LEAVING CERTIFICATE HIGHER LEVEL

Active Maths

Book 2

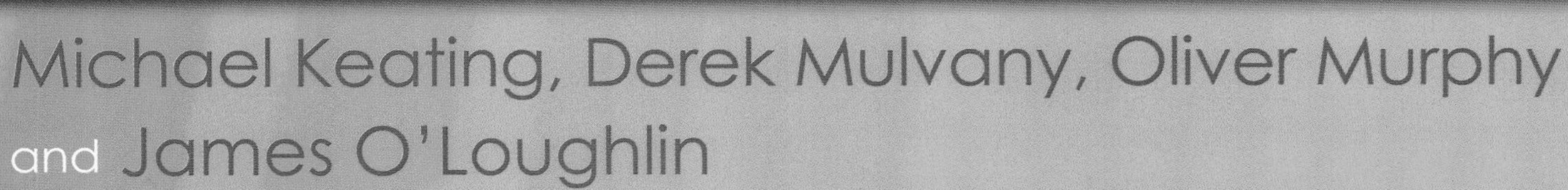

Michael Keating, Derek Mulvany, Oliver Murphy and James O'Loughlin

Special Advisors: Colin Townsend and Jim McElroy

FOLENS

Editor: Priscilla O'Connor, Aisling Hanrahan

Designer: Liz White

Layout: Compuscript

Illustrations: Compuscript, Rory O'Neill, Denis M. Baker

ISBN: 978-1-78090-609-6

Answers and worked solutions have been provided by James O'Loughlin and Jim McElroy.

Folens Publishers, Hibernian Industrial Estate, Greenhills Road, Tallaght, Dublin 24, Ireland

Acknowledgements

The authors and publisher wish to thank the following for permission to reproduce photographs: Alamy, Corbis, Getty Images, iStockphoto, Science Photo Library, Thinkstock.

The following photos were obtained from Wikimedia Commons:
Bridge collapse, 2002, near Webers Falls, Oklahoma, USA (http://commons.wikimedia.org/wiki/File:Img_3381.jpg); Rubik's Cube by Lars Karlsson (http://commons.wikimedia.org/wiki/File:Rubiks_cube_by_keqs.jpg).

Data on the world's largest companies (2009) is reproduced with permission from Bjorn Borgisky, EconomyWatch.com.

The WHO Child Growth Standards chart on length-for-age for girls aged 0–2 is reproduced with permission from the World Health Organisation (URL: http://www.who.int/childgrowth/standards/cht_lfa_girls_p_0_2.pdf; last accessed 21 July 2011).

Contents

Introduction

Active Maths 4 is a comprehensive **two-book series** covering the **complete Leaving Certificate Higher Level course**. *Active Maths 4* covers all five strands of the new Project Maths syllabus.

- **Book 1** corresponds to **Paper 1** and therefore contains **Strands 3 (Number), 4 (Algebra) and 5 (Functions).**
- **Book 2** corresponds to **Paper 2** and therefore contains **Strands 1 (Statistics and Probability) and 2 (Geometry and Trigonometry)**.

Teachers and students will find that they have the new syllabus fully covered.

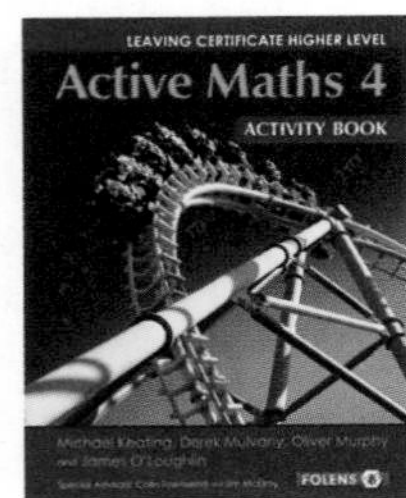

- A separate **free Activity Book** provides a wealth of activities designed to develop students' understanding of each topic in a hands-on way. The textbooks are linked throughout with the Activity Book to introduce topics and emphasise key Learning Outcomes.

Active Maths 4 is packed with student-friendly features:

- It prepares students for the new style of exam question with comprehensive **graded exercises** on each topic and **end-of-chapter revision exercises** include Project Maths-type exam questions based on all material that has been released by the NCCA and SEC.
- **Learning Outcomes** from the new syllabus are stated at the beginning of each chapter.
- Each chapter includes a **You Should Remember** section so that students can check they are fully prepared before starting the chapter.
- A list of **Key Words** at the start of each chapter helps students to consolidate learning. On first occurrence in each chapter, key words are set apart in **Definition boxes** to reinforce the importance of understanding their meaning.
- Clear and concise **Worked Examples** show students how to set out their answers, including step-by-step instructions with excellent diagrams to explain constructions.
- Essential formulae are set apart in **Formula boxes**.
- **Answers** to exercises are given at the end of each book.

  Additional **teacher resources**, **including digital activities** and **fully worked-out solutions** for the textbooks, will be available online at www.folensonline.ie.

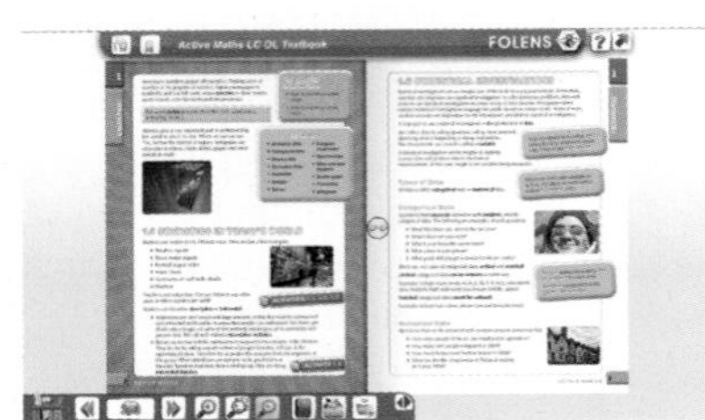

Active Maths 4 allows teachers to meet the challenge of the new syllabus for Leaving Certificate Higher Level, and encourages students to discover for themselves that mathematics can be enjoyable and relevant to everyday life.

> Note: Constructions in Book 2 are numbered according to the NCCA syllabus for Project Maths Higher Level.

Statistics I

Learning Outcomes

In this chapter you will learn about statistics, including:

- How to find, collect and organise data
- How to generate data from other sources
- Types of data
- Populations and samples
- How to select a sample
- How to use stem-and-leaf plots and histograms to display data
- Scatterplots, correlation and line of best fit

In the modern world we are inundated with statistics. When we turn on our TVs, browse the Internet or open a newspaper, we meet with numbers, charts, tables, graphs and other statistical results.

YOU SHOULD REMEMBER...

- How to write one number as a fraction and percentage of another number
- How to construct a bar chart
- How to construct a pie chart

KEY WORDS

- **Primary data**
- **Secondary data**
- **Categorical data**
- **Numerical data**
- **Population**
- **Sample**
- **Distributions**
- **Stem-and-leaf plot**
- **Histograms**
- **Correlation**
- **Scatterplot**
- **Outlier**
- **Line of best fit**

Governments are the biggest employers of statisticians. Here in Ireland the Central Statistics Office (www.cso.ie) and the Economic and Social Research Institute (www.esri.ie) are just two bodies that provide the government and the public with valuable statistics.

The word **statistics** comes from the Latin word *status* (meaning 'state').

Statistics is concerned with proper scientific methods for collecting, analysing, presenting and interpreting **data**.

Any unordered list is called **data**. When this list is ordered in some way, it becomes **information**.

Statistics are now used in such diverse areas as agriculture, biology, chemistry, economics, engineering, education, medicine, physics and political science.

Statistics can be either **descriptive** or **inferential**.

- Statisticians are often faced with large amounts of data that must be summarised and presented to the public in a way that people can understand. Bar charts, pie charts and averages are just some of the methods statisticians use to summarise and present data. We call such statistics **descriptive statistics**.
- Before an election is held, statisticians try to predict the outcome of the election. They do this by asking a small number of people how they will vote in the upcoming election. They then try to predict the outcome from the responses of this group. When statisticians try to predict or forecast based on responses from a small group, they are then doing **inferential statistics**.

Statistical Investigations

Statistical investigations are an integral part of the work of many professionals. Economists, scientists and engineers use statistical investigations to solve numerous problems. Research students use statistical investigations to prove many of their theories. Newspapers often conduct statistical investigations to gauge the public mood on various issues. The modern world is, for the most part, dependent on the information provided by statistical investigations.

A large part of any statistical investigation is the production of data. At school we often produce data for projects and experiments. An agricultural science student measuring the heights of plants she has sown in her back garden or a geography student investigating family size in Cork city are both producing data. The characteristic being recorded about each individual is called a **variable**. In the case of the agricultural science student the variable is plant height, and for the geography student the variable is family size.

1.1 TYPES OF DATA

All data is either **categorical** data or **numerical** data.

Categorical Data

Questions that cannot be answered with numbers provide **categorical data**. The following are examples of such questions:

- What colour are your eyes?
- Did you book economy or first class flights?
- Do you live in an urban area or a rural area?
- What is your favourite soccer team?
- What colour is your phone?
- What grade did you receive in your last maths test?

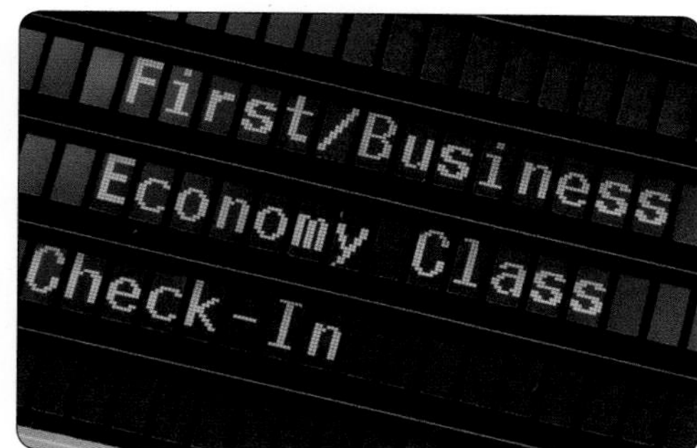

There are two types of categorical data:

- **Ordinal** categorical data
- **Nominal** categorical data

Ordinal categorical data **can be ordered** in some way. Examples include exam results (A, B, C, D, E, F, NG), stress levels (low, medium, high), and social class (lower, middle, upper).

Nominal categorical data **cannot be ordered**.
Examples include hair colour, phone colour and favourite band.

Pie charts and **bar charts** are used to display categorical data.

Numerical Data

Questions that can be answered with numbers provide **numerical** data.

- How many people in the EU are employed in manufacturing industry?
- How many Irish people emigrated in 2009?
- How many houses were built in Ireland in 2006?
- What was the temperature in Dubai at midday on 5 June 1998?
- What is the average height of Leaving Certificate students in your school?
- How many rugby Grand Slams has Ireland won?

There are two types of numerical data:

- **Continuous** numerical data
- **Discrete** numerical data

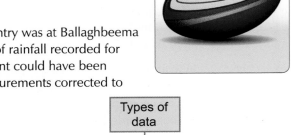

The greatest annual total rainfall recorded in this country was at Ballaghbeema Gap, Co. Kerry. The year was 1960 and the amount of rainfall recorded for the year was 3964.9 mm. Of course, this measurement could have been 3964.89764 mm, but Met Éireann gives rainfall measurements corrected to one decimal place. Rainfall measurements are an example of **continuous numerical data**, as rainfall measurements for a particular region can be any one of an infinite number of values within a given range.

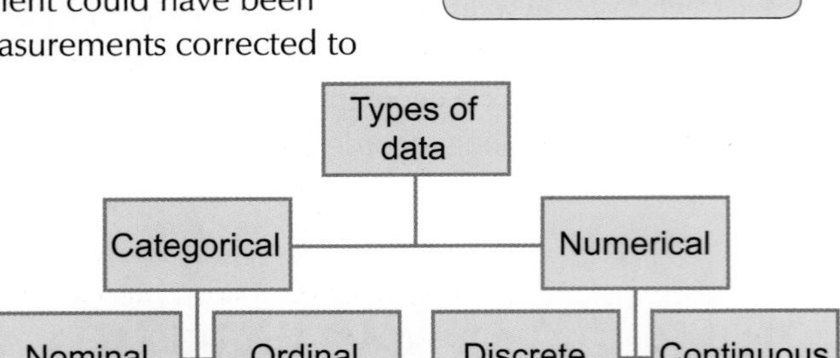

Numbers or measurements that can only have certain values, for example, shoe size and family size, are called **discrete numerical data**. Your shoe size must be a number such as 7, $7\frac{1}{2}$, 8, $8\frac{1}{2}$, 9, etc. It cannot be 8.1432.

ACTIVITY 1.2

Worked Example 1.1

Which of the following are continuous numerical data and which are discrete numerical data?

(i) The heights of basketball players

(ii) The number of gold medals won by each country in the 2008 Olympic Games

(iii) The sugar content (as a percentage of weight) in 30 brands of breakfast cereal

(iv) The time taken by each student in your class to run 100 metres

(v) The number of iPhones sold during August 2010

Solution

(i) The heights of basketball players are continuous numerical data, as these measurements can be any one of an infinite number of values within a given range.

(ii) The number of gold medals won by each country in the 2008 Olympic Games is discrete numerical data. A country may have won no gold medal or may have won some positive whole number of gold medals.

(iii) Percentage sugar content is continuous numerical data. The percentage sugar content can take on any of the infinite number of values between 0 and 100.

(iv) Time is continuous numerical data.

(v) The number of iPhones sold during August 2010 is a discrete whole number. Therefore, this is discrete numerical data.

Primary Data

Primary data is collected by or for the person who is going to use it. Therefore, the person collecting the data will organise their own study to collect the data.

There are different types of studies that generate primary data. We will look at two types of studies.

Observational Studies

In an **observational study**, the researcher collects the information of interest but does not influence events. A study into the TV viewing habits of teenagers where data is collected by means of a questionnaire is an example of an observational study.

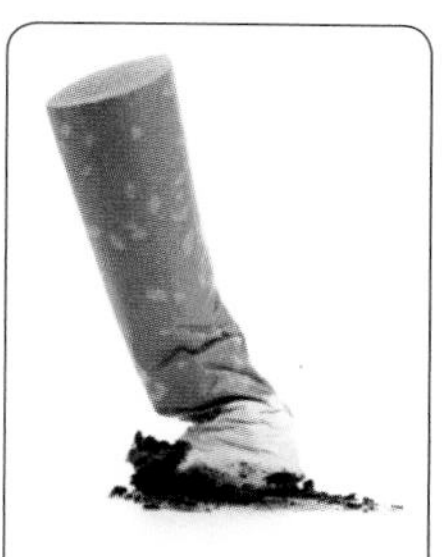

Observational studies also include **case-control** studies. For example, in a medical case-control study, two groups of people are compared. One group (the **cases**) has a disease or condition, while the other group (the **controls**) does not have the disease or condition. Researchers study the lifestyle histories of the people in each group to learn what causes the disease or condition.

A very famous case-control study in 1950 established, for the first time, the link between lung cancer and smoking. The study was carried out by Austin Hill and Richard Doll.

Designed Experiments

In a designed experiment, we apply some treatment to a group of subjects and then observe the effects of the treatment on the subjects. Pharmaceutical companies carry out many designed experiments when they are testing new drugs. In this case the drug is called an **explanatory variable** and the effect of the drug is called a **response variable**.

Worked Example 1.2

Below are descriptions of two studies.

(a) A group of car passengers who suffer from motion sickness are given magnetic bracelets, which they agree to wear in an attempt to diminish the effects of the sickness. The passengers report back to the researcher on the effectiveness of the bracelet.

(b) An examination of over 40,000 medical records of Irish men showed that those who were overweight or who had high blood pressure had a higher risk of kidney cancer.

(i) Which of the studies is an observational study, and which is an experiment?

(ii) Is the observational study a case-control study? Explain.

(iii) What is the explanatory variable and what is the response variable in the experiment?

Solution

(i) The study showing the link between certain conditions and kidney cancer is the observational study. The researcher does not influence events. The study on motion sickness is an experiment. Here the researcher tries to diminish the effects of motion sickness by having the subjects wear magnetic bracelets, i.e. he/she applies a treatment to a group of subjects and observes the effects of this treatment on the subjects.

(ii) Yes, the observational study is a case-control study. The researcher would have studied the records of people who had kidney cancer (the cases) and the records of people who did not have the disease (the controls).

(iii) The explanatory variable is the magnetic bracelet. The response variable is the effectiveness of the treatment in combating motion sickness.

Secondary Data

Secondary data is not collected by the person who is going to use it.

Sources for secondary data include the Internet, newspapers, books, historical records and databases. Here are some specific sources of secondary data:

- *The Guinness Book of Records*
- The Census of Population
- The Central Statistics Office
- Census at Schools

Exercise 1.1

1. A biology student has been studying the plants in her back garden. These tables give some of the measurements she has taken.

Heights of plants (cm)				
12.5	17.2	19.3	49.2	81.6
13.8	150.4	20.2	16.1	122.4

Colours of leaves				
Green	Yellow	Yellow	Green	Red
Green	Green	Green	Yellow	Green

(i) What variables did the student record?

(ii) State which variable is numerical and which variable is categorical.

(iii) Is the numerical variable discrete or continuous? Give a reason for your answer.

(iv) What are the units of measurements used for the numerical variable?

(v) Is the categorical variable nominal or ordinal? Explain.

2. Formulate two questions that can be answered with numerical data.

3. Formulate two questions that can be answered with categorical data.

4. A survey was carried out at a bank. Some numerical data was collected. State whether the following variables are continuous or discrete.

   (i) The number of customers who entered the bank between 10.00 am and 11.00 am

   (ii) The time taken to serve each customer

   (iii) The total amount of money withdrawn on that day

   (iv) The number of employees working on the day that the survey was carried out

5. Complete the table by naming the type of data formed by each of the measurements.

Measurement	Type of data
Number of births each month during 2009	Discrete numerical data
Concentration of volcanic ash particles in the atmosphere	
Weights of all beef slaughtered in Ireland during 2008	
Number of aeroplanes flying out of Shannon every day	
Number of pages in the books kept in the school library	
The grades of the students in your class in Junior Certificate maths	

6. (i) Give an example of an observational study which might be conducted in your school.

   (ii) Give an example of a designed experiment which might be conducted in your school.

7. Explain the terms 'explanatory variable' and 'response variable'.

8. List two sources of secondary data.

9. A sample of 500 households in Dublin was selected and several questions were asked of the householders. Which of the following is not correct?

   (i) The total household income is ordinal categorical data.

   (ii) The number of persons in the household is discrete data.

   (iii) Socioeconomic status (coded as 1 = low income, 2 = middle income and 3 = high income) is nominal categorical data.

   (iv) The primary language used at home is nominal categorical data.

   Now correct the incorrect statements.

10. Alan would like to predict the winning time for the men's 100 m final in the next Olympic Games. He gathers data from past editions of *The Guinness Book of Records*. Explain why the data collected by Alan is secondary data.

1.2 SAMPLE SURVEYS

Nowadays the news media rely on opinion polls to gauge public opinion on news issues. These polls are examples of **sample surveys**, which are designed to ask questions of a small group of people in the hope of learning something about the entire population.

Populations and Samples

Suppose that you wish to do a study on the TV viewing habits of students in your school, and now realise that it is impractical to interview everybody. You decide to interview 80 out of the 1,000 students in the school. In this case the group of all 1,000 students is called the **population**.

The **population** is the entire group that is being studied.

A **census** is a survey of the whole population.

The group of 80 students is called a **sample**.

A **sample** is a group that is selected from the population in order to gather information.

It is very important that a sample is representative of the population if you wish to make predictions about the population from the sample. For example, the sample of 80 students mentioned above would not be representative of the whole school if they were all First Year students.

Sample surveys involve working with **statistics** and **parameters**. The average amount of time spent by the sample of 80 watching television is an example of a statistic. The average amount of time spent by the population of 1,000 watching television is an example of a parameter. When it is not possible to calculate a population parameter, we use the corresponding statistic from a sample of the population to estimate the parameter.

A **parameter** is a numerical measurement describing some characteristic of a population. It is a fixed number, but in practice we do not know its value.

A **statistic** is a numerical measurement describing some characteristic of a sample. The statistic can change from sample to sample.

Bias in Sampling

Samples that are not representative are called **biased** samples. If there is a tendency for a particular group in a population to be omitted from a sample, then the sample is biased. Online polls use **voluntary response samples**. A voluntary response sample consists of people who choose themselves by responding to a general appeal. Voluntary response samples are biased because people with strong opinions, especially negative opinions, are most likely to respond. Biased samples have a tendency to underestimate or overestimate the population parameter of interest.

Simple Random Sample

In a **simple random sample**, a sample of size n is selected in such a way that every possible sample of size n from the population has an equal chance of being selected (thus avoiding bias in the sample).

If we wish to select a simple random sample of size 80 from a population of 1,000, then every possible combination of 80 must have an equal chance of being selected. A convenient way of achieving this is to assign a number to each member of the population, then draw 80 numbers out of a hat containing 1,000 numbers. Obviously, this method is not practical for larger populations, and we need to rely on a calculator, a computer or a table of random numbers to select the sample.

Stratified Random Sample

To select a **stratified random sample**, first divide the population into at least two different subgroups so that the individuals or subjects within each subgroup share the same characteristics. Then a simple random sample is drawn from each subgroup and combined to form the full sample.

Suppose that there are two candidates, one male and one female, running for president and that you would like to predict the winner of the upcoming election. You decide to select a random sample from the population. However, because the candidates are of opposite gender there is a good chance that a high proportion of the male voters will vote for the male candidate and a high proportion of the female voters will vote for the female candidate. In this case one should select a stratified random sample, i.e. randomly select the same number of males as females. This will eliminate the potential bias of having more of one gender than the other in the sample.

Systematic Random Sample

Suppose we have a population of size 10,000 and we wish to select a sample of size 500 from the population. If it is possible to assign a number to each member of the population, then we can choose a systematic sample. We begin by dividing the population size by the sample size, $\frac{10{,}000}{500} = 20$. Now, randomly choose any number from 1 to 20. Let us say that 13 is the number selected. Then 13 becomes our starting point and we select every 20th number from 13 onwards.

Cluster Sample

For **cluster sampling**, the population is divided into sections or clusters. Then some of those clusters are randomly selected and all members from those clusters are chosen.

Suppose we wanted to select a random sample of 300 maths teachers from the population of all maths teachers in the country. It is very difficult to get a list of all maths teachers from which to select our sample. However, getting a list of all second-level schools in the country is not difficult. Now randomly select, say, 40 schools (the number of maths teachers in a school will depend on the school size, but 40 schools should generate a sample of at least 300). Every maths teacher in the chosen schools is selected.

Quota Sampling

Quota sampling is an example of a non-probability sampling method. It is widely used in opinion polls and market research. Here the person selecting the sample is given a quota to fill–a certain prescribed percentage of people who come from various subgroups, e.g. men over 50, women under 25. He/she then selects the sample in the most convenient way possible. Randomisation does not play any role in the selection process, and therefore this method of sampling is open to mistakes.

Convenience Sampling

Convenience sampling is another non-probability sampling method. Subjects are chosen in the most convenient way possible. An example would be choosing just family members, as they are easily accessable.

Ethical Issues

The collection and use of data often raises ethical issues. The most complex issues of data ethics arise when we collect data from people. **Informed consent** and **confidentiality** are the two most important issues to be considered.

- Subjects must be **informed** in advance about the nature of a study and any risk of harm it may bring.
- All individuals who are subjects in a study must give their **consent** before any data is collected. In the case of very young children, the usual procedure is to get parental consent for the study. Consent should be given in writing.

When data is collected it is important to protect the subjects' privacy, by keeping all data about individuals **confidential**. Any breach of confidentiality is a serious breach of data ethics.

Clinical trials

Clinical trials are experiments that study the effectiveness of medical treatments on actual patients. A number of ethical issues arise when humans are the subjects of clinical trials.

- Experimental treatments may harm as well as heal.
- Most benefits of clinical trials go to future patients and not the subjects of the trials.
- In control trials, if a treatment is seen to be effective against a particular disease, then is it ethical to continue not giving the treatment to the control group? This is sometimes necessary in order to have a proper conclusion to the trial.

Worked Example 1.3

In each of the following, identify the type of sampling used:

(i) A marketing expert from RTÉ is conducting a survey in which 500 people will be selected from each age group of 10–19, 20–29, 30–39 and so on.

(ii) The past pupils association of Coláiste an Phiarsaigh would like to see whether past students would be interested in a reunion. They have obtained a list of all past pupils of the school. They decide to randomly select a sample of people from the list and to use this sample to gauge the interest in the reunion. They randomly select a number between 1 and 20. The person with this number is chosen and then every 20th name from the first selection onwards.

(iii) A researcher is testing a new drug. She has already administered the drug to a large number of patients. She now wants to select a sample of 20 from this group. Fortunately, she has just addressed envelopes which she will use to send information to the patients. She decides to put all the envelopes in a bag and randomly select 20.

Solution

(i) A **stratified random sample** is used. Here the population is divided into distinct groups and each group is sampled. As all the age groups should contain the same number of people, the same size sample is taken from each group. If the groups or strata were of different sizes, our samples would have to reflect these proportions, i.e. if one group contained twice as many individuals as another group, then the sample from the first group would have to be twice as big as that from the second.

(ii) A **systematic random sample** is used.

(iii) A **simple random sample** is used.

Choosing a Random Sample with a Calculator

Suppose we wish to select a random sample of size 20 from a population of 1,000. We will then have to generate 20 random numbers from all the numbers between 1 and 1,000. Here are the steps on the calculator:

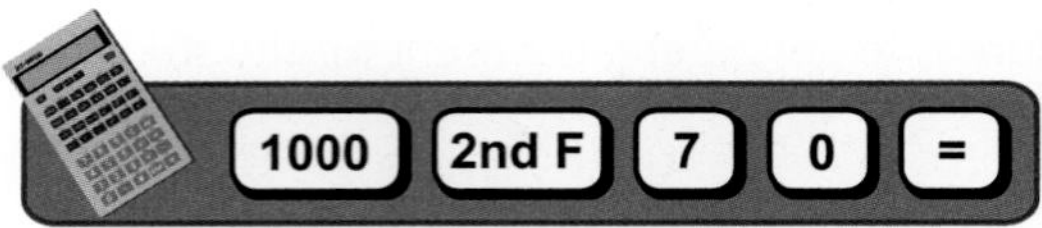

Note: Individual calculators may vary. Look for the RANDOM or RND button.

Now, press [=] 20 times to generate the 20 random numbers.

Choosing a Random Sample with Excel

When choosing a sample, it is useful to be able to choose a random set of whole numbers between two given numbers. For example, to choose a sample of size 80 from a population of 1,000, you need to generate 80 random numbers between 1 and 1,000. Most spreadsheet applications will do this for you.

Worked Example 1.4

Generate 80 random numbers between 1 and 1,000 using Excel.

Solution

Excel 2007

(i) Move the cursor to cell A1.

(ii) Type the formula =RANDBETWEEN (1,1000) and press RETURN.

(iii) Highlight cells A1 to A80.

(iv) Now use Excel's FILL DOWN command.

or

Excel 2003

(i) Move the cursor to cell A1.

(ii) Type the formula =RAND() and press RETURN.

(iii) Highlight cells A1 to A80.

(iv) Now use Excel's FILL DOWN command.

(v) Move the cursor to cell B1.

(vi) Type the formula =INT(A1*1000)+1 and press RETURN.

(vii) Highlight cells B1 to B80.

(viii) Now use Excel's FILL DOWN command.

(ix) You should now see 80 numbers randomly selected from the numbers 1–1,000.

Microsoft Excel - Book2

File Edit View Insert Format Tools Data Window Help Adobe PDF

A1 =RAND()

	A	B	C	D	E	F	G
1	0.60023	600					
2	0.69713	697					
3	0.70354	703					
4	0.26089	260					
5	0.95556	955					
6	0.6224	622					
7	0.3761	376					
8	0.6456	645					
9	0.34983	349					
10	0.16506	165					
11	0.5339	533					
12	0.32716	327					
13	0.9099	909					
14	0.0782	78					
15	0.15234	152					
16	0.78169	781					
17	0.77952	779					
18	0.27432	274					
19	0.79897	798					
20	0.85012	850					
21	0.34045	340					
22	0.18671	186					
23	0.3798	379					
24	0.3146	314					
25	0.11969	119					
26	0.70209	702					
27	0.93735	937					
28	0.58333	583					
29	0.07516	75					
30	0.81083	810					
31	0.77456	774					
32	0.01765	17					
33	0.6964	696					
34	0.09878	98					

Sheet1 / Sheet2 / Sheet3

Ready

If you wanted to generate 10 random numbers between 1 and 30, you would highlight and fill down 10 cells at steps (iii) and (iv), and you would type =INT(A1*30)+1 at step (vi).

- RAND() generates a number between 0 and 1.
- Multiplying this by 1,000 yields a number between 0 and 1,000.
- The INT function removes the decimal parts of the number, leaving only the integer part, e.g. INT(314.867) = 314. So this produces a whole number between 0 and 999.
- Adding 1 to this creates a random whole number between 1 and 1,000, as desired.

Reliability of Data

When choosing a sample from a population, try to ensure:

- That the sample is large enough
- That the sample is a random selection from the population
- That everybody has an equal chance of being selected
- As high a response rate as possible

If sample data is not collected in an appropriate way, then the data may be unreliable.

Exercise 1.2

1. Assign a number to each member of your class. Using your calculator, randomly select five people. What type of sampling have you done?

2. An electronics company manufactures four different types of components. The number of each type manufactured per day is given in the table below. The company has a policy of randomly selecting 70 components each day for quality checks.

Component	A	B	C	D
Number	200	350	50	100

   (i) How many of each type of component should be selected?
   (ii) What type of sampling is being done here?

3. What type of sampling is being used in these cases?

   (i) The Gardaí set up a checkpoint to check that drivers have car insurance. They stop every fifth driver.
   (ii) On the day of a General Election, RTÉ organise an exit poll. They randomly select 100 polling stations and all voters are surveyed as they leave the station.
   (iii) A researcher in the Department of Social Welfare has partitioned all Dublin adults into the following categories: unemployed, employed full-time and employed part-time. She is surveying 50 people from the first category, 200 people from the second category and 25 from the third category.

4. What type of sampling is being used in these cases?

   (i) In an MRBI poll of 1,000 adults, people were selected by using a computer to randomly generate telephone numbers that were then called.
   (ii) An engineer tests his new design on family members.
   (iii) The school principal decides to interview all students in the school to get their opinion on some school matter.

5. Explain why a large sample may not necessarily be a good sample.

6. After the World Trade Center in New York was destroyed, an Internet poll asked the question, 'Should the World Trade Center be rebuilt?'

   Of the 1.3 million respondants, 769,000 said 'Yes', 287,000 said 'No', and 249,000 were undecided. Given that this sample is very large, should it be considered representative of the views of the population of the USA? Explain.

7. Suppose we want to estimate the number of students who watch *Strictly Come Dancing* in a school with a population of 1,000 students. We randomly select 50 students. Our sample happens to contain 40 girls and 10 boys.

   (i) Is it possible that this sample could be biased? Explain.

   (ii) How could potential bias be eliminated in this particular case?

8. Using Excel, generate 20 random numbers between 1 and 700.

Steps in a Statistical Investigation

All statistical investigations begin with a question.
Here are the steps in a statistical investigation:

- Pose a question.
- Collect data.
- Present the data.
- Analyse the data.
- Interpret the data.

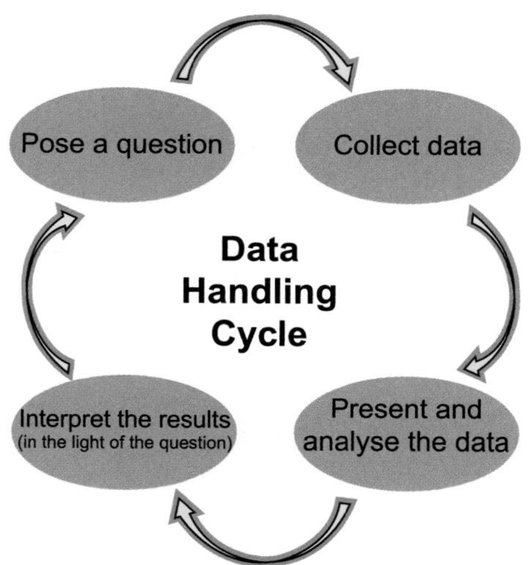

1.3 COLLECTING DATA

Statistical data can be collected in different ways.
The most common way of collecting data is by **survey**.

Surveys

Most surveys use a questionnaire. The survey can be carried out by:

- Face-to-face interview
- Telephone interview
- Sending a questionnaire by post
- Making a questionnaire available online
- Observation

Here are the advantages and disadvantages of each type of survey.

Survey	Advantages	Disadvantages
Face-to-face interview	■ Questions can be explained to the interviewee.	■ Not random. ■ Expensive to carry out.
Telephone interview	■ It is possible to select sample from almost the entire adult population. ■ Questions can be explained to the interviewee.	■ Expensive in comparison to postal and online surveys.
Postal questionnaire	■ Inexpensive.	■ People do not always reply to postal surveys and those who reply may not be representative of the whole population.
Online questionnaire	■ Very low cost. ■ Anonymity of respondents ensures more honest answers to sensitive questions.	■ Not representative of the whole population. Only those who go online and do online surveys are represented.
Observation	■ Low cost. ■ Easy to administer.	■ Not suitable for many surveys. ■ Questions cannot be explained.

Designing a Questionnaire

A **questionnaire** is an important method for collecting data.

Here are some important points to note when designing questionnaires.

A **questionnaire** is a set of questions designed to obtain data from a population.

Questionnaires should:

- Be useful and relevant to the survey you are undertaking
- Use clear and simple language
- Be as brief as possible
- Begin with simple questions to encourage people to complete them
- Accommodate all possible answers
- Be clear where answers should be recorded
- Contain no leading questions, which give a clue as to how you would like the person to respond. For example, 'Manchester United are losing a lot of games this season. Do you think their manager should resign?'
- Contain no questions which ask for a response to more than one topic. An example of this type of question is, 'Do you think the government spends too much money on sport and should be voted out of office in the next election?'

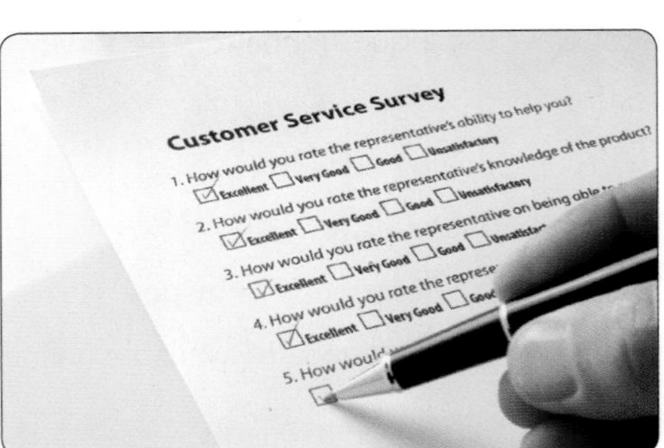

Worked Example 1.5

Britney wants to gather information on people's interest in sport. Here is the questionnaire she designs.

1. What is your favourite sport?

(i) Tennis ☐
(ii) Rugby ☐
(iii) Athletics ☐

2. How far would you travel to see a competitive sports fixture?

(i) Less than 1 km ☐
(ii) 5–10 km ☐
(iii) Greater than 20 km ☐

3. Do you participate in sport or watch sport on TV?

(i) Yes ☐
(ii) No ☐

(a) What is wrong with these questions?

(b) Design better questions for Britney to use.

Solution

Question 1

(a) The question does not allow for all possible sports. While it may not be possible to include all types of sport, it is possible to cater for everybody if an 'Other' alternative is included.

(b)

1. What is your favourite type of sport?

(i) Tennis ☐
(ii) Rugby ☐
(iii) Athletics ☐
(iv) Other ☐

Question 2

(a) There are gaps between 1 km and 5 km and also between 10 km and 20 km.

(b)

2. How far would you travel to see a competitive sports fixture?

(i) Less than 1 km ☐
(ii) 1–10 km ☐
(iii) Greater than 10 km but less than 20 km ☐
(iv) 20 km or more ☐

Question 3

(a) This question needs to be split into two questions.

(b)

3. Do you participate in sport?

(i) Yes ☐

(ii) No ☐

4. Do you watch sport on TV?

(i) Yes ☐

(ii) No ☐

1.4 FREQUENCY TABLES

When data is collected, it is often convenient to display it in a frequency table. Frequency tables show you how frequently each piece of data occurs. It is good practice to include a tally row in your table. Tallies are marks to help you keep track of counts. The marks are bunched in groups of five.

Worked Example 1.6

The table below shows the number of draws each Premier League club had during the 2009–2010 season.

5	4	6	7	13
13	9	13	11	11
14	10	11	9	11
9	10	11	9	11

(i) Sort the data into a frequency table. Include a tally column in your table.

(ii) Stoke City had the greatest number of draws during the season, and finished 11th with 47 points. How many games did Stoke win? (Win = 3 points, Draw = 1 point, Loss = 0 points.)

(iii) What percentage of clubs had fewer than nine draws?

Solution

(i)

Number of draws	4	5	6	7	8	9	10	11	12	13	14
Tally	I	I	I	I		IIII	II	~~IIII~~ I		III	I
Frequency	1	1	1	1	0	4	2	6	0	3	1

(ii) Greatest number of draws = 14

- 14 points accumulated from draws
- 47 – 14 = 33 points from wins

Number of games won $= \frac{33}{3} = 11$

(iii) $\frac{4}{20} \times 100 = 20\%$

Exercise 1.3

1. Shauna rolls a die 50 times. Her scores are listed below.

(i) Sort the data in a frequency table that includes a tally row.

(ii) How many times did Shauna throw a 6?

(iii) How many times did Shauna throw a 1?

(iv) What percentage of the rolls were 4's?

5	3	3	3	5	1	2	5	1	5
1	3	3	6	4	6	1	2	1	1
1	6	5	6	3	4	2	2	5	2
4	6	5	1	2	6	1	1	6	2
2	6	2	5	2	3	4	4	6	6

2. Below is some data selected at random from the CensusAtSchools database. The data gives the different modes of transport the group uses to go to school.

(i) Sort the data into a frequency table.

(ii) What is the most popular mode of transport?

(iii) What is the least popular mode of transport?

(iv) Use an appropriate graph to represent the sample.

Walk	Bus	Walk	Walk	Walk
Bus	Walk	Car	Car	Bus
Walk	Bus	Car	Walk	Walk
Car	Rail	Bus	Walk	Rail

(v) If it is intended to use a sample from CensusAtSchools to make predictions about the type of transport that students throughout the country use to go to school, then what questions need to be asked about such a sample?

3. A survey is made of the number of goals scored in a series of soccer matches. The findings are as follows:

(i) Sort the data into a frequency table.

(ii) How many soccer matches were played?

(iii) How many scoreless draws were there?

(iv) What is the maximum number of games that could have been drawn?

2	0	1	2	2	1	3
1	1	4	0	1	3	4
0	2	0	4	2	0	4
3	1	2	4	2	2	0
1	1	2	1	2	2	0

(v) What is the minimum number of games that could have been drawn?

4. John takes three coins from his pocket and flips the three coins together. He repeats this experiment 25 times and records his results as follows:

TTT	TTH	HTT	THT	HHH
HTH	THH	HHT	HHH	HTT
TTH	HHT	TTT	THH	HHH
THT	HTH	HTH	HTH	THH
THT	TTH	HHT	HTH	HTT

(i) Copy and complete the frequency table.

Result	3 Heads	2 Heads	1 Head	0 Heads
Tally				
Frequency				

(ii) What percentage of the throws revealed one head only?

(iii) Use an appropriate graph to display the data.

(iv) Use the random coin generator on your calculator to simulate the experiment.

To use the random coin generator on your calculator, press the following keys:

Note that individual calculators may differ.

1 = heads, and 0 = tails.

(v) Graph your results. Compare and contrast your graph with the graph of John's results.

5. The marks, out of 5, for a class of 20 pupils in a maths quiz are as follows:

4	2	3	5	4
1	1	2	3	5
4	3	1	5	3
3	1	3	5	3

(i) Show the data on a frequency table.

(ii) Represent the data on a bar chart.

(iii) If 2 is the mark needed to pass the test, then how many students failed the test?

(iv) What percentage of the class passed the test?

6. The ages of all the teachers in a school are:

21, 21, 22, 23, 23, 25, 27, 28, 30, 31, 32, 34, 34, 35, 37, 38, 39, 40, 40, 41 42, 42, 43, 44, 44, 44, 45, 46, 46, 47, 49, 49, 50, 50, 50, 54, 55, 57, 57, 58 59, 59, 60, 60, 63, 63, 64

(i) How many teachers were surveyed?

(ii) Copy and complete the frequency table below.

Age	20–29	30–39	40–49	50–59	60–69
Frequency					

(iii) You would like to know teachers' opinion on early retirement. Suggest a suitable way of selecting a sample of 12 teachers for interview on this issue.

7. A sample of young people were asked how many songs were on their iPods. Here are the results:

102	513	424	235	124
328	247	416	505	375
424	253	152	31	712
167	405	103	285	267

(i) How many people were surveyed?

(ii) What percentage of those surveyed had fewer than 300 songs?

(iii) Suppose you are asked to carry out a similar survey in your school. Outline the method you would use to select a sample.

8. What is wrong with the following question used in a questionnaire?

> Most students in this school hate the uniform. Are you in favour of changing it?
>
> Yes ☐ No ☐ Undecided ☐

9. Thomas is doing a survey on urban versus rural attitudes to drink-driving. He has included the following question in his questionnaire. What is wrong with it?

> Where did you grow up?
>
> Country ☐ Farm ☐ City ☐

10. Aisling has designed a questionnaire which includes the following question:

> How old are you?
>
> Young ☐ Middle-aged ☐ Old ☐

(i) What is wrong with the question?

(ii) Improve the question.

11. Máire is doing a survey on healthy eating habits. Design a questionnaire with three questions that would be relevant to the survey.

1.5 GRAPHING DATA

In this section we look at important methods of graphing sets of data. Data that is graphed is easier to analyse and interpret. In your Junior Certificate maths course you learned how to graph data using bar charts and pie charts. Bar charts and pie charts are used to display discrete data. You will still need to construct bar charts and pie charts.

Stem-and-Leaf Diagrams or Stemplots

Stem-and-leaf diagrams (or stemplots) represent data in a similar way to bar charts.

To make a stemplot, follow these steps:

> A **stem-and-leaf diagram** represents data by separating each value into two parts: the stem and the leaf (the final digit).

1. Separate each observation into a **stem** consisting of all but the final (rightmost) digit and a **leaf**, the final digit. Stems may have as many digits as needed, but each leaf contains only a single digit.
2. Write the stems in a vertical column with the smallest at the top, and draw a vertical line at the right of this column.
3. Write each leaf in the row to the right of its stem, **in increasing order** out from the stem.
4. Write the **key**.

Worked Example 1.7

The times in minutes between eruptions of the 'Old Faithful' geyser in Yellowstone National Park, USA, are displayed in the stem-and-leaf diagram below. This data was collected by a geologist in 1990.

Stem	Leaf
4	9, 9
5	1, 1, 5, 6, 7, 7, 8, 9
6	0, 0, 1, 5, 5, 8
7	3, 4, 5, 7, 7, 7, 8, 9, 9
8	0, 1, 2, 3, 3, 4, 4, 5, 6, 6, 7, 8, 9
9	0, 1 Key: 8|2 = 82 minutes

This key tells us that the stem denotes tens and the leaves denote units.

Using the stem-and-leaf diagram, answer the following questions:

(i) What was the shortest time interval recorded?

(ii) What was the longest time interval recorded?

(iii) How many eruptions did the geologist see while recording the data?

(iv) What percentage of time intervals recorded were greater than one hour?

Solution

(i) The shortest time interval was 49 minutes.

(ii) The longest time interval was 91 minutes.

(iii) 41 eruptions, as the number of eruptions will always be one greater than the number of time intervals.

(iv) $\frac{28}{40} \times 100 = 70\%$

Worked Example 1.8

Twenty people from the audience of a TV programme are randomly selected and each person is asked his/her age. Their ages are as follows:

15	14	25	23	33
45	13	51	62	48
19	57	47	56	44
11	38	46	21	16

(i) Represent the data on a stem-and-leaf diagram, including a key.

(ii) How many teenagers are in the audience?

Solution

(i)

Stem	Leaf
1	1, 3, 4, 5, 6, 9
2	1, 3, 5
3	3, 8
4	4, 5, 6, 7, 8
5	1, 6, 7
6	2 Key: 1|4 = 14

(ii) Reading from our stem-and-leaf diagram, we see that there are five teenagers in the audience.

Back-to-Back Stem-and-Leaf Diagrams

A back-to-back stem-and-leaf diagram is a useful way of comparing data from two different groups. A common stem is used, and the leaves on each side are ordered out from the common stem.

Worked Example 1.9

Researchers for *Consumer Reports* analysed two types of hot dog: one with meat and one with poultry. The number of calories in each hot dog was recorded. The results are as follows:

Meat			
173	179	182	180
172	147	146	139
175	136	179	153
107	185	135	140
138	135	140	142

Poultry			
129	132	102	106
94	102	87	99
107	113	135	142
86	143	152	146
144	99	112	115

(Source: *Consumer Reports*, June 1986, pp 336–367)

(i) Represent the data on a back-to-back stem-and-leaf diagram.

(ii) What feature of the plot tells you that, in general, meat hot dogs have a higher calorie count than poultry hot dogs?

Solution

(i)

Meat		Poultry
	8	6, 7
	9	4, 9, 9
7	10	2, 2, 6, 7
	11	2, 3, 5
	12	9
9, 8, 6, 5, 5	13	2, 5
7, 6, 2, 0, 0	14	2, 3, 4, 6
3	15	2
	16	
9, 9, 5, 3, 2	17	
5, 2, 0	18	
Key: 2|18| = 182 calories		Key: |15|2 = 152 calories

(ii) Much of the data on meat hot dogs is towards the bottom of the plot, whereas the data on poultry hot dogs is towards the top of the plot.

This would indicate that in general meat hot dogs have a higher calorie count than poultry hot dogs. However, we would need to do more statistical analysis on the data to increase our confidence in such a statement.

Exercise 1.4

1. Each year the Academy awards Oscars for Best Actor and Best Actress. The table below lists the ages of the Best Actor at the time of the awards ceremony. The ages are listed in order, beginning with Dustin Hoffmann's age in 1980 and ending with Seán Penn's age in 2009.

36	76	39	53	45	36
62	43	51	32	42	54
52	37	38	32	45	60
46	40	36	47	29	43
36	37	45	50	60	48

(i) Display the data on an unordered stem-and-leaf plot.

(ii) Order the data in an ordered stem-and-leaf plot.

(iii) What was the age of the oldest actor to win an Oscar in the period 1980–2009?

(iv) What was the age of the youngest actor to win an Oscar in the period 1980–2009?

(v) Describe the shape of the stem-and-leaf plot.

(vi) What does the shape tell us about the age profile of the actors?

2. John measures the heights (in centimetres) of all the students in his class. Here are his results:

160	155	166	154	150
158	170	175	156	153
140	168	170	149	145
157	160	165	180	181
165	153	139	183	160

(i) Copy and complete the stem-and-leaf diagram.

Stem	Leaf
13	9
14	
15	
16	
17	
18	Key: 13|9 = 139

(ii) What variable is John measuring?

(iii) What type of data does this variable generate?

(iv) John's height is 166 cm. What proportion of the class is taller than him?

3. A group of students were asked to choose a number between 50 and 100. Here are the results:

72	77	60	72	51	62
75	60	63	77	67	72
79	63	82	93	89	97
60	73	83	99	69	72
67	83	76	51	55	90

(i) What type of data is generated by this question?

(ii) Use your calculator to generate 30 random integers between 50 and 100. (Generate between 0 and 50, then add 50 to each number). Record your results.

(iii) Use a back-to-back stem-and-leaf diagram to compare your results with the students' results.

4. John randomly selects 20 students from his school. He asks the 20 students to take an Internet IQ test. Here are the results:

109, 100, 111, 127, 114,
103, 116, 120, 128, 132,
94, 88, 129, 108, 127,
110, 109, 104, 119, 133

(i) Show the results on a stem-and-leaf diagram.

(ii) If 100 is the average IQ score for the whole population, then how many students scored higher than average?

(iii) How many students scored lower than 100?

(iv) What percentage of students had scores between 85 and 115?

5. The tables below show maximal breadth measurements (in millimetres) of adult male Egyptian skulls from two different time periods. The first table refers to skulls dated 4000 BCE (Before Common Era) and the second table to skulls dated 150 CE (Common Era). The data was collected as part of a study to show that skull sizes changed between 4000 BCE and 150 CE as a result of Egyptians interbreeding with immigrant populations.

4000 BCE					
131	125	131	119	136	138
139	125	131	134	129	134
126	132	141	131	135	132
139	132	126	135	134	130

150 CE					
137	136	128	130	138	126
136	126	132	139	143	141
135	137	142	139	138	137
133	145	138	131	143	134

(i) Draw a back-to-back stem-and-leaf diagram that will compare the maximal breadth measurements of the skulls from the two different periods.

(ii) Does your diagram indicate a difference? Explain.

6. Fifteen plants are randomly selected and their heights measured:

49 cm, 27 cm, 44 cm, 37 cm, 43 cm, 32 cm, 40 cm, 46 cm, 45 cm, 32 cm, 38 cm, 27 cm, 40 cm, 37 cm, 45 cm

(i) Show the results on a stem-and-leaf diagram.

(ii) What is the smallest height recorded?

(iii) What is the tallest plant in the sample?

(iv) What fraction of the sample has heights greater than 43 cm?

7. The data below is from Charles Darwin's study of cross-fertilisation and self-fertilisation. Pairs of seedlings of the same age, one produced by cross-fertilisation and the other by self-fertilisation, are grown under nearly identical conditions. The data shows the final heights of each plant after a fixed period of time. All heights have been converted to centimetres.

Cross-fertilised plants				
59	55	46	58	30
30	48	55	53	58
53	54	51	54	55

Self-fertilised plants				
44	50	47	45	32
51	46	38	41	39
50	47	41	45	45

(i) Draw a back-to-back stem-and-leaf diagram that will compare the heights of cross-fertilised and self-fertilised plants.

(ii) The aim of Darwin's experiment was to demonstrate the greater vigour of the cross-fertilised plants. Based on your stem-and-leaf diagram, do you think the experiment demonstrates this?

(iii) How might Darwin have improved the experiment?

8. The following back-to-back stem-and-leaf diagram compares the pulse rates of 25 people before and after a 5 km run.

Before run		After run
7, 5, 2	5	
9, 8, 6, 4, 2, 1, 1, 0	6	
8, 8, 8, 6, 5, 3, 3, 1	7	
3, 2, 1	8	0, 2, 5
8, 5	9	8, 6
9	10	0, 0, 1, 5, 6, 6, 8, 9
	11	1, 2, 2, 6, 9
	12	7, 8, 8
	13	0, 1, 7
Key: 5|9| = 95 beats/min	14	2 Key: |11|1 = 111 beats/min

(i) How many people had pulse rates of more than 100 beats per minute after the run?

(ii) How many people had pulse rates of more than 100 beats per minute before the run?

(iii) What conclusions can you draw from the stem-and-leaf diagram?

9. Draw a back-to-back stem-and-leaf diagram that will compare the heights (in centimetres) given below of a group of men and a group of women.

Men	179, 183, 181, 186, 185, 175, 191, 171, 174, 176, 179, 184, 159, 160, 166, 170, 178, 175, 170, 161, 168, 174, 183
Women	157, 155, 148, 171, 151, 157, 167, 162, 174, 166, 165, 149, 169, 178, 158, 154, 153, 152, 155, 150, 161, 158, 163

10. Tom has randomly selected two groups of 20 students from his school. The first group consists of people who play at least one sport. The second group is made up of people who do not play any sport. Each individual in both groups is given the same puzzle to complete. Here are the times (to the nearest minute) taken to complete the puzzle.

Group 1

10	10	18	9	15	30	13	19	38	7
28	25	12	32	23	10	12	21	18	15

Group 2

24	12	24	19	18	17	26	33	15	10
25	13	34	9	17	20	16	30	22	30

(i) Draw a back-to-back stem-and-leaf diagram for the data.

(ii) What was the fastest time?

(iii) What was the slowest time?

(iv) From which groups did the fastest and slowest times come?

11. Here is some random data from the CensusAtSchools site. All lengths are measured in centimetres.

Gender	Height	Foot length	Gender	Height	Foot length
Male	167	25	Female	135	20
Female	151	22	Male	164	31
Female	171	31	Male	158	24
Male	151	24	Male	147	24
Female	158	24	Female	160	32
Male	158	24	Female	156	24
Male	170	24	Female	171	31
Female	149	21	Male	118	23
Male	154	24	Female	154	23
Female	150	22	Male	148	22

(i) Draw a back-to-back stem-and-leaf diagram that will compare the heights of males and females in the group.

(ii) Draw a back-to-back stem-and-leaf diagram that will compare the foot lengths of males and females in the group.

12. Mark conducted a survey about how accurately certain boys measured a piece of string. The piece of string was measured to the nearest millimetre. The results of the survey are given in the stem-and-leaf diagram below.

6	4, 5, 5, 7, 8
7	0, 0, 0, 0, 1, 1, 2, 3, 5
	Key: 7|1 = 71 mm

Mark then drew a second stem-and-leaf diagram.

6	4
6	5, 5, 7, 8
7	0, 0, 0, 0, 1, 1, 2, 3
7	5 Key: 7|0 = 70 mm

(i) What are the advantages of using the second stem-and-leaf diagram rather than the first?

(ii) Write down the longest measurement recorded in the survey.

(iii) Mark measured the string as 63 mm. Add Mark's measurement to the second stem-and-leaf diagram.

Histograms

Stemplots display all values of the observations, making them awkward for large data sets. Histograms break the range of values of a variable into classes and display only the count or per cent of the observations that fall into each class.

If you wish to graph height, foot length or arm span, then you could use a **histogram**.

Histograms are used to represent continuous numerical data.

Histograms are similar to bar charts. In a bar chart, the height of the bar represents the frequency. In a histogram, the area of the bar represents the frequency. However, in our course we will deal only with histograms in which the bars have a width of 1. Therefore, the **area** of the bar will have the same value as the **height** of the bar.

Worked Example 1.10

The following frequency table shows the times, in minutes, spent by a group of women in a boutique. Draw a histogram of the distribution.

Time	0–10	10–20	20–30	30–40	40–50
Number	1	4	9	7	9

Note: 10–20 means 10 or more but less than 20, and so on.

Solution

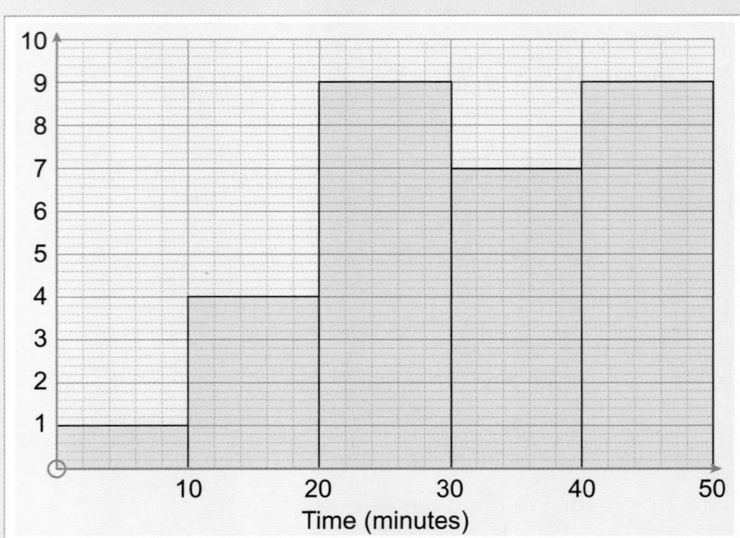

Distribution of Data

Here are the times (in minutes) taken by a group of 14 students to complete a maths problem:

4.5	1.5	2	2.5	3	4	4.5
5	5.5	5.7	6	7	7.5	9.5

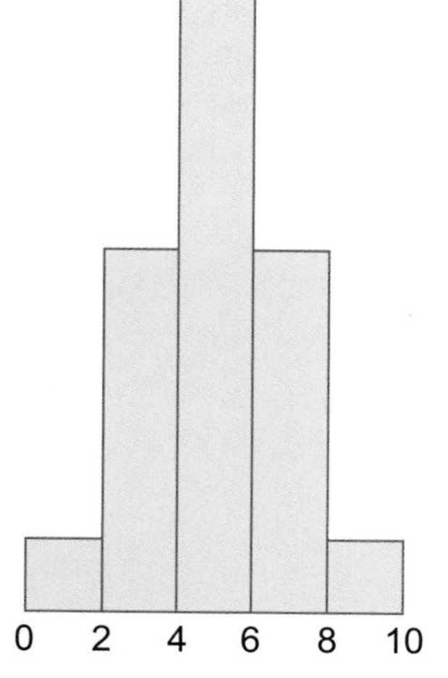

While it may not be be obvious from the list, many of the times are between 4 and 6 minutes. Also, few people had very low times or very high times. A histogram shows this distribution very well.

> We call a distribution a **symmetric distribution** if the values smaller and larger than its midpoint are mirror images of each other.

Here are the times (in minutes) taken by a group of 21 students to complete the same maths problem:

1.5	2	2.4	3.8	4	4.2	4.5
5.7	5.8	6.1	6.3	6.4	7	7.2
8.2	8.3	8.5	8.8	9	9.2	9.5

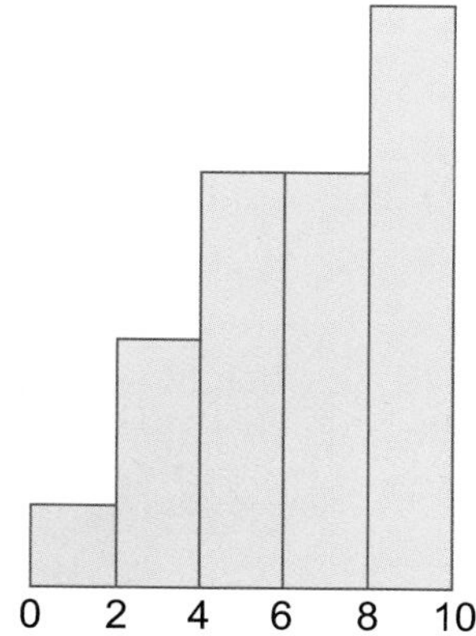

In this distribution many students would have taken a relatively long time to complete the problem. Here is the histogram for this distribution, which tails off towards the lower numbers on the left.

> We call this a **negatively skewed distribution**.
> It is also referred to as a **skewed left distribution**.

The following are the times of a group of 25 students who also completed the maths problem:

0.9	1.1	1.2	1.3	1.3	1.6	1.6	1.9	2	2
3.1	3.2	3.6	3.9	4.1	4.5	5.1	5.8	5.8	6
7.1	7.5	7.9	8	9					

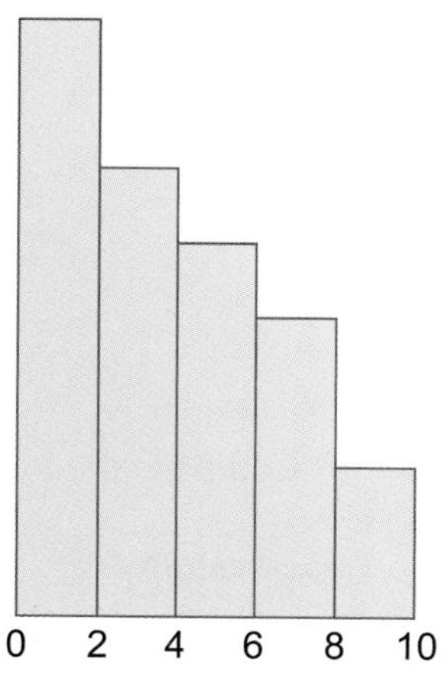

In this distribution, many students solved the problem in a short time. Here is the histogram for this distribution which tails off towards the higher numbers on the right.

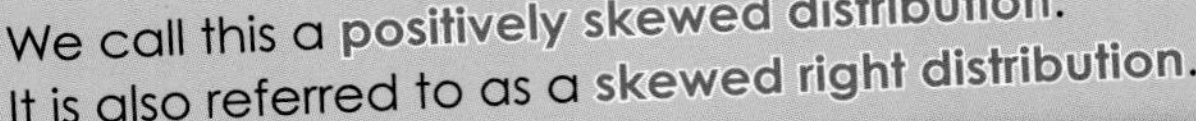

> We call this a **positively skewed distribution**.
> It is also referred to as a **skewed right distribution**.

Exercise 1.5

1. The University of Arizona, as part of a study on refuse disposal, collected data from a number of households. The data in the table below gives the weight (in kilograms) of paper disposed from 78 of the households in one week.

2.41	1.09	2.75	3.03	6.85	3.10
7.57	3.44	6.18	4.50	1.27	5.18
7.55	4.34	3.17	5.78	2.92	7.30
8.22	4.00	6.51	4.46	2.66	2.90
8.42	3.96	6.04	7.44	5.03	5.92
6.96	3.16	1.48	2.87	5.64	5.16
6.83	4.17	4.27	4.29	5.59	5.70
8.13	3.50	2.8	3.62	4.38	3.67
6.08	4.99	5.95	1.48	0.75	4.54
6.38	4.07	4.29	2.67	3.75	5.65
7.05	4.80	2.66	3.99	5.01	5.58
1.36	5.60	5.7	4.50	1.57	4.53
5.09	4.20	3.7	5.60	7.8	7.50

(i) Complete the frequency distribution table.

Weight (kg)	0.5–1.5	1.5–2.5	2.5–3.5	3.5–4.5	4.5–5.5	5.5–6.5	6.5–7.5	7.5–8.5
Tally								
Frequency								

Note: 0.5–1.5 means $0.5 < \text{Weight} \leqslant 1.5$, and so on.

(ii) Display the distribution on a histogram.

(iii) Comment on the shape of the distribution.

2. The data below gives the weights (in kilograms) of a random sample of 30 newborn babies born in a maternity ward during 2009.

2.79	3.02	3.60	2.61	2.07
3.06	2.75	3.51	3.38	3.42
2.61	3.42	3.38	2.97	2.75
2.34	2.07	3.60	2.30	3.24
3.24	3.33	2.75	3.11	3.02
3.15	3.24	2.57	3.78	2.16

(i) Complete the frequency distribution table below.

Weight (kg)	2.0–2.5	2.5–3.0	3.0–3.5	3.5–4.0
Tally				
Frequency				

Note: 2.0–2.5 means $2.0 < \text{Weight} \leqslant 2.5$ and so on.

(ii) Display the distribution on a histogram.

(iii) Write the frequency of each class interval as a percentage of 30 (30 is the total sample size). These numbers are termed the **relative frequencies of the distribution**.

(iv) Complete the following relative frequency distribution.

Weight (kg)	2.0–2.5	2.5–3.0	3.0–3.5	3.5–4.0
Relative frequency				

Note: 2.0–2.5 means 2.0 < Weight ⩽ 2.5 and so on.

(v) Display the relative frequency distribution on a histogram. Use the following scaled axes as a guide.

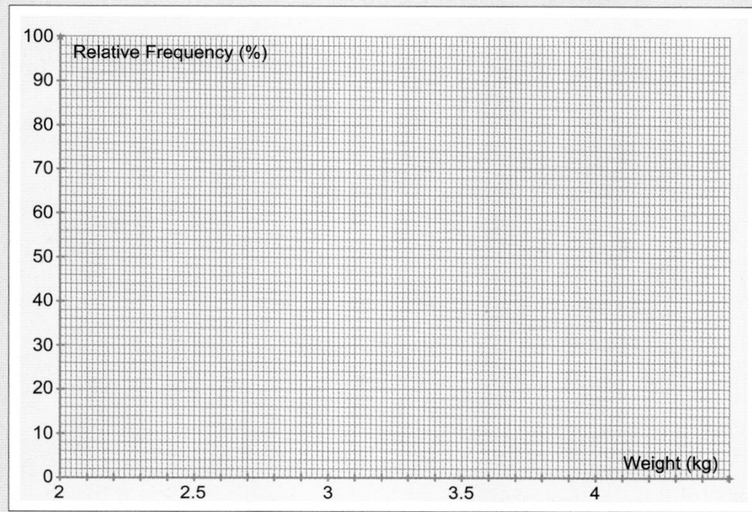

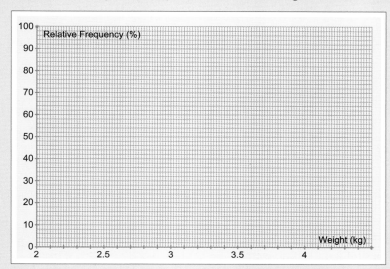

(vi) What advantage has the graph of the relative frequency distribution over the graph of the frequency distribution?

3. The time, in minutes, taken by each member of a group of students to solve a problem is represented in the histogram below.

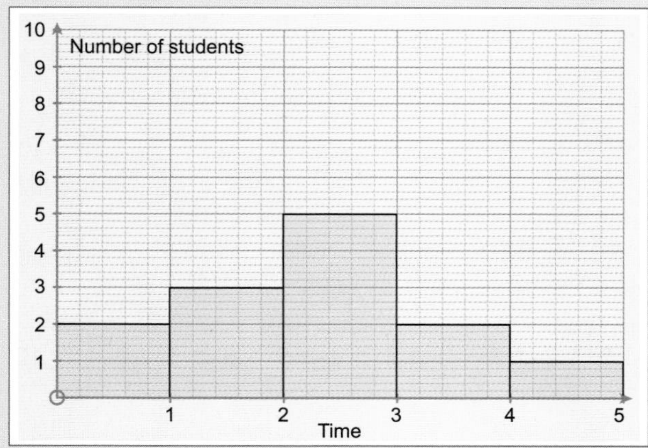

Copy and complete the following table:

Time (min)	0–1	1–2	2–3	3–4	4–5
Frequency					

Note: 0–1 means 0 or more but less than 1, and so on.

(i) How many students solved the problem in less than 3 minutes?

(ii) What percentage of students solved it in less than a minute (correct to two decimal places)?

4. The number of hours sleep taken by 50 people on a certain night was tabled as follows:

Time (hours)	0–3	3–6	6–9	9–12
Frequency	4	11	20	15

Note: 0–3 means 0 or more but less than 3, and so on.

(i) Draw a histogram that will represent the data.

(ii) What is the greatest possible number of people who had over 8 hours' sleep?

(iii) What is the least possible number who had over 8 hours' sleep?

5. The table below gives the closing weekly share price for AIB shares from January 2010 to June 2010. All prices are in euro.

AIB share prices					
0.88	0.97	1.11	0.90	0.96	1.04
1.08	1.24	1.11	1.44	1.50	1.50
1.54	1.20	1.70	1.57	1.45	1.45
0.99	1.12	1.12	1.09	1.29	1.40
1.48	1.65				

(i) Copy and complete the stem-and-leaf diagram.

0.8	
0.9	
1.0	
1.1	1, 1, 2, 2
1.2	
1.3	
1.4	
1.5	
1.6	
1.7	Key: 0.8|8 = €0.88

(ii) Using your stem-and-leaf diagram, complete the frequency distribution:

Price	0.8–0.9	0.9–1.0	1.0–1.1	1.1–1.2	1.2–1.3	1.3–1.4	1.4–1.5	1.5–1.6	1.6–1.7	1.7–1.8
Frequency										

Note: 0.8–0.9 means 0.8 or more but less than 0.9, and so on.

(iii) Display the distribution on a histogram.

(iv) 'For small data sets, stem-and-leaf plots give more information than histograms. Histograms are best used for large data sets.' Explain why this statement is true.

6. The stem-and-leaf diagram shows the time (in seconds) it took contestants to answer a general knowledge question. All contestants answered in less than 7 seconds.

2	1, 2, 2
3	2, 4, 8, 9
4	1, 3, 4, 6, 7
5	1, 5
6	8 Key: 5|1 = 5.1 sec

(i) Copy and complete the table.

Time (sec.)	2–3	3–4	4–5	5–6	6–7
Frequency		4			

Note: 2–3 means 2 or more but less than 3, and so on.

(ii) Draw a histogram to represent the data.

7. Identify the following types of distribution (skewed left, symmetric, reasonably symmetric or skewed right).

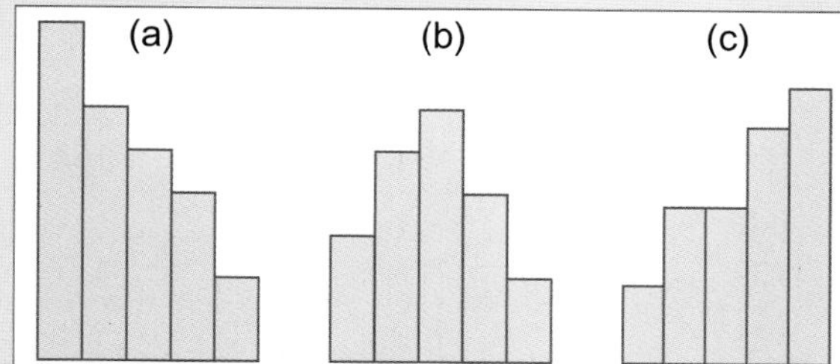

8. The following frequency distribution shows the lengths, in millimetres, of a sample of insects taken from a field:

Length	0–10	10–20	20–30	30–40	40–50
Frequency	2	8	11	10	4

Note: 0–10 means 0 or more but less than 10, and so on.

(i) Draw a histogram for this data.

(ii) Describe the distribution.

9. The frequency distribution shows the weights, in kilograms, of 25 baskets of fruit.

Weight (kg)	1–2	2–3	3–4	4–5
Frequency	10	8	4	3

Note: 1–2 means 1 or more but less than 2, and so on.

(i) Draw a histogram for this data.

(ii) Describe the distribution (symmetric, left-skewed or right-skewed).

10. The amount of rain, in millimetres, was recorded for 60 days. The results are shown in the frequency table.

Rain	0–4	4–8	8–12	12–16	16–20	20–24	24–28	28–32	32–36
No. of days	40	7	6	3	2	1	0	0	1

Note: 0–4 means 0 or more but less than 4, and so on.

(i) Represent the data on a histogram.

(ii) Describe the shape of the distribution.

1.6 SCATTER GRAPHS AND CORRELATION

Scatter graphs are used to investigate relationships between two sets of numerical data.

Always put the explanatory variable, if there is one, on the horizontal (x) axis. If there is no explanatory variable, then either variable can go on the horizontal axis.

If the points on a scatter graph are close to a straight line, then we say there is a strong **correlation** between the two sets of data.

Suppose you measure the arm span and height of all students in your class. For each height measurement, there is a corresponding arm span measurement, so the data can be **paired**.

Data that can be paired is known as paired data or bivariate data.

The following tables show the height and arm-span measurements of a group of students. All measurements are in centimetres.

Height (cm)	160	170	165	159	161	163	165	166
Arm span (cm)	159	168	162	161	162	164	164	164

Height (cm)	166	167	167	169	170	171	171	177
Arm span (cm)	165	166	167	171	169	169	170	175

Each height measurement and corresponding arm span measurement form a couple. Here are the couples for the data above:

(160, 159), (170, 168), (165, 162), (159, 161), (161, 162), (163, 164), (165, 164), (166, 164), (166, 165), (167, 166), (167, 167), (169, 171), (170, 169), (171, 169), (171, 170), (177, 175)

Here is the scatter graph for the data:

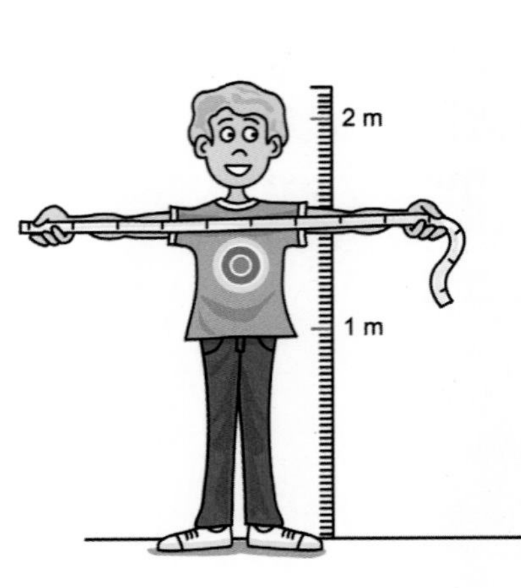

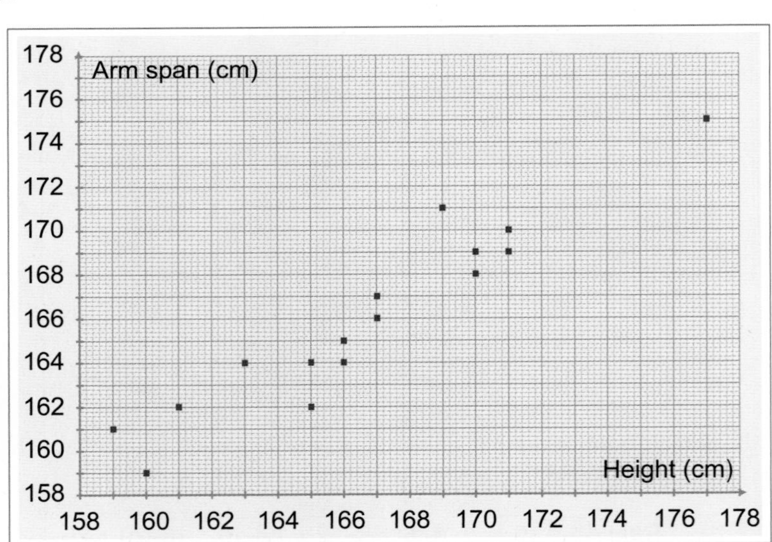

You can see from the graph that the points lie reasonably close to a straight line. We can, in this case, conclude that there is a relationship beween arm span and height. **In general**, the greater the height, the greater the arm span.

Worked Example 1.11

Listed below are the heights of mothers and the heights of their daughters. All measurements are in centimetres.

Mother's height	158	168	160	150	163	168	148	150
Daughter's height	147	162	164	153	164	169	153	158

(i) Draw a scatter diagram for the data.

(ii) Does there appear to be a linear correlation between mothers' heights and daughters' heights?

(iii) On the graph, circle the **outlier** of the data.

An outlier is an individual value that falls outside the overall pattern.

Solution

(i)

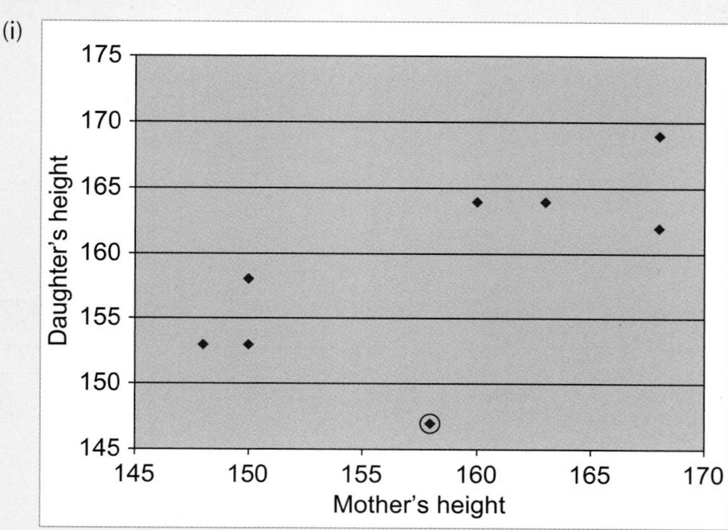

(ii) There appears to be a moderate positive linear correlation between mothers' heights and daughters' heights.

(iii) An outlier is a data point that is removed from the other points. It is circled on the graph in part (i).

The Correlation Coefficient

The **correlation coefficient**, r, is a number in the following range: $-1 \leqslant r \leqslant 1$.

The correlation coefficient is a measure of the strength of the relationship between two sets of data.

It has a value between –1 and 1.

- If r is close to 1, then there is a **strong positive correlation** between two sets of data.
- If r is close to –1, we say there is a **strong negative correlation** between the two sets.
- If r is close to 0, then there is **no correlation** between the two sets.

Types of Correlation

It is important that you state both the **direction** (positive or negative) and the **strength** of a correlation when asked for the type of correlation.

(i) Strong positive correlation

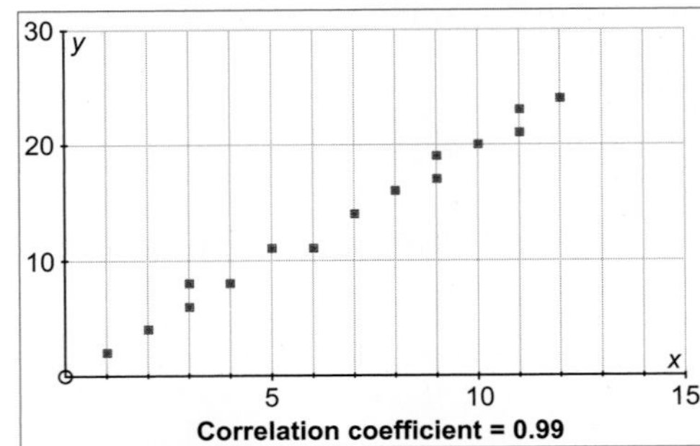

Correlation coefficient = 0.99

(iv) Weak negative correlation

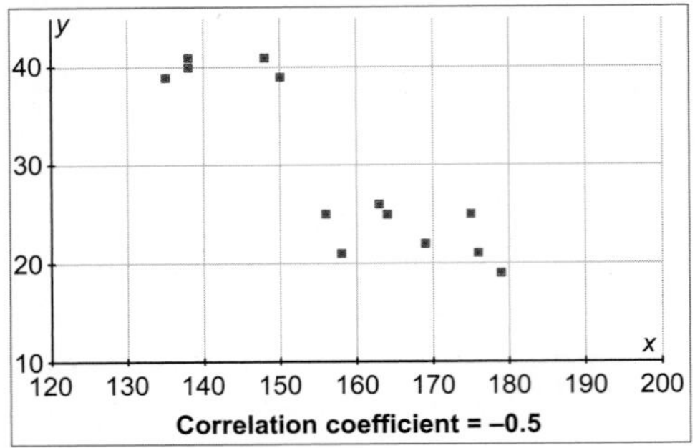

Correlation coefficient = –0.5

(ii) Strong negative correlation

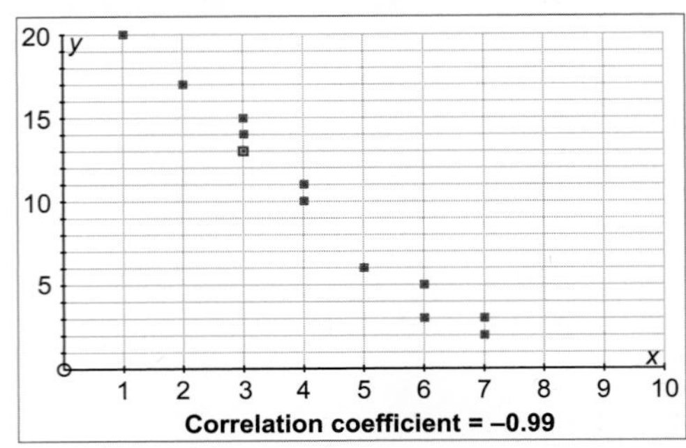

Correlation coefficient = –0.99

(v) No correlation

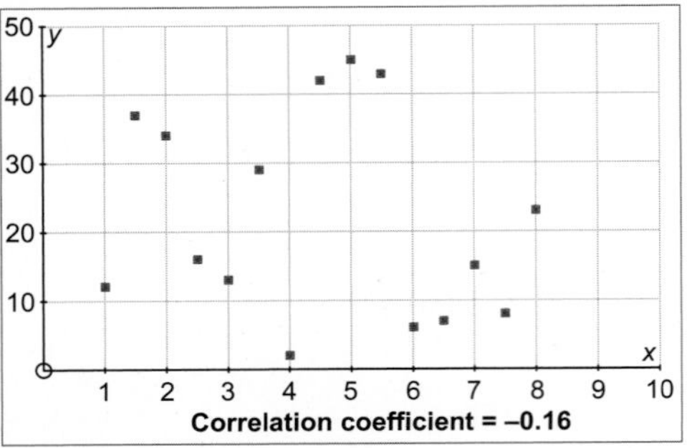

Correlation coefficient = –0.16

(iii) Weak positive correlation

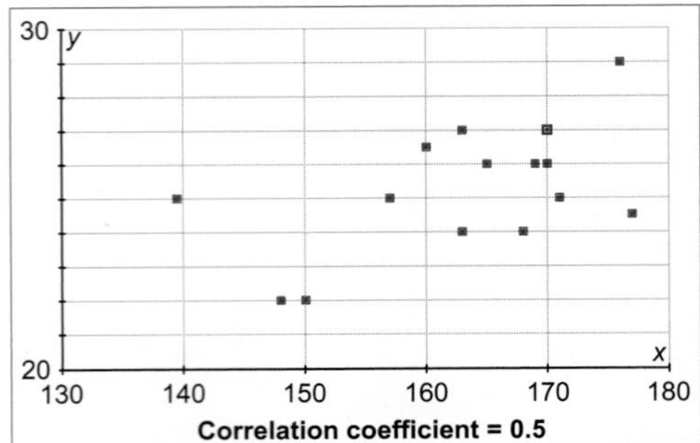

Correlation coefficient = 0.5

Calculating the Correlation Coefficient

The **correlation coefficient** is a numerical measure of the strength of the relationship between two numerical variables.

We can calculate the correlation coefficient using a calculator. Here is how we would calculate the correlation coefficient for the paired data given at the beginning of this section. The tables of data are shown below:

Height (cm)	160	170	165	159	161	163	165	166
Arm span (cm)	159	168	162	161	162	164	164	164

Height (cm)	166	167	167	169	170	171	171	177
Arm span (cm)	165	166	167	171	169	169	170	175

Always clear the calculator's memory before each question, as most calculators store previously entered data.

Step 1 Put the calculator in STAT LINE mode.

Step 2 Enter the paired data. This is how to enter the two pairs, (160, 159) and (170, 168):

Continue and enter all pairs of data.

Step 3 Calculate r, the correlation coefficient:

The value of r for this set of data is 0.95, which indicates a strong positive correlation.

This means that, in general, the taller you are, the more likely it is that you will have a wider arm span than smaller people.

Note: Individual calculators may differ, and it is important that you know how to calculate r, the correlation coefficient, on your calculator.

Worked Example 1.12

At the end of a marathon, eight athletes are randomly selected. All of the athletes are asked to give their age and their time (in minutes) for the race. The results are given in the table below.

Age	33	33	31	26	26	25	30	29
Time	132.6	132.1	133.1	134.0	134.1	134.6	133	133.5

(i) Draw a scatter graph of the data.

(ii) Calculate the correlation coefficient, correct to two decimal places.

(iii) What is the type of correlation between the two sets of data?

(iv) Describe the correlation between age and time.

(v) Explain why the correlation described in part (iv) will not apply for athletes in the 54–64 age bracket.

Solution

(i)

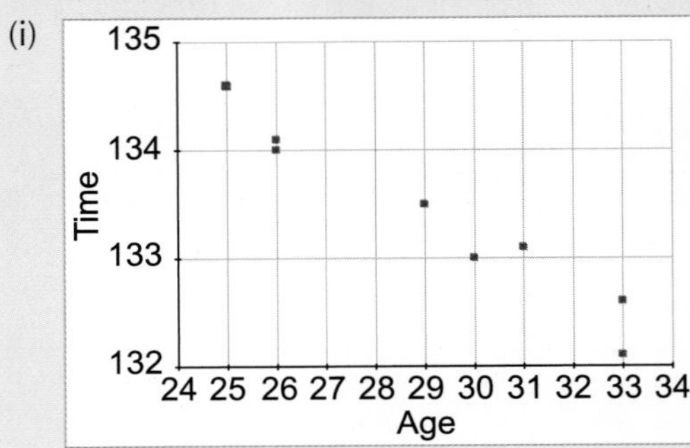

(ii) The correlation coefficient $r = -0.97$.

(iii) There is a strong negative correlation between the two sets of data.

(iv) As age increases, the times, in general, decrease.

(v) In the 54–64 age bracket, one would expect marathon times to increase as athletes get older. In the 24–34 age bracket, times improve as the athletes get older, as marathon athletes generally achieve their best times in their early thirties. Therefore, it is important that we are careful when making predictions that are outside the range of the sample data.

Correlation Versus Causality

In general, the amount of fuel burned by a car depends on the size of its engine, since bigger engines burn more petrol. We say there is a **causal relationship** between the amount of petrol used and the size of the car's engine.

If we find a statistical relationship between two variables, then we cannot always conclude that one of the variables is the cause of the other, i.e. **correlation does not always imply causality**.

During the 20 years between 1980 and 2000, there was a large increase in the sale of calculators and the sale of computers. As the sale of calculators increased, the sale of computers also increased, i.e. there was a strong positive correlation between the sale of calculators and the sale of computers. Did the increase in the sale of calculators cause an increase in the sale of computers? Of course, the answer is no. During this 20-year period, the cost of producing both these technologies decreased dramatically, leading to an increase in sales. A third variable, the cost of production, was responsible for the increase in the other variables. We call this third variable a **lurking variable**.

Exercise 1.6

1. The heights (in centimetres) and ages (in years) of 10 girls are tabled as follows:

Age	8	9	9	10	11	12	12	13	14	15
Height	145	139	140	142	147	154	153	158	160	162

(i) Using suitable scales, plot the scatter diagram for these results.

(ii) Calculate the correlation coefficient.

(iii) Describe the correlation between age and height.

2. During each heartbeat, blood pressure varies between a maximum (systolic) and a minimum (diastolic) pressure. The systolic and diastolic readings from 40 patients are displayed on the scatter graph.

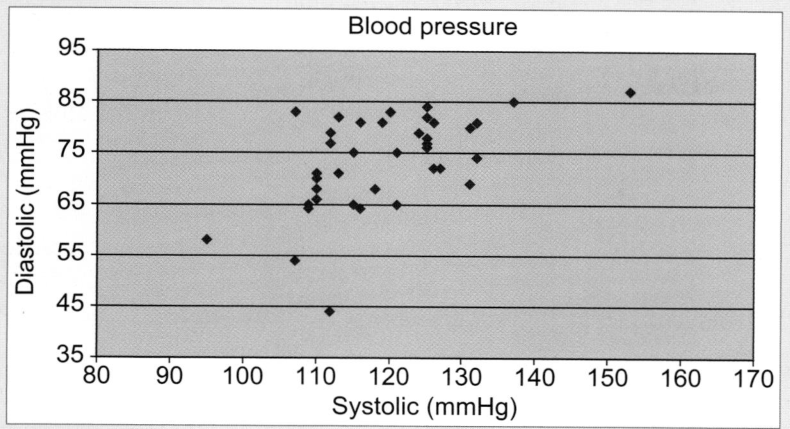

(i) Describe the correlation between systolic and diastolic blood pressure.

(ii) Select the correct value of the correlation coefficient from this list: 0.2, 0.8, –0.5, 0.6, –0.1. Justify your selection.

(iii) An **outlier** is a data point that is removed from the other data points. What is the systolic reading and the diastolic reading of the outlier in this data?

(iv) The blood pressure readings have been taken from 40 patients on a clinical trial. The trial is testing the effectiveness of a new treatment for severe migraine headaches. Outline three possible ethical issues that the trial had to address.

3. Haemoglobin is the component of red blood cells responsible for delivering oxygen from the lungs to the rest of the body. A red blood cell count is the number of red blood cells in a microlitre of blood. The scatter graph displays the haemoglobin and red blood cell count of 50 randomly selected adults.

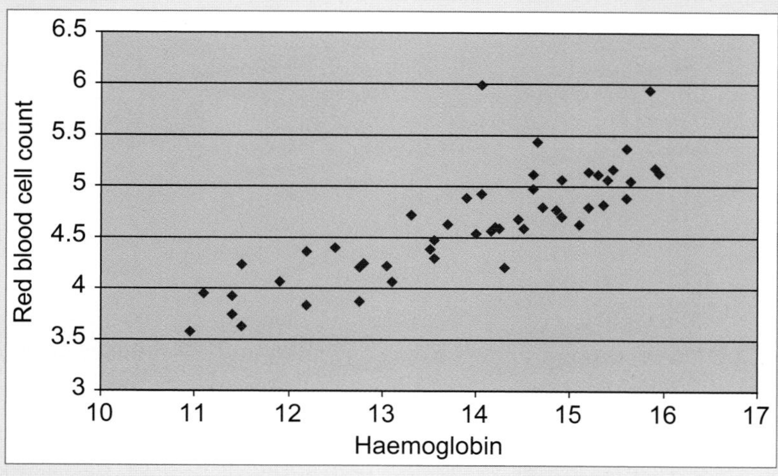

(i) Describe the correlation between haemoglobin count and red blood cell count.

(ii) Select the correct value of the correlation coefficient from this list: –0.2, 0.8, 0.5, 0.1, –0.8. Justify your selection.

(iii) From the graph, estimate the red blood cell count of the four people with the lowest haemoglobin readings.

(iv) Using the graph, estimate the haemoglobin count of the person with a red blood cell count of 6.

(v) It is known, that a high iron diet increases haemoglobin levels. If the individual with the highest blood count was to change from his current diet to a high iron diet and the change of diet increased his haemoglobin levels, would this strengthen or weaken the correlation? Explain.

4. For each of the following diagrams, describe the correlation.

(i)

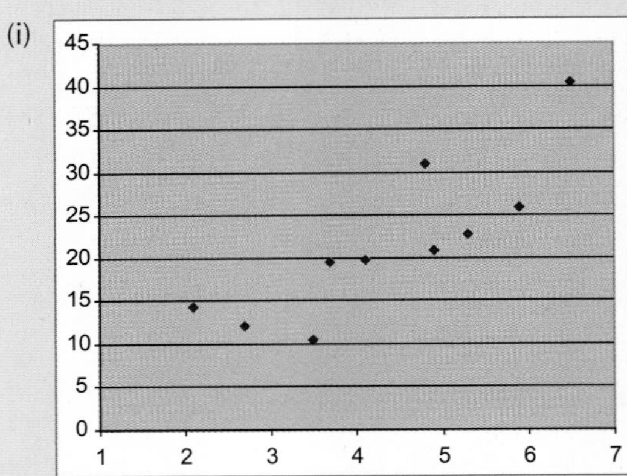

(iv)

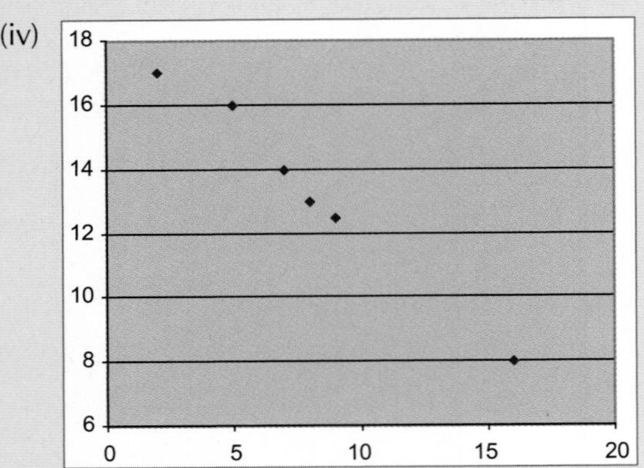

(ii)

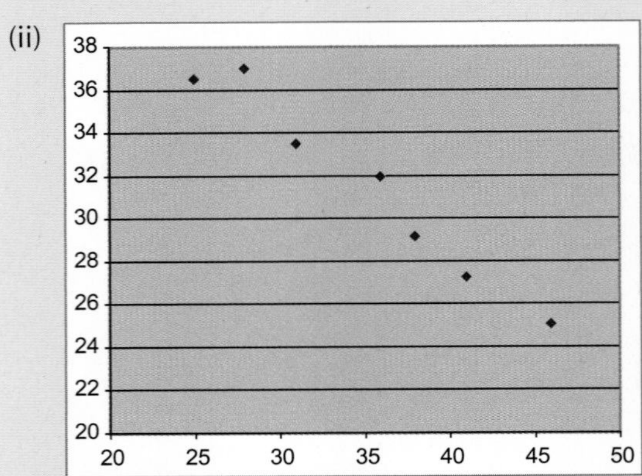

(v)

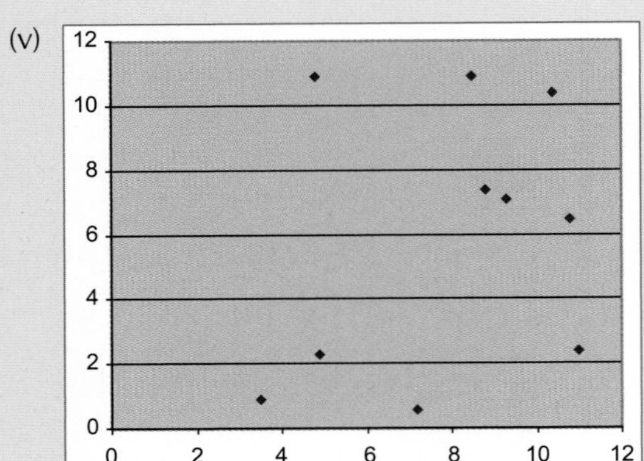

(iii)

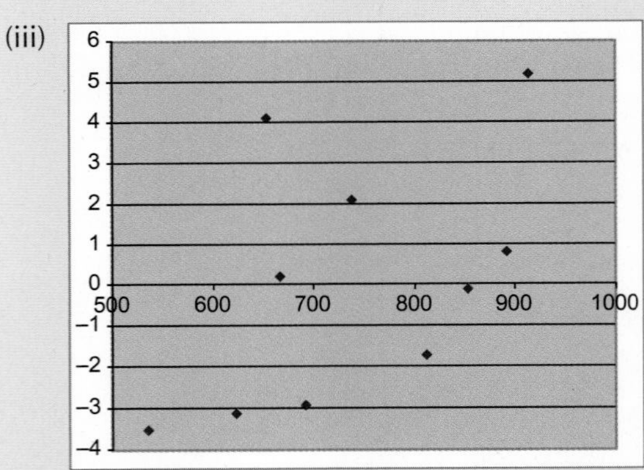

5. The table shows the marks obtained by a group of students in a maths test, and the number of hours' sleep the students had on the night before the test.

Hours slept	9	8	6	8	5	8	9	5	7	8
Mark	85	89	70	87	71	84	90	63	80	70

(i) Using suitable scales, plot the results on a scatter diagram.

(ii) Calculate the correlation coefficient.

(iii) Describe the type of correlation in the context of the question.

6. In 'The Effects of Temperature on Marathon Runners' Performance' by David Martin and John Buoncristiani (*Chance* magazine), high temperatures and times (in minutes) were given for women who won the New York City marathon in recent years. The results are shown in the table below:

Temp (°F)	55	61	49	62	70	73	51	57
Time	145.28	148.72	148.30	148.10	147.62	146.40	144.67	147.53

(i) Represent the data on a scatter graph.

(ii) Calculate the correlation coefficient.

(iii) Does it appear that winning times are affected by temperature? Explain your answer.

(iv) How might this study be improved?

7. The heights (in centimetres) and weights (in kilograms) of eight adults were as follows:

Height	157	181	203	214	197	178	162	210
Weight	59	84	81	100	92	77	61	105

(i) Plot the results on a scatter graph.

(ii) Calculate the correlation coefficient.

(iii) Comment on the correlation.

8. The scatter plot shows the fuel consumption (in litres/100 km) of seven petrol engines.

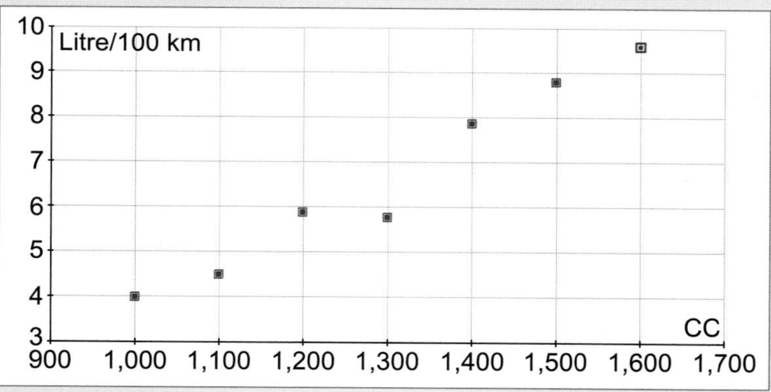

(i) What is the fuel consumption of the 1400 cc engine?

(ii) What size engine has a fuel consumption rate of 4 litres/100 km?

(iii) Calculate and describe the correlation, with reference to the information given.

(iv) 'The data shows that bigger engines are more efficient.' Is this statement true or false? Justify your answer.

9. The following table shows the age and annual income of a sample of eight employees from a large company. The income is in thousands of euro.

Age	36	25	44	48	32	50	33	40
Income	36	29	53	55	34	62	38	46

(i) Draw a scatter diagram of the data.

(ii) Explain the correlation between age and income.

10. At a job interview, eight candidates were given tests on numeracy and IT skills. The tests are marked out of 10. The following table shows the results of the tests:

Numeracy	6	9	10	4	3	5	9	5
IT skills	7	8	9	2	1	5	6	4

(i) Draw a scatter diagram of the data.

(ii) Calculate the correlation coefficient.

(iii) Explain the correlation between numeracy and IT skills.

11. The petal width and petal length of a random sample of 150 irises are plotted on the scatter graph below. Three different classes of iris are included in the sample. All measurements are in centimetres.

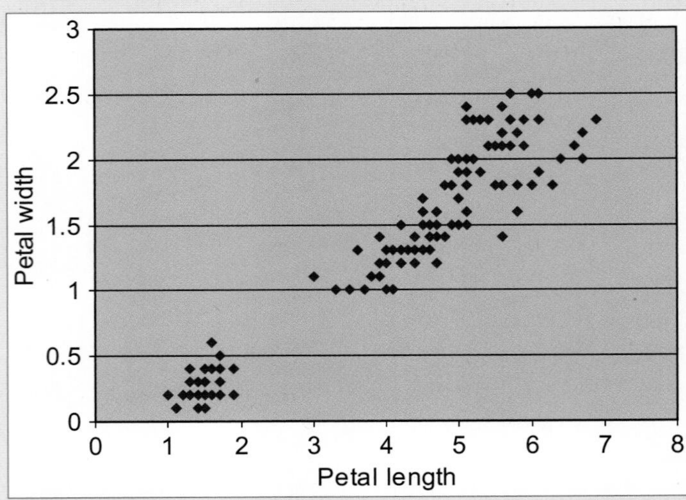

(i) Describe the correlation between petal length and petal width.

(ii) Explain the gap in the plot.

(iii) Select the correct value of the correlation coefficient from this list:
–0.2, 0.96, 0.5, 0.1, –0.8.
Justify your selection.

(iv) Explain how you would have selected this sample.

1.7 LINEAR REGRESSION

The first step in determining the relationship between two variables is to draw a scatter graph. If the scatter graph suggests a linear relationship, then we calculate the correlation coefficient to determine the strength of the relationship. The next step is to find the equation of the straight line that best fits the data. The equation of this line will describe the relationship between the two variables. We call this line **the line of best fit** or the **regression line**.

On our course we draw the line of best fit by eye, and then find its equation.

When drawing the line of best fit, draw the line in such a way as to come as close as possible to the points. We are trying to minimise the distance between the points and the line of best fit.

Worked Example 1.13

A teacher decides to investigate the connection between progress at school and the number of hours of TV watched per week. He collects data from 10 randomly selected students. The data includes the number of hours of TV watched by each student and his/her mean mark across all subjects in a recent end-of-term test.

TV hours	21	4	9	11	12	7	13	5	25	14
Mean mark	47	76	70	55	65	68	50	70	40	55

(i) Represent the data on a scatter graph.

(ii) Calculate, to two decimal places, the correlation coefficient, r.

(iii) What can you conclude from the scatter plot and the correlation coefficient?

(iv) Add the line of best fit to the scatter plot.

Solution

(i)

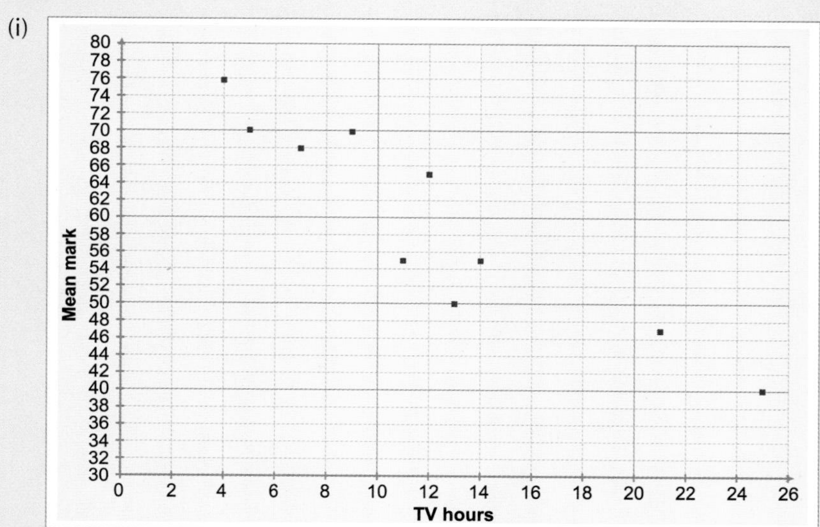

(ii) The correlation coefficient $r = -0.92$.

(iii) There is a strong negative correlation between the variables. In general, those who spend more time watching TV tend to have a lower average mark.

(iv)

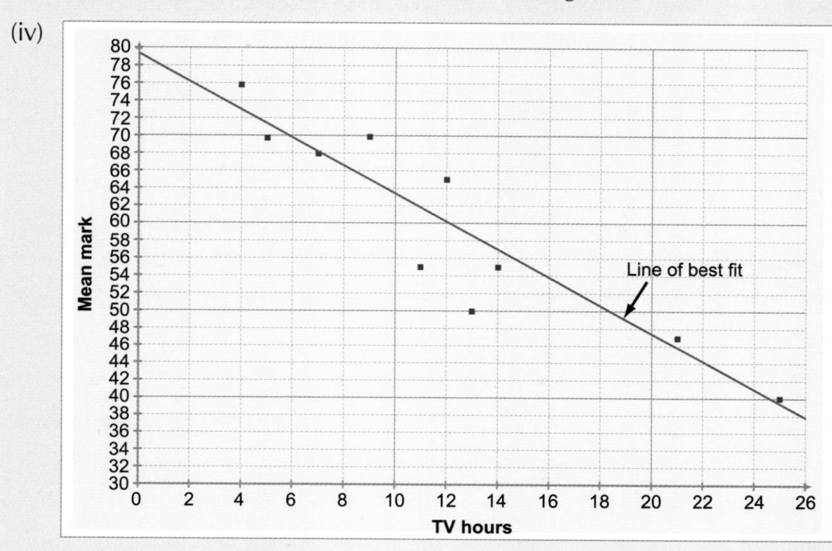

Worked Example 1.14

The manager of a company relies on travelling salespeople to sell the company's products. She wishes to investigate the relationship between sales and the amount of time spent with customers. She collects data from 10 salespeople. This data includes the sales for the month and the time (in hours) spent with customers. The results are given in the following table:

Time (hours)	3.1	4.5	3.8	5.2	6.0	4.1	5.5	5.2	5.0	7.0
Sales (€)	1,648	2,000	1,800	2,440	2,860	2,000	2,440	2,400	2,280	3,200

(i) Represent the data on a scatter graph.

(ii) Calculate the correlation coefficient.

(iii) What can you conclude from the scatter plot and the correlation coefficient?

(iv) Add the line of best fit to the scatter plot.

(v) By taking suitable readings from your plot, find the equation of the line of best fit.

(vi) Estimate the monthly sales for a salesperson who spends 5.8 hours with customers.

(vii) Explain how to interpret the slope of the line in this context.

Solution

(i)

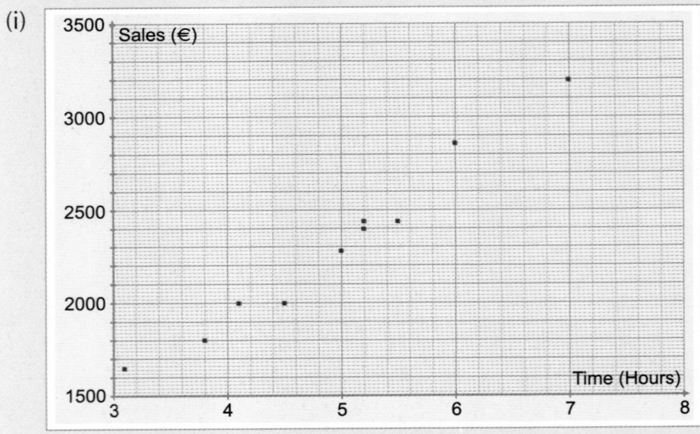

(ii) The correlation coefficient $r = 0.99$.

(iii) There is a strong positive correlation between the variables. In general, those who spend more time with their customers tend to have a higher monthly sales figure.

(iv)

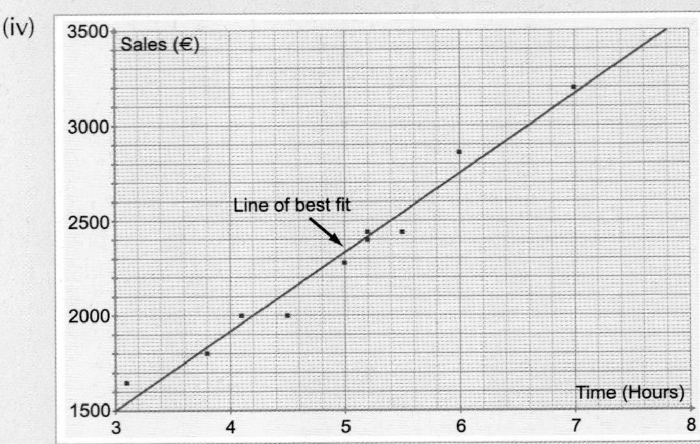

(v) From our graph, (4.2,2000) and (6.6,3000) are two points on the line of best fit.

The equation of the line of best fit should always be of the form: $y = mx + c$, or more correctly, $y = a + bx$.

Slope of the line of best fit:

$$m = \frac{y_2 - y_1}{x_2 - x_1}$$

$$m = \frac{3{,}000 - 2{,}000}{6.6 - 4.2}$$

$$m = \frac{1{,}000}{2.4} = \frac{1{,}250}{3} = 416\tfrac{2}{3}$$

Equation of the line of best fit:

$$y - y_1 = m(x - x_1)$$

$$y - 2{,}000 = \frac{1{,}250}{3}(x - 4.2)$$

$$y - 2{,}000 = \frac{1{,}250x}{3} - 1{,}750$$

$$y = \frac{1{,}250x}{3} + 250$$

(vi)

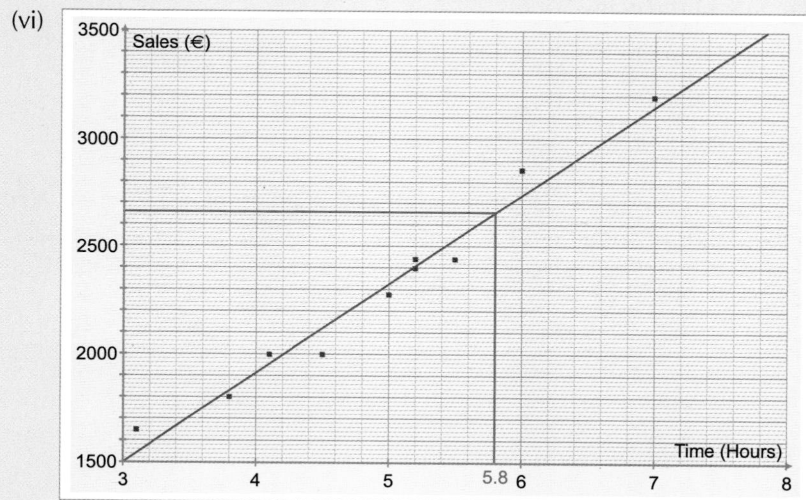

Method 1

Reading from the graph, we get an estimate of €2,660 monthly sales for a salesperson who spends 5.8 hours with the customer.

Method 2

We can also use the equation of the line of best fit to estimate the answer.

$$y = \frac{1{,}250x}{3} + 250$$

$$\therefore y = \frac{1{,}250\,(5.8)}{3} + 250 = €2{,}666.67$$

(vii) The slope represents the expected increase in sales for each additional hour spent with customers. Therefore, each extra hour will yield on average an increase of €416.67 in sales.

Exercise 1.7

1. Eleven students sat two construction studies tests. One test was a theory test and the other was a practical test. Here are the results:

Theory	6	10	8	12	21	5	7	18	13	11	16
Practical	7	9	10	15	22	9	8	17	16	9	19

   (i) Draw a scatter plot to represent the data.
   (ii) Calculate the correlation coefficient.
   (iii) Add the line of best fit to your scatter plot.

2. The table below gives the age and the maximum distance at which a randomly selected sample of drivers could read a motorway sign.

Age (years)	19	21	40	29	45	80	75	62	64	55
Distance (m)	160	165	142	149	148	120	125	100	130	145

   (i) Draw a scatter plot to represent the data.
   (ii) Calculate the correlation coefficient.
   (iii) Add the line of best fit to your scatter plot.
   (iv) Describe the correlation between the two variables.

3. The following table shows the age and annual income of a sample of eight employees from a large company. The income is in thousands of euro.

Age	38	26	43	48	35	52	33	40
Income	36	29	53	55	34	62	38	46

   (i) Draw a scatter diagram of the data.
   (ii) Calculate the correlation coefficient.
   (iii) Add the line of best fit to your scatter plot.
   (iv) Explain the correlation between age and income.
   (v) Find the equation of the line of best fit.

4. Super Stores is a convenience shop that advertises sale items each month to boost sales. The shop manager believes that there is a linear relationship between the amount spent on advertising and sales figures. Here is the data for the past 10 months. All data is in thousands of euro.

Advertising	4.3	2.8	2.1	1.8	3.4	3.8	4.1	4.4	2.2	4.1
Sales	22	17	14	13	19	21	24	25	15	20

   (i) Draw a scatter diagram of the data.
   (ii) Calculate the correlation coefficient.
   (iii) Comment on the correlation between advertising and sales.
   (iv) Add the line of best fit to your scatter plot.
   (v) Find the equation of the line of best fit.
   (vi) Use the equation of the line of best fit to predict the sales figure for a month in which €3,000 was spent on advertising.

5. The manager of Leinster Life Assurance has randomly selected 10 customers from the company's database. He wants to show the relationship between income and the amount of insurance cover a person buys. All data is in thousands of euro.

Income	35.4	40.5	42.3	50.8	40.4	48.6	61.5	56.5	48.6	39.8
Life cover	63	72	74	87	71	83	105	95	84	70

(i) Draw a scatter diagram of the data.

(ii) Calculate the correlation coefficient.

(iii) Add the line of best fit to your scatter plot.

(iv) Explain the correlation between amount of life cover and income for this sample.

(v) Find the equation of the line of best fit.

(vi) Do you think the manager should use this equation to predict the amount of life cover a future customer might take out? Explain your reasoning.

6. Peaches Beauty Salon is currently taking on beauticians at its new premises on Grafton Street. The owner of the salon wants to know what percentage of commission to pay the beauticians based on experience. A survey of 10 beauticians in Dublin was taken with the following results:

Commission (%)	41	21	25	34	45	26	36	36	42	31
Years of experience	11	2	4	9	13	5	8	9	11	6

(i) Draw a scatter diagram of the data.

(ii) Calculate the correlation coefficient.

(iii) Describe the correlation.

(iv) Add the line of best fit to your scatter plot.

(v) Find the equation of the line of best fit.

Peaches Beauty Salon has decided to adopt this equation as the model for determining the percentage of commission to pay to beauticians.

(vi) Allison has just applied to Peaches Beauty Salon for a position as a beautician. She has 10 years' experience. If Allison gets the job, what percentage of commission should she expect to receive?

Revision Exercises

1. Sonia O'Sullivan won gold for Ireland in the 5,000 m race at the World Championships in Gothenburg in 1995. She won the world title with a time of 14:46:47.

For each of the following, identify the type of data:

(i) The number of competitors in the race

(ii) The time it took O'Sullivan to win the race

(iii) The country she represented at the games

(iv) The number on her singlet

(v) The number of spectators in the stadium during the race

2. John wants to find out how fast students in his school can solve a maths problem. It is impractical to ask all students to solve the problem, so he decides to take a sample of students. He feels that students in exam years may be faster problem-solvers than students from non-exam classes.

He randomly selects two groups, one of size 12 and the other of size 20. The first group is selected from students who will be sitting the state exams in June. The second group is selected from non-exam years. He does this to reduce potential bias.

Each individual in both groups is given the same puzzle to complete. Here are the times (to the nearest minute) taken to complete the puzzle:

Group 1

12	12	20	11	17	32
15	21	40	9	20	17

Group 2

26	14	26	21	20	17	28	35	17	12
27	15	36	11	19	22	18	32	24	32

(i) Draw a back-to-back stem-and-leaf diagram for the data.

(ii) What is this type of data called?

(iii) Describe the shape of each distribution.

(iv) What type of sample has John taken?

(v) If there are 600 students in the school, how many students are sitting exams in June?

(vi) Did the fastest and slowest times come from the same group?

3. A consultant orthopaedic surgeon is trying to establish whether a relationship exists between the age of patients who have had hip replacements and the number of days, following the operation, after which they were able to walk unaided.

He chooses a simple random sample of 10 patients and tabulates for each patient their age and the number of days after which they walked without assistance.

Age of patient	69	61	54	77	58	71	65	61	50	56
Number of days	50	45	40	50	42	47	48	38	32	33

(i) Show the data on a scatter plot.

(ii) Calculate the correlation coefficient.

(iii) Describe the correlation in the context of the question.

(iv) Show the line of best fit on your plot.

(v) Find the equation of the line of best fit.

(vi) Use your equation to predict the number of days after which a 63-year-old patient walks unaided.

(vii) Comment on a possible source of bias in the sample. What type of sample should the consultant have taken to eliminate this possible source of bias?

4. In a recent study on Internet shopping in Ireland, a random selection of 1,000 adults was surveyed, and 31% of them said they used the Internet for shopping at least a few times a year.

   (i) Identify the population of interest in this study.
   (ii) Identify the sample.
   (iii) Does the study involve descriptive or inferential statistics? Explain.
   (iv) What variable is being measured in the study?
   (v) Is the variable categorical or numerical?

5. A survey company hires 20 people to go out onto the streets, stop people and ask them questions. The company asks each surveyor to get 50 responses. The data is then used to make inferences about some characteristic of the population.

   (i) What type of sample is the company collecting?
   (ii) Do you think that the people who participate in these surveys are representative of the population? Explain.
   (iii) What type of people would not participate in a survey like this?

6. The marks of 15 students in a test were as follows:

53	67	43	71	21
49	58	48	77	37
82	51	61	98	84

   (i) What variable is being measured?
   (ii) What type of data is being generated by the test?
   (iii) Use an appropriate graph to represent the data.
   (iv) Describe the distribution.

7. For each of the following, state which is the explanatory variable and which is the response variable.

   (i) The cost of a gold ring and its weight
   (ii) The mark a student receives in a mock exam and the mark the student receives in the final exam
   (iii) The distance an athlete runs in training and the time taken to do it
   (iv) The amount of electricity used to boil the water and the volume of water in an electric kettle

8. In each of the following, state the type of sampling being used, and comment on the reliability of the sample. Suggest a more reliable method where necessary.

   (i) Finding how many people have computers in their home by interviewing people outside a computer shop
   (ii) Finding out whether the potatoes are cooked by testing one with a fork
   (iii) Finding out the most popular make of car by noting the make of every fifth car that passes the school between 2.00 pm and 3.00 pm on a Tuesday afternoon
   (iv) Doing a survey on the amount of pocket money received by students in your school by using your phone to ring 15 of your friends, who all respond to the survey

9. The school principal of a co-educational school has asked a student to conduct a survey in the school to decide whether a new uniform should be introduced. The uniform has a bright blue and pink striped design. The student decides to interview a sample of students. Explain how such a sample could be collected for each of the following different sampling strategies:

(i) Cluster sampling
(ii) Simple random sampling
(iii) Stratified random sampling
(iv) Quota sampling
(v) Systematic sampling
(vi) Convenience sampling

10. An expert from a local art gallery agreed to challenge a group of contestants to correctly rank eight pieces of art. Aoife agreed to take part, and her rankings along with those of the expert were as follows:

Piece	A	B	C	D	E	F	G	H
Expert	3	1	6	8	7	2	4	5
Aoife	7	5	2	4	6	1	3	8

(i) Calculate the correlation coefficient for the two data sets.

(ii) Interpret the correlation in the context of the question.

(iii) A further five people entered the competition. The values of the correlation coefficients were 0.1, –0.4, 0.8, –0.5 and 0.9.

(a) Which of these values show that there is almost no correlation between the rankings of the expert and the rankings of the contestant?

(b) Which of these values shows the strongest correlation between the expert and the contestant?

11. Twenty students are asked how many minutes they spent watching television on a particular day. The following frequency distribution summarises their replies:

Time	0–20	20–40	40–60	60–80	80–100
Frequency	2	6	5	3	4

Note: 0–20 means 0 or more but less than 20, and so on.

(i) Draw a histogram to represent the data.

(ii) Describe the shape of the distribution.

(iii) What proportion of students spent 40 minutes or more watching television?

12. (a) Explain, with the aid of an example, what is meant by the statement:

'Correlation does not imply causality.'

(b) The data given in the table below and represented in the scatter diagram are pairs of observations of the variables x and y.

x	1	2	3	4	5	6
y	11	15	17	17	15	11

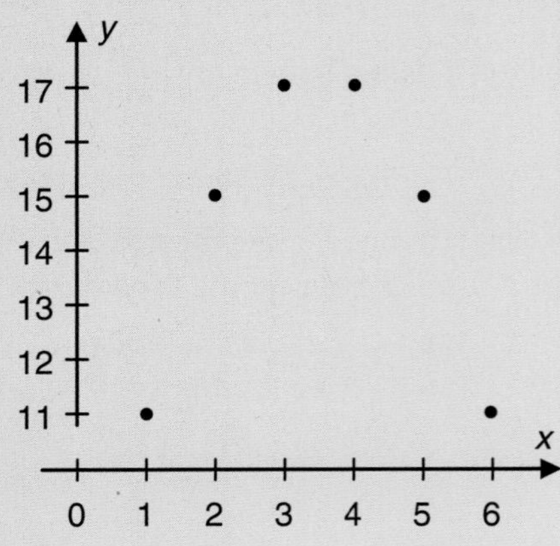

(i) Calculate the correlation coefficient.

(ii) What kind of relationship, if any, do the observed data suggest exists between x and y?

SEC, Project Maths Paper 2, Leaving Certificate Higher Level, 2011

13. A person's maximum heart rate is the highest rate at which their heart beats during certain extreme kinds of exercise. It is measured in beats per minute (bpm). It can be measured under controlled conditions. As part of a study in 2001, researchers measured the maximum heart rate of 514 adults and compared it to each person's age. The results were like those shown in the scatter plot below.

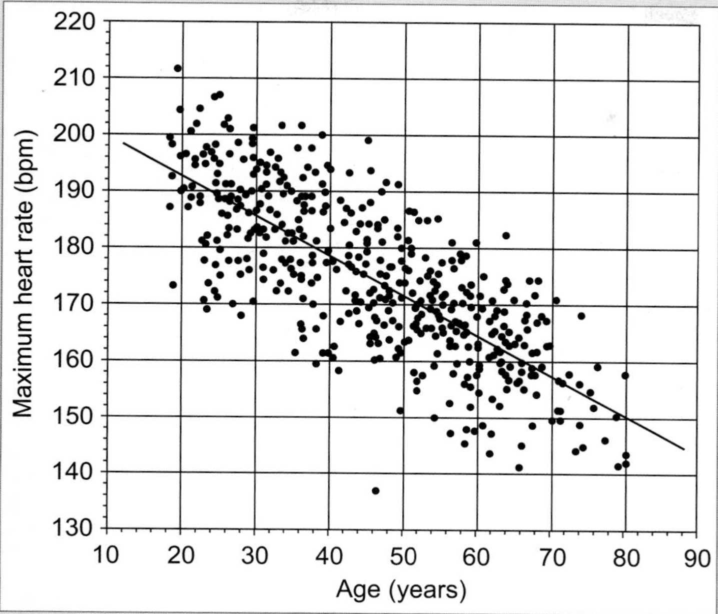

(a) From the diagram, estimate the correlation coefficient.

(b) Circle the **outlier** on the diagram and write down the person's age and maximum heart rate.

(c) The line of best fit is shown on the diagram. Use the line of best fit to estimate the maximum heart rate of a 44-year-old person.

(d) By taking suitable readings from the diagram, calculate the slope of the line of best fit.

(e) Find the equation of the line of best fit and write it in the form: MHR $= a - b \times$ (age), where MHR is the maximum heart rate.

(f) The researchers compared their new rule for estimating maximum heart rate to an older rule. The older rule is: MHR $= 220 -$ age. The two rules can give different estimates of a person's maximum heart rate. Describe how the level of agreement between the two rules varies according to the age of the person. Illustrate your answer with two examples.

(g) A particular exercise programme is based on the idea that a person will get most benefit by exercising at 75% of their estimated MHR. A 65-year-old man has been following this programme, using the old rule for estimating MHR. If he learns about the researchers' new rule for estimating MHR, how should he change what he is doing?

SEC, Project Maths Paper 2, Leaving Certificate Higher Level, 2010

Probability I

Learning Outcomes

In this chapter you will learn:

- The Fundamental Principle of Counting and how to apply it
- When and how to use the calculator buttons for ${}^nP_r$ and $n!$
- To understand the meaning of $\binom{n}{r}$ and apply it to solving problems
- To understand the difference between arranging objects and choosing objects
- To understand the idea of probability
- To apply laws of probability in real-life situations such as flipping coins, rolling dice, picking cards, birthdays falling on certain days, spinners and lotteries
- To understand the meaning of *mutually exclusive* events
- To understand conditional probability and apply it to solving problems

2.1 THE FUNDAMENTAL PRINCIPLE OF COUNTING

YOU SHOULD REMEMBER...

- Set notation
- Fractions, decimals and percentages

FORMULA

Fundamental Principle of Counting

If one event has m possible outcomes and a second event has n possible outcomes, then the total number of possible outcomes is $m \times n$.

ACTIVITIES 2.1, 2.2, 2.3, 2.4, 2.5, 2.6

KEY WORDS

- Arrangement
- Factorial
- Choice
- Probability
- Mutually exclusive
- Trial
- Outcome
- Sample space
- Event

Worked Example 2.1

In a restaurant there are three choices of main course (omelette, fish or burger) followed by two choices of dessert (ice-cream or apple pie). If you have a full meal in the restaurant, how many choices of meal will you have?

Solution

In accordance with the **Fundamental Principle of Counting**, there will be $3 \times 2 = 6$ choices. They are as follows:

1. Omelette followed by ice-cream
2. Omelette followed by apple pie
3. Fish followed by ice-cream
4. Fish followed by apple pie
5. Burger followed by ice-cream
6. Burger followed by apple pie

Worked Example 2.2

How many ways are there of arranging all the letters of the word MATH? (Math is the American for maths.)

Solution

There are four choices for the first letter, three choices for the second letter, two choices for the third letter and one choice for the last letter. Hence, there are $4 \times 3 \times 2 \times 1 = 24$ ways. Here they are:

MATH	AMTH	THAM	HATM	MTHA	ATHM	TAHM	HTAM
MAHT	AMHT	THMA	HAMT	MHAT	AHMT	TMHA	HMAT
MTAH	ATMH	TAMH	HTMA	MHTA	AHTM	TMAH	HMTA

Factorials

There is a shorthand way of writing $4 \times 3 \times 2 \times 1$.

It is 4!, which we call 'four factorial'.

Similarly, $5! = 5 \times 4 \times 3 \times 2 \times 1 = 120$.

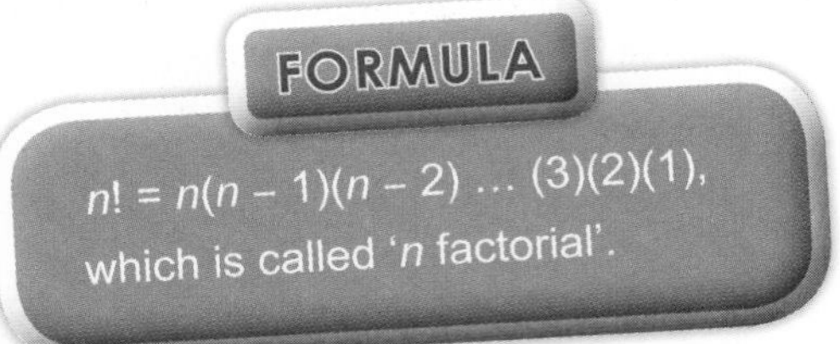

FORMULA
$n! = n(n-1)(n-2) \dots (3)(2)(1)$,
which is called 'n factorial'.

To get 5! on your calculator, press 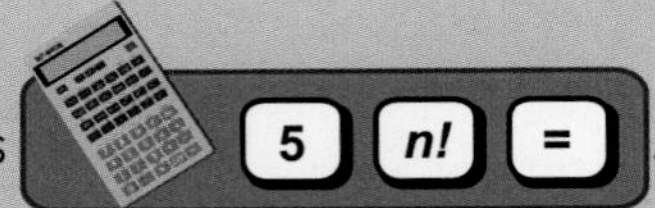 5 n! = .

The answer 120 should come up on the screen.

(On some calculators $n!$ is written as x!)

Worked Example 2.3

Six horses enter a race. Punters are asked to guess which horse will come first, which second, which third, etc. all the way down to sixth place. How many different predictions can be made?

Solution

When a punter is filling up the form, there will be six choices for first place, five choices for second place, four choices for third place, etc.

Hence, the number of different predictions is $6 \times 5 \times 4 \times 3 \times 2 \times 1 = 6! = 720$.

^nP_r : The Number of Ways of Arranging n Objects, r at a Time

Worked Example 2.4

In how many ways can the letters of the word COUNTER be arranged, taking them three at a time? No repetitions are allowed. (We can have RCE and EOU, for example – but not EEC or RRR.)

Solution

There are seven choices for the first letter, six choices for the next letter and five choices for the last letter.

This means than there are $7 \times 6 \times 5 = 210$ ways.

It is important to realise that:

$$7 \times 6 \times 5 = \frac{7!}{4!}$$

and gives the number of permutations (or arrangements) of a population of seven, taking them three at a time. It is called $^7P_3$.

In general, if you have a population of n items, and you want to arrange r of them in order, then the number of possible arrangements (or permutations) is called ^nP_r and is defined as follows:

FORMULA

$$^nP_r = \frac{n!}{(n-r)!}$$

On all good calculators there is a button labelled  nPr.

In Worked Example 2.4, the answer is $^7P_3$. We get this on a calculator by pressing:

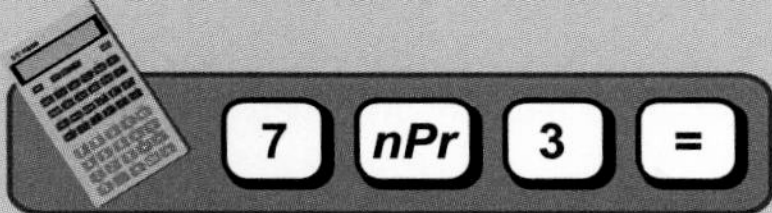

The answer 210 comes up on the screen.

Worked Example 2.5

How many numbers between 500 and 1,000 can be made from the digits 2, 4, 6 and 8:

(i) If no digit may be repeated (e.g. 824)

(ii) If digits may be repeated (e.g. 668)

Solution

We can deduce two things:

1. It will be a three-digit number.
2. The first digit will have to be either 6 or 8 (to make a number greater than 500).

(i) There are two choices for the first digit (6 and 8).

Having made this choice, there will be three choices left for the second digit.

Having made these choices, there will be two choices left for the third and last digit.

Hence, there are $2 \times 3 \times 2 = 12$ numbers.

(ii) There are two choices for the first digit (6 and 8).

There are four choices for the next digit (as a digit can be repeated).

There are again four choices for the third digit.

Hence, there are $2 \times 4 \times 4 = 32$ such numbers.

Worked Example 2.6

How many ways are there of arranging the letters of the word LEAVING:

(i) If there are no restrictions

(ii) If they must begin with N

(iii) If they must end with a vowel

(iv) If the three vowels must be together

(v) If L and N must be side by side

(vi) If L and N must be apart

Solution

(i) $7! = 5{,}040$

(ii) $1 \times 6 \times 5 \times 4 \times 3 \times 2 \times 1 = 6! = 720$ (since there is only **one** choice for the first letter)

(iii) There are three choices for the last letter, then the six remaining letters may be in any order: $6 \times 5 \times 4 \times 3 \times 2 \times 1 \times 3 = 6! \times 3 = 2{,}160$

Notice how **the place that has a restriction imposed on it is fixed up first**. Hence, we put one of the three vowels as the LAST letter and then fill the rest of the slots.

(iv) Treat the three vowels (glued together) as **one** letter. There are five letters to be arranged: L, V, N, G, [AEI]. There are 5! ways of arranging these.

But the vowels could be AEI, AIE, EAI, … etc. There are 3! ways in which they can be arranged:

Hence, the answer is $5! \times 3! = 720$

(v) Treat LN as one letter. There are six letters to be arranged: E, A, V, I, G, [LN].

But [LN] can also be [NL]. (There are 2! ways of arranging [LN].)

∴ The answer is $6! \times 2! = 1{,}440$

(vi) Use the 'subtraction method'. There are 5,040 arrangements altogether (see part (i)).

In 1,440 of these the L and N are together (see part (v)).

∴ There are $5{,}040 - 1{,}440 = 3{,}600$ arrangements in which the L and N are apart.

2.2 A SURPRISING RESULT

On your calculator press:

You might be surprised to find that the answer is 1.

Perhaps this argument may convince you:

5! = 120		
4! = 24	Divide by 5	(120 ÷ 5 = 24)
3! = 6	Divide by 4	(24 ÷ 4 = 6)
2! = 2	Divide by 3	(6 ÷ 3 = 2)
1! = 1	Divide by 2	(2 ÷ 2 = 1)
0! = 1	Divide by 1	(1 ÷ 1 = 1)

Exercise 2.1

1. Evaluate the following:

(i) $3!$
(ii) $2! + 4!$
(iii) $7! - 6!$
(iv) $\frac{8!}{7!}$
(v) $\frac{9!}{6!}$
(vi) $0! + 1! + 2! + 3!$
(vii) $\frac{11!}{10!}$
(viii) $\frac{14!}{13!}$
(ix) $\frac{20!}{19!}$
(x) $\frac{21!}{19!}$

2. In a restaurant, there are three choices of starter, seven choices of main course and two choices of dessert. How many different full meals could be eaten at this restaurant?

3. A girl has five jumpers, two pairs of jeans and three pairs of socks. Ignoring the rest of her attire, in how many different possible ways could she dress?

4. A small town introduces 'registration numbers' for bicycles. Each registration number consists of a letter followed by a single digit (F3 and Y0 for example).

What is the maximum number of bicycles that could have different registration numbers?

5. (a) Investigate if:

(i) $3! + 2! = 5!$
(ii) $3! \times 2! = 6!$
(iii) $0! + 1! = 2!$

(b) How many ways are there of arranging all the letters of these words?

(i) SUM
(ii) MATHS
(iii) TRIANGLE

6. How many ways are there of arranging the letters of THEORY if the letters are taken:

(i) Three at a time
(ii) Four at a time
(iii) Six at a time

7. How many four-digit numbers can be made from the digits 1, 3, 4 and 5 (without repetition)?

(i) How many of these are even?
(ii) How many are odd?
(iii) How many are over 4,000?

8. In how many different ways can the letters of the word RHOMBUS be arranged:

(i) Taking the letters seven at a time
(ii) Taking the letters five at a time
(iii) Taking the letters two at a time

9. How many ways are there of arranging the letters of the word MATRIX:

(i) If there are no restrictions
(ii) If they must begin with T
(iii) If they must begin with T and end with M
(iv) If they must begin with a vowel
(v) If they must **not** begin with a vowel

10. How many ways are there of arranging the letters of the word MONSTER:

(i) If there are no restrictions
(ii) If they must begin with a vowel
(iii) If they must begin with a consonant
(iv) If the vowels must be together
(v) If the vowels must be apart

11. How many ways are there of arranging the letters of the word DUBLINER:

(i) If there are no restrictions
(ii) If they must begin with B and end in L
(iii) If the three vowels must be together
(iv) If E and R must be together
(v) If E and R must be apart

12. How many ways are there of arranging the letters of the word TRIANGLES:

(i) If there are no restrictions

(ii) If the three vowels must be together

(iii) If the six consonants must be together

(iv) If the letter G must be immediately followed by the letter R

(v) If they must begin and end with a consonant

13. (a) Evaluate:

(i) $\dfrac{10!}{9!}$

(ii) $\dfrac{11!}{7!\,4!}$

(iii) $\dfrac{23!}{22!}$

(iv) $\dfrac{13!}{11!}$

(b) Simplify:

(i) $\dfrac{n!}{(n-1)!}$

(ii) $\dfrac{(n+1)!}{n!}$

(iii) $n!\left[\dfrac{1}{(n-1)!} - \dfrac{1}{n!}\right]$

(c) How many numbers between 3,000 and 10,000 can be made from the digits 1, 3, 5 and 7:

(i) If digits may not be repeated

(ii) If digits may be repeated

14. How many numbers between 500 and 1,000 do not contain the digits 0, 1 or 2?

15. How many natural numbers can be made using some or all of the digits 7, 8 and 9 – without repetitions?

16. How many natural numbers can be made using some or all of the digits 0, 1, 2 and 3, with no repetitions? (Note: Zero is not considered a natural number.)

17. A code for breaking into a computer system consists of two different letters followed by three different digits.

(i) How many different codes are possible?

(ii) A user has been given a code, but cannot remember it fully. All that she can remember is that the first letter is B and the first digit is 8. How many different possible codes fit this description?

18. How many five-digit numbers can be formed in which the first and the last digits are greater than five, the three centre digits are identical, and the last digit is odd?

19. A raffle takes place in a school. Tickets are available in three colours: pink, yellow and green. Tickets are labelled with a letter followed by three digits. How many different tickets can be sold?

(Note: Pink-N233 is not the same as Green-N233.)

20. Forty horses are entered for the Grand National. Punters are asked to guess which will come first, which will come second and which will come third. In how many different ways can this be done?

21. How many four-digits numbers satisfy all these conditions at once:

- The number is a multiple of 10.
- The first three digits are all greater than 5.
- The first digit is even.

22. How many six-digit numbers fit this description: 'It is an odd number. It is a palindrome (i.e. it reads the same backwards as forwards). The two centre digits are odd and greater than 2'?

23. Two girls and three boys are to be lined up for a photograph. How many different arrangements are possible:

(i) If there are no restrictions

(ii) If they must be boy–girl–boy–girl–boy

24. Four girls and three boys are to be lined up side by side. No two persons of the same gender may be side by side. How many arrangements are possible?

25. Four girls and five boys are to be lined up. How many arrangements are possible:

(i) If there are no restrictions

(ii) If two particular girls must be together

(iii) If two particular boys must be kept apart

(iv) If no two people of the same gender may be together

26. (i) How many six-digit numbers can be made from the digits 1, 2, 3, 4, 5 and 7 without repetitions?

(ii) How many are even?

(iii) How many are even and over 300,000?

(Hint: In part (iii), deal with those which end in 2 and 4 separately.)

27. (i) How many five-digit odd numbers can be made from the digits 5, 6, 7, 8 and 9 without repetitions?

(ii) How many of these are under 80,000?

2.3 CHOOSING

There are seven members in our club: Ann, Bob, Carol, Dee, Eve, Fred and Gus. We have to choose three of them to represent the club at the National Congress in Athlone. How many different **choices** could we possibly make?

We'll refer to the members by their initial letter. So, we could choose ABC or CDG or ADG, etc.

We have already seen that there are ${}^7P_3 = \frac{7!}{4!}$ ways of **arranging** seven letters in groups of three. But these would include ABC, ACB, BAC, BCA, CAB and CBA, all of which represent the **one team**: ABC.

Similarly, the six arrangements CDG, CGD, DCG, DGC, GCD, GDC all represent the **one team**: CDG.

In fact, there will be 3! (or six) arrangements for every one choice.

Hence, the number of choices will be $\frac{7!}{4!} \div 3! = \frac{7!}{4!3!} = 35$.

Choices

In general, the number of teams of r, which can be chosen from a population of n (where $n \geqslant r$), is called $\binom{n}{r}$.

Europeans call this 'nCr'. Americans call it 'n choose r'. There should be a button on your calculator labelled **nCr**.

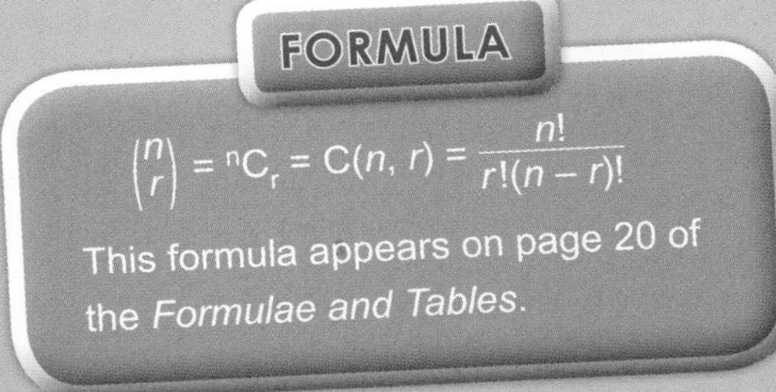

FORMULA
$\binom{n}{r} = {}^nC_r = C(n, r) = \frac{n!}{r!(n-r)!}$
This formula appears on page 20 of the *Formulae and Tables*.

Worked Example 2.7

Evaluate $\binom{11}{3}$ and $\binom{11}{8}$.

Solution

$\binom{11}{3} = \frac{11!}{3!8!} = 165$

1 1 nCr 3 =

$\binom{11}{8} = \frac{11!}{8!3!} = 165$

The Twin Rule

It is no coincidence that the two solutions in Worked Example 2.7 are equal. It is an example of the Twin Rule. Read on…

The Twin Rule states that:

$\binom{n}{r} = \binom{n}{n-r}$

For example, $\binom{14}{12} = \binom{14}{2}$. And $\binom{100}{11} = \binom{100}{89}$, etc.

The Twin Rule can be proved in the following way:

$\text{LHS} = \binom{n}{r} = \frac{n!}{r!(n-r)!}$

$\text{RHS} = \binom{n}{n-r} = \frac{n!}{(n-r)!(n-(n-r))!} = \frac{n!}{(n-r)!r!} = \text{LHS}$

There is a quick way of calculating $\binom{n}{r}$. It is this:

Think of the countdown: $n, (n-1), (n-2), \ldots, 4, 3, 2, 1$.

$$\binom{n}{r} = \frac{\text{First } r \text{ numbers in the countdown}}{\text{Last } r \text{ numbers in the countdown}}$$

For example, $\binom{10}{4} = \frac{10 \times 9 \times 8 \times 7}{4 \times 3 \times 2 \times 1} = 210$.

Of course, $\binom{10}{6}$ is also 210, under the Twin Rule.

Worked Example 2.8

There are 13 hockey players on a panel, including the captain. The manager has to choose a team of 11. How many different teams could she possibly pick:

(i) If there are no further restrictions

(ii) If the captain must be included in the 11

Solution

(i) The manager has to choose 11 players out of 13.

The number of choices $= \binom{13}{11} = \binom{13}{2} = \frac{13 \times 12}{2 \times 1} = 78.$

(ii) Since the captain must be included, the manager has to pick the remaining 10 players from the remaining 12 panel members.

The number of choices $= \binom{12}{10} = \binom{12}{2} = \frac{12 \times 11}{2 \times 1} = 66.$

Worked Example 2.9

A chess club has 11 members: six girls and five boys. A committee of five members is to be formed. How many choices are there:

(i) If there are no restrictions

(ii) If there must be more girls than boys on the committee

Solution

(i) $\binom{11}{5} = \frac{11 \times 10 \times 9 \times 8 \times 7}{5 \times 4 \times 3 \times 2 \times 1} = 462$

(ii) Here are the possibilities:

Three girls AND two boys OR four girls AND one boy OR five girls AND no boys.

$\therefore$ choices $= \binom{6}{3} \times \binom{5}{2} + \binom{6}{4} \times \binom{5}{1} + \binom{6}{5} \times \binom{5}{0}$

$= (20 \times 10) + (15 \times 5) + (6 \times 1) = 200 + 75 + 6 = 281$

The above example illustrates how, in counting, the word AND gives rise to ×, but the word OR gives rise to +.

In general, $\binom{n}{n} = 1$ and hence $\binom{n}{0} = 1$ for any number n.

Exercise 2.2

1. Evaluate the following:

$\binom{10}{2}$; $\binom{11}{3}$; $\binom{7}{4}$; $\binom{14}{1}$; $\binom{20}{2}$; $\binom{9}{3}$; $\binom{9}{6}$; $\binom{13}{11}$; $\binom{18}{4}$; $\binom{18}{14}$.

2. Verify that $\binom{13}{3} + \binom{13}{4} = \binom{14}{4}$.

3. Verify that $\binom{12}{7} - \binom{11}{7} = \binom{11}{6}$.

4. If $\binom{5}{0} + \binom{5}{1} + \binom{5}{2} + \binom{5}{3} + \binom{5}{4} + \binom{5}{3} = 2^k$, find k.

5. Investigate if $2\binom{13}{7} = \binom{14}{7}$.

6. Show that $\binom{11}{2} + \binom{11}{3} + \binom{12}{4} = \binom{13}{4}$.

7. A manager names a panel of 15 players for a hockey final. On the day of the final he must choose 11 of these.

How many different teams could the manager possibly select?

8. A student has to choose three subjects from the following range: biology, music, art, chemistry, economics, history, Greek. How many different choices can the student make:

(i) If there are no restrictions

(ii) If Greek must be included as one of the three subjects

(iii) If Greek must be excluded

9. A class consists of six girls and seven boys. A team of four tennis players must be chosen from this class.

How many different teams could be picked:

(i) If there are no restrictions

(ii) If the team must have two girls and two boys

(iii) If the team must be all female

10. How many different teams of 13 players may be chosen from a panel of 15:

(i) If any 13 players may be picked

(ii) If the captain **must** be included

11. $S = \{a, b, c, d, e, f, g, h\}$.

(i) How many subsets of S, containing five elements, can be formed?

(ii) How many of these contain h?

(iii) How many do not contain h?

(iv) How many contain h and g?

12. A committee of five persons is to be chosen from four women and seven men.

If there must be more women than men on the committee, how many different committees could be formed?

13. Thirteen people are at a party. They all shake hands with one another.

How many handshakes take place?

(*Hint*: For each handshake, you must choose two people.)

14. There are 12 teams in a league. They all play each other twice in a season.

How many matches take place in a season?

15. How many boards of five members can be chosen from a panel of four managers and five workers:

(i) If there are no restrictions

(ii) If there must be more workers than managers

(iii) If there must be only one worker

16. To fill out a card for a lottery, a person has to choose six numbers out of 45. How many different ways are there of filling out a single card?

17. (i) Evaluate $\binom{10}{5}$.

(ii) Show that there are 126 ways of dividing a group of 10 people into two groups of five.

(iii) How many ways are there of dividing up eight players into two teams for a four-a-side match?

(iv) How many ways are there of dividing 12 players into two teams for a six-a-side match?

18. Mr and Mrs Zimmerman want to give their baby a first name and a second name so that the baby's three initials are in alphabetical order.

How many different initials could the baby end up with? (for example, B, G, Z, is acceptable. But G, B, Z and B, B, Z are not acceptable.)

19. In how many ways can a committee of five be chosen from 11 people:

(i) If one particular person must be included

(ii) If one particular person must be excluded

(iii) If two particular people will not work on the same committee (that is, if one is included, the other must be excluded)

20. In how many ways may a team of four oarsmen be chosen from a panel of 13 people if two individuals refuse to work on the **same** rowing team as each other?

21. Twelve points are drawn on the circumference of a circle.

(i) How many different chords could be drawn between these points?

(ii) How many triangles may be drawn by connecting these points?

22. (i) How many different poker hands can be dealt to a player? (A poker hand consists of five cards, dealt from a pack of 52.)

(ii) How many hands include the Ace of Spades?

(iii) How many poker hands do not include the Ace of Spades?

(iv) How many hands include all four Aces?

(v) How many hands contain exactly three Aces?

23. If $\binom{n}{2} = 210$, find the value of n, where $n \geqslant 2$.

24. If $\binom{n}{3} = 15n$, $n \geqslant 3$, find the value of n.

Verify your answer.

25. Solve for $x \geqslant 3$:

$3\binom{x}{3} = 2\binom{x}{2} + 5\binom{x}{1}$. Verify your answer.

2.4 PROBABILITY

ACTIVITIES 2.10, 2.11, 2.12, 2.13

In probability we encounter many common terms that have special meanings we must be aware of.

A **trial** is the act of doing an experiment in probability.

The flipping of a coin is an example of a **trial**.

The set or list of all possible outcomes in a trial is called the **sample space**.

For a coin, the **sample space** is {head, tail}.

An **outcome** is one of the possible results of the trial.

When flipping a coin, the **outcomes** are that you could flip a head or a tail.

An **event** is the occurrence of one or more **specific outcomes**.

The flipped coin landing on a head would be an **event**.

Any subset of the sample space (S) is an event (E). If a six-sided die is rolled, S = {1, 2, 3, 4, 5, 6}. Getting an even number is an event, E = {2, 4, 6}.

The probability of an event lies between 0 and 1. The nearer the probability of an event is to 1, the more likely it is to happen. The nearer the probability of an event is to 0, the more unlikely it is to happen.

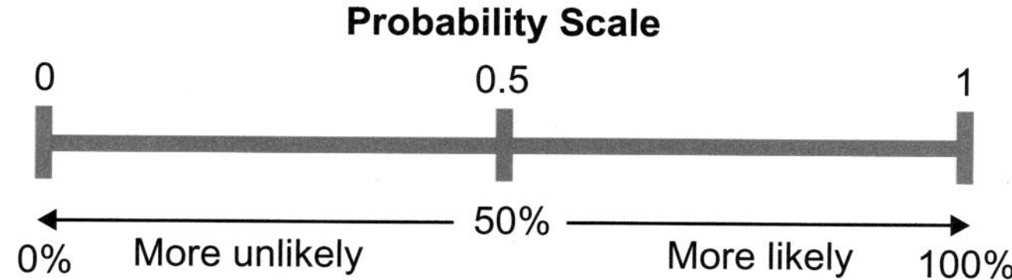

We sometimes use percentages when giving the probability of an event. If an event is certain to happen (for example, that the day after next Saturday will be a Sunday), we say its probability is 100%. If an event has an evens chance of happening (for example, getting tails when you flip a fair coin), we say the probability is 50%. If an event is impossible (for example, that you will be dealt a hand with five Aces), we say the probability is 0%.

Worked Example 2.10

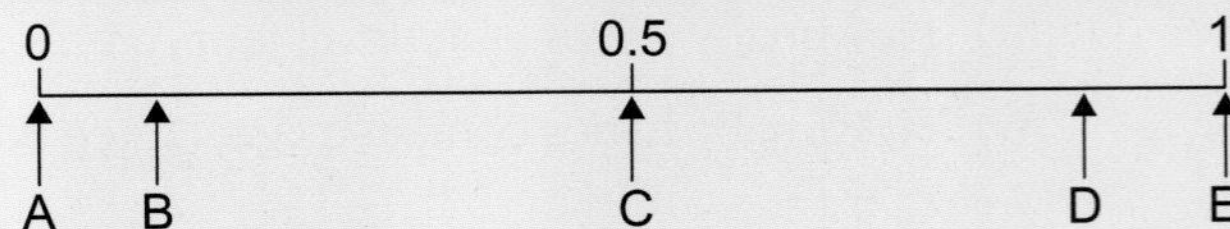

Five events (A, B, C, D and E) are shown on a probability scale. Copy and complete the following table, filling in the appropriate letters:

Event	Letter
Getting heads when you flip a fair coin once	
That next Christmas will be in December	
That someone in your family will win the Lotto	
That it will rain somewhere in Ireland next week	
Next year, I will be a year younger.	

Solution

Event	Letter	Reason
Getting heads when you flip a fair coin once	C	It's fifty–fifty, so its probability is 0.5.
That next Christmas will be in December	E	It's certain.
That someone in your family will win the Lotto	B	It's possible but not very likely. Its probability is low.
That it will rain somewhere in Ireland next week	D	It's almost, but not quite, certain.
Next year, I will be a year younger.	A	It's impossible.

2.5 RELATIVE FREQUENCY (EXPERIMENTAL PROBABILITY)

Sometimes it can be very difficult to work out the probability of an event. For example, will a football team win their next match? In this case, we can use statistical evidence from observations or experiments to determine the experimental probability or **relative frequency** of an event.

The relative frequency of an event is the number of times that an event happens in a trial out of the total number of trials.

Relative frequency is a good estimate of the true probability of an event, provided that the number of trials is sufficiently large.

$$\text{Relative frequency} = \frac{\text{frequency or number of times the event happens in a trial}}{\text{total number of trials}}$$

Worked Example 2.11

Last season, James took 20 penalties and scored 15 of them.

(i) What was the relative frequency of James scoring a penalty (give your answer as a percentage)?

(ii) If James takes 16 penalties next season, how many would you expect him to score, if the relative frequency remains the same?

Solution

(i) The relative frequency $= \dfrac{\text{number of scores}}{\text{number of penalties}} = \dfrac{15}{20} = \dfrac{3}{4} = 75\%$

(ii) James would expect to score 75% of the 16 penalties = 12 penalties.

> It is important to note that increasing the number of times an experiment is repeated generally leads to better estimates of probability.

Worked Example 2.12

An experiment is conducted to show how the number of trials improves the accuracy of the relative frequency. Michelle flips a coin and records her results every 10 flips:

After 10 flips	Total	Relative frequency
Head	6	0.6
Tail	4	0.4

After 20 flips	Total	Relative frequency
Head	13	0.65
Tail	7	0.35

After 30 flips	Total	Relative frequency
Head	13	0.43
Tail	17	0.57

After 40 flips	Total	Relative frequency
Head	18	0.45
Tail	22	0.55

After 50 flips	Total	Relative frequency
Head	24	0.48
Tail	26	0.52

Note: Results for relative frequency are rounded to two decimal places where necessary.

(i) Plot the relative frequency of tails on a trend graph.

(ii) Is a relative frequency of 0.35 more likely after 20 flips or after 50 flips?

Solution

(i)

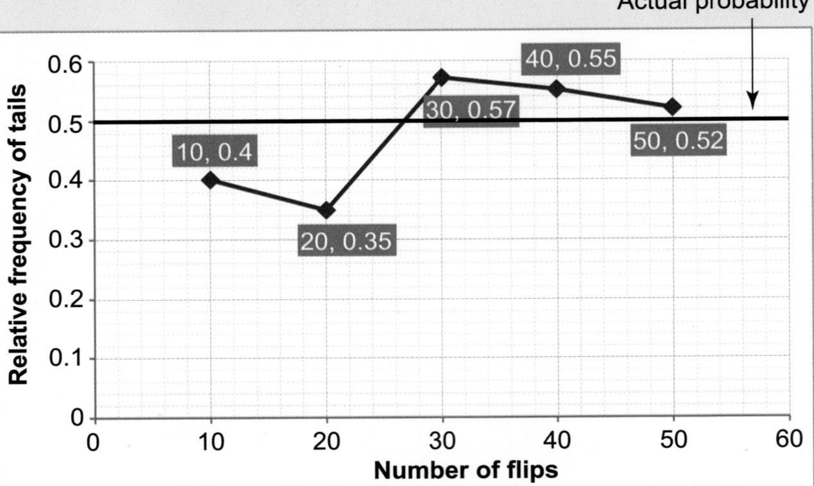

(ii) Notice that the more the experiment is repeated, the closer the relative frequency is to the actual probability (in this Worked Example: $\frac{1}{2}$ or 0.5). Therefore, a relative frequency of 0.35 is more likely after 20 flips than after 50, because after 50 flips, you would expect the relative frequency to be quite close to 0.5.

Exercise 2.3

1.

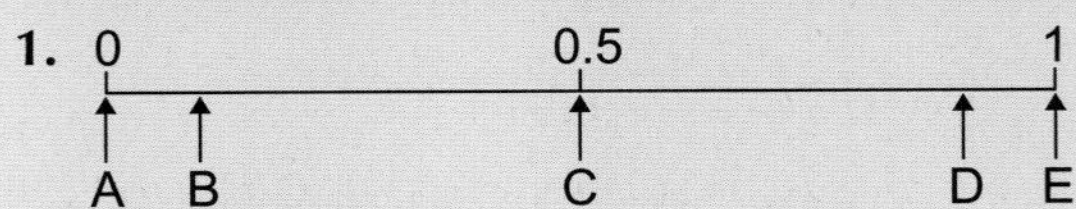

Five events (A, B, C, D and E) are shown on a probabiity scale. Copy and complete the following table:

Probability	Event
Fifty–fifty	C
Certain	
Very unlikely	
Impossible	
Very likely	

2. A gardener plants 50 parsley seeds in 50 pots. Three months later, he finds that he has 40 parsley plants: the rest were unsuccessful.

(i) What is the relative frequency of success?

(ii) If he plants 60 seeds next year, how many would he expect to grow successfully?

3. 0% 50% 100%

P Q R S T

Five events (P, Q, R, S and T) are shown on a probability scale. Copy and complete the following table, by filling in the appropriate letter in the right-hand column (P, Q, R, S or T):

Event	Letter
Getting tails on a single flip of a fair coin	
Getting a 4 on a single roll of a fair six-sided die	
Getting a 7 on a single roll of a fair six-sided die	
A person being born on a day which ends with the letter 'y'	
A person not being born on a Sunday	

4. Last year there were 167 school days and Conor was late for school 22 times.

   (i) Give the relative frequency of 'late days' for the school year as a percentage (to the nearest per cent).

   (ii) The Deputy Principal demands an improvement. The following September, Conor is late for three of the 20 school days. Has Conor's punctuality improved or disimproved? Refer to 'relative frequency' in your answer.

5. Beth flips a coin over and over. Here are the results:

Number of flips	After 20	After 40	After 60	After 80	After 100
Number of heads	14	24	31	39	51
Number of tails	6	16	29	41	49
Relative frequency of tails	0.3				

   (i) Copy the table and fill in the last row.

   (ii) Plot these results for the relative frequency of tails on a trend graph.

   (iii) Beth says, 'It is not surprising to get a relative value of 0.3 after 20 flips. It would be very surprising to get a relative frequency of 0.3 after 100 flips.' Is Beth correct? Explain your answer.

6. In the World Cup finals between 1986 and 2002, there were 211 penalties taken. Of these, 161 were successful.

   (i) What is the relative frequency of successful penalties in these finals to the nearest per cent?

   (ii) If, during the next World Cup finals, 46 penalties are awarded, how many would you expect to be successful, assuming the same relative frequency is maintained? Give your answer to the nearest whole number.

   (iii) Three pundits on different television channels make the following statements:

   Pundit A: 'When a penalty kick is taken during the World Cup finals, there is one chance in four of the kick being saved or missed.'

   Pundit B: 'Nerves play a big part in World Cup finals. Penalty kicks are more likely to be missed than scored.'

   Pundit C: 'If a player takes a penalty in the World Cup finals, there is more than a 50–50 chance that he will score.'

Which of the three statements (A, B, or C) is the most accurate?	
Which of the three statements is the least accurate?	

7. The Las Vegas Tourist Board boasts, 'Las Vegas has 210 days of total sunshine in a year. Come to Las Vegas and enjoy the sun's rays!'

   Mr and Mrs Abercrombie took a three-week holiday in Las Vegas. They wrote to the Tourist Board complaining, 'We had nine dull days in three weeks. We were very disappointed. We felt let down and misled.'

   (i) Give the relative frequency of sunny days in Las Vegas to the nearest half per cent.

   (ii) Is the complaint by Mr and Mrs Abercrombie reasonable? Justify your answer with reference to relative frequency.

8. Eoin flips a coin over and over. He keeps a tally of his results. Here they are:

	After 10 flips	After 20 flips	After 30 flips	After 40 flips	After 50 flips
No. of heads	3	11	17	21	24
No. of tails	7	9	13	19	26

(i) Copy this table and write down the relative frequencies of 'getting heads' (as a decimal) in the appropriate box; the first one has been done for you.

	After 10 flips	After 20 flips	After 30 flips	After 40 flips	After 50 flips
Relative frequency of heads	0.3				

(ii) Using this table of results, draw a trend graph of the relative frequency of heads as the number of flips increases.

(iii) After 10 flips, Eoin felt that the coin was biased in favour of tails. Given all of the above data, do you think he was right? Explain your answer.

9. In the Women's Rugby World Cup (WRWC) in 2006, there were 179 conversion attempts, 94 of which were successful. In the same tournament, there were 57 penalty kicks.

(i) What was the relative frequency (as a percentage to one decimal place) of successful conversions?

(ii) Assuming the same relative frequency, how many penalty kicks would you expect to be successful?

(iii) In fact, 31 of the penalty kicks were successful. Does this statistic satisfy you or disappoint you? Why?

(iv) A male commentator said, 'In the WRWC, place kicking was atrocious. The players missed more kicks than they scored.' Is his statement true?

10. Three students each have four coins, which they flip repeatedly. They keep a tally to record if all four coins show the same outcome or not (that is, whether or not they get HHHH or TTTT). Here are the results:

Name	Number of trials	All four coins show the same outcome	All four coins do NOT show the same outcome
Alan	40	7	33
Beth	30	3	27
Cathal	90	11	79
Total	160	21	139

(i) Which student's data is likely to give the **best estimate** of the probability of getting all four coins to show the same outcome? Give a reason for your answer.

(ii) The actual probability that all four coins will show the same outcome is $\frac{1}{8}$. How many times would you theoretically expect this to happen in 160 trials?

(iii) Give a reason why the total result of the students is different from what was theoretically expected.

11. Perhaps the most surprising mathematical law is Benford's Law. It states that if you have any set of data (e.g. the ages of humans in days, the weights of horses in kilograms, etc.) and you write down the **first digit** in each case, then the most frequent is 1, the next frequent is 2, all the way down to the least frequent, which is 9. You'd expect each digit to be equally frequent – but that is not the case! Here is a table which shows the relative frequency for the first digit of data, according to Benford's Law.

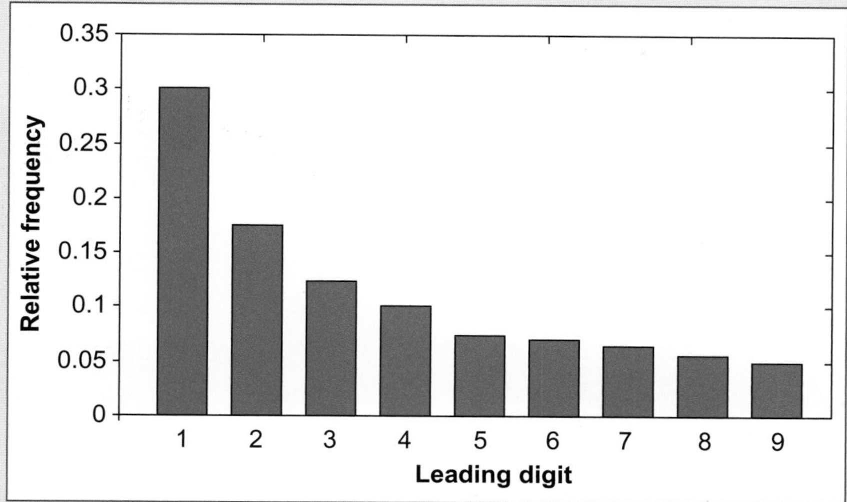

A research student looked up a social networking site and logged 1,500 numbers that appeared (e.g. 'I have five dogs', 'I hate my three sisters', 'Today is my 17th birthday'). She noted the first digit of each. Here are the results:

First digit on data	Frequency	Relative frequency (out of 1,500) as a decimal
1	444	0.296
2	255	
3	165	
4	141	
5	117	
6	108	
7	98	
8	85	
9	87	

(i) Copy and complete the table.

(ii) Does this data support Benford's Law?

(iii) Can you give any reason why Benford's Law works? Why are all first digits not equally likely?

2.6 PROBABILITY WHEN ALL OUTCOMES ARE EQUALLY LIKELY

When an experiment takes place and all outcomes are equally likely, the probability of a certain event, E, taking place is written as P(E), and is defined by:

FORMULA

$$P(E) = \frac{\text{number of elements in the event}}{\text{number of all possible outcomes}} = \frac{\#E}{\#S}$$

where S = the sample space, the set of all possible outcomes.

Worked Example 2.13

(i) A fair six-sided die is rolled. What is the probability of getting a number greater than 4?

(ii) If this die is rolled 60 times, how many times would you expect to get a number greater than 4?

Solution

(i) There are six possible outcomes. S = {1, 2, 3, 4, 5, 6}.

The desired event, E, has two elements: {5, 6}.

$\therefore P(E) = \frac{\#E}{\#S} = \frac{2}{6} = \frac{1}{3}$

(ii) You would expect to get a number higher than 4 one-third of the time. Hence, you would expect to get 'more than 4' on:

$\frac{1}{3} \times 60 = 20$ occasions

Worked Example 2.14

A card is drawn from a standard pack at random. What is the probability that the card drawn is:

(i) A Jack

(ii) A Spade

(iii) A red card

(iv) A Jack or a Spade

(v) A Spade or a red card

Solution

(i) There are 52 cards altogether in a pack. There are four Jacks.

$\therefore P(\text{Jack}) = \frac{4}{52} = \frac{1}{13}$

(ii) There are 13 Spades in a pack of 52.

$\therefore P(\text{Spade}) = \frac{13}{52} = \frac{1}{4}$

(iii) There are 26 red cards in the pack.

$\therefore$ P(red card) $= \frac{26}{52} = \frac{1}{2}$

(iv) There are 13 Spades and three **other** Jacks (we must be careful not to count the Jack of Spades twice). Hence, this event has 16 elements.

$\therefore$ P(Spade or Jack) $= \frac{16}{52} = \frac{4}{13}$

(v) There are 13 Spades and 26 red cards, making 39 altogether.

$\therefore$ P(Spade or red card) $= \frac{39}{52} = \frac{3}{4}$

2.7 PROBABILITY THEORY

Mutually Exclusive Events

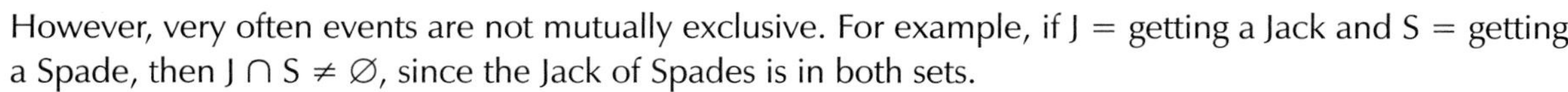

Two events E and F are said to be mutually exclusive if E ∩ F = ∅.

For example, when a card is picked from a pack, if E = getting a Diamond and F = getting a black card, then E and F are mutually exclusive since $E \cap F = \varnothing$.

If E and F are mutually exclusive, then
$P(E \cup F) = P(E) + P(F)$.

If E = getting a Diamond, then $P(E) = \frac{13}{52} = \frac{1}{4}$.

If F = getting a black card, then $P(F) = \frac{26}{52} = \frac{1}{2}$.

$P(E \cup F)$ = P(getting a Diamond or a black card) $= \frac{1}{4} + \frac{1}{2} = \frac{3}{4}$.

However, very often events are not mutually exclusive. For example, if J = getting a Jack and S = getting a Spade, then $J \cap S \neq \varnothing$, since the Jack of Spades is in both sets.

$P(J) = \frac{4}{52} = \frac{1}{13}$ $\quad$ $P(S) = \frac{13}{52} = \frac{1}{4}$

In this case,

$P(J \cup S) \neq P(J) + P(S)$ because that would be counting the Jack of Spades twice.

In general:

FORMULA
P(E ∪ F) = P(E or F) = P(E) + P(F) – P(E ∩ F)

Let's check this out in the above case:

$P(J) = \frac{4}{52} = \frac{1}{13}$ $\quad$ $P(S) = \frac{13}{52} = \frac{1}{4}$

$J \cap S = \{\text{Jack of Spades}\}$

$\therefore P(J \cap S) = \frac{1}{52}$

$\therefore P(J \cup S) = P(\text{Jack or Spade}) = P(J) + P(S) - P(J \cap S)$

$$= \frac{1}{13} + \frac{1}{4} - \frac{1}{52}$$

$$= \frac{4 + 13 - 1}{52}$$

$$= \frac{16}{52}$$

$$= \frac{4}{13}$$

This result agrees with our result in Worked Example 2.14.

Conclusion:

FORMULA

1. $P(E \cup F) = P(E) + P(F) - P(E \cap F)$
2. If E and F are mutually exclusive, then $P(E \cap F) = 0$, and so:

   $P(E \cup F) = P(E) + P(F)$

Worked Example 2.15

Given the Venn diagram, write down:

(i) $P(E)$ (ii) $P(F)$ (iii) $P(E \cap F)$ (iv) $P(E \cup F)$

(v) Verify that:

$P(E \cup F) = P(E) + P(F) - P(E \cap F)$

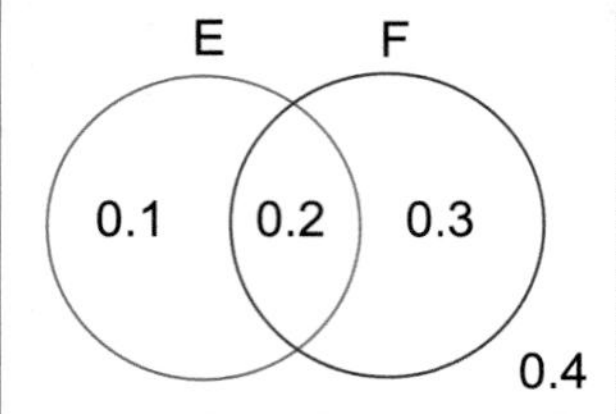

Solution

(i) $P(E) = 0.1 + 0.2 = 0.3$

(ii) $P(F) = 0.2 + 0.3 = 0.5$

(iii) $P(E \cap F) = 0.2$

(iv) $P(E \cup F) = 0.1 + 0.2 + 0.3 = 0.6$

(v) To verify that $P(E \cup F) = P(E) + P(F) - P(E \cap F)$:

LHS = 0.6

RHS = 0.3 + 0.5 – 0.2 = 0.6 = LHS **QED**

Note that the sum of all probabilities in S is 0.1 + 0.2 + 0.3 + 0.4 = 1, which is essential in all Venn diagrams of probabilities.

Worked Example 2.16

(i) Two fair six-sided dice are rolled. What is the probability that there will be a total of 8 on the two dice?

(ii) If, in a game, a pair of dice is rolled 1,000 times, how many times (to the nearest integer) would you expect to get a total of 8?

Solution

In accordance with the Fundamental Principle of Counting, there are $6 \times 6 = 36$ possible outcomes.

This sample space can first be represented by a two-way table in which the number on the left represents the outcome from the first die and the number on top represents the outcome from the second die.

		Second die					
		1	2	3	4	5	6
First die	1						
	2						*
	3						
	4						
	5						
	6						

For example, the asterisk represents when you get 2 on the first die and 6 on the second.

(i) There are five different ways of getting a total of 8, as shown by the five orange cells in the table. Hence:

$$P\text{ (Total is 8)} = \frac{\#E}{\#S} = \frac{5}{36}$$

(ii) If you rolled a pair of dice 1,000 times, then the number of times you would expect to get a total of 8 is:

$$\frac{5}{36} \times 1{,}000 = \frac{5{,}000}{36} = 139 \text{ (to the nearest integer)}$$

Exercise 2.4

1. An unbiased coin is flipped once. What is the probability of getting 'heads'?

2. An unbiased six-sided die is rolled. What is the probability that the number which appears will be:

   (i) An odd number (ii) A factor of 6 (iii) A factor of 4

3. A letter is chosen at random from the word PARALLEL. What is the probability that the letter chosen will be:

   (i) A vowel (ii) An L (iii) Not an L

4. In a class there are 14 boys and 16 girls. Three of the boys and two of the girls wear glasses. A student is chosen at random from this class.

Find the probability that this student will be:

(i) A girl

(ii) A boy

(iii) A person who wears glasses

(iv) A boy who wears glasses

If a person is chosen at random from this same class every day for 180 days, on how many days would you expect to find that a girl who wears glasses would be chosen?

5. A card is chosen from a standard pack. Find the probability that the card is:

(i) A Diamond

(ii) A black card

(iii) A King

(iv) A Diamond or a black card

(v) A Diamond or a King

(vi) A black card or a King

6. A person is asked to write down the name of one of the days of the week (Monday, Tuesday, etc.).

Find the probability that the day:

(i) Begins with T

(ii) Begins with S or T

(iii) Ends with Y

(iv) Begins with Q

7. State, giving a reason, if the events E and F are mutually exclusive in each case:

	Experiment	**E and F**	**Mutually exclusive?**	**Reason**
(i)	A six-sided die is rolled.	E = Getting an odd number. F = Getting a 6.		
(ii)	A card is drawn from a standard pack.	E = Getting a black card. F = Getting a King.		
(iii)	A person is asked which day of the week they were born on.	E = It is a weekday. F = It begins with the letter S.		
(iv)	A female student sits the Leaving Certificate exam.	E = She gets A in maths. F = She gets A in Irish.		
(v)	An Irish cyclist takes part in the Tour de France.	E = He fails to finish. F = He wins the Tour de France.		
(vi)	A couple have two children.	E = The first-born is a daughter. F = The second-born is a son.		
(vii)	A coin is flipped 10 times.	E = The first nine flips all show heads. F = The 10th flip shows heads.		
(viii)	A male student sits the Leaving Certificate exam.	E = He gets A in maths. F = He fails maths.		
(ix)	You follow an Irish soccer team.	E = They win the FAI cup next season. F = They win the League of Ireland Championship next season.		
(x)	A woman gives birth to twins.	E = They are identical twins. F = One is a boy and one is a girl.		

8. 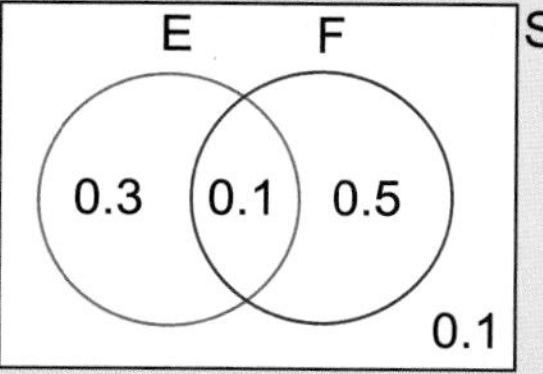

Given the Venn diagram, write down:

P(E), P(F), P(E ∩ F), P(E ∪ F)

Verify that:

P(E ∪ F) = P(E) + P(F) – P(E ∩ F)

9. The Venn diagram shows the **number of elements** in each subset, e.g. #(A ∩ B) = 3.

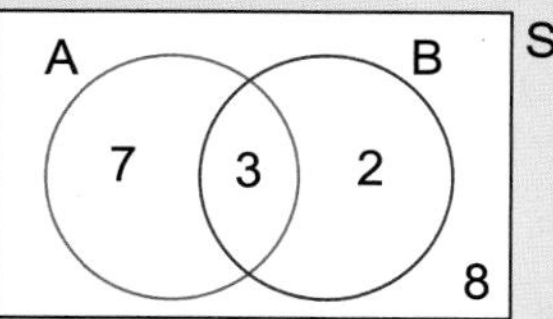

(a) An element is chosen at random from the set S, as shown. Write down the probability that the element will be in the set:

(i) A
(ii) B
(iii) A ∩ B
(iv) A ∪ B
(v) A \ B
(vi) (A \ B) ∪ (B \ A)
(vii) A′
(viii) (A ∪ B)′

(b) Verify the following:

(i) P(A \ B) = P(A) – P(A ∩ B)
(ii) P(A ∪ B) = P(A) + P(B) – P(A ∩ B)

10. There are 24 people in a class. Eighteen play basketball, 11 play chess and three play neither.

Copy and fill out the following Venn diagram. (B = the set of basketball players; C = the set of chess players.)

The class

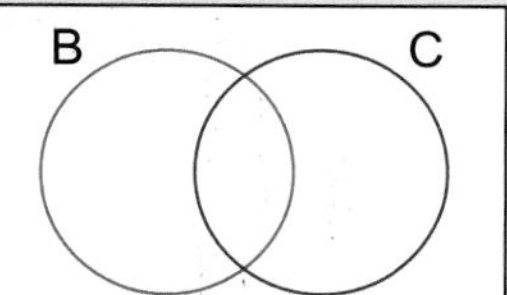

A person is chosen from the class at random. If P(X) is taken to mean the probability that the person is from set X, write down:

(i) P(B)
(ii) P(C)
(iii) P(B ∩ C)
(iv) P(B ∪ C)
(v) P(B′)

Investigate if the following are true or false:

(vi) P(B ∪ C) = P(B) + P(C)
(vii) P(B ∪ C) = P(B) + P(C) – P(B ∩ C)
(viii) P(B \ C) = P(B) – P(C)
(ix) P(B \ C) = P(B) – P(B ∩ C)
(x) P(B′) = 1 – P(B)

11. A card is drawn randomly from a pack.

Q = getting a Queen.

R = getting a red card.

S = getting a Spade.

(a) Write down the values of:

(i) P(Q)
(ii) P(R)
(iii) P(S)
(iv) P(Q ∩ R)
(v) P(R \ Q)
(vi) P(R ∪ Q)
(vii) P(S′)
(viii) P(Q ∪ R ∪ S)

(b) Show that the following are true:

(i) P(R ∪ Q) = P(R) + P(Q) – P(R ∩ Q)
(ii) P(R \ Q) = P(R) – P(R ∩ Q)
(iii) P(S′) = 1 – P(S)

12. P(B) = 0.8

P(A ∩ B) = 0.3

P(A′) = 0.6

(a) Find (i) P(A) and (ii) P(A ∪ B).

(b) Verify that:

P(A ∪ B) = P(A) + P(B) – P(A ∩ B)

13. A pair of fair six-sided dice is rolled. Find the probability that the total on the pair of dice is:

(i) Equal to 4

(ii) 4 or less

(iii) Greater than 9

(iv) An even number

(v) Less than 6 or equal to a prime number

(vi) Exactly twice as great as other possible totals

(vii) 10 or less

14. Three fair coins are flipped. Copy and complete the sample space, S:

S = {(H, H, H), (H, H, T), (H, T, H), ...}

Hence find:

(i) The numbers of elements in S

(ii) The probability of getting three tails

(iii) The probability of getting at least one head

(iv) The probability of getting two or more heads

15. A fair six-sided die is rolled and an unbiased coin is flipped.

Represent the sample space in a two-way table.

Find the probability of getting:

(i) A five followed by a head

(ii) A prime number followed by a tail (Note: 1 is **not** a prime number.)

(iii) An even number with a head or an odd number with a tail

16. There are 20 tickets in a bag numbered 1–20. The numbers 1–10 are red, 11–16 are blue and 17–20 are green. A ticket is drawn at random from the bag.

(a) Find the probability of getting:

(i) A green ticket

(ii) A ticket which is not blue

(iii) A ticket which is red or even-numbered

(iv) A ticket which is green or odd-numbered

(v) A ticket which is red and even-numbered

(b) Is it true to say that 'getting a multiple of 7' and 'getting a green ticket' are mutually exclusive events?

17. A bag contains 11 yellow marbles, 13 green marbles and n blue marbles. When a marble is drawn at random, the probability of getting a blue marble is $\frac{1}{4}$. Find the value of n.

18. The data shows the number of boys and girls aged either 17 or 18 on a school trip, in which only these 50 students took part.

	Boys	**Girls**
Aged 17	18	12
Aged 18	15	5

A student is chosen at random from the party. Find the probability that the student:

(i) Is a boy

(ii) Is aged 18

(iii) Is a girl of 18 years

(iv) Is a girl aged 17 or a boy aged 18

19. A fair six-sided die is rolled three times.

(i) What is the number of elements in the sample space?

(ii) What is the probability that three 6's appear?

(iii) What is the probability that the first roll yields a 6 and that the sum on all three rolls is 14?

(iv) What is the probability that the first roll is an even number and that the sum on all three rolls is 14?

20. There were 31 days in January and 28 in February in 1997. A person was born in 1997.

Write down, correct to two significant figures, the probability that the person was born:

(i) In January

(ii) In February

(iii) In January or February

21. 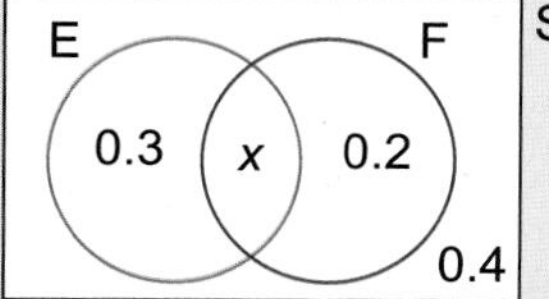

(i) Given the probability Venn diagram, find the value of x.

(ii) Are E and F mutually exclusive?

(iii) Write down:
$P(E)$, $P(F)$, $P(E \cap F)$, $P(E \cup F)$.

(iv) Verify that:
$P(E \cup F) = P(E) + P(F) - P(E \cap F)$

22. 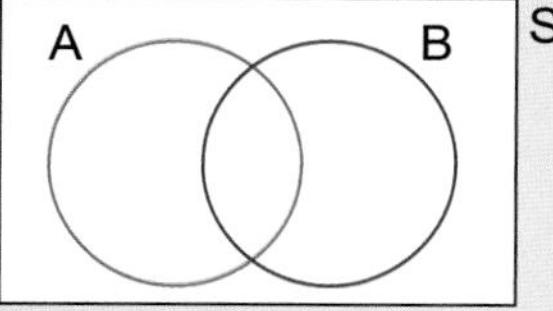

$P(A \cup B) = 0.8$

$P(A) = 0.35$

$P(A \cap B) = 0.2$

(i) Find $P(B)$. (ii) Find $P(B')$.

(iii) Verify that:
$P(A \cup B) = P(A) + P(B) - P(A \cap B)$

23. 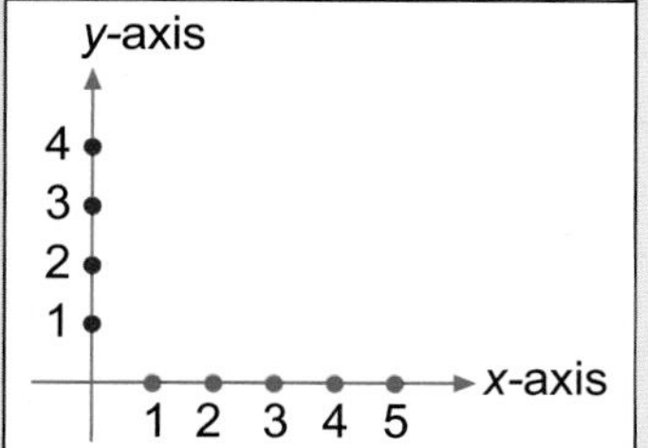

A point is chosen randomly from one of the green points (1,0) (2,0) (3,0) (4,0) (5,0) on the x-axis. Another point is chosen randomly from the blue points (0,1) (0,2) (0,3) (0,4) on the y-axis.

A line segment is drawn linking the two points. Use this two-way table to represent the sample space. Fill in the lengths in the table.

	(0,1)	**(0,2)**	**(0,3)**	**(0,4)**
(1,0)	$\sqrt{2}$			$\sqrt{17}$
(2,0)				
(3,0)				
(4,0)	$\sqrt{17}$			
(5,0)				

Find the probability (as a percentage) that the line segment will:

(i) Be 5 units long

(ii) Be greater than 5 units long

(iii) Have a slope of –1

24. 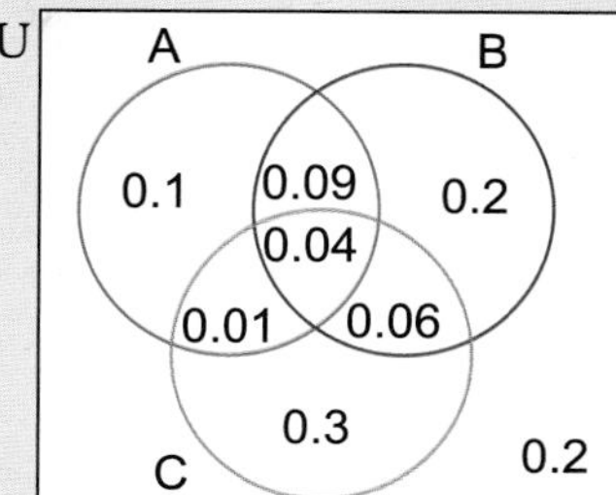

Given the Venn diagram which shows the probabilities of various sets, write down:

(i) $P(A \cap B)$ (iii) $P(C \setminus A)$

(ii) $P(A \cup C)$ (iv) $P(C \setminus (A \cup B))$

Verify that:

$P(B \cup C) = P(B) + P(C) - P(B \cap C)$

25. 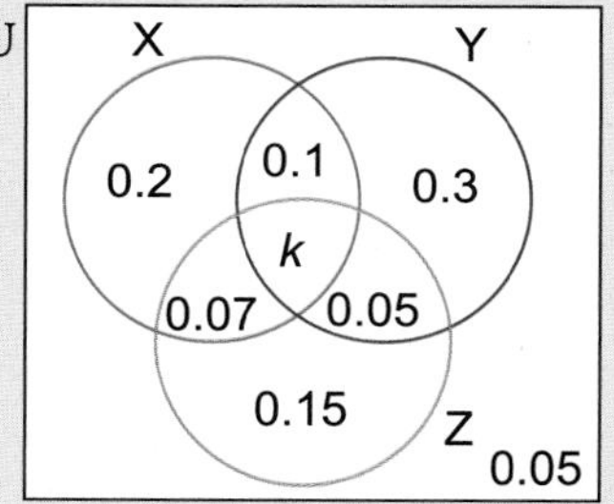

(a) Use the probability Venn diagram to find the value of:

(i) k (iv) $P(Y \setminus (X \cup Z))$

(ii) $P(X \cup Z)$ (v) $P(Z')$

(iii) $P(X \cap Z)$

(b) Verify that:

(i) $P(Y \cup Z) = P(Y) + P(Z) - P(Y \cap Z)$

(ii) $P(Y') = 1 - P(Y)$

26. A number is chosen randomly from the set $A = \{1, 2, 3, 4, 5\}$.

Another number is chosen randomly from the set $B = \{6, 7, 8, 9, 10\}$.

(a) Use a two-way table to represent the sample space.

(b) E = {The sum of the numbers is less than 9}

F = {The product of the numbers is greater than 20}

(i) Find P(E) and P(F).

(ii) Are E and F mutually exclusive?

Explain your answer.

(iii) Find P(E ∪ F).

(iv) Kate and Kevin play a game. They use two spinners to choose a number from A and a number from B. Kate wins if the product of the two numbers is less than 23, Kevin if the product is greater than 23. Is this fair?

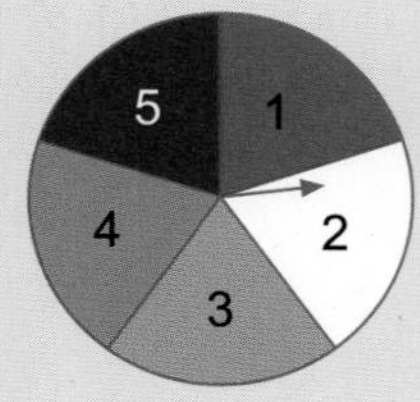

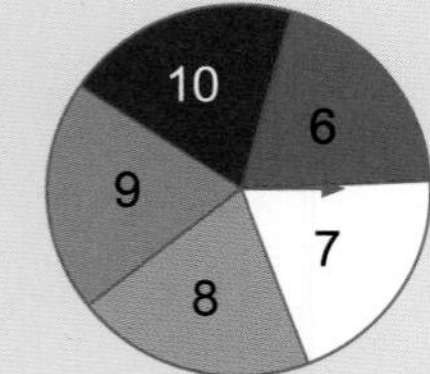

27. Two fair six-sided dice are rolled.

(i) Copy and complete the table for the probabilities of different possible sums:

Sum on two dice	2	3	4	5	6	7	8	9	10	11	12
Probability					$\frac{5}{36}$						$\frac{1}{36}$

(ii) Copy and complete the bar chart, showing the probabilities, using one 'brick' for every $\frac{1}{36}$.

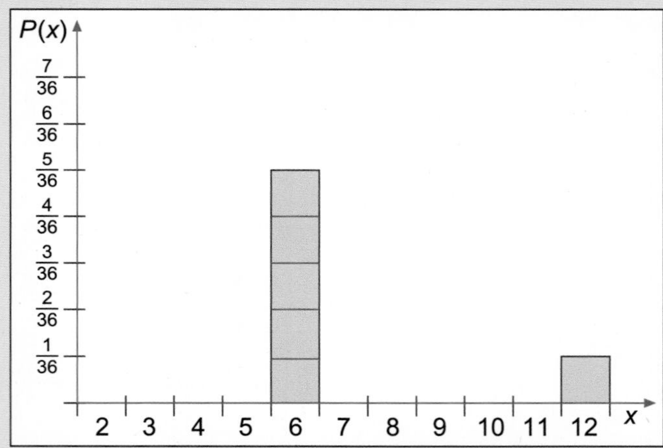

(iii) Kilian and Shane play a game. They roll a pair of fair dice. If the total on the dice is 4, 5, 6 or 7, Kilian wins. If the total is anything else, Shane wins. Is this fair?

(iv) They now change the game so that it *is* fair. Kilian now wins if the total on the dice is one of four consecutive numbers. Write down two possible lists of these four consecutive numbers.

(v) A spinner is designed so that the probability of each outcome is the same as the total when two fair dice are rolled. Write down the angle for each outcome (one has already been filled in for you).

Sum on two dice	2	3	4	5	6	7	8	9	10	11	12
Angle on spinner						60°					

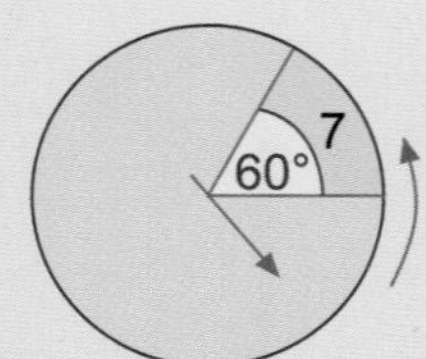

2.8 CONDITIONAL PROBABILITY

In a class there are 15 male students, five of whom wear glasses and 10 female students, three of whom wear glasses. We will let M = {Male students}, F = {Female students} and G = {Students who wear glasses}.

A student is picked at random from this class. What is the probability that the student is female, given that the student wears glasses?

Mathematically, we write this probability as:

$P(F \mid G)$ ['The probability of F, given G']

To find $P(F \mid G)$, we examine the set of those who wear glasses (G). This set has eight members.

Of this set, the number of females is three. Hence, $P(F \mid G) = \frac{3}{8}$.

Note that three is the number of elements in $(F \cap G)$, and eight is the number of elements in G. Hence, it should be clear that:

$$P(F \mid G) = \frac{\#(F \cap G)}{\#(G)} = \frac{P(F \cap G)}{P(G)}$$

In general, $P(A \mid B)$, the probability of A given B, is determined by:

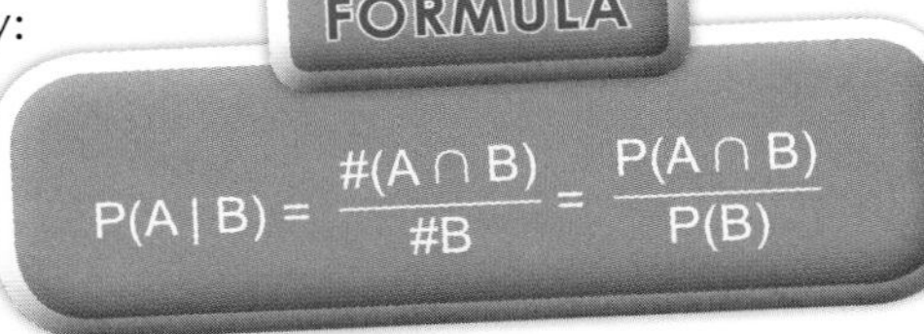

Worked Example 2.17

A couple have three children. Find the probability that all three are girls, given that at least one is a girl.

Solution

Taking the three children in order of age, there are eight elements in the outcome space:

S = {BBB, BBG, BGB, GBB, BGG, GBG, GGB, GGG}

Let A = {All three are girls} = {GGG}

Let B = {At least one is a girl} = {BBG, BGB, GBB, BGG, GBG, GGB, GGG}

$\therefore A \cap B = \{GGG\}$

$$P(A \mid B) = \frac{\#(A \cap B)}{\#B} = \frac{1}{7}$$

Worked Example 2.18

Given the Venn diagram, find P(X | Y) and P(Y | X).

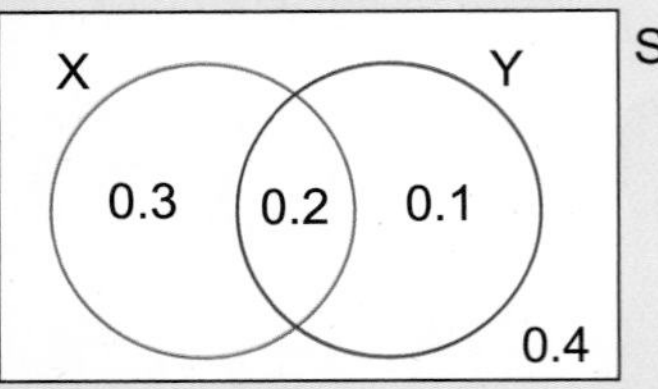

Solution

$$P(X \mid Y) = \frac{P(X \cap Y)}{P(Y)} = \frac{0.2}{(0.2 + 0.1)} = \frac{0.2}{0.3} = \frac{2}{3}$$

$$P(Y \mid X) = \frac{P(X \cap Y)}{P(X)} = \frac{0.2}{(0.3 + 0.2)} = \frac{0.2}{0.5} = \frac{2}{5}$$

From this, it is clear that P(X | Y) and P(Y | X) are not necessarily equal.

Worked Example 2.19

In a certain country, there are only two parties: the Red Party and the Blue Party. In elections, 60% of the country votes Red, and 40% votes Blue. Of the Red supporters, 70% favour disarmament. Of Blue supporters, 10% favour disarmament.

A voter is chosen at random and announces that she favours disarmament. What is the probability that she supports the Blue Party?

Solution

Let R = {Red Party supporters} $\therefore$ P(R) = 0.6

Let B = {Blue Party supporters} $\therefore$ P(B) = 0.4

Let D = {Disarmament supporters}

$P(D) = 70\%$ of $60\% + 10\%$ of $40\% = (0.7)(0.6) + (0.1)(0.4) = 0.46$

$P(B \cap D) = 10\%$ of $40\% = (0.1)(0.4) = 0.04$

We are required to find $P(B \mid D) = \dfrac{P(B \cap D)}{P(D)} = \dfrac{0.04}{0.46} = \dfrac{2}{23}$

Exercise 2.5

1.

The probabilities of two events, E and F, are given in the Venn diagram.

Find:

(i) P(E | F)

(ii) P(F | E)

2. Two fair six-sided dice are rolled.

A = The total is over 8.

B = At least one die shows a 6.

(a) List the elements of A, B and A ∩ B.

(b) Find:

(i) P(B | A) (ii) P(A | B)

3. A team wins 60% of home matches and 20% of away matches. Half of their matches are at home and half are away. They won their last match. Find the probability that:

(i) It was at home. (ii) It was away.

4. A family has three children. Complete the outcome space:

{GGG, GGB, …}, where GGB means the first two are girls and the third is a boy.

Find the probability that all three children are girls, given that the family has at least two girls.

5. $P(A) = \frac{1}{2}$ $P(B) = \frac{1}{3}$ $P(A \cap B) = \frac{1}{4}$

Find:

(i) $P(A \mid B)$
(ii) $P(B \mid A)$
(iii) $P(A' \mid B)$
(iv) $P(A \mid B')$
(v) $P(A \cup B)$
(vi) $P[A \mid (A \cup B)]$

6. In a school, there are 150 girls and 100 boys. One hundred and twenty of the girls and 50 of the boys play hockey.

A student is picked at random. Find the probability that this student:

(i) Is a girl, given that the student plays hockey
(ii) Plays hockey, given that the student is a girl

7. In a certain county, 70% of the population live in a townland, and 30% live in a rural area. Fifty per cent of townlanders listen to the local radio station, whereas only 20% of rural dwellers listen to the local radio station. A person from the county is picked at random. Find the probability that this person is a townlander, given that the person listens to the local radio station.

8. $P(A) = 0.5$ $P(A \cup B) = 0.6$
$P(A \mid B) = 0.75$

Find P(B).

(Hint: Let $P(B) = x$ and let $P(A \cap B) = y$. You should be able to set up a pair of 'simultaneous equations'.)

9. E and F are two events such that $P(E) = \frac{2}{5}$, $P(F) = \frac{1}{2}$, and $P(E \mid F) = \frac{1}{9}$.

Find:

(i) $P(E \cap F)$ (ii) $P(F \mid E)$ (iii) $P(E \cup F)$

10. You meet a man who tells you that he has two children. Later you meet his wife, who tells you that one of the children is a girl. What is the probability that the other child is:

(i) A boy (ii) A girl

11. A pair of fair six-sided dice is rolled.

E = {The sum on the two dice is 7}

F = {3 appears on at least one die}

Find $P(F \mid E)$ and $P(E \mid F)$.

12. A bag contains 11 snooker balls numbered 1 to 11. A ball is drawn at random from the bag and the number is noted.

A = {The number is even}

B = {The number is greater than 6}

Find $P(A \mid B)$ and $P(B \mid A)$.

13. In a certain school, 27% of students got an A in Junior Certificate maths, 15% got an A in science and 9% got an A in both. A student is selected at random. Find the probability that:

(i) This student got an A in maths, given that she got an A in science.
(ii) This student got an A in science, given that she got an A in maths.
(iii) This student got an A in maths or science.
(iv) This student got an A in neither maths nor science.

14. A and B are two events such that $P(A) = \frac{3}{10}$, $P(B) = \frac{1}{2}$ and $P(A \cup B) = \frac{3}{5}$.

Find $P(A \mid B)$ and $P(B \mid A)$.

15. If $A \subset B$, prove that $P(B \mid A) = 1$.

16. The Venn diagram shows the probability of events A, B and C.

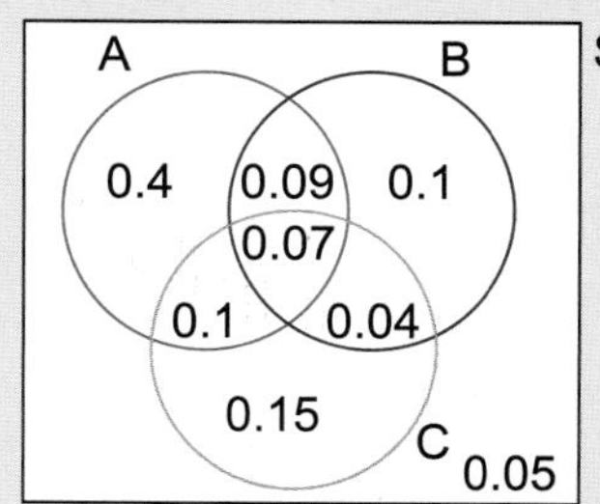

Find:

(i) P(A)
(ii) $P(A \cap B)$
(iii) $P(A \mid B)$
(iv) $P(B \mid A)$
(v) $P(A \mid (B \cup C))$
(vi) $P(C \mid (A \cap B))$

17. 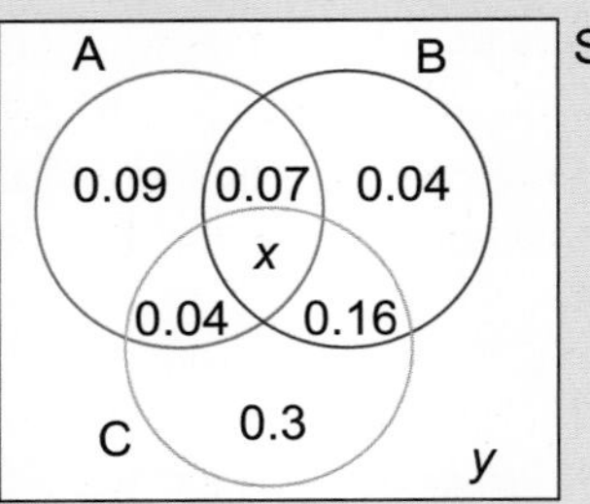

(i) Given that P(A) = 0.3, find the values of x and y.

(ii) Find P(B | C) and P(C | B).

(iii) Find P(B | (A ∪ C)).

(iv) Find P((A ∩ C) | (A ∪ B ∪ C)).

(v) Find P((A \ B) | (A ∪ B)).

18. 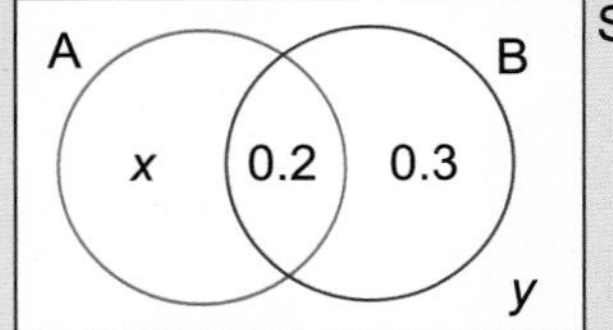

(i) Given that $P(B \mid A) = \frac{1}{2}$, find the values of x and y.

(ii) Find, also, P(A | B).

19. 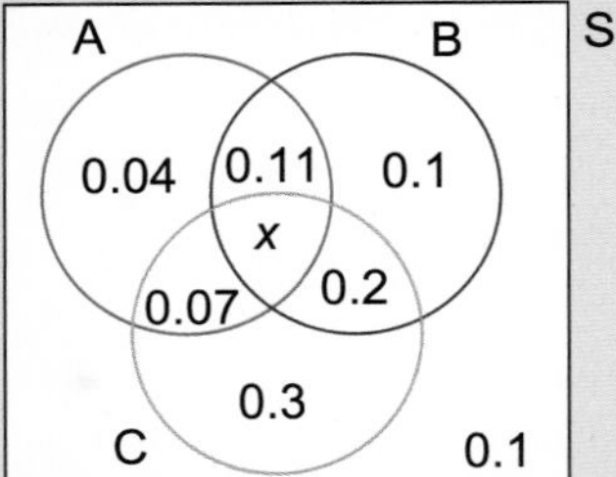

Given the probability Venn diagram, find:

(i) The value of x

(ii) P(A | B)

(iii) P(A | (B ∪ C)

(iv) P((B ∩ C) | A)

20. A couple have four children.

(i) Find the probability that all four are boys, given that three are boys.

(ii) 'If your first three children are boys, your fourth child is more likely to be a girl.'

Is this statement true? Give a reason for your answer.

Revision Exercises

1. (a) (i) How many arrangements are there of the letters of the word MUNSTER?

(ii) How many of these begin and end with a vowel?

(b) Two fair six-sided dice are rolled. Use a two-way table to find the probability of getting:

(i) 6 on each of the two dice

(ii) 6 on at least one of the dice

(iii) A total of 6 on the two dice

2. (i) How many ways are there of arranging the letters of the word NICHOLAS, taking them three at a time?

(ii) In how many different ways can you choose three letters from the word NICHOLAS?

(iii) If you choose three letters from the word NICHOLAS, what is the probability of getting three vowels?

(iv) If you choose three letters from the word NICHOLAS, what is the probability of getting at least one consonant?

3. 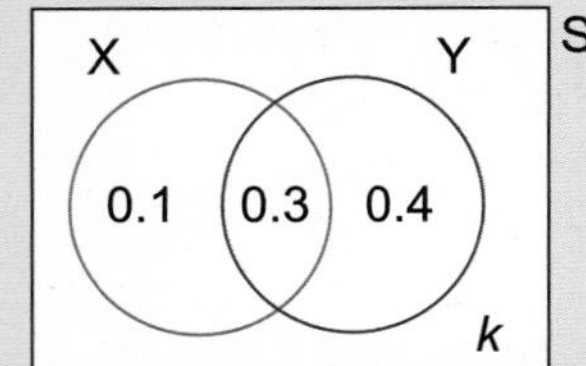

(i) Find the value of k.

(ii) Evaluate P(X), P(Y), P(X∩Y).

(iii) Verify that P(X∪Y) = P(X) + P(Y) − P(X∩Y).

(iv) Find P(X | Y).

(v) Is P(X | Y) = P(Y | X)? Justify your answer.

4. Two spinners are shown below.

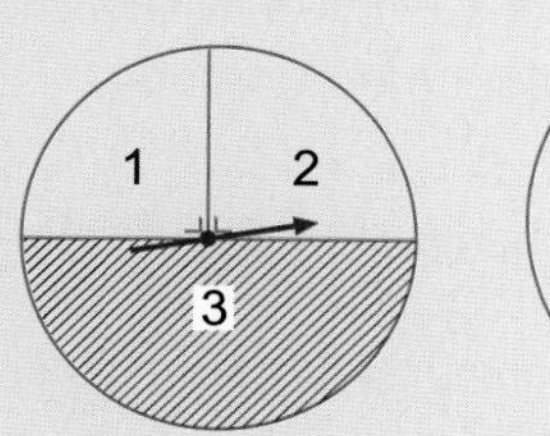

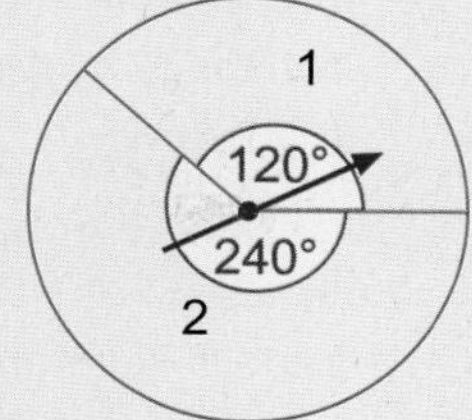

(i) If these two spinners are spun, which are you more likely to get: a **sum** of 3 from the two outcomes, or a **product** of 3 from the two outcomes? Justify your answers.

(ii) Calculate the probabilities of all the different possible **sums** when the two spinners are spun.

(iii) Design a single spinner whose outcomes have the same probabilities as the **sum** of these two spinners.

5. (a) How many numbers between 5,000 and 10,000 can be made from the digits 1, 3, 5, 7 and 9 if no digit may be repeated?

(b) (i) How many ways are there of arranging the letters of the word IRELAND?

(ii) How many of these arrangements begin with L and end with a vowel?

(iii) How many of these arrangements have the three vowels side by side?

(iv) The letters of the word IRELAND are arranged at random. What is the probability that the three vowels will be together?

6. A subcommittee of three people is to be chosen from a committee of 10.

(i) How many subcommittees are possible?

(ii) How many subcommittees are possible if two particular people on the committee refuse to work together on the subcommittee?

(iii) If the subcommittee is chosen at random, what is the probability that the two people who refuse to work together will both end up on the subcommittee?

7. Last year the local soccer team (The Hamiltonian Academicals) played 21 home games and 20 away games. They won 14 of their home games and only four of their away games.

(i) Find (as a fraction in its lowest terms) the relative frequency of their winning a home game last year.

(ii) Find (as a fraction in its lowest terms) the relative frequency of their winning an away game.

(iii) Taking these values as determining the probabilities, find the probability that their final match was a home game, given that they won.

8. (i) How many ways are there of arranging the letters of the word EUCLID?

(ii) In how many arrangements are the three vowels together?

(iii) The letters of EUCLID are arranged at random. Find the probability that the three vowels will be together.

9. S = {a, b, c, d, e, f, g}

(i) How many different subsets with four elements can be chosen from S?

(ii) How many of these contain *f*?

(iii) How many do not contain *f*?

(iv) A subset of four elements is chosen at random from S. What is the probability that it will include *f*?

10. The police in a certain town reported that during one year there were 25 muggings in the town in 365 days. The mayor of the town makes a speech saying that things will improve.

(i) In the 31 days of January of the next year, there are two muggings. Have things improved or disimproved, and by how much? Make reference to relative frequency (using percentages).

(ii) Over the first six months of the next year, there was a 20% reduction in muggings. How many muggings took place during those six months?

11. (a) A traffic light goes green for 50 seconds, then orange for 5 seconds and then red for 25 seconds. If a car arrives at random, find the probability that:

(i) It will get a green light.

(ii) It will not get a green light.

(b) If $\binom{n}{2} = 91$, find the value of $n \in N, n \geqslant 2$.

12. A coin is flipped twice and then a four-sided die (with numbers 1, 2, 3 and 4) is rolled. The coin and the die are both fair.

(i) Copy and complete the sample space: {HH1, HH2, ...}.

(ii) What is the probability of getting TT3?

(iii) What is the probability of getting two heads followed by an even number?

(iv) What is the probability of getting one head, one tail and an odd number?

13. (i) Three letters are chosen at random from the letters of the word FACETIOUS. How many different choices are possible?

(ii) How many of these choices consist of two vowels and a consonant?

(iii) If three letters are chosen at random from the word FACETIOUS, what is the probability of getting an A, E and I (in any order)?

(iv) Sue says, 'If I choose three letters from the word FACETIOUS at random, the chances of getting the letters of my name (S, U, E) is a little under 1%.'

Is this statement true or false? Justify your answer.

14. An online club is formed and is called the Alphabetical Order Club. In order to be a member, your first name, middle name and surname must have initials which are in alphabetical order. The same initial cannot be repeated, e.g. they do not allow BBK, HPP or RRR. Only one person with particular initials is allowed into the club. So, if Alan Craig Peterson (ACP) is a member, they will not allow Alice Carol Partridge to join.

(i) State which of the following names are acceptable: Fred Harry Murphy, Yvonne Victoria Sullivan, Leah Nadia Nagle, Oisín Oscar Walsh.

(ii) What is the maximum number of members that the club could have?

Probability II

Learning Outcomes

In this chapter you will learn:

- To solve problems in which one event happens after another
- To use tree diagrams to help solve such problems
- The meaning of *expected value* and how to calculate it
- The strict definition of *independent events*
- The binomial distribution formula and how to apply it to problems
- The normal distribution table and how to use it
- To solve real-life problems which involve normal distributions
- About random samples

3.1 INDEPENDENT EVENTS

Two events are said to be independent if the outcome of one in no way affects the outcome of the other. In this chapter, we will look more formally at this definition.

YOU SHOULD REMEMBER...

- $P(A \cup B) = P(A) + P(B) - P(A \cap B)$
- $P(A \mid B) = \frac{P(A \cap B)}{P(B)} = \frac{\#(A \cap B)}{\# B}$

KEY WORDS

- **Independent events**
- **Expected value**
- **Binomial distribution**
- **Normal distribution**

For example, suppose a coin is flipped and then a die is rolled. Let E = {Getting a tail on the coin} and F = {Getting a 6 on the die}. Clearly, if you get a tail on the coin, this will have no bearing whatsoever on whether you will get a 6 on the die. These events are **independent**.

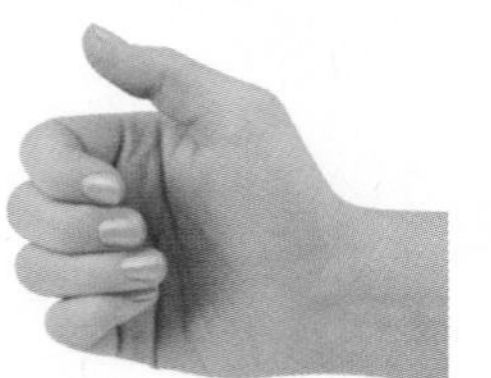

However, suppose you roll a fair die twice. E = {Getting a 6 on the first roll}. F = {Getting a total of 10 or more on the two rolls}. Clearly, if you get a 6 on the first die, you are more likely to get a high total. These events are **not** independent.

Three Laws of Probability

Law 1

$0 \leqslant P(E) \leqslant 1$, where P(E) is the probability of any event E.

Law 2

If p is the probability of an event E happening, then the probability that E will not happen is $1 - p$.

Law 3 The Multiplication Law

If p is the probability of an event E happening, and if q is the probability of an independent event F happening, then the probability that, in two successive experiments, E happens and then F happens is pq.

One Event After Another

If you roll a fair six-sided die and then flip an unbiased coin, the probability of getting a 5 and then a tail is $\frac{1}{6} \times \frac{1}{2} = \frac{1}{12}$, in accordance with Law 3 above, since these events are independent. If you draw one card and then another from a pack, the probability that the first is a King and the second is a Queen is $\frac{4}{52} \times \frac{4}{51} = \frac{4}{663}$. These events are not independent, but we can use the amended multiplication law: P(A and then B) = P(A) P(B | A).

In this example, $\frac{4}{52}$ is the probability that the first is a King, and $\frac{4}{51}$ is the probability that the second is a Queen, given that the first is a King. In other words, we assume that the sequence of events **does** happen, and calculate the probabilities accordingly.

Worked Example 3.1

Two cards are drawn from a standard pack, without replacement.
Find the probability that:

(i) They are both Hearts.

(ii) At least one is not a Heart.

Solution

(i) There are 13 Hearts in a pack of 52. Therefore, the probability that the first card is a Heart is:

$$\frac{13}{52} = \frac{1}{4}$$

When the second card is drawn, there will be 51 cards left in the pack, and only 12 of these will be Hearts. Hence, the probability that the second card is a Heart is:

$$\frac{12}{51} = \frac{4}{17}$$

Under the Multiplication Law, the probability that **both** are Hearts is:

$$\frac{1}{4} \times \frac{4}{17} = \frac{1}{17}$$

(ii) If at least one is not a Heart, then they cannot both be Hearts. Hence, the probability that at least one is not a Heart is:

$$1 - \text{P(both Hearts)} = 1 - \frac{1}{17} = \frac{16}{17} \quad \text{(by Law 2)}$$

Worked Example 3.2

Three cards are chosen at random from a standard pack. Find the probability that:

(i) All three are Kings.

(ii) None of the three cards is a King.

(iii) At least one is a King.

(iv) Exactly two are Spades.

Solution 1

The step-by-step method

(i) P(all three are Kings) = P(1st is a King **and** 2nd is a King **and** 3rd is a King)

$$= \frac{4}{52} \times \frac{3}{51} \times \frac{2}{50} = \frac{1}{5{,}525}$$

Here we assume that the event **does** happen and calculate the probabilities accordingly.

(ii) P(none is a King) = P(1st is not a King **and** 2nd is not a King **and** 3rd is not a King)

$$= \frac{48}{52} \times \frac{47}{51} \times \frac{46}{50} = \frac{4{,}324}{5{,}525}$$

(iii) P(at least one is a King) = 1 – P(none is a King)

$$= 1 - \frac{4{,}324}{5{,}525} = \frac{1{,}201}{5{,}525}$$

(iv) P(exactly two are Spades) = P(Spade, Spade, not Spade)

$+$

P(Spade, not Spade, Spade)

$+$

P(not Spade, Spade, Spade)

$$= \left(\frac{13}{52} \times \frac{12}{51} \times \frac{39}{50}\right) + \left(\frac{13}{52} \times \frac{39}{51} \times \frac{12}{50}\right) + \left(\frac{39}{52} \times \frac{13}{51} \times \frac{12}{50}\right)$$

$$= \frac{117}{850}$$

Solution 2

The choosing method

(i) P(all three are Kings)

$$= \frac{\text{\# ways of choosing 3 Kings out of 4}}{\text{\# ways of choosing 3 cards from 52}} = \frac{\binom{4}{3}}{\binom{52}{3}} = \frac{4}{22{,}100} = \frac{1}{5{,}525}$$

(ii) P(none is a King)

$$= \frac{\text{\# ways of choosing 3 non-Kings from 48}}{\text{\# ways of choosing 3 cards from 52}} = \frac{\binom{48}{3}}{\binom{52}{3}} = \frac{17{,}296}{22{,}100} = \frac{4{,}324}{5{,}525}$$

(iii) P(at least one is a King) = 1 – (none is a King) $= 1 - \frac{4{,}324}{5{,}525} = \frac{1{,}201}{5{,}525}$

(iv) P(exactly two are Spades)

$$= \frac{\text{\# ways of choosing 2 Spades (from 13) \textbf{and} 1 non-Spade (from 39)}}{\text{\# ways of choosing 3 cards from 52}}$$

$$= \frac{\binom{13}{2} \times \binom{39}{1}}{\binom{52}{3}} = \frac{3{,}042}{22{,}100} = \frac{117}{850}$$

Worked Example 3.3

Four people are asked 'On what day of the week were you born?' Find, correct to two decimal places, the probability that at least two were born on the same day of the week.

Solution

First, we will find the probability that they were all born on different days of the week.

- The first person can have any day at all: $P = \frac{7}{7}$.
- The second person's birthday must be on one of the six other days of the week: $P = \frac{6}{7}$.
- That leaves five days for the third person: $P = \frac{5}{7}$.
- And, finally, four days for the last person: $P = \frac{4}{7}$.

$\therefore$ P(all different) $= \frac{7}{7} \times \frac{6}{7} \times \frac{5}{7} \times \frac{4}{7} = \frac{120}{343} = 0.35$

Again, we assume that the event **does** happen and calculate the probabilities accordingly.

$\therefore$ P(at least two are the same)

= 1 – P (all different)

= 1 – 0.35

= 0.65

Exercise 3.1

1. A fair coin is flipped twice. Find:

   (i) The probability of getting two heads

   (ii) The probability of getting at least one tail

2. A fair six-sided die is rolled three times. Find the probability of getting:

   (i) Three 6's

   (ii) A 6 followed by an even number followed by an odd number

3. A fair coin is flipped four times. Find the probability of getting:

   (i) Four heads

   (ii) At least one tail

4. A couple have five children. What is the probability that:

   (i) They are all girls.

   (ii) At least one is a boy.

5. A classroom contains 14 girls and 16 boys. A student is picked at random and leaves the room. Another student is then picked at random. Find the probability that:

   (i) Both are boys.

   (ii) Both are girls.

   (iii) At least one is a boy.

6. A card is drawn from a standard pack but not replaced. Then another card is drawn from the remainder of the pack. Find the probability that:

   (i) The first card is a Jack and the second is a Queen.

   (ii) Both of the cards are Jacks.

   (iii) Neither of the cards is a Jack.

   (iv) At least one of the cards is a Jack.

7. Three cards are drawn from a standard pack without replacement. Find the probability that:

   (i) All three are Queens.

   (ii) At least one is not a Queen.

8. (a) Last season, a centre-forward took 20 penalties and scored 12. Find the probability that she scores a penalty, using the relative frequency.

   (b) If, in a match, the centre-forward takes two penalty kicks, find the probability that:

   (i) She scores both.

   (ii) She scores neither.

   (iii) She scores at least once.

   (iv) She scores one but not the other.

9. (a) Last year, a certain student was late for school 21 times out of 168 days.

   Find the probability that this student will be on time for school on a specific day, using the relative frequency.

   (b) Find, correct to three significant figures, the probability that this student will be on time:

   (i) For two successive days

   (ii) For three successive days

   (iii) For five successive days

10. Jim, Ken and Leah are given a maths problem to solve. Their probabilities of success are shown in this table:

Person	Jim	Ken	Leah
Probability of success	$\frac{1}{2}$	$\frac{1}{4}$	$\frac{1}{3}$

Find the probability that:

   (i) All three are successful.

   (ii) All three fail.

   (iii) At least one is successful.

3.2 TREE DIAGRAMS

Worked Example 3.4

A bag contains seven green marbles and three red ones. Two marbles are drawn at random but not replaced. Use a tree diagram to find the probability that they will have different colours.

Solution

There are two ways that this can happen: The first is green **and** the second is red **or** the first is red **and** the second is green. We show these on a tree diagram:

1st Draw	2nd Draw	Outcome	Probability
$\frac{7}{10}$ G	$\frac{6}{9}$ G	G, G	$\frac{7}{10} \times \frac{6}{9} = \frac{7}{15}$
	$\frac{3}{9}$ R	G, R	$\frac{7}{10} \times \frac{3}{9} = \frac{7}{30}$
$\frac{3}{10}$ R	$\frac{7}{9}$ G	R, G	$\frac{3}{10} \times \frac{7}{9} = \frac{7}{30}$
	$\frac{2}{9}$ R	R, R	$\frac{3}{10} \times \frac{2}{9} = \frac{1}{15}$

Check: Total = 1

We are looking for the probability that the two marbles drawn will have different colours.

The desirable outcomes are Green, Red **or** Red, Green.

$$\therefore \text{P(different colours)} = \frac{7}{30} + \frac{7}{30} = \frac{14}{30} = \frac{7}{15}$$

Worked Example 3.5

The table shows the ages and gender of 28 students on a school tour.

	Boys	Girls
Aged 17	4	6
Aged 18	8	10

Two students are chosen from this group at random.
Find the probability that:

(i) One is a girl and one is a boy.

(ii) Both have the same age and gender.

Solution

(i)

1st Student	2nd Student	Outcome	Probability
$\frac{12}{28}$ Boy	$\frac{11}{27}$ Boy	B, B	$\frac{12}{28} \times \frac{11}{27} = \frac{11}{63}$
	$\frac{16}{27}$ Girl	B, G	$\frac{12}{28} \times \frac{16}{27} = \frac{16}{63}$
$\frac{16}{28}$ Girl	$\frac{12}{27}$ Boy	G, B	$\frac{16}{28} \times \frac{12}{27} = \frac{16}{63}$
	$\frac{15}{27}$ Girl	G, G	$\frac{16}{28} \times \frac{15}{27} = \frac{20}{63}$

Check: Total = 1

P(one girl and one boy) = P(G, B) + P(B, G)

$$= \frac{16}{63} + \frac{16}{63}$$

$$= \frac{32}{63}$$

(ii) There are four branches on the 'probability tree':

1st Student		2nd Student	Outcome	Probability
$\frac{4}{28}$ B(17)	$\frac{3}{27}$	B(17)	B(17), B(17)	$\frac{4}{28} \times \frac{3}{27} = \frac{1}{63}$
$\frac{8}{28}$ B(18)	$\frac{7}{27}$	B(18)	B(18), B(18)	$\frac{8}{28} \times \frac{7}{27} = \frac{2}{27}$
$\frac{6}{28}$ G(17)	$\frac{5}{27}$	G(17)	G(17), G(17)	$\frac{6}{28} \times \frac{5}{27} = \frac{5}{126}$
$\frac{10}{28}$ G(18)	$\frac{9}{27}$	G(18)	G(18), G(18)	$\frac{10}{28} \times \frac{9}{27} = \frac{5}{42}$

For this probability tree, we show only the branches that we are interested in:

∴ P(both have the same age and gender)

$$= \frac{1}{63} + \frac{2}{27} + \frac{5}{126} + \frac{5}{42}$$

$$= \frac{47}{189}$$

Exercise 3.2

1. A bag contains five black marbles and two white ones. Two marbles are taken out, without replacement. What is the probability that one is white and the other is black?

2. Two cards are taken from a standard pack, without replacement. What is the probability that one will be a Club and the other a Spade?

3. When a certain player takes a penalty, the probability that he will score is $\frac{5}{6}$ each time. In a match, he takes two penalties. What is the probability that he will score exactly once?

4. A fair six-sided die is rolled twice. Find the probability that one result is odd and the other even.

5. A student sits a multiple choice test. In each question, four possible answers are offered, but only one is correct. The student guesses the answers to two of the questions.
What is the probability that she gets exactly one of these right?

6. Three-quarters of all light bulbs in a country are made by Glare, and one-quarter are made by Brighteyes. Five per cent of all Glare lightbulbs last for a year (or more). Ten per cent of all Brighteyes lightbulbs last for a year (or more).
If you buy a lightbulb at random in this country, what is the probability that it will last for at least a year?

7. If a day is fine, the probability that Mary will be late for school is 0.4. If the day is wet, the probability goes up to 0.5. In Ireland, 20% of all days are wet.
Find the probability that on a random day in Ireland, Mary will be late for school.

8. A bag contains five red sweets and four green ones. Pete takes three sweets out in succession and eats them.
What is the probability that:

    (i) All three are red.

    (ii) One is red and two are green.

9. A bag contains five green, three blue and four red marbles. Two marbles are withdrawn, without replacement.
Find the probability that:

(i) Both are green.

(ii) Both are green or both are blue.

(iii) Both are the same colour.

(iv) They are different colours.

(v) One is red and one is not red.

For the remaining questions, use tree diagrams **or** multiplication of probabilities **or** ^nC_r as appropriate.

10. A bag contains eight black, three white and five red beads. Three beads are picked at random, without replacement.
Find the probability that:

(i) All three have the same colour.

(ii) One is white and the others are not white.

(iii) All three are of different colours.

(iv) At least two are the same colour.

11. Nine tickets, numbered 11, 12, 13, 14, 15, 16, 17, 18 and 19, are placed in a hat. One ticket is taken out but not replaced. Another ticket is taken out.
Find the probability that:

(i) Both are prime numbers.

(ii) Both are even or both are odd.

(iii) One is prime but the other is not.

12. Twenty tickets are numbered 1–20. Numbers 1–10 are red, 11–16 are yellow, and 17–20 are green. A ticket is picked at random and replaced. A second ticket is then picked at random. Find the probability that:

(i) Both are red.

(ii) Both are yellow and even-numbered.

(iii) Both are yellow or even-numbered.

(iv) The sum of the numbers on the two tickets is 36.

13. (i) A tennis player gets 50% of his first serves 'in' and 80% of his second serves 'in'. Find the probability that this player will get a 'double fault' (where both first and second serves go out).

(ii) Another player gets 70% of both her first and her second serves 'in'. What is the probability that this player will get a 'double fault'?

14. Three people are picked at random. What is the probability that:

(i) All three have birthdays in different months.

(ii) At least two have their birthdays in the same month.

(N.B. Take all months to be equally likely.)

15. (i) A poker hand of five cards is dealt randomly from a pack of 52. Find, correct to four decimal places, the probability of being dealt a flush of Spades (where all five cards are Spades).

(ii) Find the probability of being dealt a flush in **any** suit.

16. Five people are chosen at random. Find the probability that two or more were born:

(i) On the same day of the week

(ii) In the same month (taking all months to be equally likely)

17. (i) Four people are asked their birthday (e.g. 10th Nov., 25th Jan. etc.) Show that the probability that two or more of them have the same birthday is (correct to four decimal places) 0.0164. (Ignore 29th Feb.)

(ii) The Famous Birthday Problem: There are 23 people in a room. Show that the probability that two or more have the same birthday is greater than 0.5.

18. Three girls and one boy meet and discuss their birthdays. They discover that three of them have their birthdays in the same week (i.e. a seven-day week). Find the probability that:

(i) The three whose birthdays lie in that week are all girls.

(ii) All four were born on different days of the week.

19. Four people are asked (independently) to think of one letter in the word TRIANGLES. Find the probability that:

(i) They all think of the letter T.

(ii) They all think of vowels.

(iii) They all think of different letters.

20. Three people are asked to choose at random one of the numbers between 1 and 10 (inclusive). Find the probability that:

(i) They all choose the same number.

(ii) They all choose different numbers.

(iii) At least two choose the same number.

21. A wheel of fortune is divided into eight sections, each of which is equally likely to end up the 'winning' sector (where the arrow points). Sections 1, 2 and 3 are grey. Sections 4, 5, 6 and 7 are black. Section 8 is white.

The wheel is turned twice.
Find the probability that:

(i) Black wins twice.

(ii) The same colour wins twice.

(iii) The total of the two winning numbers is 13.

22. Two people are asked (independently of one another) to choose two letters (each) from the letters of the word FRACTION.
Find the probability that:

(i) They both choose two consonants.

(ii) One chooses two consonants and the other chooses two vowels.

(iii) They have no letters in common.

(iv) They both choose the same pair of letters.

23. There are 11 white socks and n black socks in a drawer. A person draws out two socks, at random. The probability that both are black is $\frac{1}{12}$. Find n.

24. There are four black balls, 10 white balls and n red balls in a bag. Two balls are drawn without replacement. The probability that one is red and one is not red is found to be $\frac{7}{15}$. Find two possible values for n.

25.

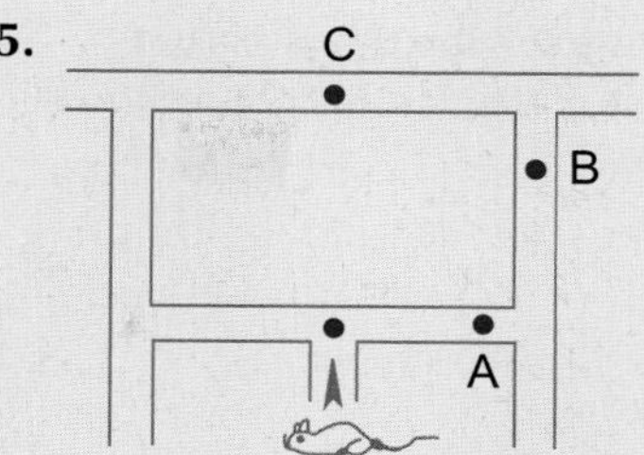

A rat is placed in a maze as shown. When it goes for a walk, it turns left at a 'T-junction' twice as often as it turns right.
What is the probability that:

(i) It passes A after one turn.

(ii) It passes B after two turns.

(iii) It passes C after three turns.

26. Seven people are picked at random. Find the probability (correct to two significant figures) that their birthdays in a certain year (ignore leap years):

(i) Fall on different days of the week

(ii) Fall in different months (taking all months as equally likely)

(iii) Fall on different dates of the year

27. A fair cubic die is relabelled so that it has three 1's, two 2's and one 6. The die is rolled.

T = {The number showing is 2}

E = {The number showing is even}

O = {The number showing is 1}

(a) Find:

(i) P(T)	(v) P(E′)
(ii) P(E)	(vi) $P(T \cap E)$
(iii) P(O)	(vii) $P(E' \cap T)$
(iv) P(T′)	(viii) $P(O' \cap T')$

(b) Are these pairs of sets mutually exclusive?

(i) T and E	(iii) E and O
(ii) T and O	(iv) T′ and O′

28. Eva has a bag into which she is placing copper coins and silver coins. She places six copper coins and x silver coins in the bag. She then draws a coin at random from the bag.

(a) Find the value of x:

(i) If P (the coin is copper) = 0.5

(ii) If P (the coin is silver) = 0.25

(iii) If P (the coin is copper) = 0.2

(b) Why is it impossible for:

P (the coin is silver) = 0.2

29. In a certain city, 60% of the cars are from country A, 30% from country B and 10% from country C. Thirty per cent of cars from country A, 25% of cars from country B and 20% of cars from country C last for 10 years or more.

Find the probability that:

(i) A car, bought at random in this city, will last for 10 years or more.

(ii) A car will last for 10 or more years, given that it is not from country A.

(iii) A car is from country C, given that it is 10 years old.

30. Three fair six-sided dice are rolled.
Find the probability that the total on all three dice is 5 or less.

31. A soccer team has five penalty takers (*A*, *B*, *C*, *D* and *E*) for a penalty shoot-out. Each of the five has to take one penalty. The probabilities for each player's success is given in the following table:

Player	*A*	*B*	*C*	*D*	*E*
Probability of scoring	0.9	0.8	0.75	0.5	0.4

Find the probability that:

(i) All five score their penalties.

(ii) At least one misses.

(iii) They all score, except for *E*.

(iv) They all score, except for *D*.

(v) Exactly four of the five score.

32. A university student walks, cycles or drives to college with probabilities 0.1, 0.3 and 0.6, respectively. If she walks, she has a probability of 0.35 of being late. If she cycles, the probability of being late is 0.1. If she drives, the probability of being late is 0.55.

Find, correct to three decimal places, the probability that:

(i) She will be late on a particular day.

(ii) She walked, given that she was late.

(iii) She walked, given that she was **not** late.

33. During the season, a hurling team (called the Random Variables) played 32 matches. Twenty of these matches were in fine weather and they won 16 of them. The other 12 were in rainy weather and they won only four of these.

Give your answers to the following questions as fractions in their lowest terms.

(i) What is the relative frequency of the Random Variables winning in fine weather?

(ii) What is the relative frequency of the Random Variables winning in rainy weather?

(iii) The Random Variables are playing in the Cup Final next Sunday. The weather forecasters say that the probability of fine weather is $\frac{3}{4}$ and the probability of rainy weather is $\frac{1}{4}$. Using the relative frequencies as probabilities, find the probability that they will win.

34. A teacher has one euro coin and three 50c coins in his back pocket. He has two euro coins and one 50c coin in his left pocket. He has three euro coins only in his right pocket. He rolls a die. If it comes up as 1, 2 or 3, he will give a coin randomly from his back pocket as a prize to the best pupil. If a 4 or 5 comes up, he will give a coin from his left pocket. If a 6 comes up, he will give a coin from his right pocket.
What is the probability that the coin given will be a euro?

3.3 EXPECTED VALUE

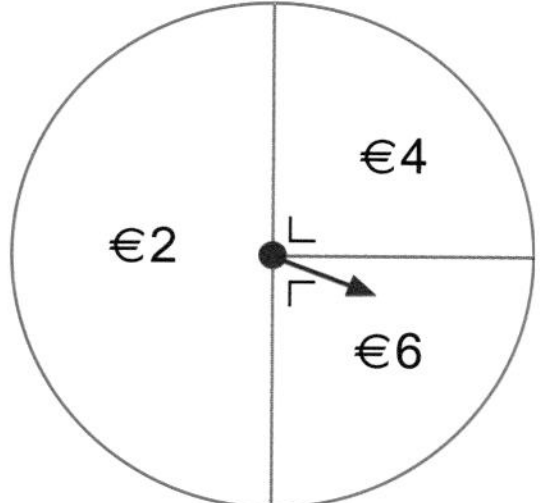

Here is a spinner. You bet €5, then spin the wheel and you win whatever amount the arrow is pointing to. Is this a good or a bad bet? We can decide mathematically by calculating the **expected value** (or mean). The expected value E(X) is defined as E(X) = $\sum x \,.\, P(x)$ (where $\sum$ means 'the sum of'). In this case, the probability of getting €2 is $\frac{1}{2}$, of getting €4 is $\frac{1}{4}$ and of getting €6 is $\frac{1}{4}$.

The expected return = $E(X) = \sum x \,.\, P(x)$

$$\therefore E(X) = 2\left(\frac{1}{2}\right) + 4\left(\frac{1}{4}\right) + 6\left(\frac{1}{4}\right)$$

$$= 1 + 1 + 1.5$$

$$= 3.5$$

$$\therefore E(X) = €3.50 \text{ (in money)}$$

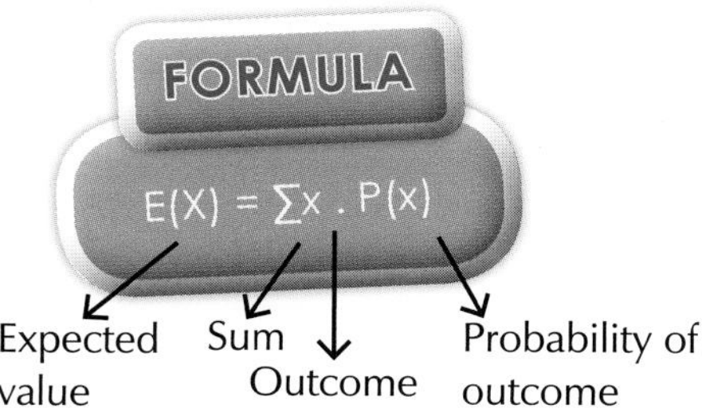

But you paid out €5, so the expected value of the transaction is:

$$€(3.50 - 5) = -€1.50$$

This means that you expect to lose €1.50. It is therefore a bad bet.

Worked Example 3.6

The two arrows in spinners A and B are spun, and the product of the two numbers is found. Find the expected value.

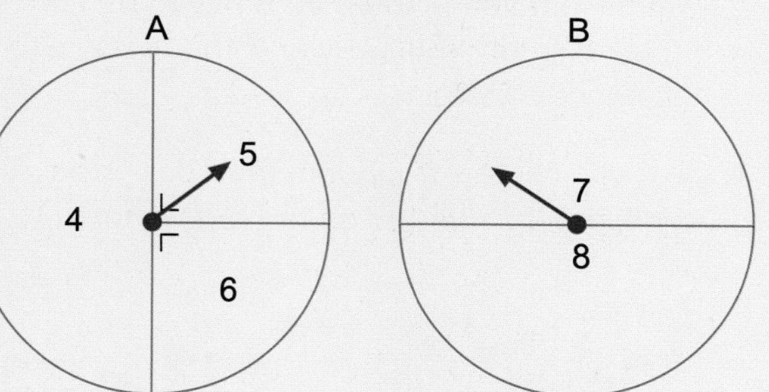

Solution

There are six possible products:

$4 \times 7 = 28 : P(28) = \frac{1}{2} \times \frac{1}{2} = \frac{1}{4}$

$5 \times 7 = 35 : P(35) = \frac{1}{4} \times \frac{1}{2} = \frac{1}{8}$

$6 \times 7 = 42 : P(42) = \frac{1}{4} \times \frac{1}{2} = \frac{1}{8}$

$4 \times 8 = 32 : P(32) = \frac{1}{2} \times \frac{1}{2} = \frac{1}{4}$

$5 \times 8 = 40 : P(40) = \frac{1}{4} \times \frac{1}{2} = \frac{1}{8}$

$6 \times 8 = 48 : P(48) = \frac{1}{4} \times \frac{1}{2} = \frac{1}{8}$

$$E(X) = \sum x \,.\, P(x)$$

$$= 28\left(\frac{1}{4}\right) + 35\left(\frac{1}{8}\right) + 42\left(\frac{1}{8}\right) + 32\left(\frac{1}{4}\right) + 40\left(\frac{1}{8}\right) + 48\left(\frac{1}{8}\right)$$

$$\therefore E(X) = 35.625$$

It is worth noting that the expected value does not necessarily have to be an actual possible outcome. For example, in this Worked Example, the expected value is 35.625 even though this is not one of the six possible products (28, 35, 42, 32, 40 and 48). This can be true of any mean: for example, the average family might have 2.4 children, even though it is not possible to give birth to 2.4 children.

Exercise 3.3

1. When a fair six-sided die is rolled, show that the expected value is 3.5.

2.

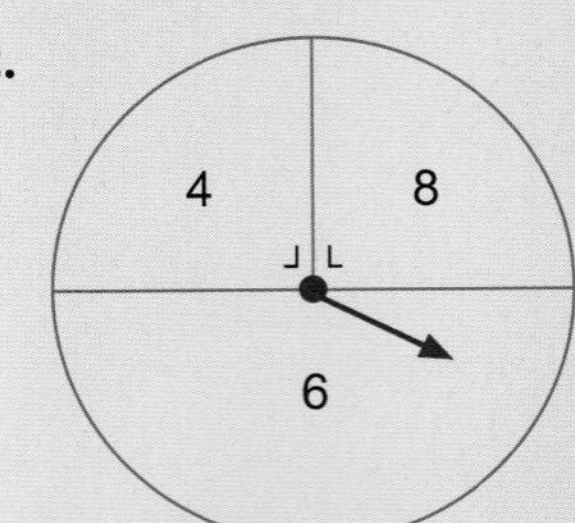

Find the expected value when this spinner is spun.

3.

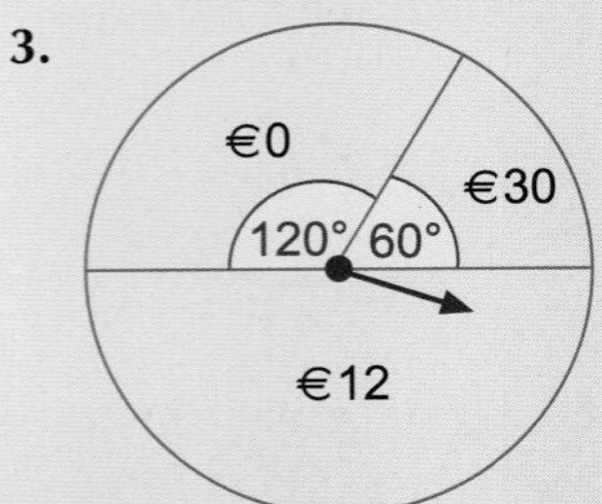

You bet €10. Then spin the spinner and you win the amount pointed at. Is this a good or bad bet? Justify your answer with reference to the expected value.

4. A card is chosen at random from this poker hand and the number on the card is noted.

(i) Copy and complete this probability distribution table:

Number on card	10	5
Probability		

(ii) Find the expected value of the number on the card.

(iii) Is the expected value one of the possible outcomes?

5. A friend of yours offers you a bet: you have to bet €1. Then you pick a card from a pack.

- If you choose the Ace of Spades you win €20.
- If you pick any Diamond card, you win €2.

Is this a good bet? Justify your answer with reference to the expected value.

6. A pair of fair six-sided dice is rolled and the total on the two dice is noted.

(i) Copy and complete the following probability distribution table:

Total (x)	2	3	4	5	6	7	8	9	10	11	12
P(x)	$\frac{1}{36}$				$\frac{5}{36}$						$\frac{1}{36}$

(ii) Calculate the expected value.

(iii) Is the expected value a possible outcome?

7.

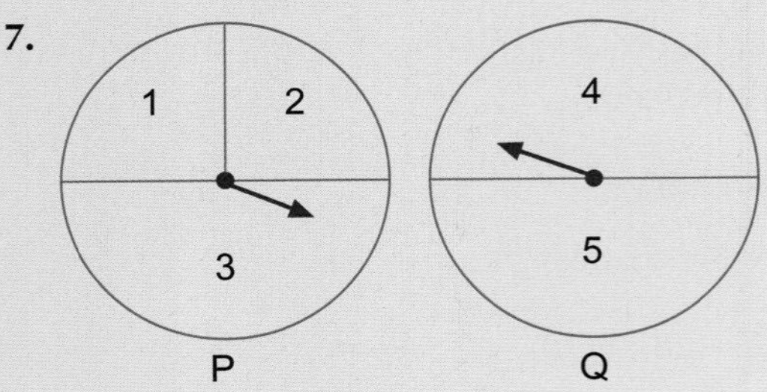

Two spinners P and Q are spun and the sum total is noted.

(i) Copy and complete the probability distribution table:

Total (x)	5	6	7	8
P(x)	$\frac{1}{8}$			

(ii) Calculate the expected value of the sum.

8. 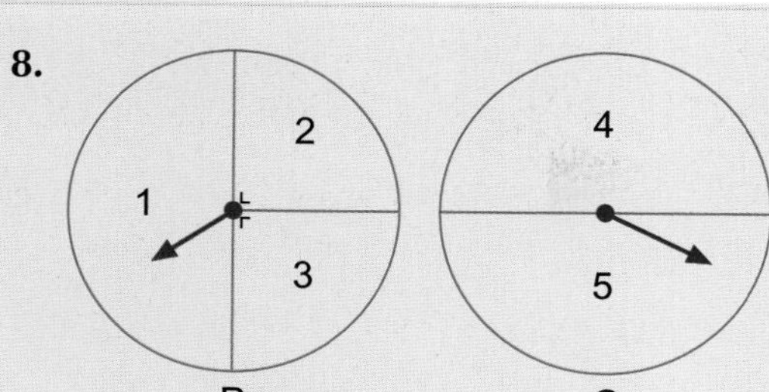

Spinners P and Q are spun and the product of the two numbers is noted. Calculate the expected value of the product.

9. In a game, a contestant is given the chance to choose one of five plain white envelopes, but must pay €10 for this game. The contestant keeps the contents of the envelope.

One envelope is empty, one contains a €5 note, one a €10 note, one a €20 note, and finally, one a €50 note.

Is this a good game for the contestant to play? Explain your answer with reference to the expected value.

10. 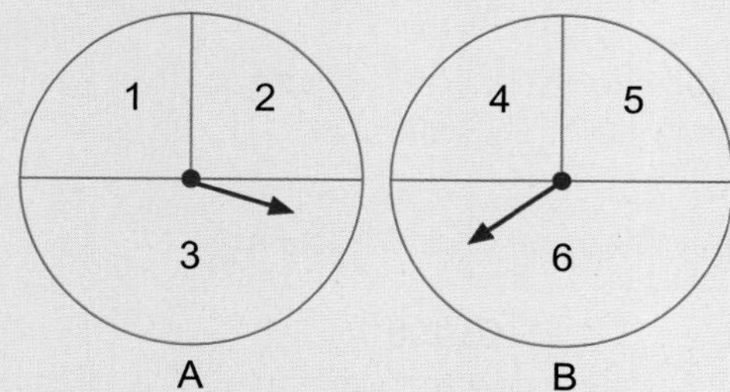

Spinners A and B are spun and the sum of the outcomes is noted.

(i) Calculate the expected value.

(ii) Design a single spinner with the same probabilities as the sum of A and B, showing the degrees in each sector.

11. 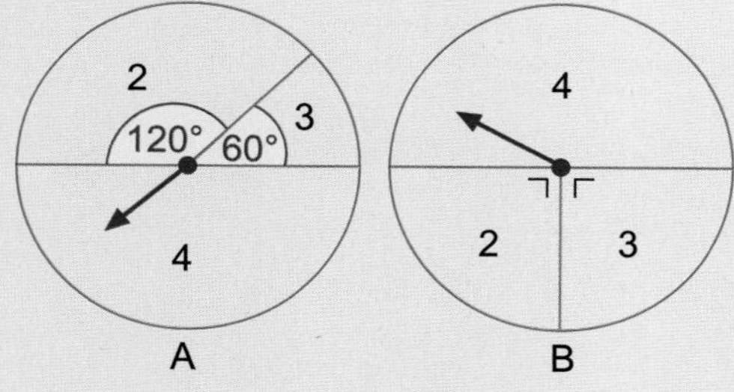

(i) Which has the higher expected value, A or B?

(ii) If both spinners are spun, find the expected value for the **sum** of A and B.

(iii) If both spinners are spun, find the expected value for the **product** of A and B.

(iv) Design a single spinner whose outcomes have the same probability as the sum of A and B.

12. A girl is in a show on television. She has answered a question correctly and so she has won €1,000. Now she is offered three choices:

Choice 1: She can take the money and go.

Choice 2: She can pick a card at random from a standard pack of cards, and if she picks an Ace, she wins €10,000. (In this case, she does not get the €1,000 as well.) If she does not get an Ace, she goes home with nothing.

Choice 3: She can roll a pair of fair six-sided dice and if she throws a double 6, she wins €100,000. (In this case also, she does not get the €1,000 as well.) If she does not throw a double 6, she goes home empty-handed.

(i) Copy and complete the following table:

Choice	Expected value
Choice 1	€1,000
Choice 2	
Choice 3	

(ii) What should the girl do? Justify your answer.

13. A country holds a lottery every week. You have to choose six numbers out of 45. If your six numbers come up, you will win €3,000,000. It costs €1 to buy a ticket.

(i) How many ways are there of choosing six numbers out of 45?

(ii) What is the probability of winning, correct to three significant figures?

(iii) Is it good value to buy a ticket for this lottery? Justify your answer with reference to expected value.

14. The table below gives motor insurance information for fully licensed, 17–20-year-old drivers in Ireland in 2007. All drivers who had their own insurance policy are included.

	Number of drivers	Number of claims	Average cost per claim
Male	9,634	977	€6,108
Female	6,743	581	€6,051

(Source: Adapted from: Financial Regulator. *Private Motor Insurance Statistics 2007*.)

Questions (a) to (e) refer to drivers in the table above only.

(a) What is the probability that a randomly selected male driver made a claim during the year?

Give your answer correct to three decimal places.

(b) What is the probability that a randomly selected female driver made a claim during the year?

Give your answer correct to three decimal places.

(c) What is the expected value of the cost of claims on a male driver's policy?

(d) What is the expected value of the cost of claims on a female driver's policy?

(e) The male drivers were paying an average of €1,688 for insurance in 2007, and the female drivers were paying an average of €1,024. Calculate the average surplus for each group, and comment on your answer.

(Note: the surplus is the amount paid for the policy minus the expected cost of claims.)

(f) A 40-year-old female driver with a full licence has a probability of 0.07 of making a claim during the year. The average cost of such claims is €3,900. How much should a company charge such drivers for insurance in order to show a surplus of €175 per policy?

(Leaving Certificate Project Maths Paper 2, 2010)

15. The number of laptops per household in a survey of 100 houses in a town gave the following frequency distribution:

Number of laptops	0	1	2	3
Frequency	10	75	10	5

(i) Draw up a probability distribution table for the variable X, where X is the number of laptops in a house picked at random in the town.

(ii) Find the expected value for X.

(iii) Find the probability that a household has three laptops, given that there is at least one laptop in the house.

16. The random variable X has the following probability distribution:

x	1	2	3	4	5
$P(X = x)$	0.1	a	b	0.2	0.1

(i) Given that the expected value $E(X) = 2.9$, find the value of a and the value of b.

(ii) Find $P(X = 5 \mid X > 3)$.

Independent Events: A Formal Approach

We saw earlier in this chapter that when we say that two events (E and F, say) are **independent**, we mean that the outcome of one in no way affects the outcome of the other. There is a more formal, mathematical definition of independence:

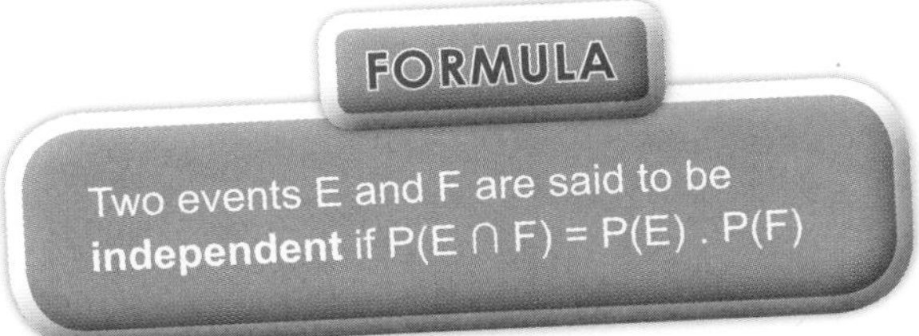

FORMULA
Two events E and F are said to be
independent if P(E ∩ F) = P(E) . P(F)

It is not at all obvious that these two definitions are compatible, but we can prove that they are.

Proof: To say that the outcome of E in no way affects the outcome of F means that:

$P(E \mid F) = P(E)$ (Since the probability that E will happen does NOT depend on whether F happens or not)

$$\Leftrightarrow \frac{P(E \cap F)}{P(F)} = P(E)$$

$$\Leftrightarrow P(E \cap F) = P(E) \,.\, P(F) \qquad \text{Q.E.D.}$$

The following Worked Example illustrates that our intuitive idea of independence and the strict mathematical definition are one and the same.

Worked Example 3.7

Let a fair six-sided die be rolled twice.

Let E = {6 turns up on the first roll}.

Let F = {6 turns up on the second roll}.

Let G = {The total on the two rolls is 8 or more}.

Our intuition would tell us that E and F are independent, whereas E and G are NOT independent. (Surely, a total of 8 or more is made more likely by the fact that the first roll produced a 6?)

Prove mathematically that:

(i) E and F are independent.

(ii) E and G are not independent.

Solution

S = OUTCOME SPACE = {(1, 1), (1, 2), (1, 3), …, (6, 5), (6, 6)} #S = 36

E = {6, 1), (6, 2), (6, 3), (6, 4), (6, 5), (6, 6)} #E = 6

F = {(1, 6), (2, 6), (3, 6), (4, 6), (5, 6), (6, 6)} #F = 6

G = {(2, 6), (3, 5), (3, 6), (4, 4), (4, 5), (4, 6), (5, 3), (5, 4), (5, 5), (5, 6), (6, 2), (6, 3), (6, 4), (6, 5), (6, 6)} #G = 15

$E \cap F = \{(6, 6)\}$ $\#(E \cap F) = 1$

$E \cap G = \{(6, 2), (6, 3), (6, 4), (6, 5), (6, 6)\}$ $\#(E \cap G) = 5$

(i) $P(E) = \frac{6}{36} = \frac{1}{6}$, $P(F) = \frac{6}{36} = \frac{1}{6}$ $\therefore P(E) . P(F) = \frac{1}{6} \cdot \frac{1}{6} = \frac{1}{36}$

$P(E \cap F) = \frac{1}{36}$

Since $P(E \cap F) = P(E) . P(F)$, E and F are independent.

(ii) $P(E) = \frac{1}{6}$, $P(G) = \frac{15}{36} = \frac{5}{12}$ $\therefore P(E) . P(G) = \frac{1}{6} \cdot \frac{5}{12} = \frac{5}{72}$

$P(E \cap G) = \frac{5}{36}$

$P(E) . P(G) \neq P(E \cap G)$

$\therefore$ E and G are NOT independent.

Worked Example 3.8

A and B are independent events such that:

P(A) = 0.3 and P(A ∪ B) = 0.5

Find P(B).

Solution

Let P(B) = x.

P(A ∪ B) = P(A) + P(B) – P(A ∩ B)

⇒ P(A ∪ B) = P(A) + P(B) – P(A) . P(B) (Since A, B are independent.)

⇒ $0.5 = 0.3 + x - 0.3x$

⇒ $5 = 3 + 10x - 3x$ (Multiplying by 10)

⇒ $2 = 7x$

⇒ $x = \frac{2}{7}$

Answer: P(B) = $\frac{2}{7}$

It is useful to know de Morgan's Laws, namely:

$(A \cup B)' = A' \cap B'$ and $(A \cap B)' = A' \cup B'$

Exercise 3.4

1. 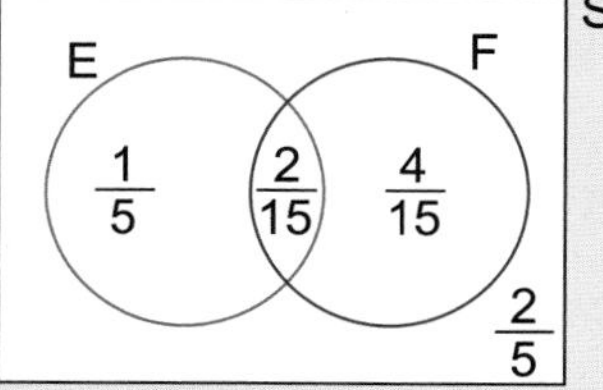

Prove that E and F are independent events, given the Venn diagram above.

2. A and B are independent events, such that P(A) = $\frac{1}{2}$ and P(B) = $\frac{3}{4}$.

Find:

(i) P(A ∩ B)

(ii) P(A ∪ B)

3. E and F are subsets of an outcome space, S, in which all single elements are equally likely.

#(E \ F) = 1 #(F \ E) = 9

#(E ∩ F) = 7 #S = 20

Investigate if E and F are independent.

4. E and F are independent events, such that P(E) = 0.2 and P(F) = 0.5. Evaluate P(E ∪ F).

5. 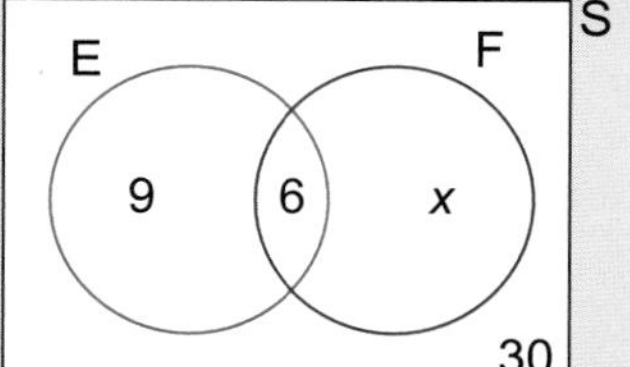

E and F are independent events, whose cardinal numbers are given in the Venn diagram. Find the value of x.

You may assume that all single elements are equally likely.

6. A fair six-sided die is rolled twice.

E = {2 appears on the first roll}.

F = {The total on the two rolls is an even number}.

G = {The total on the two dice is less than 5}.

Investigate if:

(i) E and F are independent.

(ii) E and G are independent.

7. E and F are independent events, such that P(E) = $\frac{2}{5}$ and P(E ∪ F) = $\frac{3}{5}$.

Find P(F).

8. A card is drawn from a pack at random. E is the event that the chosen card is a Spade. F is the event that the chosen card is a 'picture card' (i.e. a Jack, Queen or King).

Prove that E and F are independent.

9. A green six-sided die and a red six-sided die are rolled. E is the event that the score on the green die is 1. F is the event that the total on the two dice is 7.

Investigate if E and F are independent.

10.

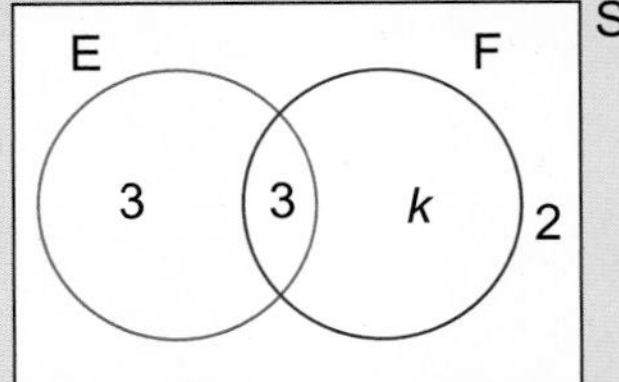

E and F are two independent events of an outcome space, S, as shown in the Venn diagram. Assume that all singletons are equally likely.

(i) Find the value of k.

(ii) Find P(E′), P(F′) and P(E′ ∩ F′).

(iii) Investigate if E′ and F′ are also independent.

11. There are 20 raffle tickets in a hat, numbered 1 to 20. Four of the tickets (numbers 5, 10, 15, 20) are green. The rest are pink.

A ticket is picked at random from the hat and then replaced in the hat.

Once more, a ticket is picked from the hat.

E is the event that the first ticket is pink.

F is the event that the total on the two numbers is 35 or more.

(i) Without listing them, state the number of elements in the outcome space S for picking two tickets.

(ii) Find P(E), P(F) and P(E ∩ F).

(iii) Are E and F independent events? Justify your answer.

12. A fair coin is flipped four times. List the remaining 13 elements of the outcome space:

S = {*hhhh*, *hhht*, *hhth*, …}

- E is the event that the first three flips all give 'heads'.
- F is the event that the fourth flip gives a 'head'.

Prove that E and F are independent.

3.4 THE BINOMIAL DISTRIBUTION: BERNOULLI TRIALS

There are 300 girls and 100 boys in a school. Each weekday, the headmistress chooses one student at random to read the announcements at Assembly. Over a certain five-day week, find the probability that the headmistress chooses a girl exactly three times and a boy twice.

It is easy to be misled here. One might imagine that she must choose a girl for the first three days and a boy for the next two days. Hence, the probability would be:

$$\frac{3}{4} \times \frac{3}{4} \times \frac{3}{4} \times \frac{1}{4} \times \frac{1}{4} = \frac{27}{1{,}024}$$

But this answer is too restrictive, since it is allowable to have the sequence:

Girl-Girl-Boy-Girl-Boy, with a probability of

$$\frac{3}{4} \times \frac{3}{4} \times \frac{1}{4} \times \frac{3}{4} \times \frac{1}{4} = \frac{27}{1{,}024}$$

or Girl-Boy-Girl-Boy-Girl, again with a probability of $\frac{27}{1{,}024}$ or, indeed, ANY acceptable order, each of which yields a probability of $\frac{27}{1{,}024}$.

So, the correct answer will be $k\left(\frac{27}{1{,}024}\right)$ where k is the number of different ways in which the three girls and two boys can be ordered.

PROBABILITY II

So, what is k?

k, in this case, is 10 because there are 10 ways of ordering three girls and two boys:

GGGBB, GGBGB, GBGGB, BGGGB, GBGBG,

GBBGG, BGGBG, GGBBG, BGBGG, BBGGG

The **reason** why there are 10 is that we are **choosing** three days out of five for the girls.

There are $\binom{5}{3} = 10$ ways of doing this.

Here the correct answer is:

$$\binom{5}{3}\left(\frac{3}{4}\right)^3\left(\frac{1}{4}\right)^2 = 10\left(\frac{27}{1{,}024}\right) = \frac{135}{512}$$

In general, let us conduct the **same** experiment n times – each with two possible outcomes which we will call 'success' and 'failure'. Let the probability of success be p and the probability of failure be q (where $q = 1 - p$). The probability of getting exactly r successes (where $r \leqslant n$) will be:

This formula appears on page 33 of the *Formulae and Tables*.

The formula above is a term in the binomial expansion of $(p + q)^n$. Hence the name 'binomial distribution'.

It is important for you to recognise when to use the binomial distribution formula. Remember to use the formula when the following four criteria are satisfied:

- There is a finite number of trials (n).
- There are only two outcomes – success and failure.
- Trials are independent of each other.
- The probability of success (p) is the same for each trial.

Each trial is often referred to as a **Bernoulli trial**, after the Swiss mathematician Jakob Bernoulli (1655–1705).

Worked Example 3.9

A couple have six children. Find the probability that they have four girls and two boys.

Solution

We will let 'success' be 'having a girl' and 'failure' be 'having a boy' (although each is, of course, as much a success as the other).

$\therefore p = \frac{1}{2}$ and $q = \frac{1}{2}$

We require four successes out of six. $\therefore n = 6, r = 4$.

$$\text{Probability} = \binom{6}{4}\left(\frac{1}{2}\right)^4\left(\frac{1}{2}\right)^2 = (15)\left(\frac{1}{16}\right)\left(\frac{1}{4}\right) = \frac{15}{64}$$

Worked Example 3.10

One person in 10 is left-footed. Eleven football players are picked at random. Find as a percentage the probability that less than two will be left-footed (to the nearest per cent).

Solution

'Success' = Being left-footed. $\therefore p = 0.1$

'Failure' = Being right-footed. $\therefore q = 0.9$

P(less than two are left-footed) = P(None is left-footed) + P(One is left-footed)

$$= \binom{11}{0}(0.1)^0(0.9)^{11} + \binom{11}{1}(0.1)^1(0.9)^{10}$$

$$= (1)(1)(0.3138106) + (11)(0.1)(0.3486784)$$

$$= 0.3138106 + 0.3835462$$

$$= 0.697 \text{ (correct to three decimal places)}$$

$$= 70\%$$

Exercise 3.5

1. In each case, put a tick (✓) in the box if the problem is solved using the binomial distribution formula. If not, put a cross (✗) in the box.

(There is no need to solve these problems.)

	Problem	Binomial distribution formula?
1	The probability of getting two tails when a fair coin is flipped five times.	
2	A coin is flipped until four heads turn up.	
3	In 100 football games, the probability of getting 50 wins, 30 losses and 20 draws.	
4	In a family of seven children, the probability of having four girls and three boys.	
5	A bag contains 10 white and five green balls. Three balls are taken out in turn. The probability that only one is green if:	(i)
	(i) The ball is replaced each time. (ii) The ball is **not** replaced each time.	(ii)
6	The probability of finding exactly two left-handed tennis players in a class of 20 students.	
7	The probability of being dealt exactly two Aces when you are dealt a poker hand of five cards.	
8	When 50 people take a certain medicine, the probability that two or more suffer side-effects.	

2. A couple has five children. Find the probability that they have two girls and three boys.

3. A fair six-sided die is rolled four times. Find the probability that a 6 comes up exactly one time.

4. A fair coin is flipped eight times. Find the probability that heads comes up:

(i) Exactly four times

(ii) Exactly seven times

(iii) Seven times or more

5. In the first 56 days of school, Samantha was late 14 times. Take the relative frequency as the probability that she will be late.

In five consecutive days, find the probability that she will be late:

(i) Never

(ii) Once only

(iii) More than once

6. In a family of six children, what is the probability of having three girls and three boys?

Of 400 such families, how many would you expect to have three girls and three boys?

7. One-eighth of the Irish population is left-handed. Three Irish people are chosen at random. Find the probability that one (and one only) is a left-hander.

8. In Ireland, 40% of the cars are Japanese. Ten cars pass a point in Ireland randomly. What is the probability that exactly four are Japanese?

9. A survey shows that 60% of the population of Dublin is female. Four Dubliners are picked at random. Find the probability that at least two are female.

10. Show that in five throws of an unbiased six-sided die, the probability of throwing one 6 is the same as the probability of throwing no 6.

11. A fair coin is flipped n times. Show that the probability of getting one head or less is $\frac{n+1}{2^n}$.

12. A student is doing a multiple choice test. Only one answer (of the four possible answers) in each question is correct. The student answers five questions, using guesswork alone. What is the probability (to three significant figures) of getting three or more correct?

13. If you drop a drawing pin on a wooden floor, it will face point up 80% of the time. A person drops five drawing pins.
Find the probability that:

(i) Exactly two will face point up.

(ii) Two or less will face point up.

14. Whenever Jimmy fires an arrow he has $\frac{1}{4}$ chance of hitting a target. He fires 10 arrows. Find the probability (to the nearest percentage) that:

(i) He hits the target the first three times but misses the rest.

(ii) He hits the target exactly three times.

(iii) He hits the target at least once.

15. When Susan rings her mother, the chance that her mother will answer the phone is $\frac{3}{5}$.

Susan rings her mother every day for a week. Find the probability that her mother answers:

(i) Exactly four times

(ii) Six or more times

(iii) On Monday and Tuesday only

16. An insurance firm calculates that a client has a $\frac{1}{20}$ chance of having one or more accidents during a given year. If this client is insured for 10 consecutive years, find the probability that:

(i) He will have no accidents.

(ii) He will have an accident in more than one year.

17. Leah is the team's penalty taker. Last season, she took 20 penalties and scored 16 times. Use the relative frequency as the probability of scoring.

During the next season she takes eight penalties. Find the probability (correct to two decimal places) that:

(i) She scores the first six penalties but misses the last two.

(ii) She scores exactly six penalties.

(iii) She scores six or more.

18. In a certain country, 30% of the population is suffering from AIDS. If a sample of 10 people from this country are chosen at random, find the probability that exactly 30% of these will be found to be suffering from AIDS.

19. When a certain drug is used, there is a 5% chance that side-effects will be suffered. Twenty people are given the drug. Find the probability that:

(i) None will suffer side-effects.

(ii) More than one will suffer side-effects.

3.5 THE BINOMIAL DISTRIBUTION EXTENDED

Worked Example 3.11

A fair six-sided die is thrown repeatedly until a 6 appears for the third time. Find the probability that this will take exactly 15 throws. Give your answer to the nearest per cent.

Solution

There is only one way this can happen: if there are exactly two 6's in the first 14 throws **and** the 15th throw is a 6.

The probability that this will happen is:

$\binom{14}{2}\left(\frac{1}{6}\right)^2\left(\frac{5}{6}\right)^{12} \times \frac{1}{6}$

$= \binom{14}{2}\left(\frac{1}{6}\right)^3\left(\frac{5}{6}\right)^{12}$

$= 0.04725$

$= 5\%$ (to the nearest per cent)

Worked Example 3.12

A coin is flipped repeatedly until 10 heads appear. Find the probability that this will take exactly 17 flips. Give your answer correct to three decimal places.

Solution

There is only one way this can happen: if there are nine heads in the first 16 flips **and** the 17th flip gives a head.

$P = \binom{16}{9}\left(\frac{1}{2}\right)^9\left(\frac{1}{2}\right)^7 \times \frac{1}{2}$

$= \binom{16}{9}\left(\frac{1}{2}\right)^{17}$

$= 0.087$ (correct to three decimal places)

Exercise 3.6

1. A fair coin is flipped repeatedly until exactly four heads appear. Find the probability that this will take exactly six flips.

2. A fair six-sided die is rolled repeatedly until two 6's appear.
Find the probability that this will take exactly 10 rolls.

3. A couple decide to keep having children until they have exactly two boys.
Find the probability that this will happen:
   (i) At the birth of their second child
   (ii) At the birth of their fifth child

4. When a thumb tack is thrown on the floor, the probability that it lands pin up is $\frac{1}{5}$.
The thumb-tack is thrown repeatedly onto the floor until it lands pin up for the third time.
Find the probability that this will take exactly 10 throws.

5. A card is drawn randomly from a standard pack, noted and replaced. This procedure is repeated over and over again until two spades appear. Find the probability that this will happen when the eighth card is drawn.

6. People are stopped at random on a street and asked what day of the week they were born on. This process is repeated until two people who were born on Sunday are stopped.
Find the probability that this will take exactly 12 people. (You may assume they all know the day of their birth).

7. A golfer has a 30% chance of landing the ball on the green each time he tees off from a par-three hole. He decides to keep hitting balls until he gets three balls on the green.
Find the probability that this will happen after only six balls.

8. A woman phones householders randomly. She finds that only 20% of householders reply to her questions. She decides to keep ringing until she gets four householders who reply to her questions.
Find the probability that this will take 10 calls.

9. In the USA, 10% of the population is left-handed. A researcher stops people randomly in a street in the USA until she comes across two left-handed people.
Find the probability (correct to two significant figures) that she will stop exactly 15 people.

10. A missile has a 25% chance of hitting a target. How many missiles must be fired to ensure that there is a greater than 90% chance that the target will be hit at least once?

11. How many times must a fair six-sided die be rolled so that the chances of getting at least one 6 is greater than 90%?

12. How many times must a fair coin be flipped in order to ensure that there is at least a 99% chance of getting at least one tail?

3.6 THE NORMAL DISTRIBUTION

When you roll a pair of dice and evaluate the total of the numbers which turn up, the possible outcomes are the following:

$$\{2, 3, 4, 5, 6, 7, 8, 9, 10, 11, 12\}$$

There is a *countable* number of *individual* elements in this outcome space. We call such a set a **discrete** set. It is important to note that only whole number outcomes are possible; hence, outcomes of $7\frac{1}{2}$ or 5.34 are both impossible. Now every time we roll this pair of dice, we cannot be sure which outcome is going to turn up. The result varies randomly, from roll to roll. However, we CAN say that some outcomes are more likely than others. Indeed, we can graph the probabilities of each outcome:

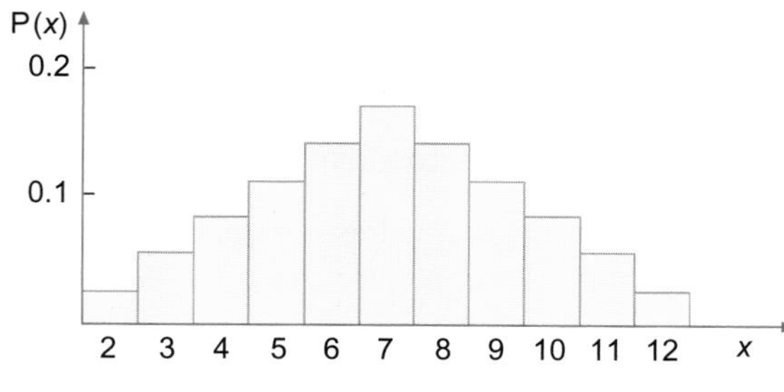

PROBABILITY II

The set of outcomes when any pair of dice is rolled is called a **discrete random variable** (**discrete**, because the possible outcomes are individual and countable; **random**, because the results are unpredictable; **variable**, because the results vary from roll to roll).

The mean of this data is 7 and the standard deviation from the mean is 2.415.

Another example of a discrete random variable would be the results of picking houses randomly in Ireland and asking how many occupants are in each house. The results of this might have a mean of 2.3 with a standard deviation of 0.6.

Now let us look at a random variable which is NOT discrete. We will pick people at random and ask 'What is your weight in kilograms?' The set of possible outcomes, in this case, is an infinite continuous set, since all positive real numbers are now possible. (Your weight could be 60.00387543… kg, etc.) We call such variables **continuous random variables**. We graph the probabilities of such variables with a continuous, smooth curve:

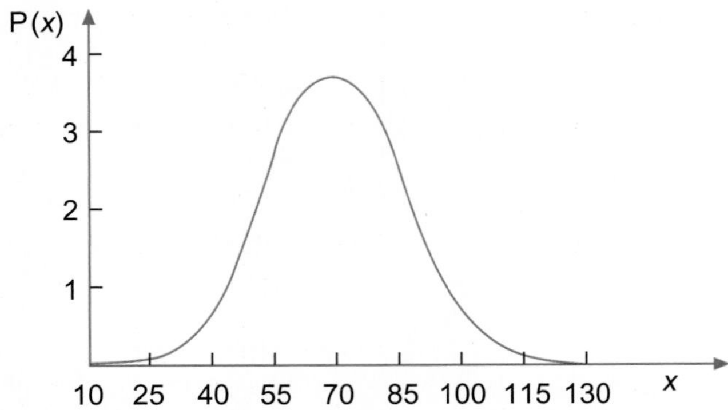

In this case, the mean is 70 kg, with a standard deviation of 15 kg.

Another continuous random variable is the heights of Irish soldiers (in centimetres). The mean is 170 cm, with a standard deviation of 3 cm. Here is the graph of the probabilities:

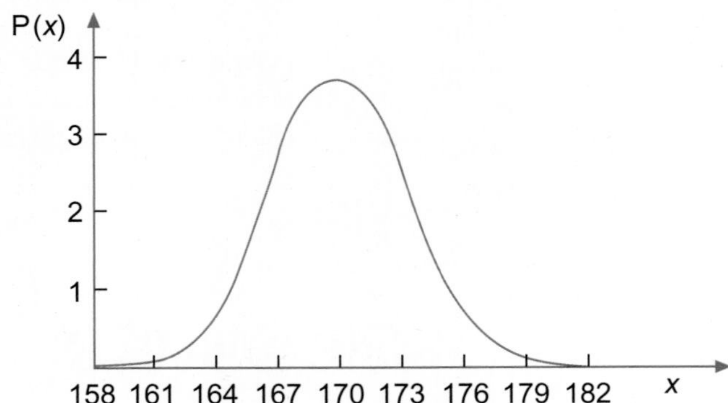

These two curves are remarkably similar. Many other curves which occur in real life have exactly this shape. Any random variable whose graph has this shape is said to have **normal distribution**. The curve is often described as bell-shaped.

In the above cases, the probability that a result will be within one standard deviation of the mean will be the same. That is to say, the probability that a person's weight will be between 55 kg and 85 kg will be the same as the probability that an Irish soldier's height will be between 167 cm and 173 cm.

If a random variable has normal distribution with mean μ and standard deviation σ, we say it has distribution $N(\mu, \sigma^2)$, for short. For example, the heights of Irish soldiers have distribution $N(170, 9)$.

Note: Below is the Normal Distribution Table as it appears on pages 36–37 of the *Formulae and Tables*.

NORMAL DISTRIBUTION TABLE

z	0.00	0.01	0.02	0.03	0.04	0.05	0.06	0.07	0.08	0.09
0.0	0.5000	.5040	.5080	.5120	.5160	.5199	.5239	.5279	.5319	.5359
0.1	0.5398	.5438	.5478	.5517	.5557	.5596	.5636	.5675	.5714	.5753
0.2	0.5793	.5832	.5871	.5910	.5948	.5987	.6026	.6064	.6103	.6141
0.3	0.6179	.6217	.6255	.6293	.6331	.6368	.6406	.6443	.6480	.6517
0.4	0.6554	.6591	.6628	.6664	.6700	.6736	.6772	.6808	.6844	.6879
0.5	0.6915	.6950	.6985	.7019	.7054	.7088	.7123	.7157	.1790	.7224
0.6	0.7257	.7291	.7324	.7357	.7389	.7422	.7454	.7486	.7517	.7549
0.7	0.7580	.7611	.7642	.7673	.7704	.7734	.7764	.7794	.7823	.7852
0.8	0.7881	.7910	.7939	.7967	.7995	.8023	.8051	.8078	.8106	.8133
0.9	0.8159	.8186	.8212	.8238	.8264	.8289	.8315	.8340	.8365	.8389
1.0	0.8413	.8438	.8461	.8485	.8508	.8531	.8554	.8577	.8599	.8621
1.1	0.8643	.8665	.8686	.8708	.8729	.8749	.8770	.8790	.8810	.8830
1.2	0.8849	.8869	.8888	.8907	.8925	.8944	.8962	.8980	.8997	.9015
1.3	0.9032	.9049	.9066	.9082	.9099	.9115	.9131	.9147	.9162	.9177
1.4	0.9192	.9207	.9222	.9236	.9251	.9265	.9279	.9292	.9306	.9319
1.5	0.9332	.9345	.9357	.9370	.9382	.9394	.9406	.9418	.9429	.9441
1.6	0.9452	.9463	.9474	.9484	.9495	.9505	.9515	.9525	.9535	.9545
1.7	0.9554	.9564	.9573	.9582	.9591	.9599	.9608	.9616	.9625	.9633
1.8	0.9641	.9649	.9656	.9664	.9671	.9678	.9686	.9693	.9699	.9706
1.9	0.9713	.9719	.9726	.9732	.9738	.9744	.9750	.9756	.9761	.9767
2.0	0.9772	.9778	.9783	.9788	.9793	.9798	.9803	.9808	.9812	.9817
2.1	0.9821	.9826	.9830	.9834	.9838	.9842	.9846	.9850	.9854	.9857
2.2	0.9861	.9864	.9868	.9871	.9875	.9878	.9881	.9884	.9887	.9890
2.3	0.9893	.9896	.9898	.9901	.9904	.9906	.9909	.9911	.9913	.9916
2.4	0.9918	.9920	.9922	.9925	.9927	.9929	.9931	.9932	.9934	.9936
2.5	0.9938	.9940	.9941	.9943	.9945	.9946	.9948	.9949	.9951	.9952
2.6	0.9953	.9955	.9956	.9957	.9959	.9960	.9961	.9962	.9963	.9964
2.7	0.9965	.9966	.9967	.9968	.9969	.9970	.9971	.9972	.9973	.9974
2.8	0.9974	.9975	.9976	.9977	.9977	.9978	.9979	.9979	.9980	.9981
2.9	0.9981	.9982	.9982	.9983	.9984	.9984	.9985	.9985	.9986	.9986
3.0	0.9987	.9987	.9987	.9988	.9988	.9989	.9989	.9989	.9990	.9990

3.7 THE NORMAL DISTRIBUTION TABLE

If the variables have a normal distribution, we can use the table on pages 36–37 of the *Formulae and Tables* to calculate probabilities.

The normal distribution table on this page is based on a variable, z, with a mean 0 and a standard deviation 1. That is, it has distribution $N(0, 1)$.

If we are asked: 'Find $P(z \leqslant 1.3)$', we are really being asked: 'Find the probability that the result will be less than (or equal to) 1.3 standard deviations above the mean.' We look up the value of 1.3 and find that $P(z \leqslant 1.3) = 0.9032$.

This means that 90.32% of the population of any normally distributed random variable will give readings which are less than (or equal to) 1.3 standard deviations above the mean.

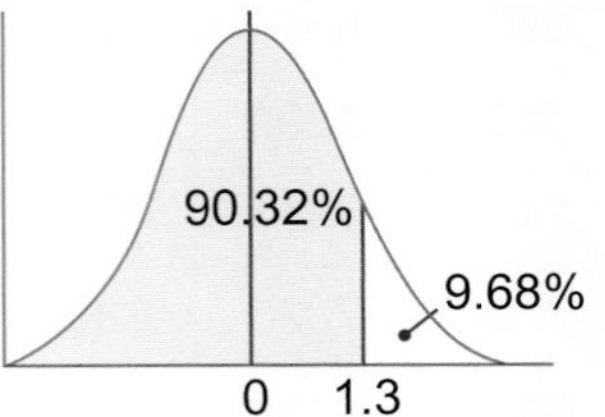

The total area under the curve is 1. The total percentage is 100%.

If you are asked to find $P(z < -1.3)$, this means 'Find the probability that the result is less than 1.3 standard deviations below the mean.'

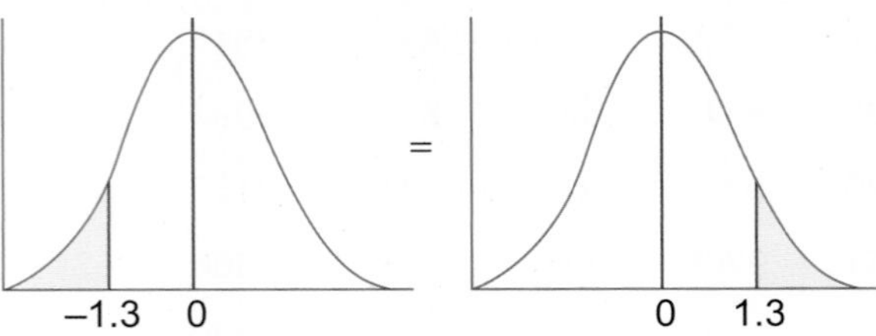

The curve is symmetrical. We use this to work out answers when the values of z are on the negative side.

By symmetry, $P(z < -1.3) = P(z > 1.3) = 1 - P(z \leqslant 1.3)$

$$= 1 - 0.9032$$

$$\therefore P(z < -1.3) = 0.0968$$

If we are asked 'What is $P(-1.3 \leqslant z \leqslant 1.3)$?' we mean 'What is the probability that the result will be within 1.3 standard deviations of the mean?'

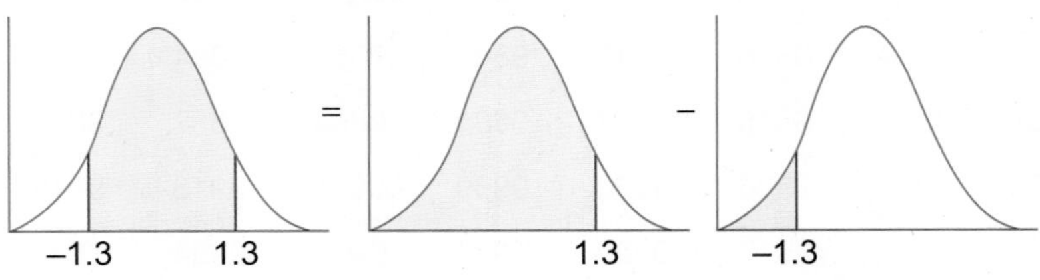

Always start by drawing a normal curve and shading in the desired area approximately.

$$\begin{aligned} P(-1.3 \leqslant z \leqslant 1.3) &= P(z \leqslant 1.3) - P(z < -1.3) \\ &= 0.9032 - 0.0968 \\ &= 0.8064 \end{aligned}$$

$P(z < k)$ and $P(z \leqslant k)$ give the same result, because the probability that z is exactly equal to k is infinitely small.

Worked Example 3.13

z has the standard normal distribution $N(0, 1)$.

If $P(-k < z < k) = 0.1428$, find the value of k.

Solution

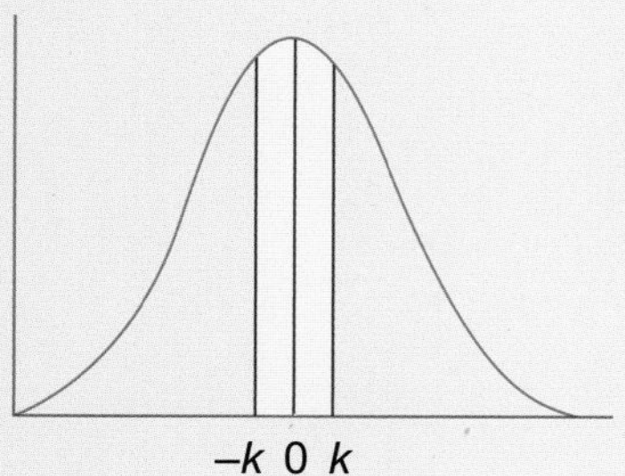

Start by drawing a normal curve and shading in the area required.

Since $P(-k < z < k) = 0.1428$, it follows (because of symmetry) that:

$P(0 < z < k) = \frac{1}{2}(0.1428) = 0.0714$

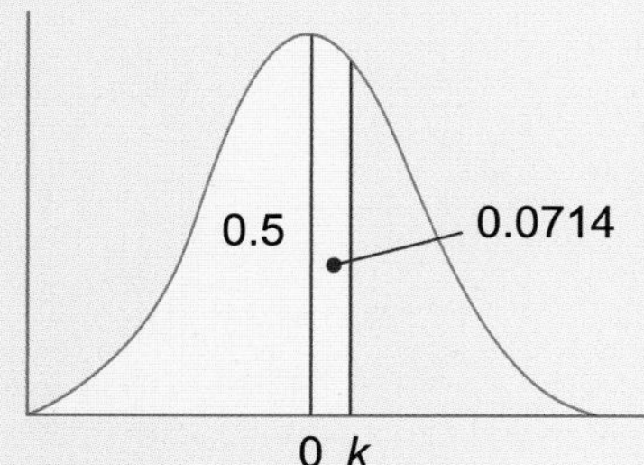

Since the area under the whole curve is 1, the area under half the curve must be 0.5.

Hence, $P(z < k) = 0.5 + 0.0714 = 0.5714$.

$\therefore z = 0.18$, from the table on pages 36–37 of the *Formulae and Tables*.

Exercise 3.7

1. Evaluate the following:

(i) $P(z \leqslant 1.6)$

(ii) $P(z > 1.6)$

(iii) $P(z \geqslant 1.6)$

(iv) $P(1.2 \leqslant z \leqslant 1.8)$

(v) $P(1 < z < 2)$

(vi) $P(1.1 < z < 2.2)$

(vii) $P(z < -1.2)$

(viii) $P(-1.5 \leqslant z \leqslant 1.8)$

(ix) $P(-1.2 < z < 2.2)$

(x) $P(-0.3 < z < 0.5)$

(xi) $P(-0.5 < z < 0.3)$

(xii) $P(-2.5 < z < 2.5)$

(xiii) $P(-3 < z < -2)$

(xiv) $P(-1.2 < z < -1.1)$

(xv) $P(-1.5 < z < 1.5)$

(xvi) $P(z \leqslant 1.77)$

(xvii) $P(z < -2.35)$

(xviii) $P(-1.12 \leqslant z \leqslant 1.12)$

(xix) $P(-1.96 < z < 1.96)$

(xx) $P(-1.645 < z < 1.645)$

2. Find, to the nearest unit, the percentage of a normally distributed population which lies within:

   (i) One standard deviation of the mean (i.e. $P(-1 < z < 1)$)

   (ii) Two standard deviations of the mean

   (iii) Three standard deviations of the mean

3. Find the values of k in each case, where z has distribution $N(0, 1)$:

   (i) $P(z < k) = 0.9671$

   (ii) $P(z > k) = 0.1788$

   (iii) $P(z < k) = 0.2643$

   (iv) $P(-k < z < k) = 0.5098$

   (v) $P(-k < z < k) = 0.34$

4. If 95% of a normally distributed population lies within x standard deviations of the mean, what is the value of x?

5. A normally distributed population, $N(0, 1)$, is divided into three equal parts by two vertical lines at $x = -k$ and $x = k$.

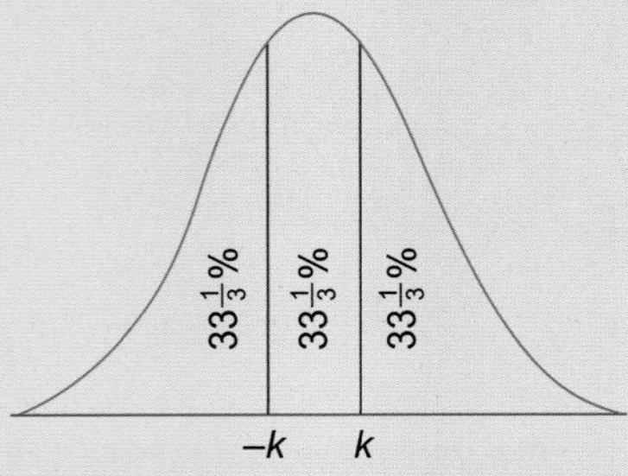

Find the value of k as accurately as the tables allow.

6. Find the value of k if $P(1.1 < z < k) = 0.125$.

7. Find the value of t if $P(-0.51 \leqslant z \leqslant t) = 0.32$.

8. A normally distributed population, $N(0, 1)$, is divided into four quartiles (each containing 25% of the population) by three vertical lines. Find the equations of the lines.

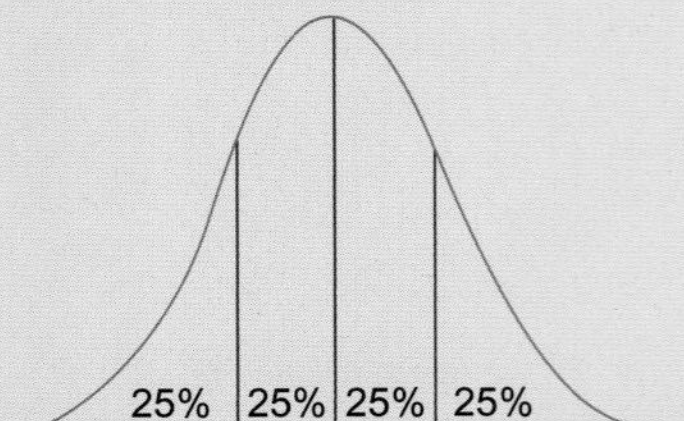

9. A normally distributed population, $N(0, 1)$, is divided into three sections by the lines $x = k$ and $x = t$. The sections contain 20%, 50% and 30% of the population, respectively.

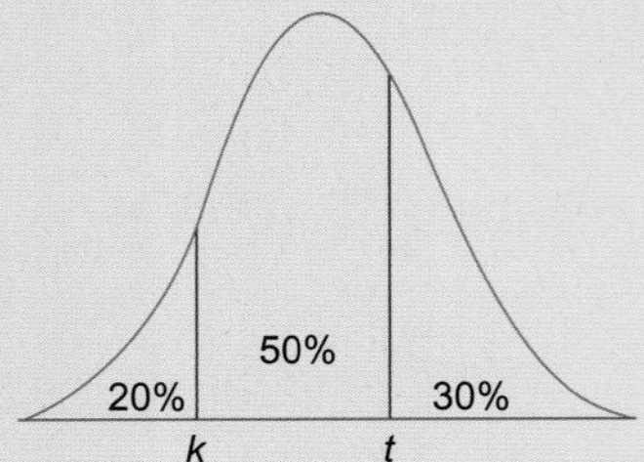

Find the values of k and t, correct to two decimal places.

10. Ninety-nine per cent of a normally distributed population lies within k standard deviations of the mean. Find the value of k correct to two decimal places.

3.8 SOLVING PROBLEMS INVOLVING NORMAL DISTRIBUTION

In this section we will look at real-life situations in which we can find the probabilities of normally distributed variables. If x is normally distributed with mean μ and standard deviation σ, then the formula for converting x to z (which is normally distributed with mean 0 and standard deviation 1) is as given here.

FORMULA

$$z = \frac{x - \mu}{\sigma}$$

This formula appears on page 34 of the *Formulae and Tables*.

Worked Example 3.14

The mean total score in Irish Basketball Superleague games is 137 with a standard deviation of 10. If you go to a match, what is the probability that there will be 150 or more points scored by the two teams?

Solution

Let x be the number of points scored. The question asks: 'What is $P(x \geqslant 150)$?'

To solve such problems, use the following steps:

Step 1 Convert the x-values to z-values, using the formula $z = \frac{x - \mu}{\sigma}$.

Step 2 Draw a rough sketch of a normal curve, and shade in the desired values of z.

Step 3 Look up the normal distribution table to find the probability of getting the required values for z (as before).

Step 1 In this case, $\mu = 137$ and $\sigma = 10$.

$$P(x \geqslant 150) = P\left(z \geqslant \frac{x - \mu}{\sigma}\right) = P\left(z \geqslant \frac{150 - 137}{10}\right) = P(z \geqslant 1.3)$$

Note: This means that the number 150 is 1.3 standard deviations above the mean.

Step 2 Draw a rough sketch of the normal curve and shade in the desired values of z.

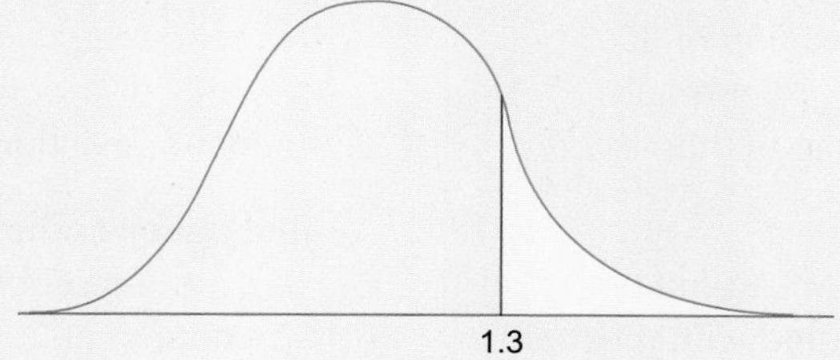

Step 3 Look up the normal distribution table to find the probability of getting the required values for z (as before):

$$\begin{aligned} P(z \geqslant 1.3) &= 1 - P(z < 1.3) \\ &= 1 - 0.9032 \\ &= 0.0968 \end{aligned}$$

Worked Example 3.15

The heights of women in Ireland are normally distributed with mean 163 cm and standard deviation 5 cm. A film producer is seeking an Irish actress whose height is between 170 cm and 175 cm. The director says to the producer, 'You are being too fussy. The chance of finding an actress with the right height is less than 5%.' Is this statement correct?

Solution

Step 1 Let x be the height. In this case, $\mu = 163$ and $\sigma = 5$.

We are asked to find $P(170 \leqslant x \leqslant 175)$. Convert the x-values to z-values using the formula $z = \frac{x - \mu}{\sigma}$.

$$P(170 \leqslant x \leqslant 175) = P\left(\frac{170 - 163}{5} \leqslant z \leqslant \frac{175 - 163}{5}\right) = P(1.4 \leqslant z \leqslant 2.4)$$

Step 2 Draw a rough sketch of the normal curve and shade in the desired values of z.

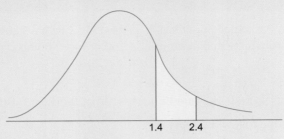

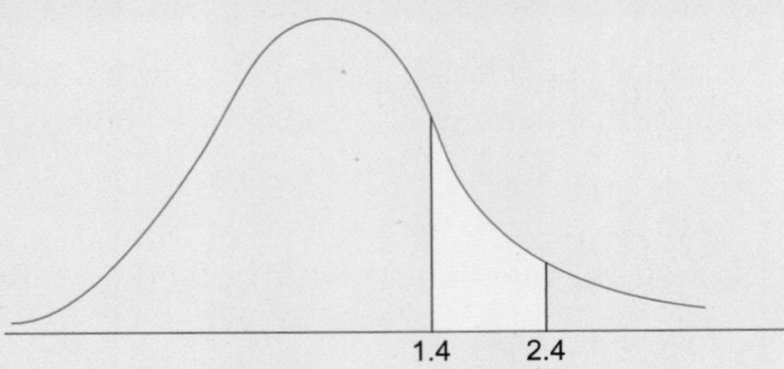

Step 3 Look up the normal distribution table to find the probability of getting the required values for z (as before):

$$P(1.4 \leqslant z \leqslant 2.4) = P(z \leqslant 2.4) - P(z < 1.4)$$
$$= 0.9918 - 0.9192$$
$$= 0.0726$$
$$= 7.26\% > 5\%$$

Therefore, it is not true to say that the chance of finding such an actress is less than 5%.

Exercise 3.8

1. The mean cricket score in a 50-over match is 200, with a standard deviation of 50. Assuming that such scores are normally distributed, what percentage of these scores are greater than 300?

2. If Leaving Certificate Higher Level maths marks are normally distributed with mean 68 and standard deviation 10, what percentage of students will get an A?

3. The heights of men in Ireland are normally distributed with a mean of 168 cm and a standard deviation of 6 cm. Find the probability that an Irishman selected at random will be greater than 180 cm in height.

4. The weights of people in Ireland are normally distributed with a mean of 68 kg and a standard deviation of 10 kg. If an Irish person, chosen at random, has a weight of x kg, find the probability that:

   (i) $x < 61$
   (ii) $63 < x < 73$
   (iii) $60 < x < 61$

5. The life expectancy of a newborn baby in Japan is normally distributed with mean 81 years and standard deviation 8 years. Is the following statement true or false?

   'Less than 1% of Japanese newborn babies will live to be 100.'

6. The number of hours of sleep got by pupils in a school has a distribution $N(9,1)$, i.e. normally distributed with mean 9 and standard deviation 1.

   (i) A pupil is chosen at random in this school. Find the probability that this pupil got more than 10.5 hours of sleep.
   (ii) If there are 350 students in this school, how many would you expect to get between 9.4 and 10.7 hours of sleep?

7. The number of runs scored by the Irish cricket team in Twenty-20 matches is normally distributed with a mean of 157 and a standard deviation of 16. In a match against Bangladesh, the opponents score 168. The Irish team must score 169 or more to win the game.

   (i) What is the probability that they will win?
   (ii) An online bookie is offering odds of 2-1 for an Irish victory at this point. (This means that if you bet €100, you win €200 if Ireland wins.) Is this a good bet? Justify your answer with reference to the expected value.

8. The wages of workers in the motor industry in Ireland are normally distributed with a mean of €38,430 and a standard deviation of €6,400. What percentage of workers in the motor industry in Ireland earn over €50,000? Give your answer to the nearest per cent.

9. The annual number of hours of sunshine in Ireland is normally distributed with a mean of 1,550 hours and a standard deviation of 150 hours. What is the probability that next year there will be:

(i) Less than 1,300 hours of sunshine in Ireland

(ii) More than 1,800 hours of sunshine in Ireland

(iii) Between 1,300 and 1,800 hours of sunshine in Ireland

10. The height of American males is normally distributed with mean 177 cm and standard deviation 7.5 cm. What percentage of American males are 6 feet or more in height? Give your answer to the nearest per cent. (The following information is given: 1 inch = 2.54 cm; 1 foot = 12 inches.)

11. Every day the maximum air temperature at Athlone is measured. The mean maximum air temperature for Athlone is 9.6°C with a standard deviation of 8°C. Assuming that the maximum temperatures are normally distributed:

(i) Find the probability that the temperature will reach 25°C or higher on a random day.

(ii) On how many days of next year will the temperature reach 25°C or higher at Athlone? Give your answer to the nearest whole number.

(iii) A weatherman says that he would expect the temperature at Athlone to break over 30°C on two days in the year. Is this a reasonably accurate statement?

12. The life span of a light bulb is normally distributed with a mean of 1,020 hours. Find the standard deviation if 12% of the light bulbs have a life span of 1,067 hours or more.

13. The time (in minutes) taken by a group of students to complete a maths test is normally distributed with a mean of 60 and a standard deviation of σ. If 34% of these students took between 51.2 and 68.8 minutes, find the value of σ.

14. The heights of male Gardaí have a normal distribution with a mean of 173 cm and a standard deviation of 2. If the tallest 2.5% of male Gardaí have heights greater than x cm, find the value of x.

Revision Exercises

1. (a) A fair six-sided die is rolled five times. Find the probability of getting:

(i) No 6

(ii) Exactly one 6

(iii) More than one 6

(b) A fair six-sided die is rolled over and over until two 6's appear. Find the probability that this will happen on the sixth roll.

(c) E and F are independent events, such that $P(E) = \frac{1}{5}$ and $P(F) = \frac{5}{8}$.

Find:

(i) $P(E \cap F)$

(ii) $P(E \cup F)$

2. (a) z is a normally distributed random variable with mean 0 and standard deviation 1.

(i) Find $P(-1.11 < z < 1.11)$

(ii) If $P(-k < z < k) = 0.7776$, find the value of k.

(b)

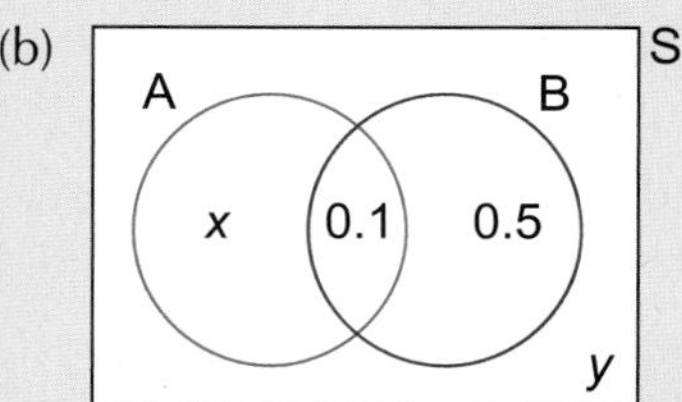

If A and B are independent events, find the value of:

(i) x (ii) y (iii) $P(A \mid B)$

3. Paula and Rose enter the school sports competition. They both take part in the 100 m and 200 m race. The probabilities that they will win are given in the following table:

	Probability that Paula wins	Probability that Rose wins	Probability that neither wins
100 m	$\frac{1}{2}$	$\frac{3}{8}$	$\frac{1}{8}$
200 m	$\frac{1}{4}$	$\frac{1}{8}$	x

(i) Find the value of x.

(ii) Find the probability that Rose wins both races.

(iii) Find the probability that Paula and Rose win one race each.

4. The Venn diagram shows the number of elements in each subset. An element is picked at random from S.

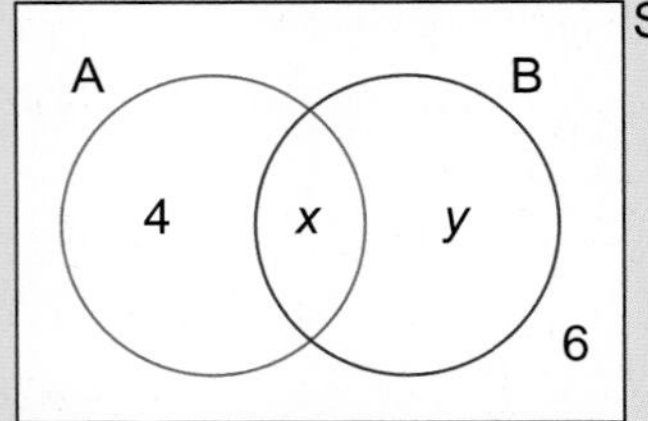

If $P(A) = \frac{1}{3}$ and $P(B) = \frac{7}{9}$:

(i) Find the values of x and y.

(ii) Investigate if $P(A \mid B) = P(B \mid A)$.

(iii) Investigate if A and B are independent.

5. (a) If z is a normally distributed random variable with mean 0 and standard deviation 1, find:

(i) $P(z < 0.6)$

(ii) $P(-0.6 < z < 0.6)$

(b) A team plays the same number of games at home and away. They win $\frac{2}{5}$ of their home games and $\frac{1}{4}$ of their away games.

Find the probability that:

(i) They will win their next two home games.

(ii) Their last game was at home, given that they won.

(iii) They will win exactly four of their next six home games.

6. (a) Three cards are drawn from a standard pack, without replacement. What is the probability that:

(i) All three are red cards.

(ii) At least one is a black card.

(b) $S = \{-1, -2, -3, -5, 2, 7, 8, 10, 12\}$ is a set of nine elements.

(i) If two numbers are chosen at random from S, what is the probability that their product is greater than zero?

(ii) If three numbers are chosen at random from S, what is the probability that their product is greater than zero?

(iii) If three numbers are chosen at random from S, what is the probability that their product is less than zero?

7. (a)

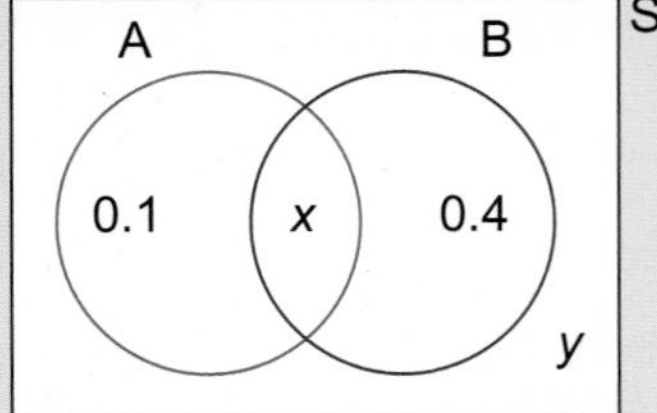

Given that A and B are independent events, find two possible values of x and the corresponding values of y.

(b) Three students, Ann, Barry and Cathal, have the following probabilities of solving a mathematical problem:

	Ann	Barry	Cathal
Probability	0.8	0.7	0.6

All three are given a maths problem. Find the probability that:

(i) All three get it right.

(ii) All three get it wrong.

(iii) At least one gets it right.

8. (a) Five people are chosen at random. Find, correct to two significant figures, the probability that:

(i) All five were born in different months.

(ii) At least two were born in the same month. (Take all months as equally likely.)

(b) A friend of yours offers you a bet. You must bet €5. Then you roll a fair six-sided die. If you get a 6, the friend will give you €20. If you get a 5, the friend will give you €10. Otherwise, you'll get nothing. Is this a good bet? Explain your answer, referring to the expected value.

9. Two spinners are shown below.

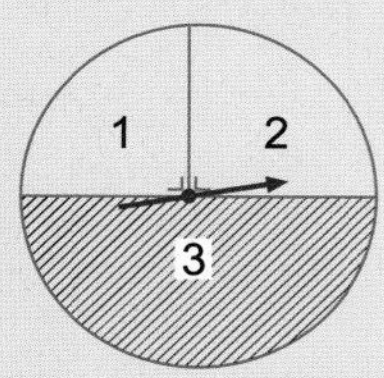

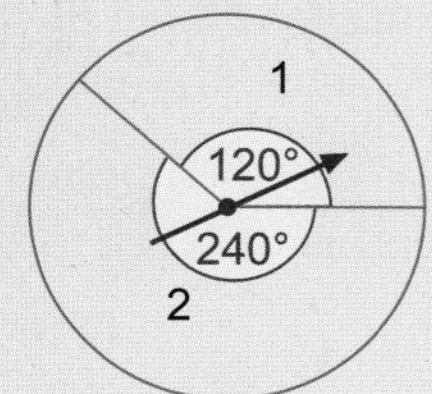

(i) If these two spinners are spun, which are you more likely to get: a **sum** of 3 from the two outcomes, or a **product** of 3 from the two outcomes? Justify your answer.

(ii) Calculate the probabilities of all the different possible **sums** when the two spinners are spun.

(iii) Design a single spinner whose outcomes have the same probabilities as the **sum** of these two spinners.

10. A circular room has a radius of 5 m. There is a circular rug on the floor, of radius 3 m.

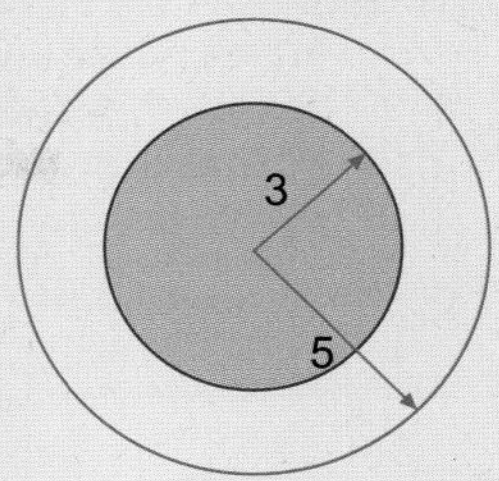

(i) A speck of dust falls at random on the floor. Find the probability that it will land on the rug.

(ii) If two specks of dust fall, what is the probability that one falls on the rug but the other does not?

(iii) If three specks of dust fall, what is the probability that all three land on the rug or all three land off the rug?

(iv) Your friend offers you a bet. He will drop a feather from high up in this room, so that it lands at a random place on the floor. If it lands on the rug, you win and he will give you €3. If it lands off the rug, he wins and you will give him €4. Is this a good bet for you? Refer to expected value when justifying your answer.

(v) Feathers are dropped at random onto the floor until three land on the rug. Find the probability that this will take seven drops.

11. James says, 'There are six people in the next office. I reckon there is a 50-50 chance that two or more were born in the same month.'

Karen says, 'You are wrong. I will offer you a bet. If the six were all born in different months, you win and I will give you €2. If two or more are born in the same month, I win – but you will have to give me only €1, since I feel confident of winning.'

'You're on,' replies James, 'since that is a good bet for me.'

'No, it's a good bet for me,' says Karen.

(i) Find the probability that all six people are born in different months (assuming that all months are equally likely).

(ii) Find the probability that two or more were born in the same month.

(iii) Who has the better bet, James or Karen? Justify your answer with reference to the expected value.

(iv) There are k people in a room. The probability that they are all born in different months is zero. What is the lowest possible value of k?

12. (a)

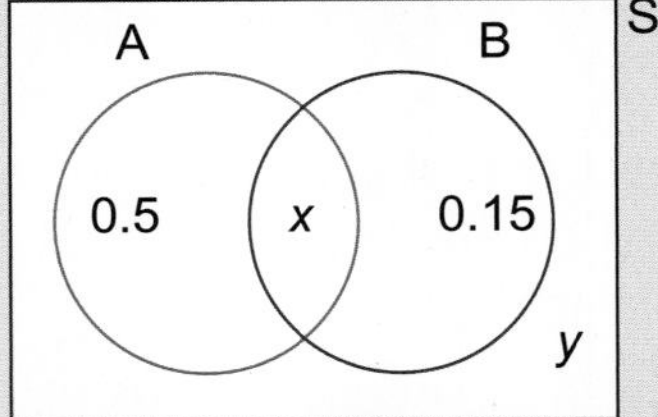

(i) Given $P(A \mid B) = \frac{5}{8}$, find the values of x and y.

(ii) Investigate if A and B are independent.

(b) (i) A couple have five children. By chance, all five were born in December (though in different years). If the couple have another child, what is the probability that the child will be born in December?

(ii) In this question, we assume that all months are equally likely. Give a reason why this might not, in fact, be perfectly correct.

13. Three fair six-sided dice are rolled.

(i) Use the Fundamental Principle of Counting to find the number of outcomes in the sample space [e.g. (3, 5, 4) is one outcome].

(ii) What is the probability that the total is 17 or more?

(iii) What is the probability that the total is less than 17?

(iv) What is the probability that the numbers on the three dice are all different?

(v) The three dice are now rolled four times. Find the probability that all three numbers are different on exactly two occasions.

(vi) The three dice are now rolled repeatedly until all three numbers are different on exactly four occasions. Find the probability that this will happen when the three dice are rolled for the seventh time.

14. E and F are two events of an outcome space, S. The probabilities of E and F are shown in the Venn diagram below:

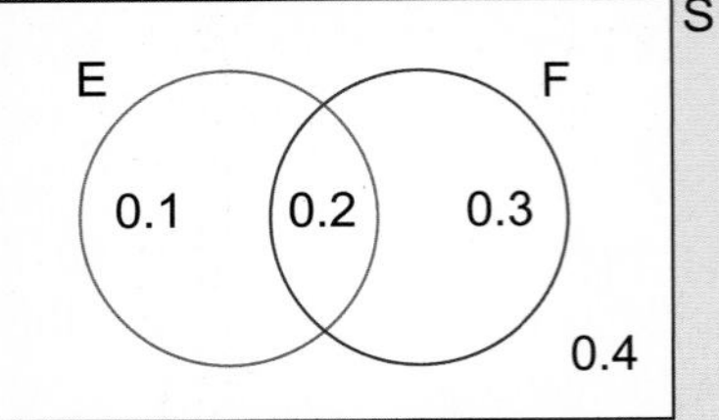

(i) Write down P(E), P(F) and $P(E \cap F)$.

(ii) Find $P(E \mid F)$.

(iii) What do we mean when we say that two events are 'independent'? Give a verbal answer and a mathematical answer.

(iv) Investigate if E and F are independent.

15. (a) A certain car is designed to give a mean of 9.2 km/litre, with a standard deviation of 0.2. Assume that the distribution is normal. If you buy one of these cars, what is the probability that you will get more than 9.5 km/litre?

(b) Take the set {1, 2, 3, 4, ... 100}.

(i) What is the mean of this set?

(ii) Suggest a method of taking a random sample of 10 elements of this set (with replacement).

(iii) Use this method to make a random sample of 10 elements.

(iv) Find the mean of the random sample.

(v) Find the percentage error in the mean of the random sample (from the true mean of the entire set).

(vi) 'Usually, the bigger the sample, the closer the sample mean will be to the population mean.' Is this statement true? Give a reason for your answer.

16. A €2 coin has diameter 26 mm. It is dropped at random onto lined paper. The lines are 40 mm apart. The task is to calculate the probability that the coin will **not** land on a line. The key is to work out where the **centre** of the €2 coin must land.

(i) Let's say the coin lands between the two lines drawn here. Shade in the area where the **centre** of the coin must land in order that the coin will not land on a line.

(ii) Show that the probability that the coin will not land on a line is 0.35.

(iii) If six €2 coins land on the lined paper at random, find the probability that exactly four of them land on a line.

(iv) A €2 coin lands on **squared** paper, the lines of which are 40 mm apart. Show that the probability that the coin will not land on a line is 0.1225.

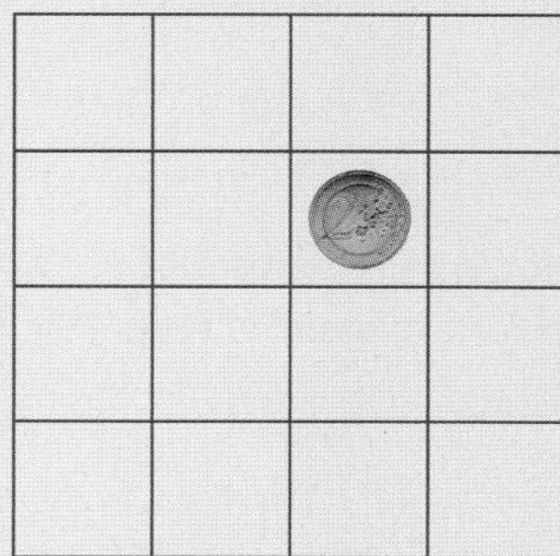

(v) At a funfair, there is a game in which you roll your own €2 coin onto squared paper of sides 40 mm. If your coin lands on a line, you lose it. If it doesn't land on a line, you win €10. Is this a good bet? Justify your answer with reference to expected value.

17. Two events A and B are such that $P(A) = 0.2$, $P(A \cap B) = 0.15$ and $P(A' \cap B) = 0.6$.

(a) Complete the Venn diagram.

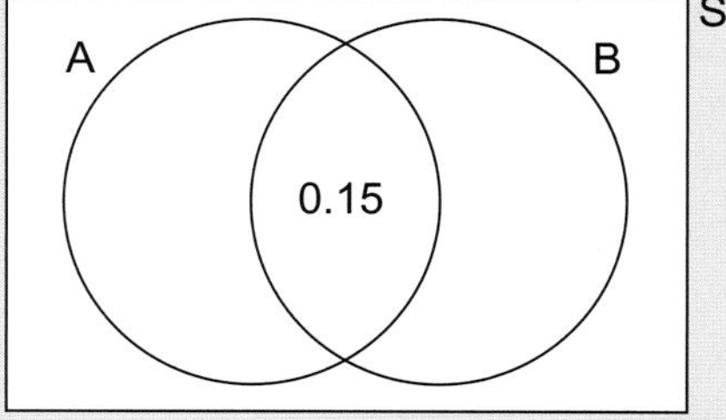

(b) Find the probability that neither A nor B happens.

(c) Find the conditional probability $P(A \mid B)$.

(d) State whether A and B are independent and justify your answer.

(Leaving Certificate Project Maths Paper 2, 2010)

18. A slot machine displays three fruit at random. Each fruit can appear as a banana, apple, orange, cherry, pear, kiwi, pineapple or plum. You put in €1 and pull the lever.

- If the three fruit which appear are all different, you lose your money.
- If all three fruit are the same, you win the jackpot of €25.
- If two fruit only are the same, you get your money back.

(i) Find the probability that (in one go) you lose your euro.

(ii) Find the probability (in one go) of winning the jackpot.

(iii) Deduce the probability that two fruit only are the same.

(iv) Evaluate the expected value when you play once, to the nearest cent.

(v) Is this game good value? Justify your answer.

(vi) The manufacturer of this gaming machine alters the jackpot prize so that the game is perfectly fair (so that the expected value is 'breaking even'). What is the new jackpot prize?

(vii) Sam says, 'Every time you play that slot machine, you are twice as likely to lose as to get any money back.' Is this statement accurate? Explain your answer.

(viii) If you play this game 10 times, what is the probability (to the nearest half per cent) of winning the jackpot exactly once?

19. A golfer called Rory has one round to go in a competition. His scores for one round are normally distributed with mean 71.5 and standard deviation 2. To win the competition, he must score 68 or less in the final round.

(i) What is the probability that he will win? (Give your answer correct to one significant figure.)

(ii) A bookie at the golf course is offering odds of 10–1 (ten to one) against Rory winning. Would it be wise to bet €20 that Rory will win, given those odds? Justify your answer.

Statistics II

Learning Outcomes

In this chapter you will learn about:

- Measures of centre
- Sampling variability
- Measures of variation
- Measures of relative standing
- The normal distribution and the empirical rule
- Distributions
- Margin of error
- Hypothesis testing

When describing and comparing data sets, **measure of centre**, **measure of spread**, **distribution** and **outliers** are the key characteristics we look for.

A **measure of centre**, sometimes called an average, is a number that is typical of most numbers in the data set.

A **measure of spread**, sometimes called a **measure of variation**, measures how spread out the data points are from the centre of the data set.

As we have already seen in Chapter 1:

The **distribution** describes the shape of a plot of the data set.

Outliers are extreme values that are not typical of the other values to a set.

YOU SHOULD REMEMBER...

- How to construct a bar chart
- How to construct a pie chart
- How to construct a histogram
- How to construct a stem-and-leaf plot

- **Mean, median and mode**
- **Range**
- **Quartiles and interquartile range**
- **Standard deviation**
- **The normal distribution and the empirical rule**
- **Percentiles**
- **Z-scores**
- **Margin of error**
- **Population proportion**
- **Sample proportion**
- **Confidence interval**
- **Hypothesis test**

  H_0: the null hypothesis

  H_1: the alternative hypothesis

4.1 MEASURES OF CENTRE

Measures of centre are sometimes called **measures of location** or **averages**. Statisticians use different measures of centre, depending on the type and distribution of the data being analysed. We will look at three measures of centre: **the mean**, **the mode** and the **median**.

The Mean

The **mean** uses all values in the data. It is calculated by adding all the values in the data set and dividing by the number of values.

For example, the mean of the set {2, 2, 3, 5, 9, 9} is:

$$\text{Mean} = \frac{2 + 2 + 3 + 5 + 9 + 9}{6} = \frac{30}{6} = 5$$

The **mean** of a set of values is the sum of all the values divided by the number of values.

The Mode

For example, the mode of the set {2, 2, 2, 3, 3, 3, 3, 5, 5} is 3, as 3 occurs more often than any other value.

The **mode** of a data set is the value that has the greatest frequency (occurs the most often).

The Median

The **median** is the value that divides an ordered data set in two equal parts.

The **median** of a set of values is the middle value when the values are arranged in order.

The first step in finding the median is to arrange the data in order of increasing magnitude. Suppose we want to find the median of the following set:

{4, 7, 11, 9, 12, 10, 8, 11, 14, 2, 6}.

Ranking the set gives:

Arranging the values of a set in order is known as ranking.

{2, 4, 6, 7, 8, (9), 10, 11, 11, 12, 14}.

The number in the middle of the ranked set is called the median, which in this case equals 9. There are five values greater than 9 and five values less than 9; therefore 9 has divided the data set in two equal parts.

What happens if the set contains an even number of values?
For example, the set {2, 1, 4, 3} contains an even number of values.

First, ranking the set gives {1, 2, 3, 4}. The median is the mean of the middle two numbers.
In this case, we sum the two middle numbers, 2 and 3, and divide our result by 2:

Median $= \frac{2+3}{2} = \frac{5}{2} = 2.5$. There are two values greater than 2.5 and two values less than 2.5.

Worked Example 4.1

Listed below are measured amounts of lead in the air (in μg/m^3).

4.80 0.56 1.20 0.85 0.43 1.75 0.66 5.20

Find:

(i) The median of the sample

(ii) The mean of the sample

Solution

(i) First, rank the data by arranging them in order.

0.43 0.56 0.66 0.85 1.20 1.75 4.80 5.20

There is an even number of data points, so the median will be the mean of the two middle numbers:

Median $= \frac{0.85+1.20}{2} = 1.025$ μg/m^3

(ii) Mean $= \frac{0.43+0.56+0.66+0.85+1.20+1.75+4.80+5.20}{8} = 1.93125$ g/μm^3

Worked Example 4.2

The stem-and-leaf diagram displays the predicted high-water tides at the North Wall, Dublin, for 15 consecutive days in April 2010.

Find the median predicted high-water mark at the North Wall during this period.

Stem	Leaf
3.2	7, 7
3.3	6, 9
3.4	9
3.5	7
3.6	1
3.7	0, 3, 7
3.8	1, 5, 6
3.9	6
4.0	1 Key: 3.3|6 = 3.36 m

Solution

To find the median, cross out the smallest number and the largest number (3.27 and 4.01), then the second largest and the second smallest, and so on until you are left with the number in the middle. This number is the median.

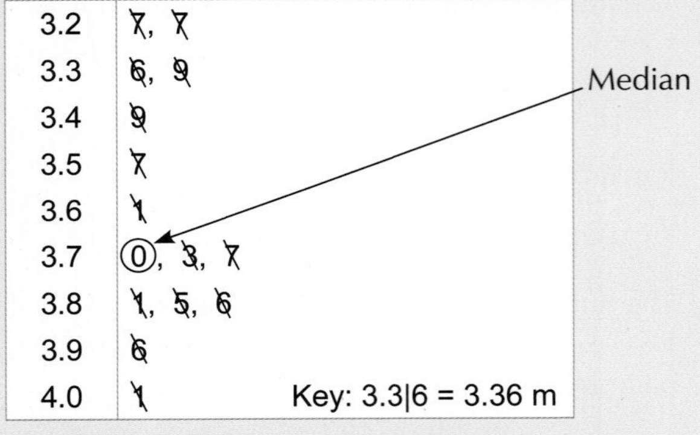

The median predicted high-water mark is 3.70 m.

Mean of a Grouped Frequency Distribution

When working with data in a grouped frequency distribution, we do not know the exact values falling within a particular class interval. To make calculations possible, we give all values in a particular class a value equal to the mid-interval value of the class.

Worked Example 4.3

A group of 82 randomly selected adults have their resting pulse rates measured. The table summarises the results of the survey. All measurements are in beats per minute.

Pulse rate	60–70	70–80	80–90	90–100	100–110	110–120
Frequency	5	8	22	29	13	5

Note: 60–70 means that 60 is included but not 70, and so on.

(i) Find the mean of the distribution.

(ii) What percentage of the sample had a pulse rate greater than or equal to 110 bpm?

Solution

(i) We can see from the table that five people had a pulse rate between 60 and 70 beats per minute. However, the table does not tell us the exact pulse rates of each person.
In order to estimate the mean resting pulse rate, each person has to be assigned a resting pulse rate. We choose the mid-interval times as the rate for each group.

Here is how we calculate the mid-interval values (M.I.V.):

M.I.V.	$\frac{60+70}{2}$	$\frac{70+80}{2}$	$\frac{80+90}{2}$	$\frac{90+100}{2}$	$\frac{100+110}{2}$	$\frac{110+120}{2}$
Frequency	5	8	22	29	13	5

We can now continue and estimate the mean:

M.I.V.	65	75	85	95	105	115
Frequency	5	8	22	29	13	5

$$\text{Mean} = \frac{(65)(5) + (75)(8) + (85)(22) + (95)(29) + (105)(13) + (115)(5)}{(5 + 8 + 22 + 29 + 13 + 5)} = \frac{7{,}490}{82}$$

$= 91$ beats per minute

This answer is correct to the nearest beat.

(ii) Five adults had a pulse rate greater than or equal to 110 bpm.

$\therefore$ Percentage $= \frac{5}{82} \times 100$

$= 6.10\%$ (correct to two decimal places)

Sampling Variability

In Chapter 1, we learned how to select random samples from a population. The value of the mean, median or mode of the random sample depends on the particular values in the sample, and it generally varies from sample to sample. This variation is called **sampling variability**.

Exercise 4.1

1. Find the mean and the median of these sets of numbers:

   (i) {67.2, 82.5, 66.7, 93.0, 82.6, 75.4, 73.6, 81.4, 99.4, 67.7}

   (ii) {41.6, 42.8, 39.0, 40.2, 36.2, 43.2, 38.7, 41.0, 43.8, 37.3}

   (iii) {6.0, 6.7, 5.7, 6.2, 5.5, 6.0, 5.7, 6.8, 7.8, 6.6}

   (iv) {23.6, 26.3, 26.3, 32.6, 29.2, 26.4, 27.9, 33.0, 38.6}

   (v) {98, 99, 97, 95, 98, 98, 98}

2. The stem-and-leaf diagram below records the weights (in grams) of 35 plums.

Stem	Leaf
2	6
3	1, 3, 4
3	6, 6, 8, 8, 9
4	2, 2, 2, 3, 4, 4, 4, 4
4	5, 5, 5, 6, 6, 7, 7, 7, 7, 9
5	0, 1, 2, 2
5	6, 7, 8
6	1

Key: 4|5 = 45 g

   (i) Describe the shape of the distribution.

   (ii) What are the mean and the median of the distribution?

3. Consider the data sets shown below. For each data set, randomly select four samples of size 5. Then find the mean of each of the four samples.

A = {157, 33, 186, 78, 538, 3, 143, 193, 378, 96, 59, 108, 54, 275, 498, 806}

B = {0.7, 1.6, 0.2, 1.2, 1.0, 3.4, 3.7, 0.8, 0.0, 2, 0.75, 1.9, 0.8, 1.1, 0.1}

C = {19, 14, 19.5, 14.5, 20, 15, 20.5, 15.5, 16, 24.5, 25, 17.5, 18.5, 19}

(i) What is the term used to describe the differences between the means of the samples?

(ii) Find the mean of set A. Write down the value of the sample mean closest to the mean of A.

(iii) Find the mean of set B. Write down the value of the sample mean furthest from the mean of B.

(iv) Find the mean of set C. Write down the value of the sample mean closest to the mean of C.

(v) Randomly select four samples of size 7 from set A. Find the mean of the samples. Are these sample means closer to the mean of A than the sample of size 5? Explain your findings.

4. The table below shows average monthly sea temperatures, in degrees Celsius, at Malin Head, Co. Donegal, for the year 2009. Average monthly readings for the period 1961–1990 are also given.

Year/month	2009	1961–1990
January	7.3	7.3
February	6.9	6.7
March	7.6	7
April	8.8	8.1
May	10.4	9.9
June	12.4	12
July	14.3	13.8
August	15.3	14.6
September	14.4	14
October	13.6	12.4
November	11.1	10.2
December	8.8	8.5

Source: http://www.met.ie/marine/marine_climatology.asp

(i) Using the monthly averages, estimate the mean annual sea temperature at Malin Head for 2009. (Give your answer correct to two decimal places.)

(ii) Using the monthly averages, estimate the mean annual sea temperature at Malin Head for the period 1961 to 1990. Comment on the difference between the 2009 figure and the 1961–1990 figure. (Give your answer correct to two decimal places.)

(iii) Is the comparison made in part (ii) a fair comparison? Explain.

5. The table below gives the number of vehicles licensed in Ireland for the first time. The table covers the period 2000–2009.

Number of vehicles licensed for the first time, by year					
Year	2000	2001	2002	2003	2004
Number of new cars	225,269	160,908	150,485	142,992	149,635
Year	2005	2006	2007	2008	2009
Number of new cars	166,270	173,273	180,754	146,470	54,432

Source: http://www.cso.ie/

(i) In what year was the highest number of vehicles registered?

(ii) In what year was the lowest number of vehicles registered?

(iii) What was the mean number of vehicles registered for the first time during these 10 years?

(iv) What was the median number of vehicles registered for the first time during these 10 years?

6. The following frequency distribution shows the time (in minutes) taken by a group of people to complete a five-mile run.

Time	30–35	35–40	40–45	45–50	50–55
Frequency	10	6	22	29	7

Note: 30–35 means 30 is included but 35 is not, etc.

(i) Using mid-interval values, calculate the mean time.

(ii) What is the maximum number of people who could have completed the run in less than 37 minutes?

7. The frequency distribution shows the ages of people living in a street.

Age	0–20	20–30	30–50	50–80
Frequency	24	16	41	15

Note: 0–20 means 0 is included but 20 is not, etc.

(i) How many people are living on the street?

(ii) Estimate the mean age.

(iii) What percentage of the people are less than 20 years old?

8. The number of hours per day that the secretary of a construction firm spends on the phone is recorded. The following data shows the number of hours per day over a 30-day period.

4.21	1.12	0.33	1.1	3.3	3.2	5.2	1.5	3.1	0.5
1.22	2.51	0.8	0.7	1.8	5.9	1.2	2.5	5.2	1.6
4	1.4	0.9	2.8	5	0.2	1.9	2.3	1.79	4

(i) Is this data discrete or continuous? Explain.

(ii) Complete the frequency table below.

Hours	0–1	1–2	2–3	3–4	4–5	5–6
Tally						
No. of days						

Note: 0–1 means 0 is included but 1 is not, etc.

(iii) Draw a histogram of the distribution.

(iv) Describe the distribution.

(v) Rank the raw data and find the median.

(vi) Using mid-interval values, estimate the mean of the distribution.

(vii) Now using the raw data, calculate the mean.

(viii) What is the percentage error in the estimated mean?

9. The heights of a random sample of 1,000 women are given in the frequency distribution below.

Height in cm	140–145	145–150	150–155	155–160	160–165	165–170	170–175	175–180
Frequency	9	65	177	325	253	133	31	7

Note: 140–145 means that 140 is included but 145 is not, etc.

(i) Estimate the mean height.

(ii) Construct a histogram to represent the data.

(iii) Describe the shape of the distribution.

10. The following are the daily maximum temperatures in Dubai for the month of June (in degrees Celsius).

29.2	29.4	34.1	36.3	36.5	32.1	32.0	35.7	35.6	34.9
36.2	32.3	32.6	36.5	33.8	32.1	32.2	38.8	36.5	35.7
31.1	33.9	34.7	34.3	37.3	40.9	33.8	32.2	40.9	34.2

(i) Is this data discrete or continuous? Explain.

(ii) Complete the frequency table below.

Temperature	29–31	31–33	33–35	35–37	37–39	39–41
Tally						
No. of days						

Note: 29–31 means that 29 is included but 31 is not, etc.

(iii) Draw a histogram of the distribution.

(iv) Describe the distribution.

(v) Rank the raw data and find the median.

(vi) Using mid-interval values, estimate the mean of the distribution.

(vii) Now using the raw data, calculate the mean.

(viii) What is the percentage error in the estimated mean?

4.2 DECIDING WHICH AVERAGE TO USE

The mean, median and mode of a set of data are all averages, but each one has a different meaning. The average, or measure of central tendency, that we choose depends on the characteristics of the data set we are studying. The following table will help you decide when to use the mean, the median or the mode.

Average	When to use	Advantages/Disadvantages
Mode	■ If data is **categorical**, then the mode is the only sensible measure of centre to use. Therefore, for data on hair colour, eye colour, gender, etc., use only the mode. ■ The mode can also be used with **numerical** data.	*Advantages* ■ It can be used with any type of data. ■ It is easy to find. ■ It is not affected by extreme values. *Disadvantage* ■ There is not always a mode, or there are several modes.
Median	■ Used **only** with **numerical** data. ■ If there are **extreme values** in the data set, then use the median.	*Advantages* ■ It is easy to calculate. ■ It is not affected by extreme values.
Mean	■ Used **only** with **numerical** data. ■ If there are **not extreme values** in the data set, use the mean.	*Advantage* ■ It uses all the data. *Disadvantage* ■ It is affected by extreme values.

Worked Example 4.4

Eight European professional soccer players are selected at random. They are asked the following question: 'What is the most money any club has paid in transfer fees for you?' This is the data generated by the question. All amounts are in sterling.

£3 million	£80 million	£5.8 million	£18.25 million
£3.5 million	£3.7 million	£8 million	£7 million

(i) Find the mean transfer fee for the sample (correct to two decimal places).

(ii) Find the median transfer fee.

(iii) Which of the above averages is the most typical of transfer fees?

Solution

(i) Mean $= \dfrac{3 + 80 + 5.8 + 18.25 + 3.5 + 3.7 + 8 + 7}{8} = \dfrac{129.25}{8} = £16.16$ million

(ii) Median $= \{\cancel{3}, \cancel{3.5}, \cancel{3.7}, 5.8, 7, \cancel{8}, \cancel{18.25}, \cancel{80}\}$

$= \dfrac{5.8 + 7}{2} = £6.4$ million

(iii) The median is the most typical. The extreme value of £80 million affects the mean.

Exercise 4.2

1. Decide which average you would use for each of the following. Give a reason for your answer.
   (i) The average height of students in your class
   (ii) The average eye colour of all teachers in the school
   (iii) The average mark in a maths exam
   (iv) The average colour of all cars in the school car park
   (v) The average wage of 100 workers in a company, given that 90 of the workers earn between €30,000 and €40,000 per annum, five workers earn between €60,000 and €80,000, and the remaining five workers earn over €600,000 per annum

2. Write down the type of average in each case:
   (i) This average uses all values of the data.
   (ii) This average is used with categorical data.
   (iii) This average is useful with data that contains extreme values.

3. Below is some data selected at random from the CensusAtSchools database. The data gives the different modes of transport the group uses to go to school.

Walk	Bus	Walk	Walk	Walk
Bus	Walk	Car	Car	Bus
Walk	Bus	Car	Walk	Walk
Car	Rail	Bus	Walk	Rail

   (i) What type of data is contained in this sample?
   (ii) What average are you using when you refer to the most popular mode of transport used by these students?

4. Rex has just been given the result of his last maths test. He does not know the results his classmates received, but would like to know how his result compares with those of his friends. The teacher has given the class the modal mark, the mean mark and the median mark for the test.

    (i) Which average tells Rex whether he is in the top half or the bottom half of the class?

    (ii) Is the modal mark useful to Rex? Explain.

    (iii) Which average tells Rex how well he has done in comparison to everyone else?

5. Find the mean and the median of the following set of numbers:

    1, 2, 12, 12, 18, 19, 20, 24, 188

    Which average would you use to describe these numbers? Give a reason for your answer.

6. Generate some primary data from within your class. Find the average of the data using a suitable measure.

4.3 MEASURES OF VARIATION

Variation 1: Range and Interquartile Range

Measures of centre supply us with one number to describe a set of data. However, such numbers give no indication of data variation or data spread.

Consider the sets A = {8, 8, 9, 11, 14} and B = {1, 3, 8, 17, 21}:

- The mean of set A $= \frac{8 + 8 + 9 + 11 + 14}{5} = \frac{50}{5} = 10$.
- The mean of set B $= \frac{1 + 3 + 8 + 17 + 21}{5} = \frac{50}{5} = 10$.

Both sets have the same mean, but the members of set A are more tightly bunched around the mean than the members of set B. To measure the spread of values, we could use the **range**.

$\text{Range}_A = 14 - 8 = 6$ $\qquad \text{Range}_B = 21 - 1 = 20$

This indicates that the elements of set B may have a greater spread of values.

The range of a set of data is the difference between the maximum value and the minimum value in a set.

Range = Maximum value – Minimum value.

Quartiles and the Interquartile Range

Quartiles divide a data set into four parts. There are three quartiles: the lower quartile, the median and the upper quartile. The **interquartile range** is the difference between the first, or lower, quartile (Q_1) and the third, or upper, quartile (Q_3). The interquartile range is more reliable than the range as a measure of spread, as it is not affected by extreme values, also called **outliers**.

Outliers are extreme values that are not typical of the other values in a data set.

Q_1, the lower quartile of a ranked set of data, is a value such that one-quarter of the values are less than or equal to it.
Q_2, the second quartile, is the median of the data.
Q_3, the upper quartile of a ranked set of data, is a value such that three-quarters of the values are less than or equal to it.

FORMULA
Interquartile range = $Q_3 - Q_1$

Worked Example 4.5

As part of a laboratory experiment, 19 rats are weighed. Their weights (in grams) are given in the table below.

148	158	167	176
188	190	200	149
165	176	186	195
163	176	181	146
164	176	170	

(i) Display the data on a stemplot.

(ii) Find Q_1, the lower quartile.

(iii) Find Q_2, the median.

(iv) Find Q_3, the upper quartile.

(v) Calculate the interquartile range.

Solution

(i)

14	6, 8, 9
15	8
16	3, 4, 5, 7
17	0, 6, 6, 6, 6
18	1, 6, 8
19	0, 5
20	0 Key: 17|0 = 170 g

(ii) **Step 1**

Count the number of leaves in the stemplot. There are 19 leaves in total.

Step 2

Find $\frac{1}{4}$ of 19, which is 4.75. As this is not a whole number, we round up to the nearest whole number (always round up), which is 5. The fifth value in the plot is Q_1, the lower quartile.

$Q_1 = 163$ g

(iii) Find $\frac{1}{2}$ of 19 which is 9.5. Round up to 10, the next whole number. The 10th value in the plot is Q_2, the median.

$Q_2 = 176$ g

(iv) Find $\frac{3}{4}$ of 19 which is 14.25. Round up to 15, the next whole number. The 15th value in the plot is Q_3, the upper quartile.

$Q_3 = 186$ g

(v) The interquartile range is

$Q_3 - Q_1 = 186 - 163 = 23$ g.

Worked Example 4.6

Set B is a list of the ages in years of a group of people at a birthday party.

B = {6, 7, 8, 9, 9, 10, 10, 12, 14, 15, 15, 22}

(i) Represent the data on a stem-and-leaf plot.

(ii) Find, Q1, the lower quartile, and Q3, the upper quartile of the data.

(iii) What is the interquartile range?

Solution

(i) Stem-and-leaf plot

0	6, 7, 8, 9, 9
1	0, 0, 2, 4, 5, 5
2	2 Key: 1|2 = 12 years

(ii) **Step 1**

Count the leaves in the stem-and-leaf plot. The number of leaves in this plot is 12.

Step 2

Lower quartile

0	6, 7, 8, •, 9, 9
1	0, 0, 2, 4, •, 5, 5
2	2

Upper quartile

Find $\frac{1}{4}$ of 12, which is 3. This is a whole number, so the lower quartile will lie midway between the third and fourth value in the stem-and-leaf plot. So the lower quartile is:

$\frac{8+9}{2} = 8.5 \quad \Rightarrow Q1 = 8.5$ years

Step 3

Now, find $\frac{3}{4}$ of 12, which is 9, a whole number. In this case, the upper quartile will lie midway between the ninth and 10th value. So, the upper quartile is:

$\frac{14+15}{2} = 14.5 \quad \Rightarrow Q3 = 14.5$ years

(iii) The interquartile range is:
$Q_3 - Q_1 = 14.5 - 8.5 = 6$ years.

Exercise 4.3

1. Find the lower quartile, the upper quartile and the interquartile range for the following sets:

(i) {2, 5, 7, 3, 3, 2, 8}
(ii) {5, 8, 6, 4, 5, 3, 4, 12}
(iii) {8, 7, 6, 5, 4, 3, 2, 1}
(iv) {8, 7, 8, 7, 6, 5, 6, 5, 4, 3, 4, 3}
(v) {–3, –2, –1, 0, 1, 2, 3}
(vi) {1, 2, –3, 8, 7, –5, –2}

2. Consider the following set:

A = {139, 131, 136, 141, 121, 126, 121, 131, 131, 145, 143, 141, 130, 150}

(i) Display the data on a stem-and-leaf diagram.
(ii) Find the lower quartile and the upper quartile for the set.
(iii) What percentage of values lies between the lower quartile and the upper quartile?
(iv) Find the interquartile range.

3. The stem-and-leaf plot gives the ages of 31 people attending a meeting about a government proposal not to grant medical cards to all people over the age of 70.

5	1, 4, 4, 4
5	5, 9, 9, 9, 9
6	3, 3, 3, 4, 5
6	6, 6, 7, 7, 8, 8, 9
7	1, 1, 2, 3, 3, 3, 3, 3, 4
7	5 Key: 6|6 = 66 years

(i) Find Q_1, the lower quartile.
(ii) Find Q_3, the upper quartile.
(iii) Calculate the interquartile range.
(iv) Describe the shape of the distribution.
(v) Explain the shape of the distribution in the context of this question.

4. The following data indicates the electricity consumption (in kilowatt-hours) for 20 typical two-bedroom apartments in Dublin.

9	11	16	10	11	9	8	13	11	9
13	11	7	9	7	12	14	13	11	7

(i) Draw a stem-and-leaf diagram to illustrate the data.
(ii) Describe the distribution.
(iii) Find the range.
(iv) Find the median.
(v) Find the interquartile range.

5. The data below gives the diameter (in inches) at 54 inches above the ground for a sample of 30 black cherry trees in the Allegheny National Forest, Pennsylvania.

8.3	10.8	11.4	12.9	14.2	17.5
8.6	11.0	11.4	13.3	14.5	17.9
8.8	11.1	11.7	13.7	16.0	18.0
10.5	11.2	12.0	13.8	16.3	18.0
10.7	11.3	12.9	14.0	17.3	20.6

(i) Draw a stem-and-leaf diagram to illustrate the data.
(ii) Describe the distribution.
(iii) Find the range.
(iv) Find the median.
(v) Find the interquartile range.

6. The percentage of silica was calculated in each of 22 meteorites. The data is displayed below.

20.77 22.56 22.71 22.99 26.39 27.08 27.32 27.33 27.57 27.81
28.69 29.36 30.25 31.89 32.88 33.23 33.28 33.40 33.52 33.83
33.95 34.82

(a) Provide the following summary statistics.

(i) The mean
(ii) The median
(iii) The minimum value
(iv) The maximum value
(v) The range
(vi) The interquartile range

(b) (i) What is the difference between the mean and the median for the data set given above?
(ii) What does this difference tell us about the shape of the distribution?

7. The data give sets of salinity values (parts per thousand) for three separate water masses in the Bimini Lagoon, the Bahamas.

Area 1	Area 2	Area 3
37.54	40.17	39.04
37.01	40.80	39.21
36.71	39.76	39.05
37.03	39.70	38.24
37.32	40.79	38.53
37.01	40.44	38.71
37.03	39.79	38.89
37.70	39.38	38.66
37.36		38.51
36.75		40.08
37.45		
38.85		

Copy and complete the following table.

	Area 1	Area 2	Area 3
Mean			
Minimum			
Q_1			
Median			
Q_3			
Maximum			
IQR			
Range			

Variation II: Standard Deviation

Standard deviation measures the average deviation or spread from the mean of all values in a set. It is a reliable measure of spread, as it takes account of all values in the set, unlike the range or interquartile range. However, if there are extreme values in the data set, it is best to use the interquartile range as a measure of spread.

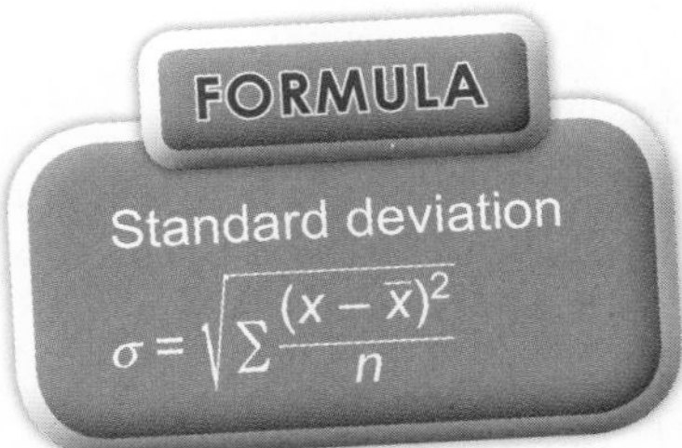
FORMULA
Standard deviation
$\sigma = \sqrt{\sum \frac{(x-\bar{x})^2}{n}}$

Note:
σ is the standard deviation.
Σ means 'sum of'.
x is the variable.
$\bar{x}$ is the mean.
n is the number of variables.

Worked Example 4.7

Set A = {8, 8, 9, 11, 14} and set B = {1, 5, 9, 14, 21}.

(i) Show that A and B have the same mean.

(ii) Find the range of A and the range of B.

(iii) Comment on the range as a measure of spread in the context of this question.

(iv) Why is the standard deviation a better measure of spread than the range?

(v) Calculate the standard deviation from the mean of both sets.

Solution

(i) The mean of set A, $\bar{x}_A = \frac{8+8+9+11+14}{5} = \frac{50}{5} = 10.$

The mean of set B, $\bar{x}_B = \frac{1+5+9+14+21}{5} = \frac{50}{5} = 10.$

(ii) $\text{Range}_A = 14 - 8 = 6$ $\quad$ $\text{Range}_B = 21 - 1 = 20$

(iii) The range indicates that set B has a greater spread than set A. However, as a measure of spread, it is limited to just two values in the set, the maximum value and the minimum value. If an outlier or extreme value exists in the data, then this will distort the true measure of spread.

(iv) The standard deviation uses all values in the set to calculate the spread and is therefore a much better measure.

(v) We can calculate the standard deviation using the formula $\sigma = \sqrt{\sum \frac{(x-\bar{x})^2}{n}}$

The work can be summarised in the following tables.

Set A			
x	$\bar{x}$	d	d^2
8	10	−2	4
8	10	−2	4
9	10	−1	1
11	10	1	1
14	10	4	16
			26

Set B			
x	$\bar{x}$	d	d^2
1	10	−9	81
5	10	−5	25
9	10	−1	1
14	10	4	16
21	10	11	121
			244

Note: $d = x - \bar{x}$

$\sigma_A = \sqrt{\frac{26}{5}}$ $\sigma_B = \sqrt{\frac{244}{5}}$

$\sigma_A = \sqrt{5.2}$ $\sigma_B = \sqrt{48.8}$

$\sigma_A \approx 2.28$ $\sigma_B \approx 6.99$

Worked Example 4.8

One hundred students are given a maths problem to solve. The times taken to solve the problem are tabled as follows:

Time (minutes)	10–14	14–18	18–22	22–26	26–30
Number of students	13	28	26	21	12

Note: 14–18 means 14 is included and 18 is not, etc.

Using mid-interval values, estimate the mean of the distribution, and hence, estimate the standard deviation from the mean. Give your answers to two decimal places.

Solution

We can summarise our work as follows:

M.I.V. x	**Number**		**Mean** $\overline{x}$	**Deviation** d	**Deviation^2** d^2	fd^2
	f	xf				
12	13	156	19.64	–7.64	58.3696	758.8048
16	28	448	19.64	–3.64	13.2496	370.9888
20	26	520	19.64	0.36	0.1296	3.3696
24	21	504	19.64	4.36	19.0096	399.2016
28	12	336	19.64	8.36	69.8896	838.6752
	100	1964				2371.04

Estimated mean, $\overline{x} = \frac{1{,}964}{100} = 19.64$

Standard deviation $\sigma = \sqrt{\frac{2{,}371.04}{100}} = \sqrt{23.7104} \approx 4.87$

The statistics functions on your calculator can also be used to find standard deviation. Here are the keystrokes for this problem. Note that individual calculators may differ.

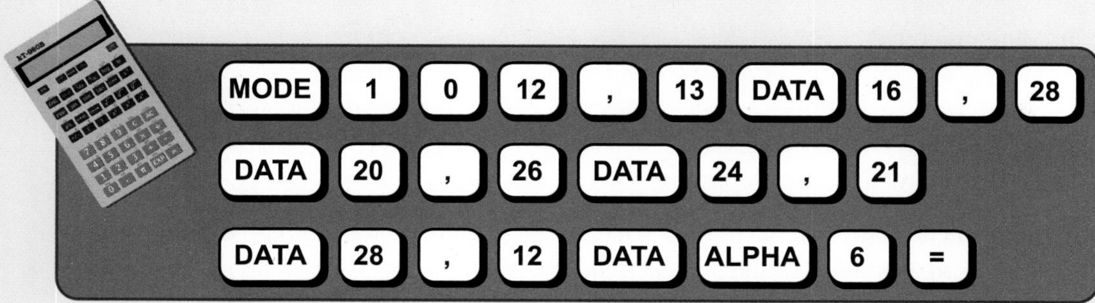

Exercise 4.4

1. Examine the data sets A and B. Without doing any calculations, decide which set has the larger standard deviation. Then check by doing the standard deviation by hand.

(i) A = {11, 13, 15, 17, 19} B = {10, 12, 14, 16, 18}

(ii) A = {11, 15, 16, 17, 21} B = {16, 20, 21, 22, 26}

(iii) A = {500, 600, 700, 800} B = {50, 60, 70, 80}

(iv) A = {2, 5, 8, 9} B = {22, 25, 28, 29}

2. Examine the data sets X and Y. Without doing any calculations, decide which set has the larger standard deviation. Then check by doing the standard deviation by hand.

(i) X = {15, 17, 19, 21, 23} Y = {14, 16, 18, 20, 22}

(ii) X = {9, 13, 14, 15, 19} Y = {14, 18, 19, 20, 24}

(iii) X = {x, x + 1, x + 2, x + 3} Y = {x + 10, x + 11, x + 12, x + 13}

(iv) X = {x + 2, x + 5, x + 8, x + 9} Y = {x + 22, x + 25, x + 28, x + 29}

3. Statisticians sometimes estimate the standard deviation using $\sigma = \frac{\text{Range}}{4}$.

Using the rough estimate $\sigma = \frac{\text{Range}}{4}$ rather than the formula $\sigma = \sqrt{\sum \frac{(x - \bar{x})^2}{n}}$, calculate the percentage error on set A = {98.6, 98.6, 98.0, 99.0, 98.4, 98.4, 98.4}.

4. The table shows the prices on 1 August 2010 of a sample of Sunday newspapers.

Newspaper	Price (€)	Newspaper	Price (€)	Newspaper	Price (€)
Sunday Independent	2.50	*Independent on Sunday*	1.80	*Observer*	2.30
Sunday World	2.30	*Sunday People*	1.30	*Sunday Express*	1.40
Sunday Tribune	2.50	*Sunday Mirror*	1.30	*Sunday Telegraph*	2.90
Sunday Business Post	2.50	*Irish Mail on Sunday*	1.50	*Sunday Times*	2.50
Star on Sunday	2.10	*News of the World*	1.40	*Sunday Racing Post*	2.50

(a) Provide the following summary statistics for the prices of the Sunday newspapers shown in the table.

(i) Count (i.e. the number of newspapers in the sample)

(ii) Minimum price

(iii) Maximum price

(iv) Mean price

(v) Standard deviation from the mean

(b) For most data sets, it is unusual to have a data value more than two standard deviations away from the mean. Comment in the context of this question.

5. The gross national product (GNP) is the value of all goods and services produced by an economy in a year. The table gives Ireland's GNP (in €m) for the period 2006–2009.

Year	2006	2007	2008	2009
GNP	154,078	162,853	154,672	131,241

Source: www.cso.ie

(i) Calculate the mean and the standard deviation for the data.

(ii) Why would an economist be interested in the standard deviation from the mean?

(iii) In what year was the maximum value of GNP?

(iv) In what year was the minimum value of GNP?

(v) In your opinion, is the economy in recession? Explain your answer.

6. A group of medical students measure the blood pressure of the same person. The systolic readings (in mmHg) are given below.

139 131 136 141 121 126 121

131 131 145 143 141 130 150

(i) Give two possible reasons why there is variation in the readings.

(ii) Plot the data on a stem-and-leaf diagram.

(iii) Circle the outlier in the data. Give a possible reason for the outlier in this data.

(iv) Describe the shape of the distribution.

(v) Calculate the mean and the standard deviation of the distribution.

(vi) If a group of qualified doctors had taken the readings, would you expect the standard deviation to be greater or less? Explain your answer.

7. Twenty students are asked how many minutes they spent watching television on a particular day. The following frequency distribution summarises their replies.

Time (min)	0–40	40–60	60–80	80–100	100–120
Frequency	2	6	5	3	4

Note: 0–40 means 0 is included but 40 is not, etc.

(i) Estimate the mean time spent watching television by the group.

(ii) Find to the nearest minute the standard deviation from the mean.

8. The frequency distribution shows the ages of 100 people.

Age	0–10	10–20	20–30	30–50	50–80
Frequency	10	19	25	30	16

Note: 0–10 means 0 is included but 10 is not, etc.

(i) Estimate the mean age.

(ii) Find to the nearest integer the standard deviation from the mean.

9. A garage owner recorded the amount of money spent by customers on petrol over a day. The frequency distribution shows the results.

Amount (€)	0–10	10–20	20–30	30–50	50–100
Freq.	50	150	400	300	100

Note: 0–10 means 0 is included but 10 is not, etc.

(i) Estimate the mean amount spent.

(ii) Find to the nearest euro the standard deviation from the mean.

10. The heights (in centimetres) of 140 plants are measured and recorded in the table below.

Height	55–60	60–65	65–70	70–75	75–80	80–85	85–90
Frequency	1	11	37	54	28	8	1

Note: 55–60 means 55 is included and 60 is not, etc.

(i) Using mid-interval values, estimate the mean height of the plants.

(ii) Estimate the standard deviation from the mean.

11. Weights (in grams) of samples of the contents in cans of regular Coke and Diet Coke are given below.

Regular Coke				
370	371	369	371	363
362	369	367	367	365

Diet Coke				
352	352	349	354	353
352	350	354	357	351

(i) Complete the grouped frequencies for the data.

Regular Coke			
Weight (g)	360–365	365–370	370–375
Frequency			

Note: 360–365 means 360 is included but 365 is not, etc.

Diet Coke			
Weight (g)	345–350	350–355	355–360
Frequency			

Note: 345–350 means 345 is included but 350 is not, etc.

(ii) Display the grouped frequency distributions on two histograms.

(iii) Using only evidence from your histograms, state which set has the greater standard deviation.

(iv) Confirm your answer to part (iii) by calculating the standard deviation for both distributions.

4.4 MEASURES OF RELATIVE STANDING

In this section we will introduce measures that can be used to compare values within a data set or to compare values from different data sets. These measures are known as **measures of relative standing**. You have already met with some measures of relative standing, e.g. the lower quartile, the median and the upper quartile. The other measures of relative standing you will study are percentiles and z-scores.

Percentiles

Generally speaking, when we take tests we are more interested in how we compare to everybody else (our relative standing) than in our actual score on the test. The most common way to report relative standing is by using **percentiles**.

The values that divide a data set into 100 equal parts are called **percentiles**.

There are 99 percentiles in a data set. Usually, percentiles are denoted by $P_1, P_2, P_3, \ldots, P_{99}$.

A percentile is not a score. Suppose your score on a particular test is reported to be the 75th percentile. This does not mean you have scored 75% in the test. It means that 75% of the students' scores were lower than yours.

- The median is the 50th percentile.
- The lower quartile is the 25th percentile.
- The upper quartile is the 75th percentile.

Calculating P_k – the kth percentile

Step 1 Rank the data.

Step 2 Find the number c, which is k% of the total number of numbers in the set.

$$c = \frac{n \times k}{100}$$

where n = sample size and k = the required percentile.

Step 3 (a) If c **is** a whole number, find the average of the values in the c and $c + 1$ positions in the ordered set. The average value will be the required percentile.

Step 3 (b) If c is **not** a whole number, round up to the next whole number. Locate this position in the ordered set. The value in this location is the required percentile.

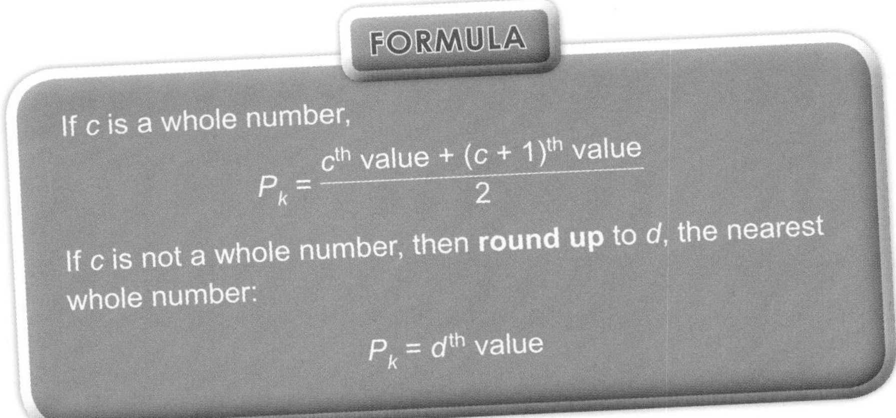

FORMULA

If c is a whole number,

$$P_k = \frac{c^{th} \text{ value} + (c+1)^{th} \text{ value}}{2}$$

If c is not a whole number, then **round up** to d, the nearest whole number:

$$P_k = d^{th} \text{ value}$$

Finding the percentile value of a data point

If you scored 85% on your last maths test, then what percentile will the teacher report for you?

You need to know x, the number of students who had a smaller score than yours.

$$\text{Percentile value} = \frac{x}{\text{Total number of values}} \times 100$$

Worked Example 4.9

Find (i) P_{30} and (ii) P_{80} for the following data set:

{98, 92, 95, 87, 96, 90, 65, 92, 95, 93, 98, 94, 98, 95, 96}

Solution

(i) To find P_{30}:

Step 1 Rank the data:

65, 87, 90, 92, 92, 93, 94, 95, 95, 95, 96, 96, 98, 98, 98

Step 2 Find c, 30% of 15:

$$c = \frac{15 \times 30}{100} = 4.5$$

Step 3 4.5 is not a whole number, so we round up to 5:

P_{30} = fifth value = 92

(ii) To find P_{80}:

Step 1 Rank the data:

65, 87, 90, 92, 92, 93, 94, 95, 95, 95, 96, 96, 98, 98, 98

Step 2 Find c, 80% of 15:

$$c = \frac{15 \times 80}{100} = 12$$

Step 3 12 is a whole number, so $P_{80} = \dfrac{\text{12th value} + \text{13th value}}{2}$

$$P_{80} = \frac{96 + 98}{2} = 97$$

Worked Example 4.10

The table below gives the marks of 30 students in a maths test.

43	63	72	59	73
61	45	83	88	61
72	87	52	63	79
78	64	72	56	97
98	89	63	85	58
68	75	77	58	67

(i) Display the data on a stemplot.

(ii) Calculate P_{20} and $P85$.

(iii) John has scored 85 in the test. What is John's relative standing in the group for this test?

Solution

(i)

4	3, 5
5	2, 6, 8, 8, 9
6	1, 1, 3, 3, 3, 4, 7, 8
7	2, 2, 2, 3, 5, 7, 8, 9
8	3, 5, 7, 8, 9
9	7, 8 Key: 5|6 = 56 marks

(ii) Calculate P_{20}:

$c = \frac{30 \times 20}{100} = 6$

c is a whole number, so

$P20 = \frac{6^{\text{th}} \text{ value} + 7^{\text{th}} \text{ value}}{2}$

$P20 = \frac{58 + 59}{2} = 58.5$

Calculate P_{85}:

$c = \frac{30 \times 85}{100} = 25.5$

c is not a whole number, so round up to 26:

$P_{85} = 26^{\text{th}}$ value

$P_{85} = 87$

(iii) Twenty-four students scored lower than John.

John's percentile ranking $= \frac{24}{30} \times 100 = 80^{\text{th}}$ percentile.

80% of the class scored lower than John in the test.

z-Scores

We use **z-scores** to compare values within a set and to compare values from different sets.

A z-score is the number of standard deviations a given value x is above or below the mean of a given data set.

z-scores are measures of position in the sense that they describe the location of a value relative to the mean. The z-score is affected by an outlier, as the outlier directly affects the mean and the standard deviation.

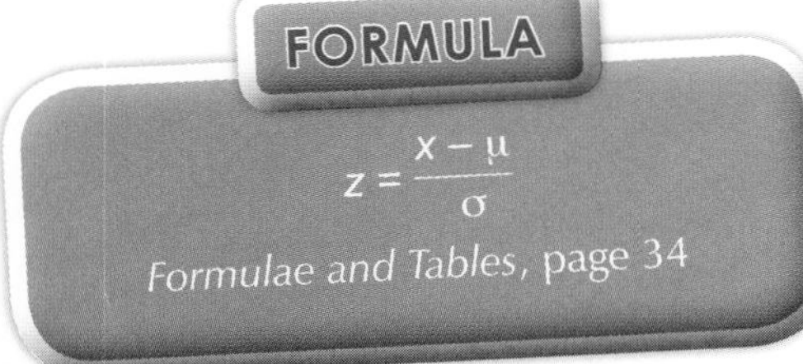
FORMULA
$z = \frac{x - \mu}{\sigma}$
Formulae and Tables, page 34

Note:
x is a population value.
μ is the population mean.
σ is the population standard deviation.

For most distributions, a value that is more than two standard deviations from the mean would be considered unusual.

Unusual values for z-score: $z < -2$ or $z > 2$

Worked Example 4.11

Dublin's maximum February temperatures average 6.5°C with a standard deviation of 0.75°C, while in July the mean maximum temperature is 18°C with a standard deviation of 1.5°C.
In which month is it more unusual to have a maximum temperature of 10°C?

Solution

February: $z = \frac{10 - 6.5}{0.75}$

$z = 4.6$

July: $z = \frac{10 - 18}{1.5}$

$z = -5\frac{1}{3}$

It is more unusual to have a maximum temperature of 10°C in July because $5\frac{1}{3} > 4.6$.

Note that both *z*-scores are unusual values, as they lie outside $-2 \leqslant z \leqslant 2$.

ACTIVITY 4.5

Exercise 4.5

1. Consider the following data:

80	77	81	85	73
72	80	83	54	73
54	75	55	68	60
59	61	54	62	53
56	53	81	56	53
51	74	78	80	52

(i) Display the data on an ordered stem-and-leaf diagram.

Calculate:

(ii) P_{90}

(iii) P_{10}

(iv) Q_1

(v) Q_3

(vi) P_{60}

(vii) P_{40}

2. The table below gives the marks of a class on an end-of-term maths test.

100	94	89	77	67
56	99	95	87	76
65	48	97	47	43
98	90	86	74	61
95	89	83	71	58
18	87	88	42	56

(i) Display the data on an ordered stem-and-leaf diagram.

(ii) Calculate the 40th percentile.

(iii) Calculate the 70th percentile.

(iv) Interpret the meaning of the numbers calculated, in the context of this question.

(v) How would you evaluate the performance of the student who scored 61 on the test?

3. A group of Fifth Year students recorded their pulse rates (in beats per minute) when they were in a relaxed state. The results of the survey are shown in the table.

84	68	63	80	68	63	80	69	63	68	62	53
55	63	69	57	63	70	58	64	71	58	63	55
63	70	59	65	73	75	65	59	62	67	69	83

(i) Display the data on an ordered stem-and-leaf diagram.

(ii) Describe the distribution.

(iii) Calculate the 85th percentile.

(iv) Calculate the 15th percentile.

(v) Interpret the meaning of the numbers calculated, in the context of the question.

(vi) Calculate the difference between the 90th percentile and the 10th percentile.

4. Kevin is studying the cost of history books in his local bookshop. He presents the results of his survey on a stem-and-leaf diagram.

0	6, 9
1	0, 0, 0, 2, 2, 8, 9, 9, 9, 9
2	0, 0, 0, 2, 2, 2, 3, 5, 7, 9, 9, 9, 9, 9
3	0, 0, 7, 7, 8, 9, 9, 9, 9
4	0, 0, 0, 5, 9, 9, 9
5	5, 8, 9
6	5, 9 Key: 2|7 = €27

(i) Describe the distribution.

(ii) Find the median of the data.

(iii) Find the interquartile range of the data.

(iv) Find the difference between the 15th percentile and the 85th percentile of the data.

5. The women's shot putt event at the 2009 World Athletics Championships was won by Valerie Vili of New Zealand. The table below gives the qualifying performances of the 28 competitors in the event. All distances are in metres.

19.70	19.36	19.12	19.08	18.92	18.69	18.62
18.53	18.44	18.25	18.14	18.10	17.99	17.95
17.92	17.89	17.86	17.71	17.61	17.30	17.25
17.19	16.92	16.80	16.60	16.09	16.01	14.98

(i) Copy and complete the frequency distribution table.

Distance (m)	14.25–15.00	15.00–15.75	15.75–16.50	16.50–17.25	17.25–18.00	18.00–18.75	18.75–19.50	19.50–20.25
Frequency								

Note: 14.25–15.00 includes 14.25 but not 15.00 and so on.

(ii) Draw a histogram of the distribution.

(iii) Describe the shape of the distribution.

(iv) Calculate the 90th percentile.

(v) Austra Skujyte of Lithuania was the only competitor to have a 'personal best' in the qualifying rounds. She putted a distance of 17.86 m. How would you evaluate Austra's performance in relation to the other competitors?

6. A sample consists of heights of Irish wolfhounds, measured in centimetres. If the height of one particular wolfhound is converted to a z-score, what units are used for the z-score?

7. For a large data set, Q_3 (the upper quartile) is 155. What does it mean when we say that 155 is the upper quartile?

8. Men have heights with a mean of 176 cm and a standard deviation of 7 cm. John Keats (1795–1821), the English Romantic poet, had a height of 153 cm.

   (i) What was the difference between Keats' height and the mean?

   (ii) How many standard deviations is his height from the mean?

   (iii) Convert Keats' height to a z-score.

   (iv) Is Keats' height usual or unusual? Explain.

9. IQ scores have a mean of 100 and a standard deviation of 16. Albert Einstein had an IQ of 160.

   (i) What was the difference between Einstein's IQ and the mean?

   (ii) How many standard deviations is his IQ from the mean?

   (iii) Convert Einstein's IQ to a z-score.

   (iv) Is Einstein's IQ usual or unusual? Explain.

10. Human body temperatures have a mean of 36.8°C and a standard deviation from the mean of 0. 2°C. Convert the following temperatures to z-scores.

    (i) 36.2° (ii) 37.2° (iii) 36° (iv) 38°

11. Which is relatively better, a score of 84 on an English test or a score of 48 on a maths test? Scores on the English test have a mean of 90 and a standard deviation of 10. Scores on the maths test have a mean of 55 and a standard deviation of 5.

4.5 THE NORMAL DISTRIBUTION AND THE EMPIRICAL RULE

In nature, there are many continuous distributions that are symmetric. For example, if one were to measure the heights of all adult males in Ireland, one would find a high proportion of the adult male population with heights close to the mean height of the population. As measurements increase or decrease away from the mean, the proportion of the population with these heights begins to decrease. This results in a symmetric distribution.

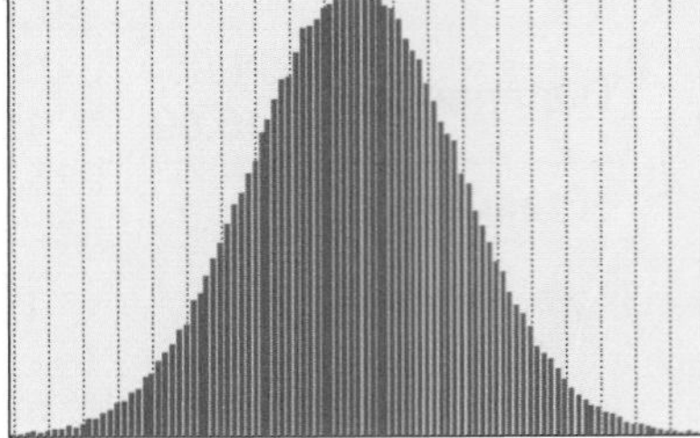

If the distribution is very large and we allow the class intervals (base width of the rectangles) to become sufficiently small, the distribution forms a symmetrical bell-shaped smooth curve called the **normal distribution curve**.

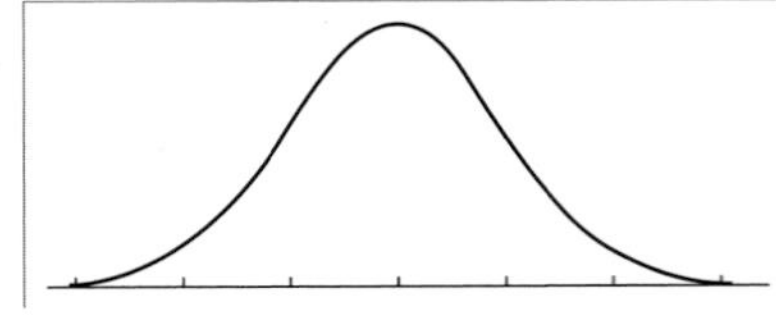

The famous French mathematician Abraham de Moivre (1667–1754) discovered a mathematical formula for constructing the normal curve. If we wish to find the equation of the normal curve for a particular normal distribution, we substitute (i) the mean and (ii) the standard deviation from the mean into de Moivre's formula.

In any normal distribution:

(i) Approximately 68% of the population lies within one standard deviation of the mean, i.e. 68% lies in the range $[\bar{x} - \sigma, \bar{x} + \sigma]$.

(ii) Approximately 95% of the population lie in the range $[\bar{x} - 2\sigma, \bar{x} + 2\sigma]$

(iii) Approximately 99.7% of the population lie in the range $[\bar{x} - 3\sigma, \bar{x} + 3\sigma]$

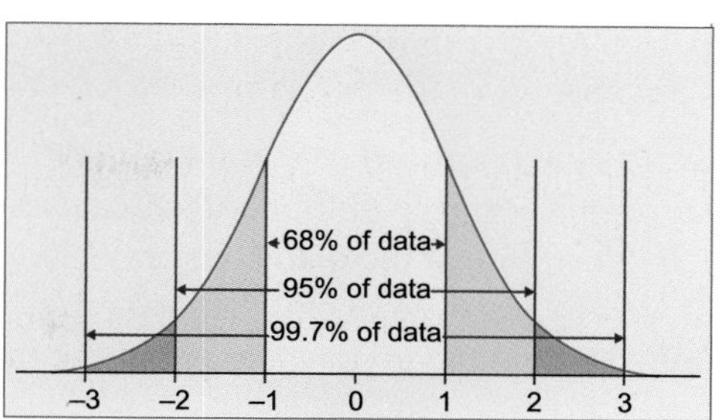

Worked Example 4.12

The frequency table below shows the number of hits a website received each day during a particular week.

Day	Mon.	Tue.	Wed.	Thu.	Fri.
Number of hits	50	80	120	40	20

(i) Calculate $\bar{x}$, the mean number of hits per day during that week.

(ii) Calculate σ, the standard deviation from the mean.

(iii) Now find the range $[\bar{x} - \sigma, \bar{x} + \sigma]$.

Solution

(i) $\bar{x} = \dfrac{50 + 80 + 120 + 40 + 20}{5} = 62$

(ii) $\sigma = 34.9$ (calculator)

(iii) $[62 - 34.9, 62 + 34.9] = [27.1, 96.9]$

Worked Example 4.13

The distribution of heights of a large group of students is normal, with a mean of 158 cm and a standard deviation from the mean of 10 cm. The empirical rule says that approximately 68% of a normally distributed population lies within one standard deviation of the mean.

(i) Using the empirical rule, find the range of heights within which 68% of this population lies.

(ii) If a student is chosen at random from the population, find the probability that the student has a height between 148 cm and 168 cm.

Solution

(i) Range $= [\bar{x} - \sigma, \bar{x} + \sigma]$

$= [158 - 10, 158 + 10] = [148 \text{ cm}, 168 \text{ cm}]$

(ii) From part (i), we know that 68% of the population has heights in the range [148 cm, 168 cm]. Therefore, the probability that the student has a height between 148 cm and 168 cm is 0.68.

Worked Example 4.14

Washers are produced so that their inside diameter is normally distributed with a mean of 1.25 cm. If 95% of the diameters are between 1.2375 cm and 1.2625 cm, then what is the approximate standard deviation from the mean?

Solution

The empirical rule tells us that approximately 95% of the diameters will be in the range $[1.25 - 2\sigma, 1.25 + 2\sigma]$.

Therefore, $1.25 - 2\sigma = 1.2375$

$-2\sigma = 1.2375 - 1.25$

$-2\sigma = -0.0125$

$\sigma = 0.00625$ cm

Exercise 4.6

1. In a normal distribution:

(i) Approximately what proportion of observations lie within one standard deviation of the mean?

(ii) Approximately what proportion of observations lie within two standard deviations of the mean?

(iii) Approximately what proportion of observations lie within three standard deviations of the mean?

2. The principal of Fermat High School records the number of pupils absent each day during a week in December. The results are displayed in the table below.

Day	Monday	Tuesday	Wednesday	Thursday	Friday
Number	12	19	17	25	20

(i) Calculate $\bar{x}$, the mean number of students absent per day during that week.

(ii) Calculate σ, the standard deviation from the mean.

(iii) Now find the range $[\bar{x} - \sigma, \bar{x} + \sigma]$.

3. In each of the following the mean ($\bar{x}$) and standard deviation (σ) of the normal distributions are given. For each distribution, find the range within which 68% of the distribution lies.

(i) $\bar{x} = 200, \sigma = 25$ (ii) $\bar{x} = 100, \sigma = 20$ (iii) $\bar{x} = 20, \sigma = 2$ (iv) $\bar{x} = 25, \sigma = 2.5$

4. In each of the following, the mean ($\bar{x}$) and standard deviation (σ) of the normal distributions are given. For each distribution, find the range within which 95% of the distribution lies.

(i) $\bar{x} = 280, \sigma = 35$ (ii) $\bar{x} = 120, \sigma = 30$ (iii) $\bar{x} = 25, \sigma = 2$ (iv) $\bar{x} = 35, \sigma = 5.5$

5. In each of the following, the mean ($\bar{x}$) and standard deviation (σ) of the normal distributions are given. For each distribution, find the range within which 99.7% of the distribution lies.

(i) $\bar{x} = 150, \sigma = 25$ (ii) $\bar{x} = 300, \sigma = 15$ (iii) $\bar{x} = 20, \sigma = 2$ (iv) $\bar{x} = 100, \sigma = 5$

6. In each of the following, the mean ($\bar{x}$) and standard deviation (σ) of the normal distributions are given. For each distribution, find the range within which 68% of the distribution lies.

(i) $\bar{x} = 300, \sigma = 30$ (ii) $\bar{x} = 115, \sigma = 20$ (iii) $\bar{x} = 40, \sigma = 3$ (iv) $\bar{x} = 35, \sigma = 2.5$

7. In each of the following, the mean ($\bar{x}$) and standard deviation (σ) of the normal distributions are given. For each distribution, find the range within which 95% of the distribution lies.

(i) $\bar{x} = 200, \sigma = 25$ (ii) $\bar{x} = 100, \sigma = 20$ (iii) $\bar{x} = 20, \sigma = 2$ (iv) $\bar{x} = 25, \sigma = 2.5$

8. In each of the following, the mean ($\bar{x}$) and standard deviation (σ) of the normal distributions are given. For each distribution, find the range within which 99.7% of the distribution lies.

(i) $\bar{x} = 40, \sigma = 5$ (ii) $\bar{x} = 100, \sigma = 15$ (iii) $\bar{x} = 22, \sigma = 6$ (iv) $\bar{x} = 30, \sigma = 2$

9. IQ scores are normally distributed with a mean of 100 and a standard deviation of 15. Isaac de Moivre has taken an IQ test and scored 130. His friend Eoin has remarked that Isaac's score is in the top 5% of all IQ scores. Isaac disagrees and says that he is in the top 2.5%. Is Isaac's remark correct? Explain your reasoning.

10. Men's heights are normally distributed with a mean of 172.5 cm and a standard deviation from the mean of 7 cm. Séamus the statistician has designed a house with doorways high enough to allow all men, except the tallest 2.5%, to pass through without bending. What doorway height has Séamus used?

11. Human body temperatures are normally distributed with a mean of 36.8°C and a standard deviation from the mean of 0.2°C. Rita has a body temperature of 40.5°C. Should Rita be concerned? Explain your reasoning.

12. Birth weights in Ireland are normally distributed with a mean of 3.42 kg and a standard deviation of 0.5 kg. What percentage of babies born will weigh between 2.92 kg and 3.92 kg? Explain your answer.

4.6 DISTRIBUTIONS

In Chapter 1, you learned about symmetric and skewed distributions. In this section, you will learn how the shape of a distribution affects the mean and standard deviation.

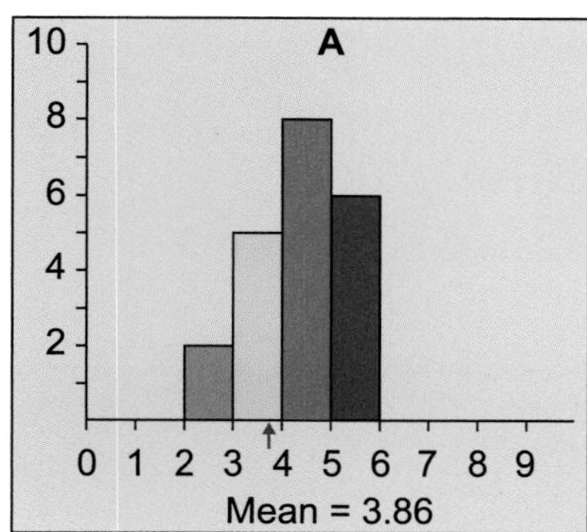

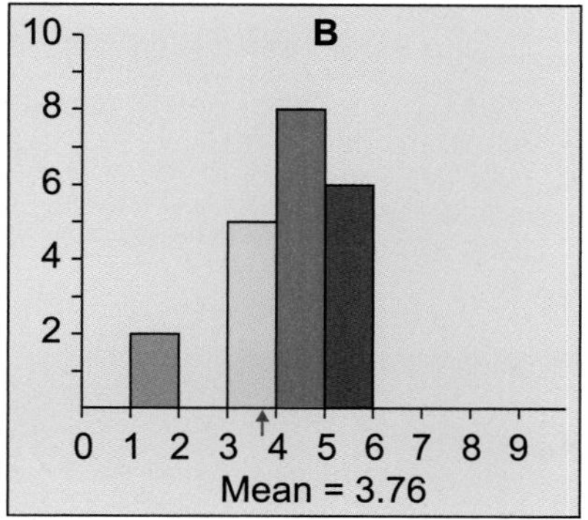

The mean of the distribution shown in diagram A is 3.86. If we change the value of the green bar from 2.5 to 1.5 (mid-interval values), what happens to (a) the mean and (b) the standard deviation? The results are shown in diagram B.

(a) The mean changes from 3.86 to 3.76, i.e. the mean is shifted to a slightly lower value. This occurs as smaller values (1.5 instead of 2.5) are now being used in the calculation of the mean.

(b) What happens to the standard deviation? Does it increase, decrease or remain the same? First, all deviations from the mean will change. The red, blue and green bar are now further from the mean. The yellow bar is closer to the mean.

The larger frequencies of the red and blue bars, coupled with increases in deviation, will outweigh the few values in the yellow bar that had a slight decrease in deviations. Therefore, the standard deviation will be larger for the second distribution.

Worked Example 4.15

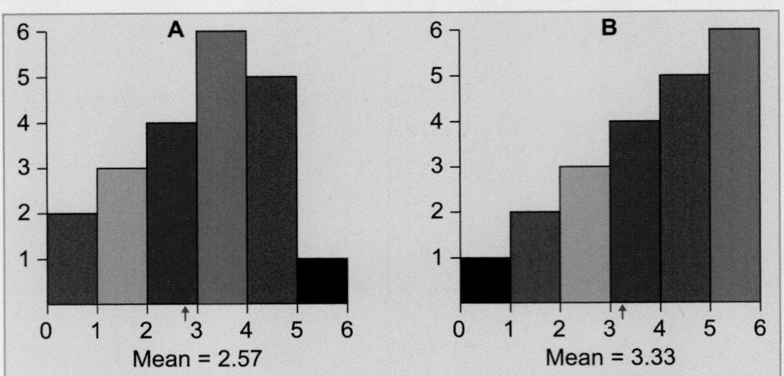

Which distribution has the larger standard deviation?

Solution

Distribution B has the larger standard deviation. The values with the higher frequencies are closer to the mean in distribution A than in distribution B. In general, a skewed distribution would have a larger standard deviation than a symmetric distribution.

Worked Example 4.16

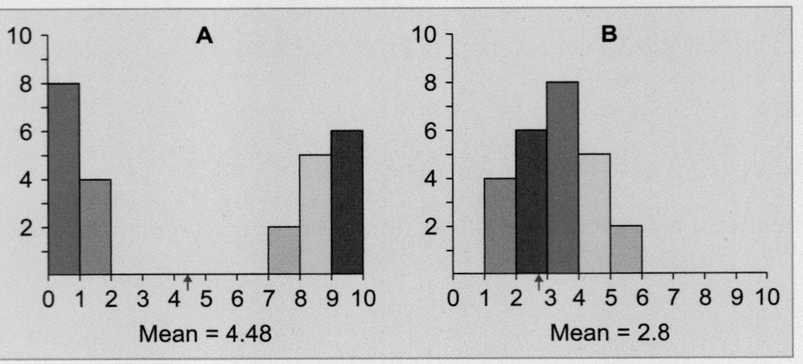

Which distribution has the larger standard deviation?

Solution

Distribution A has the larger standard deviation. The values with the higher frequencies are closer to the mean in distribution B, than in distribution A.

Worked Example 4.17

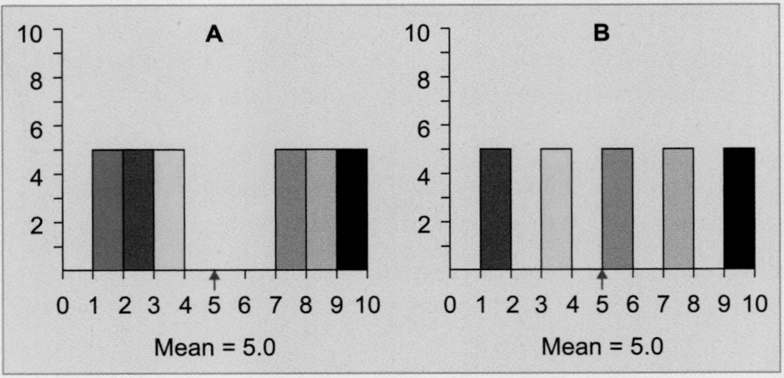

Which distribution has the larger standard deviation?

Solution

Consider distribution A. If we move the blue bar to the position where it has a value of 5.5, and if the lilac bar is removed completely, then distribution A and distribution B would be identical. Removing the lilac bar reduces the standard deviation of A, as does moving the blue bar to the new position. Therefore, distribution A has the larger standard deviation.

Worked Example 4.18

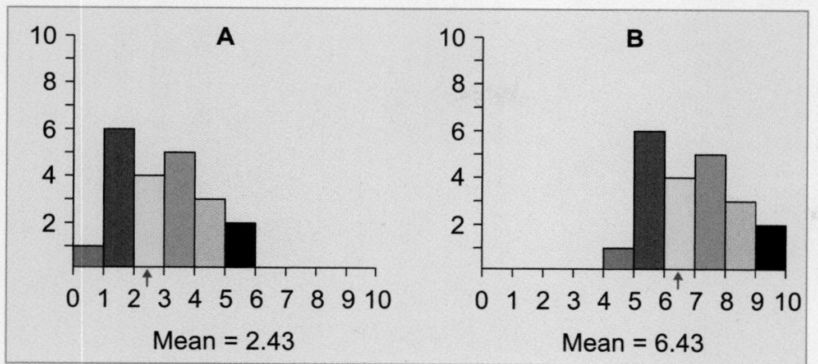

Which distribution has the larger standard deviation?

Solution

Note: Mean is based on raw data.

Distributions A and B both have the same standard deviation. As you can see from the diagram, both distributions have an identical shape and therefore have the same standard deviation.

Exercise 4.7

For each of the following distributions, state whether $\sigma_A = \sigma_B$, $\sigma_A > \sigma_B$ or $\sigma_A < \sigma_B$, where σ_A is the standard deviation of distribution A and σ_B is the standard deviation of distribution B.

1. 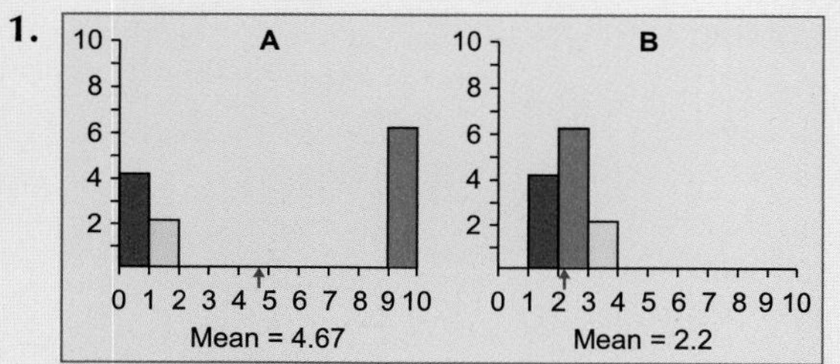

2. 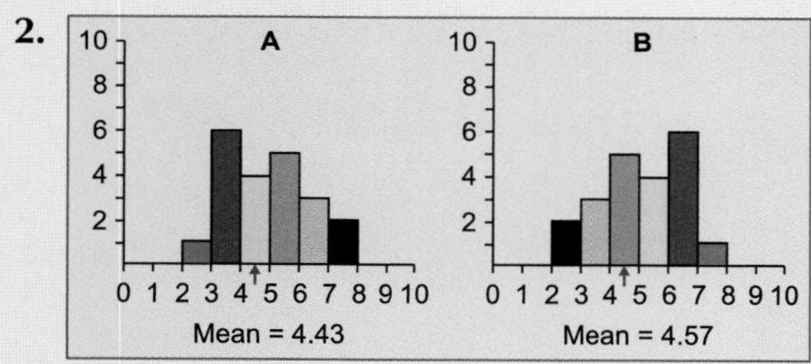

3. 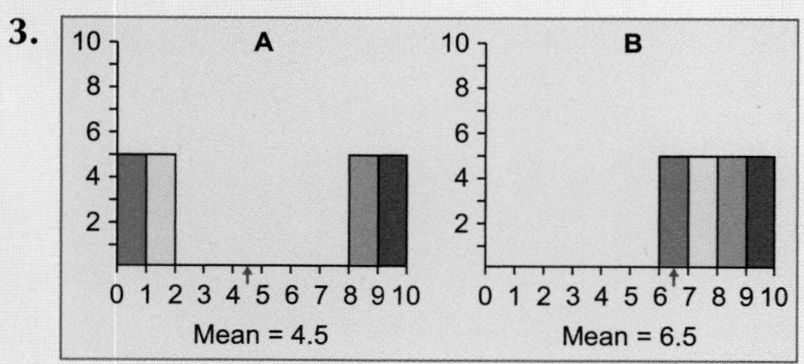

4. 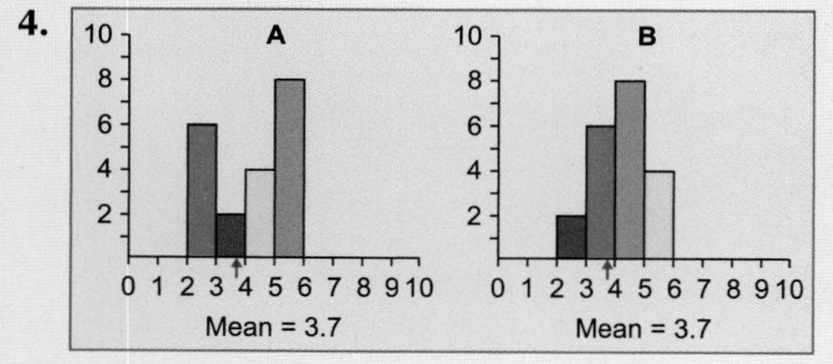

5. 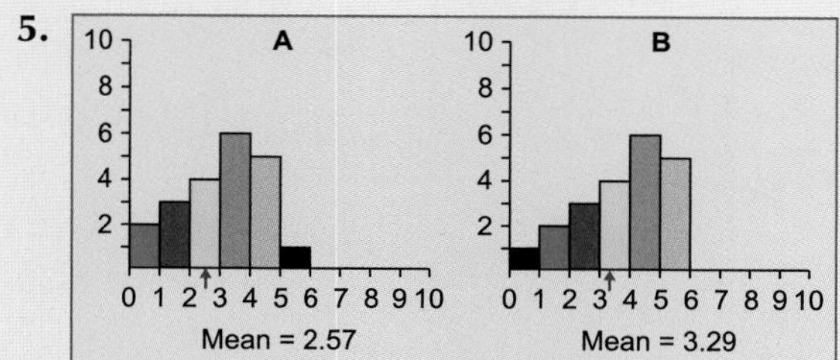

6. 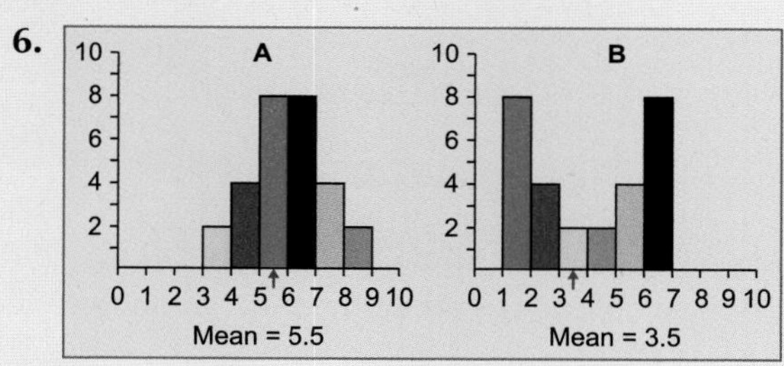

7. 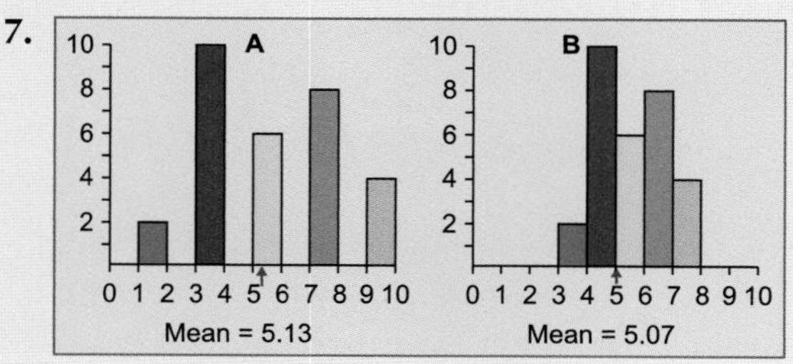

8. 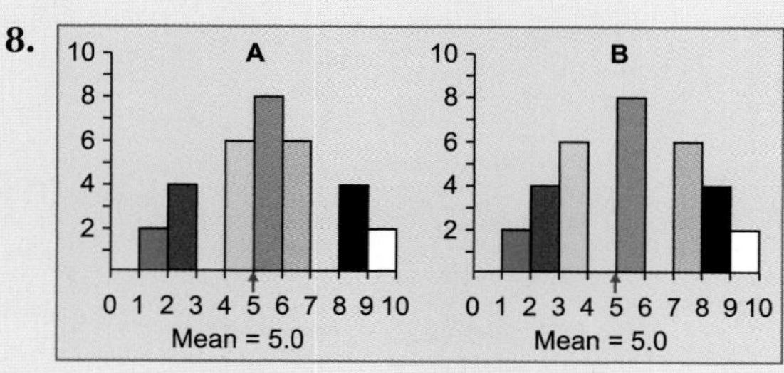

9.

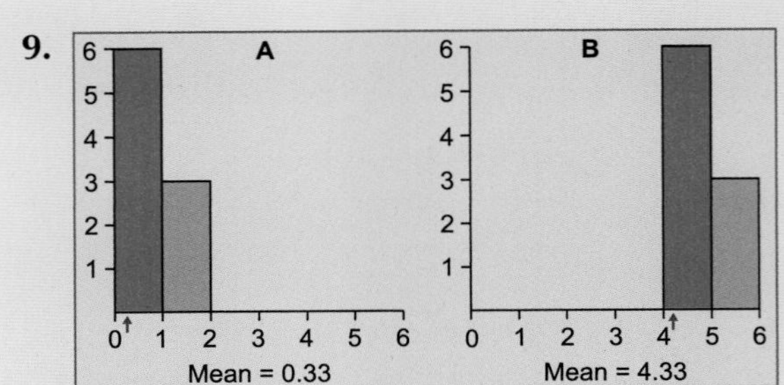

10.

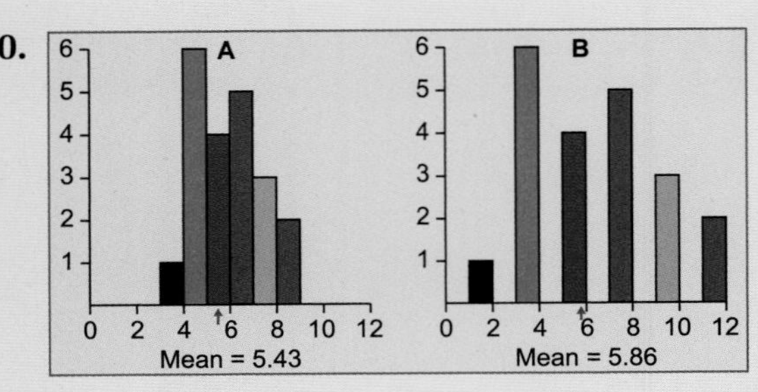

4.7 SAMPLING

Sample data must be collected in an appropriate way, such as through the process of random selection.

A **census** is the collection of data from every member of the population.

A **sample** is a subset of members selected from the population.

In a particular school, 85% of the students play sport. The figure of 85% is a **parameter**, as it is based on the entire population of the school.

A **parameter** is a numerical measurement describing some characteristic of a population.

Based on a sample of 400 First Year college students, it is found that 45% of them achieved more than 400 points in their Leaving Certificate. The figure of 45% is a **statistic** because it is based on a sample, not on the entire population of all First Year college students.

A **statistic** is a numerical measurement describing some characteristic of a sample.

When we select a sample from a population and the sample is representative of the population, then we can make inferences about the population from the sample.

The Sampling Distribution of a Statistic

The **sampling distribution** of a statistic is the distribution of all values of that statistic when all possible samples of the same size are taken from the same population.

OR

The **sampling distribution** of a sample statistic calculated from a sample of n measurements is the probability distribution of the statistic.

Worked Example 4.19

A census was carried out and the following measurements were recorded for the population:

1, 1, 2, 2, 2, 3, 3

(i) Show the distribution in a frequency table.

(ii) Is the mean of the data a parameter or a statistic? Explain.

(iii) What is the mean of the data?

(iv) How many different possible samples of size 6 can be taken from the population?

(v) List all the possible samples of size 6.

(vi) Find the mean of each sample listed in part (v).

(vii) Is the mean of each sample an example of a parameter or a statistic? Explain.

(viii) Show the sampling distribution of the sample mean in a frequency table.

(ix) Find the mean of the sampling distribution. What do you notice?

Solution

(i)

Measurement	1	2	3
Frequency	2	3	2

(ii) The mean of the data is a parameter, as it is a measurement describing a characteristic of the population.

(iii) $\mu = \frac{1(2) + 2(3) + 3(2)}{2 + 3 + 2}$

$= \frac{14}{7}$

$\therefore \mu = 2$

μ = population mean

σ = population standard deviation

(iv) $\binom{7}{6} = 7$

(v) 1, 1, 2, 2, 2, 3

1, 1, 2, 2, 2, 3

1, 1, 2, 2, 3, 3

1, 1, 2, 2, 3, 3

1, 1, 2, 2, 3, 3

1, 2, 2, 2, 3, 3

1, 2, 2, 2, 3, 3

(vi)

Sample number	Sample	Mean
1	1, 1, 2, 2, 2, 3	$1\frac{5}{6}$
2	1, 1, 2, 2, 2, 3	$1\frac{5}{6}$
3	1, 1, 2, 2, 3, 3	2
4	1, 1, 2, 2, 3, 3	2
5	1, 1, 2, 2, 3, 3	2
6	1, 2, 2, 2, 3, 3	$2\frac{1}{6}$
7	1, 2, 2, 2, 3, 3	$2\frac{1}{6}$

(vii) The mean of each sample is an example of a statistic, as it is a measurement describing a characteristic of a sample.

(viii)

Sample mean	$1\frac{5}{6}$	2	$2\frac{1}{6}$
Frequency	2	3	2

(ix) $\bar{x} = \frac{1\frac{5}{6}(2) + 2(3) + 2\frac{1}{6}(2)}{2 + 3 + 2}$

$= \frac{14}{7}$

$\therefore \bar{x} = 2$

$\bar{x}$ = sample mean

The mean of the sampling distribution is equal to the mean of the population ($\bar{x} = \mu$).

The Central Limit Theorem

When selecting a simple random sample of size n from a population with mean μ and standard deviation σ, then:

(a) If $n > 30$, the sample means for a given sample size have a distribution that can be approximated by a normal distribution with mean μ and standard deviation $\frac{\sigma}{\sqrt{n}}$. (This guideline is commonly used regardless of the distribution of the underlying population; in other words, the population measurements may or may not be normal.)

(b) If $n \leqslant 30$ and the underlying population is normal, then the sample means for a given sample size have a normal distribution with mean μ and standard deviation $\frac{\sigma}{\sqrt{n}}$.

The standard deviation of the sampling distribution of the sample means is often referred to as the standard error of the mean.

In the case of (a) and/or (b), the corresponding z-score for the sample mean is:

FORMULA
$z = \frac{\bar{x} - \mu}{\left(\frac{\sigma}{\sqrt{n}}\right)}$

Central Limit Theorem Summary

Mean: $\mu_{\bar{x}} = \mu$

Standard deviation: $\sigma_{\bar{x}} = \frac{\sigma}{\sqrt{n}}$

Formulae and Tables, pages 34–5

Worked Example 4.20

A car battery manufacturer claims that the distribution of the lengths of life of its premium battery has a mean of 54 months and a standard deviation of 6 months. A consumer magazine tests a random sample of 50 batteries to investigate the company's claim.

(i) Describe the sampling distribution of the mean lifetime of a sample of 50 batteries, assuming the company's claim is true.

(ii) What theorem have you used in answering part (a)?

(iii) Sketch the sampling distribution described in part (a).

(iv) Assuming that the company's claim is true, what is the probability that the magazine's sample has a mean life of 52 months or less?

(v) If the magazine's sample had a mean life of 52 months and you were the journalist at the magazine reporting on the company's claim, what would you conclude regarding the claim?

Solution

(i) Approximately normal with mean = 54 months and standard deviation of $\frac{6}{\sqrt{50}} \approx 0.85$ months.

(ii) The Central Limit Theorem, which states that if $n > 30$, then the sampling distribution of the sample mean (sample size n) will be approximately normal with mean μ (population mean) and standard deviation of $\frac{\sigma}{\sqrt{n}}$ (where σ is the population standard deviation).

(iii)

51.45 52.3 53.15 54 54.85 55.7 56.55

−1 +1

−2 +2

−3 +3

Number of standard errors from mean

(iv) $z = \frac{\bar{x} - \mu}{\left(\frac{\sigma}{\sqrt{n}}\right)}$

$= \frac{52 - 54}{0.85}$

≈ -2.35

$P(z \leqslant -2.35) = 1 - P(z < 2.35)$

$= 1 - 0.9906$

$= 0.0094$

$= 0.94\%$

(v) I would conclude that the investigation provides evidence that the company's claim is **not** true. If the company's claim were true, there would be a less than 1% chance of a random sample of size 50 having a sample mean of 52 or less.

OR

As $|z| > 2$, we dismiss the company's claims. A z-score of –2.35 seems to suggest that the true mean is lower than what the company is claiming.

Worked Example 4.21

In a computer simulation, random samples of size 400 are selected from a population. The mean measurement of each sample is recorded. Five thousand such sample means are recorded.

Describe the expected distribution of the sample means.

Solution

The sample means will have an approximately normal distribution. The mean of the distribution will approximate the mean of the population. The Central Limit Theorem tells us that the mean of the sampling distribution is the mean of the population.

The standard deviation of the distribution will approximate $\frac{\sigma}{\sqrt{400}}$, where σ is the standard deviation of the population.

Worked Example 4.22

A simple random sample of 400 is selected from a population having a mean height of 1.77 m and a standard deviation of 0.0775 m.

Find the probability that the sample mean $\bar{x}$ lies in the range $1.76 \text{ m} \leqslant \bar{x} \leqslant 1.78 \text{ m}$.

Solution

Since $n > 30$, the sampling distribution of the means is approximately normal, with a mean $\mu_{\bar{x}} = \mu = 1.77$ and a standard deviation of $\sigma_{\bar{x}} = \frac{\sigma}{\sqrt{n}} = \frac{0.0775}{20} = 0.003875$.

We will now convert 1.76 and 1.78 to standard z-scores using the formula $z = \frac{\bar{x} - \mu}{\left(\frac{\sigma}{\sqrt{n}}\right)}$.

$$z_1 = \frac{1.76 - 1.77}{0.003875} \approx -2.58$$

$$z_2 = \frac{1.78 - 1.77}{0.003875} \approx 2.58$$

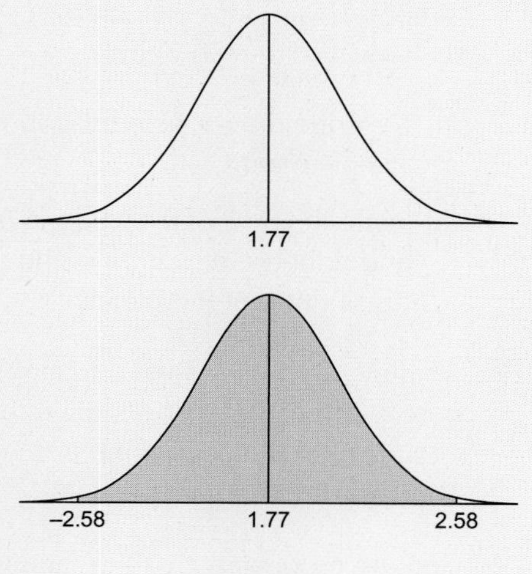

Therefore, the probability that the sample mean $\bar{x}$ lies in the range $1.76 \text{ m} \leqslant \bar{x} \leqslant 1.78 \text{ m}$ is given by:

$$P(-2.58 \leqslant z \leqslant 2.58) = 2P(z \leqslant 2.58) - 1$$
$$= 2(0.9951) - 1$$
$$= 0.9902$$

There is a probability of approximately 99.02% that the sample mean lies in the range $1.76 \text{ m} \leqslant \bar{x} \leqslant 1.78 \text{ m}$.

Worked Example 4.23

A population is normally distributed with a mean of 11 and a standard deviation of 3. Find the sample size such that $P(\bar{x} > 11.5) = 0.05$, where $\bar{x}$ is the sample mean.

Solution

$P(z > z_1) = 0.05$

$P(z \leqslant z_1) = 0.95$

$\therefore z_1 = 1.645$

$$1.645 = \frac{11.5 - 11}{\frac{3}{\sqrt{n}}}$$

$$\frac{0.5\sqrt{n}}{3} = 1.645$$

$$\sqrt{n} = 9.87$$

$$n = 97.4169$$

Sample size = 98 (Round up)

Exercise 4.8

1. Numerical data for a large population is stored on a database. The data has a mean of μ and a standard deviation of σ. A computer simulation randomly selects samples of size 400 from the database and calculates the mean of each sample. This is done repeatedly until 1,200 such means are recorded.

   (i) Describe the expected distribution of the sample means.

   (ii) Write in terms of μ and σ the mean and standard deviation of the sampling distribution of the means.

2. A simple random sample of size 49 is chosen from a population that is known to be normal. The mean of the population is 9 with a standard deviation of 2.

   Find the probability that the sample mean is greater than 10.

3. Women's heights in Ireland are normally distributed with a mean given by $\mu = 164.4$ cm and a standard deviation given by $\sigma = 6.25$ cm (Source: Jaume Garcia and Climent Quintana-Domeque, 'The evolution of adult height in Europe', *Economics and Human Biology* 5(2) (2007), pp 340–349).

   (i) If a woman is selected at random, find the probability that her height is less than 167 cm.

   (ii) A simple random sample of 25 women are selected. Find the probability that the mean height of the sample is less than 167 cm.

   (iii) Explain why you were able to use the Central Limit Theorem in part (ii), even though the sample size does not exceed 30.

4. Men's heights in Ireland are normally distributed with a mean given by $\mu = 177.5$ cm and a standard deviation given by $\sigma = 6.3$ cm (Source: Garcia and Quintana–Domeque, 'The evolution of adult height in Europe').

(i) If a man is selected at random, find the probability that his height is between 173 cm and 182 cm.

(ii) A simple random sample of 25 men is conducted. Find the probability that they have a mean height of between 173 cm and 182 cm.

5. A ski lift has a maximum capacity of 12 people or 910 kg. The capacity will be exceeded if 12 people have weights with a mean greater than $\frac{910 \text{ kg}}{12} = 75.8$ kg. As men tend to weigh more than women, a 'worst case' scenario involves 12 passengers who are all men. Men's weights are normally distributed with a mean of 78.1 kg and a standard deviation of 13.2 kg.

(i) Find the probability that if an individual man is selected at random, his weight will be greater than 75.8 kg.

(ii) Find the probability that 12 randomly selected men will have a mean weight greater than 75.8 kg.

(iii) Does the ski lift appear to have the correct weight limit?

6. The manager of a hotel finds that guests spend a mean of 12.5 minutes each day in the shower. Assume shower times are normally distributed with a standard deviation of 2.8 minutes.

(i) Find the percentage of guests who shower for more than 13 minutes.

(ii) The hotel has installed a hot water system that can provide enough hot water, provided that the mean shower time for 100 guests is less than 13 minutes. Find the probability that there will not be enough hot water on a morning that the hotel has 100 guests.

7. A normal distribution has a mean of 80 and a standard deviation of 8. A sample of size n is selected at random and the mean of the sample is $\bar{x}$.

Find n if the $P(\bar{x} > 82) = 0.1977$.

8. A sample is chosen at random from a population that is strongly skewed to the left.

(i) Describe the shape of the sampling distribution of the means if the sample size is large.

(ii) Describe the mean and standard deviation of the sampling distribution of the means in terms of the underlying population.

9. Records indicate that the value of homes in a large town is positively skewed with a mean of 150,000 and standard deviation of 65,000. To check the accuracy of the records, officials plan to conduct a survey of 100 randomly selected homes.

Draw and label an appropriate sampling model for the mean value of the homes selected.

10. The distribution of the hourly earnings of all employees in Ireland in October 2009 is shown in the diagram. It can be seen that the distribution is positively skewed.

- The mean is €22.05.
- The median is €17.82.
- The standard deviation is €10.64.
- The lower quartile is €12.80.
- The upper quartile is €26.05.

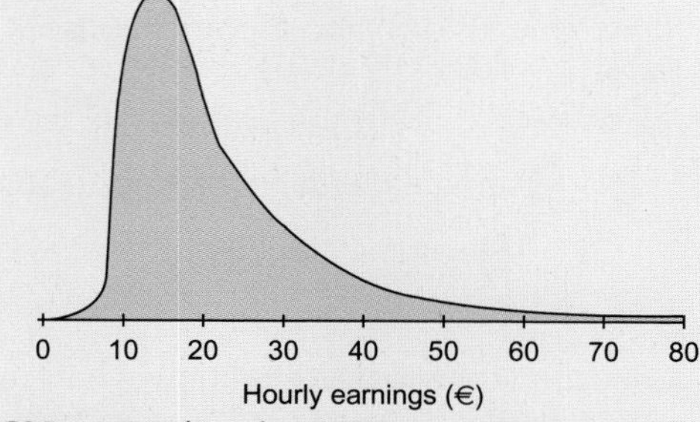

(Source: Adapted from: CSO. *National Employment Survey 2008 and 2009*)

(i) If six employees are selected at random from this population, what is the probability that exactly four of them had hourly earnings of more than €12.80?

In a computer simulation, random samples of size 200 are repeatedly selected from this population and the mean of each sample is recorded. A thousand such sample means are recorded.

(ii) Describe the expected distribution of these sample means. Your description should refer to the shape of the distribution and to its mean and standard deviation.

(iii) How many of the sample means would you expect to be greater than €23?

SEC Project Maths Sample Paper 2, Leaving Certificate Higher Level, 2012

11. Perfluoro-octanoic acid (PFOA) is a chemical used in Teflon-coated cookware. The US Environmental Protection Agency (EPA) is investigating if PFOA causes cancer. It is known that the blood concentration of PFOA in the general population has a mean of 6 ppb (parts per billion) and a standard deviation of 10 ppb. Tests for PFOA exposure were conducted on a sample of 326 people who live near DuPont's Teflon-making plant in West Virginia.

(i) What is the probability that the average blood concentration of PFOA in the sample is greater than 7.5 ppb?

(ii) What assumption did you make in answering part (i)?

(iii) If the actual study resulted in a sample mean of 7 ppb, what inference would you make about the true mean PFOA concentration for the population that lives near the DuPont Teflon facility?

12. On 1 May 1994, the triple World Champion, Ayrton Senna, was killed at the San Marino F1 Grand Prix at Imola, Italy, following a mechanical failure in his car. Later research revealed that the time x (in hours) to the first mechanical failure in an F1 Grand Prix is distributed with mean of 0.1 and standard deviation of 0.1; i.e. $x \sim (0.1, 0.01)$.

A random sample of 40 F1 Grand Prix is selected by a computer.

(i) Describe the distribution of the sample mean (sample size of 40).

(ii) Sketch this distribution.

(iii) Find the probability that the sample mean time for the first mechanical failure exceeds 0.13 hours.

(iv) A computer generates 1,500 random samples each of 40 F1 Grand Prix. How many of these 1,500 random samples would you expect to have a sample mean exceeding 0.13 hours?

(v) Describe the expected distribution of the 1,500 sample means referred to in part (iv).

4.8 MARGIN OF ERROR AND HYPOTHESIS TESTING

In this section, we begin working with **inferential statistics**, as we use sample data to make inferences (draw conclusions) about populations.

The two main applications of inferential statistics that we will study involve the use of sample data to:

(1) Estimate the value of a population proportion

(2) Test some claim (hypothesis) about a population proportion

To begin, you will need to know what statisticians mean by a **population proportion** and a **sample proportion**. Suppose you want to know the percentage of Leaving Certificate students in Ireland who will go on to third-level education next year. To find out, you decide to survey your class and use the result to infer the percentage of students for the whole country. (Not a great sample! Why?)

Suppose the survey reveals that 25 out of the 30 students in your class are going on to third-level education next year. Then $\frac{25}{30}$ or $0.8\dot{3}$ is the sample proportion. We use the symbol $\hat{p}$ to denote the sample proportion.

The population proportion is the proportion of the whole population (in this case, this year's Leaving Certificate students) who will go on to third-level education. We use p to denote the population proportion.

We can never find the exact value of p from $\hat{p}$. We can only estimate p.

Margin of Error

To understand the margin of error, we need to know about confidence intervals.

Out of 50 randomly selected students in an all girls school, 15 said they liked rock music, i.e. the sample proportion $\hat{p}$ is $\frac{15}{50} = 0.3$ The school population is 500. Using only information from the sample, can we give the exact proportion of girls in the school who like rock music? The answer is no, but we can give a range within which we can state, with a certain degree of confidence, the proportion of students who like rock music lie.

A statistician might say, 'I can say with a confidence level of 95% that the proportion of girls in this school who like rock music lies in the interval $0.1586 < p < 0.4414$.' This interval is called a **confidence interval**. How does the statistician determine the interval and what does he mean by 'a confidence level of 95%'?

First, we calculate the margin of error using the formula shown, where n is the size of the sample. There are other ways of calculating the **margin of error**, but we will use this formula on our course.

The **margin of error** is the maximum likely difference between the sample proportion, $\hat{p}$ and the population proportion, p.

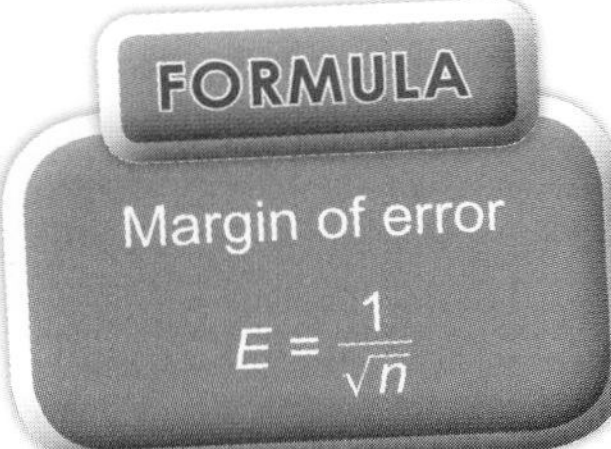
FORMULA
Margin of error
$E = \frac{1}{\sqrt{n}}$

In this example, $n = 50$, so $E = \frac{1}{\sqrt{50}} = 0.1414$.

This means that the population proportion p will differ from the sample proportion $\hat{p}$ by at most 0.1414, 95% of the time. In other words, if we were to take 100 random samples of size 50 from any population, 95 of the samples would have proportions that would differ from the population proportion by at most 0.1414. When we use this formula, our level of confidence is always 95%.

The confidence interval for the proportion is:

FORMULA
$\hat{p} - \frac{1}{\sqrt{n}} < p < \hat{p} + \frac{1}{\sqrt{n}}$

Worked Example 4.24

A company wishes to estimate the proportion, p, of its employees who went on sick leave during the past year. A random sample of 20 employees was taken. Nine of the sample went on sick leave during the past year. Construct a 95% confidence interval for p.

Solution

Step 1 Calculate the sample proportion, $\hat{p}$.

$$\hat{p} = \frac{9}{20} = 0.45$$

Step 2 Find E, the margin of error.

$$E = \frac{1}{\sqrt{20}} = 0.2236$$

Step 3 Construct the confidence interval.

$$0.45 - 0.2236 < p < 0.45 + 0.2236$$

$$0.2264 < p < 0.6736$$

The margin of error in Worked Example 4.19 is quite big, 0.2236 or 22.36%. Margins of error that are this big are of little use. However, we can quite easily reduce the margin of error, simply by increasing the size of our sample.

Worked Example 4.25

What size sample is required to have a margin of error of 0.04 or 4%?

Solution

Let n be the sample size.

$$\frac{1}{\sqrt{n}} = 0.04$$

$$\frac{1}{n} = 0.0016$$

$$0.0016n = 1$$

$$n = \frac{1}{0.0016}$$

$$n = 625$$

Hypothesis Testing

Hypothesis testing is an important aspect of statistics.

A **hypothesis** is a claim or statement about a property of a population.

A **hypothesis test** is a procedure for testing a claim about a population.

The following statement is an example of an hypothesis about a population: '65% of all heavy smokers will contract a serious lung or heart ailment before the age of 60.' To accept or reject this statement, you must collect a random sample of medical records of heavy smokers under the age of 60 and find the proportion of the sample who have contracted serious heart or lung ailments. Then you must set up a hypothesis test to prove or disprove the claim. In our course, we will only test claims about a population proportion.

Procedure for hypothesis testing for a population proportion

Step 1 State clearly the **null hypothesis**, H_0, and the alternative hypothesis, H_1.

H_0, the **null hypothesis**, is a statement which defines the population.

For example, '65% of all heavy smokers will contact a serious lung or heart ailment before the age of 60.' Usually you are hoping to show that the null hypothesis is **not** true and so the alternative hypothesis, H_1, is often the hypothesis you want to establish. In the example just given, the alternative hypothesis, H_1, is that '65% of all heavy smokers will **not** contract a serious lung or heart ailment before the age of 60.'

Step 2 Calculate $\hat{p}$, the sample proportion.

Step 3 Set up a confidence interval for p, the population proportion.

- If the proportion for the population stated in the null hypothesis is within the confidence interval, then accept H_0, the null hypothesis.
- If the population proportion is outside the confidence interval, then reject the null hypothesis and accept H_1.

Worked Example 4.26

Irish Express Newspapers surveyed 800 randomly selected voters to find out whether or not they would vote for the government parties in the next election. Of the sample, 40% indicated that they would vote for the government in the next election. A month later, a rival newspaper surveyed 900 voters and 315 said they would support the government. Had support for the government changed during this month?

Solution

Step 1 H_0 – Government support has remained unchanged.

H_1 – Government support has changed.

Step 2 Calculate confidence intervals for both samples.

Sample proportion $\hat{p}_1 = \frac{315}{900} = 0.35$

Step 3 Margin of error $E_1 = \frac{1}{\sqrt{900}} \approx 0.03$

Step 4 Confidence interval (1) $= 0.32 < p_1 < 0.38$

Sample proportion $\hat{p}_2 = 0.4$

Margin of error $E_2 = \frac{1}{\sqrt{800}} = 0.04$

Confidence interval (2) $= 0.36 < p_2 < 0.44$

As there is an overlap between Confidence Interval (1) and Confidence Interval (2), we fail to reject the null hypothesis and accept that support for the government has not changed.

Worked Example 4.27

A local newspaper is investigating a claim made by the CEO of a large multinational company. The CEO claimed that 80% of the company's 500,000 customers are satisfied with the service they receive. Using simple random sampling, the newspaper surveyed 200 customers. Among the sampled customers, 146 said they were satisfied with the company's service. Based on these findings, can we reject the CEO's claim that 80% of customers are satisfied with the company's service?

Solution

Step 1 H_0 – The company's satisfaction rating is 80%.

H_1 – The company's satisfaction rating is **not** 80%.

Step 2 Sample proportion $\hat{p} = \frac{146}{200} = 0.73$ or 73%.

Step 3 Margin of error $E = \frac{1}{\sqrt{200}} \approx 0.071$.

Step 4 CI for the population proportion is $0.73 - 0.071 < p < 0.73 + .071$.

CI: $0.659 < p < 0.801$

The population proportion is within the confidence interval. Therefore, we accept the null hypothesis that the satisfaction rating is 80%, and hence, we are not rejecting the CEO's claim.

Exercise 4.9

1. A manufacturer of computer components wishes to estimate the proportion, p, of its present stock of components that are defective. A random sample of 500 components is selected, and 10 are found to be defective.

   Construct a 95% confidence interval for p, the proportion of all components that are defective.

STATISTICS II

2. A bank randomly selected 120 customers with savings accounts and found that 90 of them also had cheque accounts.

   Construct a 95% confidence interval for the true proportion of savings-account customers who also have cheque accounts.

3. In a survey of 1,000 people, 740 said that they voted in a recent general election. Voting records show that 71% of eligible voters actually did vote.

   (i) Find a 95% confidence interval estimate of the proportion of people who say they voted.

   (ii) Are the survey results consistent with the actual voter turnout? Explain.

4. In a recent poll, 1,000 randomly selected adults were surveyed and 27% of them said that they use the Internet for shopping at least once a year. Construct a 95% confidence interval for the true proportion of adults who shop on the Internet.

5. A company wishes to estimate the proportion of its employees who would accept an extra week of holidays instead of the annual rise in salary.

   If the maximum margin of error the company will accept for the proportion is 4%, then find the necessary sample size at the 95% level.

6. In a study of 10,000 car crashes, it was found that 5,550 of them occurred within 10 kilometres of the driver's home. Test the hypothesis that 50% of car crashes occur within 10 kilometres of home.

7. A coin is tossed 100 times and heads occur 57 times. Test the hypothesis that the coin is biased.

8. A six sided die is thrown 180 times and a 6 occurs 40 times. Can we conclude that the die is biased?

9. A pharmaceutical company is replacing one of its pain-killing drugs with another drug that the company has developed and tested. The company's records show that the old drug provided relief for 70% of all patients who were administered it. A random sample of 625 patients were administered the new drug, and 450 of these claimed that the new drug provided relief.

   Test the hypothesis that the new drug is different to its old counterpart.

10. The World Health Organisation percentile chart below gives the heights or lengths of baby girls aged between zero and two years.

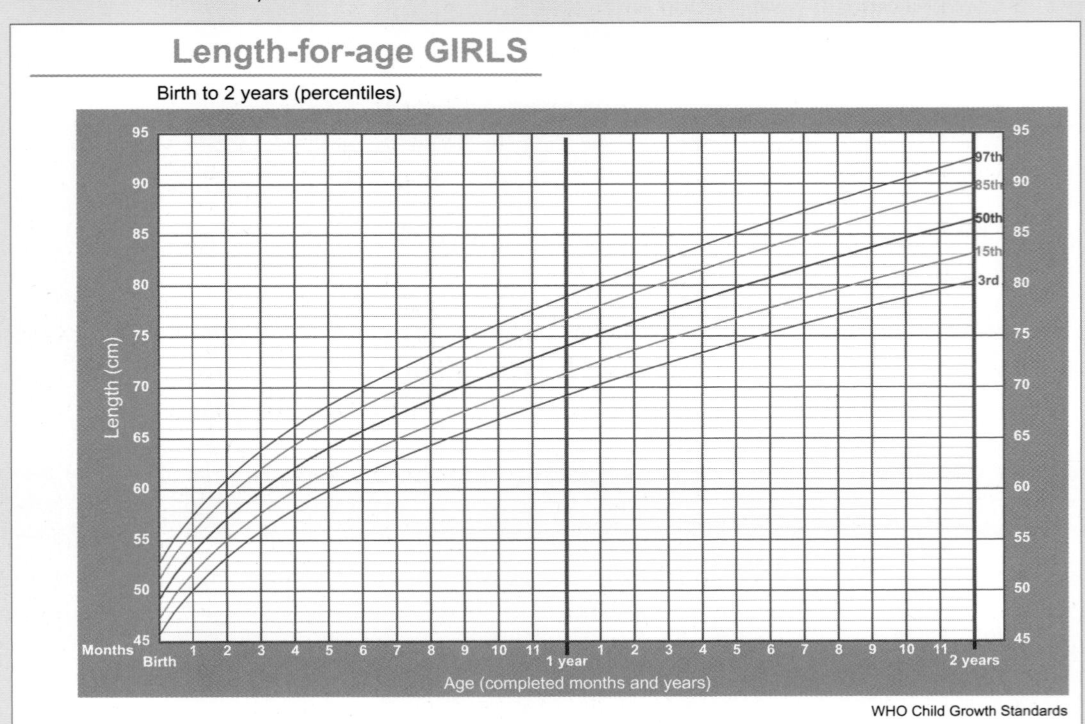

(i) Copy and complete the following table:

Age (months)	0	1	2	3	4	5	6	7	8	9
Median height (cm)										

(ii) If a baby girl aged two months has a height of 57 cm, what percentage of baby girls of the same age are taller than her?

(iii) A baby girl aged one year has a height of 80 cm. Is this height unusual? Explain your reasoning.

(iv) Calculate the range of heights between the 3rd and 97th percentiles for a baby girl aged 11 months.

(v) Give one similarity and one difference between a length-for-age girls percentile chart and a length-for-age boys percentile chart.

Revision Exercises

1. The data gives the survival time of patients suffering from chronic granulocytic leukaemia, measured in days from the time of diagnosis.

7	47	58	74	177	232	273	285	317
429	440	445	455	468	495	497	532	571
579	581	650	702	715	779	881	900	930
968	1077	1109	1,314	1,334	1,367	1,534	1,712	1,784
1,877	1,886	2,045	2,056	2,260	2,429	2,509		

The following histogram shows the distribution:

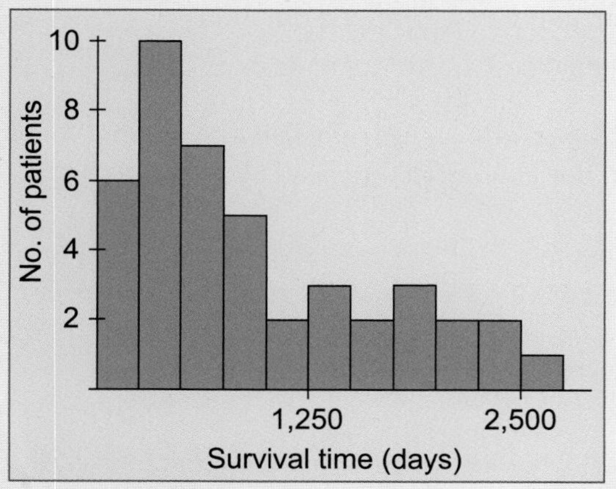

(i) Using the information above, construct a frequency distribution.

(ii) Calculate the mean survival time for the sample.

(iii) Describe the shape of the distribution.

(iv) Explain the shape of the distribution in the context of the question.

(v) Do you think the mean calculated in part (ii) is a good measure of centre? Explain.

(vi) Do you think that a doctor should give a patient the median or mean as the average survival time for patients with granulocytic leukaemia? Explain.

(vii) This data was collected in 1969. If a similar sample were taken today, do you think the distribution would be different? If so, which summary statistics (minimum, maximum, mean, standard deviation, median, IQR) would be different?

STATISTICS II

2. The following are the prices in euro of 30 different wooden toys in a rural craft shop.

8.20	4.50	11.36	5.45	5.12	4.99	8.75	5.39	15.40	15.60
6.00	9.12	8.69	7.90	4.90	13.80	6.15	1.99	5.85	5.74
10.30	6.00	9.80	6.60	5.35	1.70	7.00	10.00	6.85	16.20

(i) Using suitable intervals, construct a frequency distribution (have six intervals).

(ii) Display the distribution on a histogram.

(iii) Comment on the shape of the distribution.

(iv) Calculate an appropriate measure of centre.

(v) Calculate an appropriate measure of spread.

(vi) The proprietor of the craft shop decides to add €2 to the price of all toys in the shop. How will this affect the summary statistics (minimum, maximum, mean, standard deviation, median, IQR)?

3. The following are cholesterol readings (mg/dl) for a randomly selected group of 36 adults.

522	127	740	49	230	316	590	466	121	578	78	265
250	265	273	272	972	75	138	139	638	613	762	303
690	31	189	957	339	416	120	702	1252	288	176	277

(i) Display the distribution on an appropriate graph.

(ii) Describe the distribution.

(iii) Calculate the 85th percentile.

(iv) Calculate the 15th percentile.

(v) Interpret the meaning of the numbers calculated, in the context of the question.

(vi) Calculate the difference between the 90th percentile and the 10th percentile.

4. Chinese woman Yao Defin claims to be the world's tallest woman with a height of 233 cm. Women have heights with a mean of 159 cm and a standard deviation from the mean of 6.25 cm.

(i) What is the difference between Yao Defin's height and the mean?

(ii) How many standard deviations is the difference from the mean?

(iii) Convert Defin's height to a *z*-score.

(iv) In statistical terms, is Defin's height usual or unusual? Explain.

5. In each of the following, the mean $\bar{x}$ and standard deviation σ of the normal distributions is given. For each distribution, find the range within which 68%, 95% and 99.7% of the distribution lie.

(i) $\bar{x} = 200, \sigma = 25$

(ii) $\bar{x} = 100, \sigma = 20$

(iii) $\bar{x} = 20, \sigma = 2$

(iv) $\bar{x} = 25, \sigma = 2.5$

6. 'Dowsing' is a type of divination employed in attempts to locate groundwater, buried metals or ores, gemstones, oil, grave sites, etc. A person who practices dowsing is known as a dowser. Dowsers claim that the forked stick they carry vibrates when something of interest, such as groundwater, is located directly below.

In a rural area, about 30% of the wells drilled find adequate water at a depth of 35 m or less. A local dowser claims that he is able to find water with a forked stick. A survey of 80 randomly selected customers of his reveals that 27 have wells less than 35 m in depth.

Test the hypothesis that the dowser has a different success rate to the water drillers.

7. (a) For each of the four scatter plots below, estimate the correlation co-efficient.

(i)

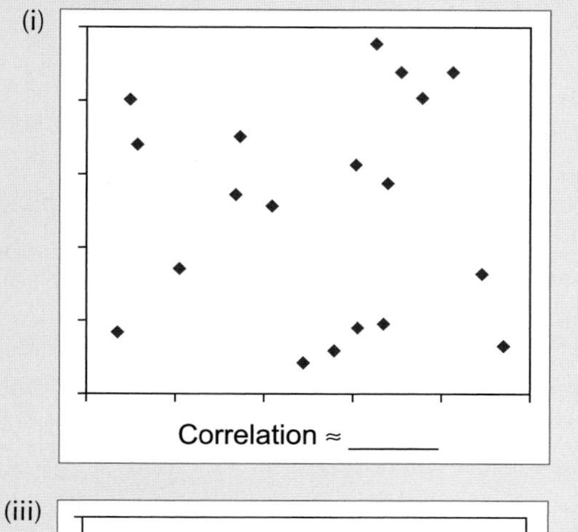

Correlation ≈ ______

(ii)

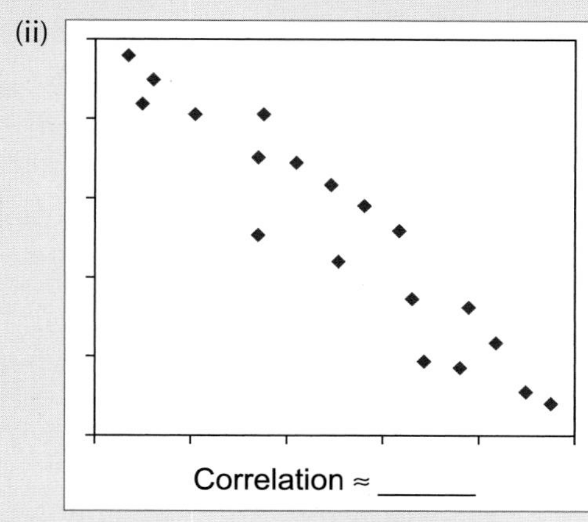

Correlation ≈ ______

(iii)

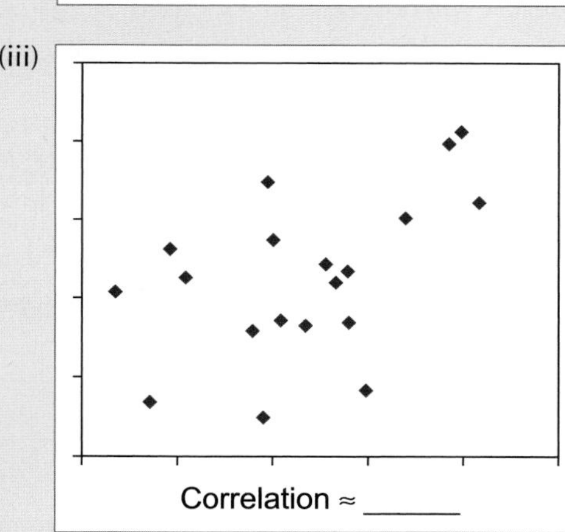

Correlation ≈ ______

(iv)

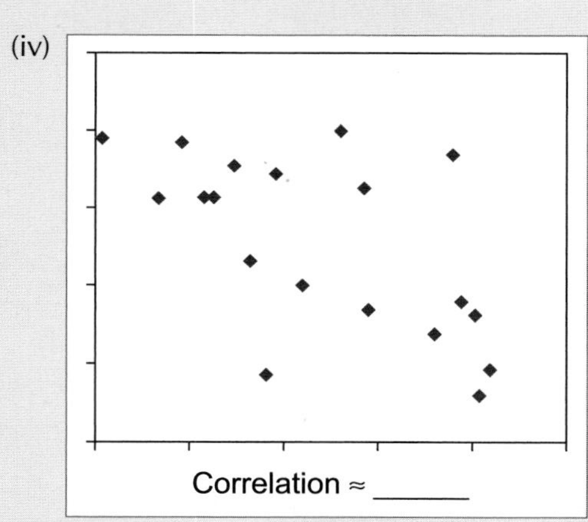

Correlation ≈ ______

(b) Using your calculator, or otherwise, find the correlation co-efficient for the data given in the table. Give your answer correct to two decimal places.

x	y
0.0	0.5
5.0	1.3
5.2	3.3
6.1	6.7
9.3	4.5
9.5	4.6
9.9	6.5

NCCA Pre-Leaving Certificate Project Maths Paper 2, February 2010

8. Some research was carried out into the participation of girls and boys in sport. The researchers selected a simple random sample of 50 male and 50 female teenagers enrolled in GAA clubs in the greater Cork area. They asked the teenagers the question: How many sports do you play?

The data collected were as follows:

Boys	Girls
0, 4, 5, 1, 4, 1, 3, 3, 3, 1,	3, 3, 3, 1, 1, 3, 3, 1, 3, 3,
1, 2, 2, 2, 5, 3, 3, 4, 1, 2,	2, 2, 4, 4, 4, 5, 5, 2, 2, 3,
2, 2, 2, 3, 3, 3, 4, 5, 1, 1,	3, 3, 4, 1, 6, 2, 3, 3, 3, 4,
1, 1, 1, 2, 2, 2, 2, 2, 3, 3,	4, 5, 3, 4, 3, 3, 3, 4, 4, 3,
3, 3, 3, 3, 3, 3, 3, 3, 3, 3	1, 1, 3, 2, 1, 3, 1, 3, 1, 3

(a) Display the data in a way that gives a picture of each distribution.

(b) State **one difference** and **one similarity** between the distributions of the two samples.

(c) Do you think that there is evidence that there are differences between the two populations? Explain your answer.

(Note: you are not required to conduct a formal hypothesis test.)

(d) The researchers are planning to repeat this research on a larger scale. List **two** improvements they could make to the design of the research in order to reduce the possibility of bias in the samples. Explain why each improvement you suggest will reduce the likelihood of bias.

NCCA Pre-Leaving Certificate Project Maths Paper 2, February 2010

9. The shapes of the histograms of four different sets of data are shown below.

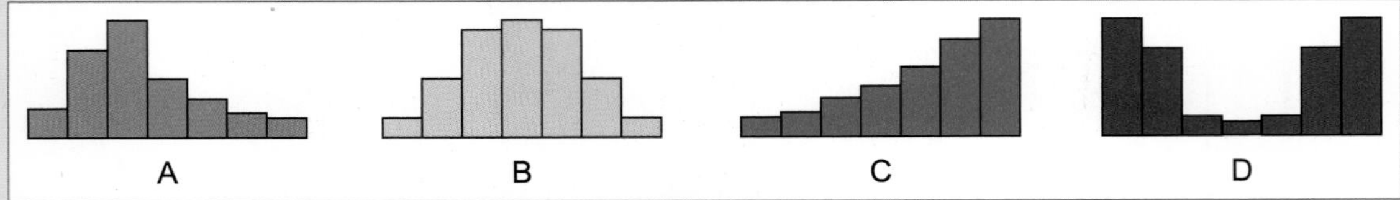

(a) Complete the table below, indicating whether the statement is correct (✓) or incorrect (×) with respect to each data set.

	A	B	C	D
The data are skewed to the left.				
The data are skewed to the right.				
The mean is equal to the median.				
The mean is greater than the median.				
There is a single mode.				

(b) Assume that the four histograms are drawn on the same scale. State which of them has the largest standard deviation, and justify your answer.

Leaving Certificate Project Maths Sample Paper 2, 2010

10. Below is a table of the world's largest companies for 2009.

Company name	Country	Industry	Market capitalisation (approx.)	% Change on a year earlier
PetroChina	China	Petroleum	$390 billion	–46.8
Exxon Mobil	US	Petroleum	$345 billion	–30.9
Industrial & Commercial Bank of China	China	Banking	$250 billion	–26.4
China Mobile	China (HK)	Telecoms	$210 billion	–39.9
Microsoft	US	Software	$205 billion	–15.9
Wal-Mart Stores	US	Retail	$198 billion	–4.6
China Construction Bank	China	Banking	$195 billion	–5.6
Johnston & Johnston	US	FMCG, Medical	$172 billion	–11.9
Proctor & Gamble	US	FMCG	$170 billion	–11.3
Royal Dutch Shell	UK & Netherlands	Petroleum	$169 billion	–38.6
HSBC	UK	Banking	$168 billion	–17.8
Petrobras	Brazil	Petroleum	$166 billion	–33.3

Bjorn Borgisky, EconomyWatch.com

(a) Market capitalisation is the current value of a company's shares. Economists often use this value to determine the size of a company. Choose an appropriate graph or chart to display this information.

(b) Calculate an appropriate measure of centre for the market capitalisation values.

(c) What measure of spread should be used for the data? Calculate this value.

(d) Are there any outliers in the data?

(e) Use a suitable graph to display the change in the value of each of the companies from the previous year.

(f) Copy and complete the following table of summary statistics:

Summary statistics	2008	Summary statistics	2009
Count		Count	
Maximum		Maximum	
Minimum		Minimum	
Range		Range	
Mean		Mean	
Median		Median	
Standard deviation		Standard deviation	
Lower quartile		Lower quartile	
Upper quartile		Upper quartile	
IQR		IQR	

(g) How has the world recession affected the summary statistics?

11. An aircraft strobe light is designed so that the time between flashes is normally distributed, with a mean of 3 seconds and a standard deviation of 0.4 seconds.

(a) Find the probability that an individual time is greater than 4 seconds.

(b) Find the probability that the mean for 60 randomly selected times is greater than 3.10 seconds.

12. According to a National Business Travel Association 2008 survey, the average salary of a travel management professional is \$97,300. Assume that the standard deviation of such salaries is \$30,000. Consider a random sample of 50 travel management professionals.

(a) What is the mean of the sampling distribution of the sample mean with sample size 50?

(b) What is the standard deviation of the same sampling distribution?

(c) Describe the shape of this sampling distribution.

(d) Sketch this sampling distribution.

(e) Find the z-score for a value of \$89,500 for the sample mean.

(f) What is the probability that a random sample of size 50 will have a sample mean of less than \$89,500?

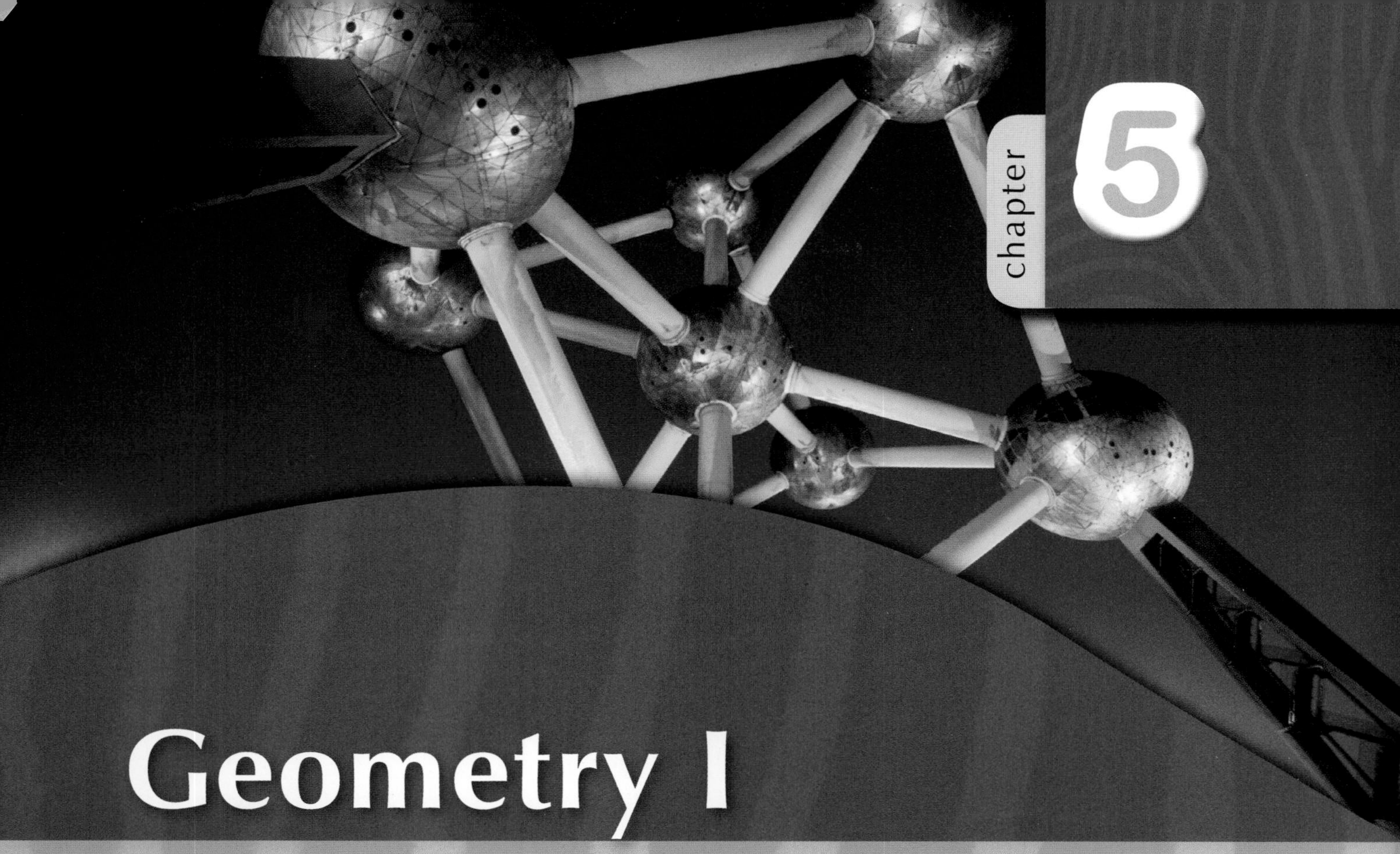

Geometry I

Learning Outcomes

In this chapter you will learn:

- The basic concepts of geometry and geometry notation
- What an axiom is and use axioms to solve problems
- The following terms: *axiom, theorem, proof, corollary, converse* and *implies*
- Theorem 1. Vertically opposite angles are equal in measure.
- Theorem 2. In an isosceles triangle the angles opposite the equal sides are equal. Conversely, if two angles are equal, then the triangle is isosceles.
- Theorem 3. If a transversal makes equal alternate angles on two lines then the lines are parallel (and converse).
- Theorem 4. The angles in any triangle add to 180°.
- Theorem 5. Two lines are parallel if, and only if, for any transversal, the corresponding angles are equal.
- Theorem 6. Each exterior angle of a triangle is equal to the sum of the interior opposite angles.
- Axiom 4. Congruent triangles (SSS, SAS, ASA and RHS)
- Theorem 7. In a triangle, the angle opposite the greater of two sides is greater than the angle opposite the lesser side. Conversely, the side opposite the greater of two angles is greater than the side opposite the lesser angle.
- Theorem 8. Two sides of a triangle are together greater than the third.
- Theorem 9. In a parallelogram, opposite sides are equal and opposite angles are equal.
- Corollary 1. A diagonal divides a parallelogram into two congruent triangles.
- Theorem 10. The diagonals of a parallelogram bisect each other.
- Theorem 11. If three parallel lines cut off equal segments on some transversal line, then they will cut off equal segments on any other transversal.
- Theorem 12. Let ABC be a triangle. If a line l is parallel to BC and cuts $[AB]$ in the ratio $m : n$, then it also cuts $[AC]$ in the same ratio.

5.1 GEOMETRY

When we study figures and their properties in two- or three-dimensional space, we are studying geometry. We encounter geometrical shapes everywhere in our daily lives – in buildings, in works of art and in countless other objects.

Geometry comes from the Greek word meaning 'earth measurement' (*γεωμετρία*; *geo* = earth, *metria* = measure). Many of the theorems and proofs that we use today were first recorded by Euclid of Alexandria, a Greek mathematician. His book *The Elements*, written about 300 BCE, is one of the most famous mathematics textbooks ever written and is still in use more than 2,000 years later!

We encounter geometry in many aspects of everyday life, and a knowledge of geometry is essential in many careers. Carpenters, engineers and architects, to name but a few, must have a knowledge of geometry to do their jobs.

YOU SHOULD REMEMBER...

- Geometry notation
- Types of angles
- Types of triangles
- Parallel
- Perpendicular
- Junior Certificate geometry theorems

KEY WORDS

- **Axiom**
- **Theorem**
- **Corollary**
- **Converse**
- **Vertically opposite**
- **Alternate**
- **Corresponding**
- **Isosceles triangle**
- **Interior angle**
- **Exterior angle**
- **Congruent**
- **SSS, SAS, ASA, RHS**
- **Quadrilateral**
- **Parallelogram**

5.2 BASIC CONCEPTS

The Plane

A **plane** is a flat two-dimensional surface. It has length and width, but it has no thickness.

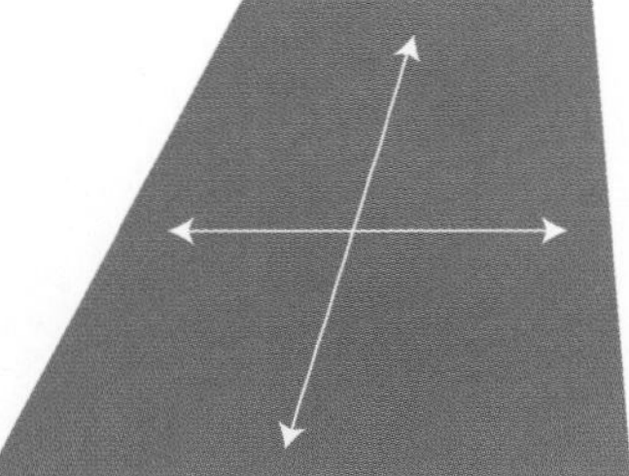

A plane stretches on to infinity. Points and lines are shown on a plane.

Points on the Plane

A **point** is a position on a plane. It has no dimensions.

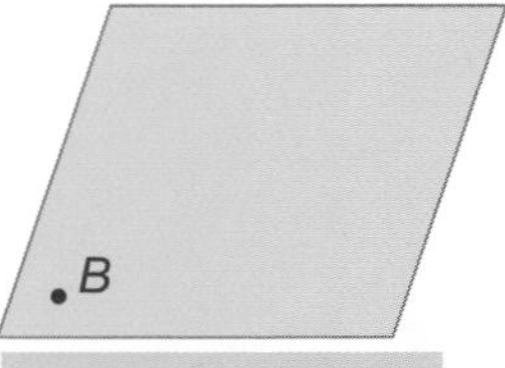

This is the point *B*.

A point is denoted by a capital letter and a dot.

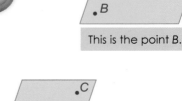

If points lie on the same plane they are said to be **coplanar**.

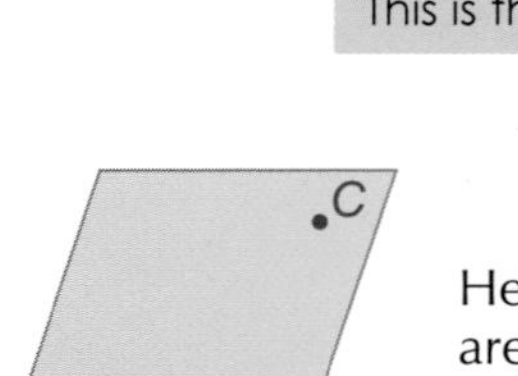

Here, *B* and *C* are coplanar.

Lines

A line can be named by any two points on the line or by a lower-case letter. It has an infinite number of points on it.

A **line** is a straight, infinitely thin 'line' that continues forever in both directions; it has no endpoints.

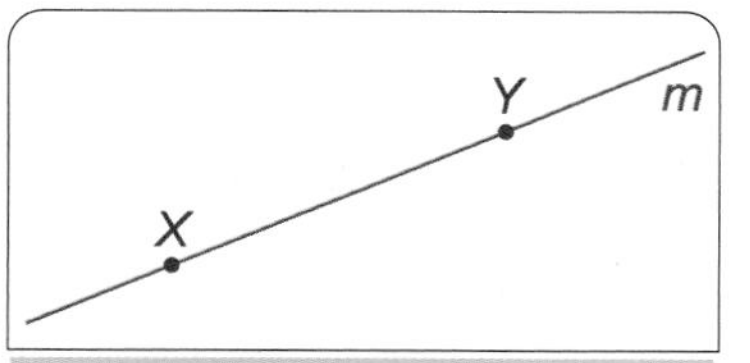

The line XY or the line m.

Points that lie on the same line are called **collinear points.**

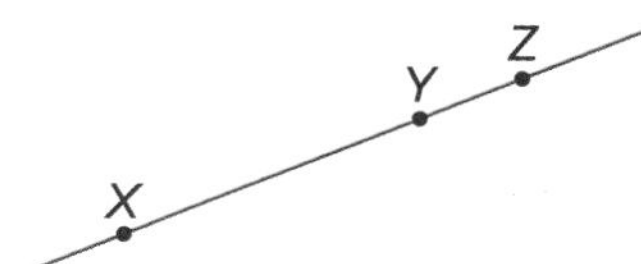

The points X, Y and Z are collinear.

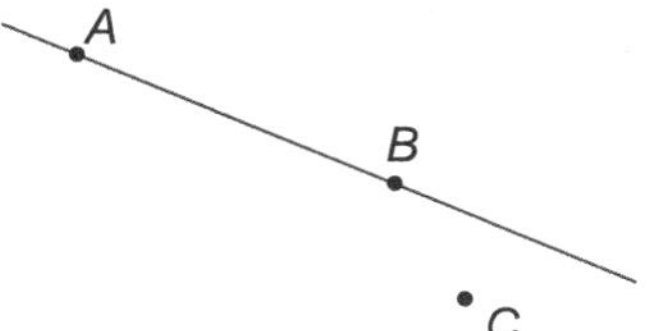

The points A, B and C are not collinear.

Perpendicular and Parallel Lines

The line a is perpendicular to the line b.

We denote this as $a \perp b$.

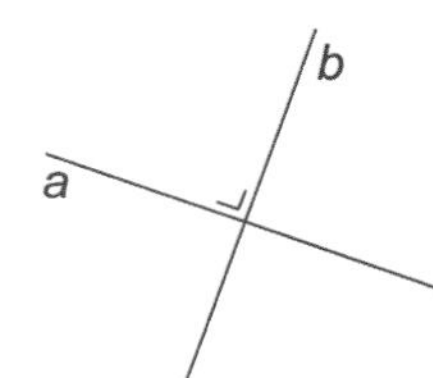

Perpendicular lines are lines which are at right angles or 90° to each other.

The line d is parallel to the line e.

We denote this as $d \parallel e$.

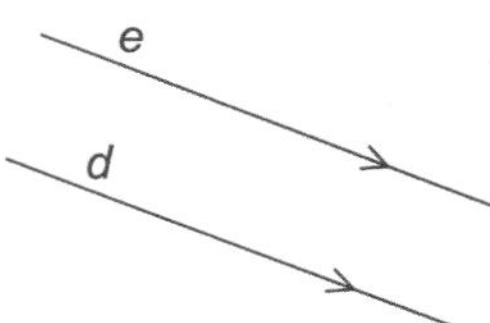

Parallel lines are lines which are the same distance apart. They never meet.

Line Segment

The line segment shown has one endpoint A and another endpoint B. This is the line segment $[AB]$ or $[BA]$.

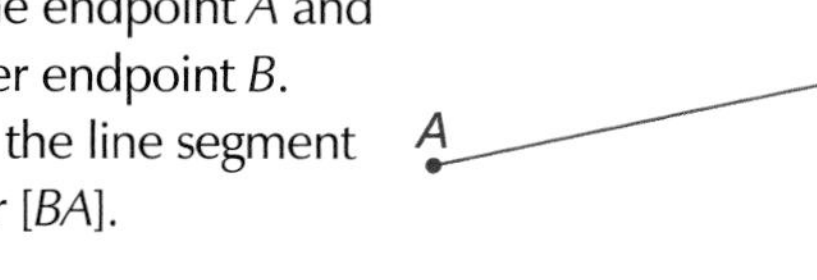

A **line segment** is part of a straight line. It has two endpoints and can be measured using a ruler.

We can use a ruler to measure a line segment.

When we write an actual measurement, we use the | | symbols to show this.

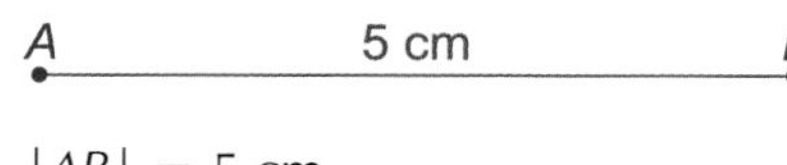

$|AB| = 5$ cm.

Ray

A **ray** is part of a line that originates at a point and goes on forever in only one direction.

This is the ray $[AB$.

The other end goes on to infinity. It is sometimes called a half-line.

A single square bracket is used to denote where the ray originates from.

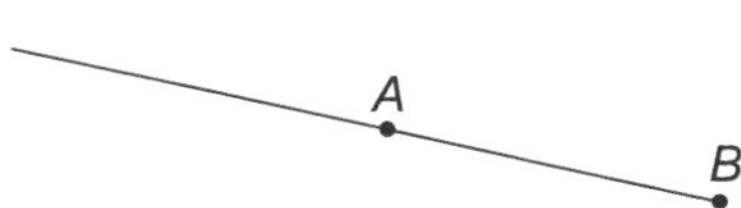

This is the ray $[BA$.

5.3 ANGLES

When two rays meet at a point called the **vertex**, they make an **angle**.

Angle Notation

There are many different ways to label an angle:

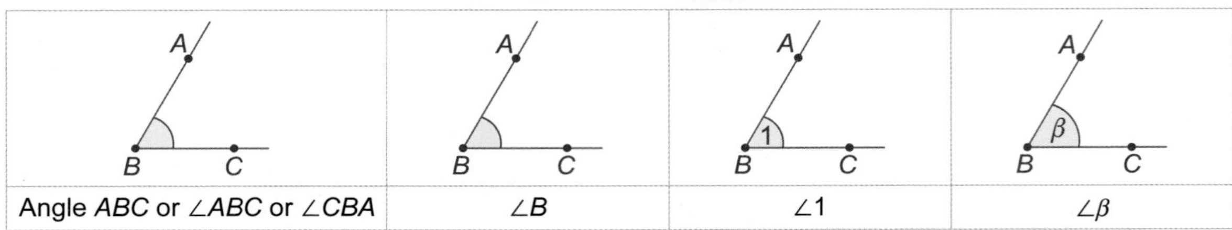

Identify Different Types of Angles

Angles can be divided into many different types.

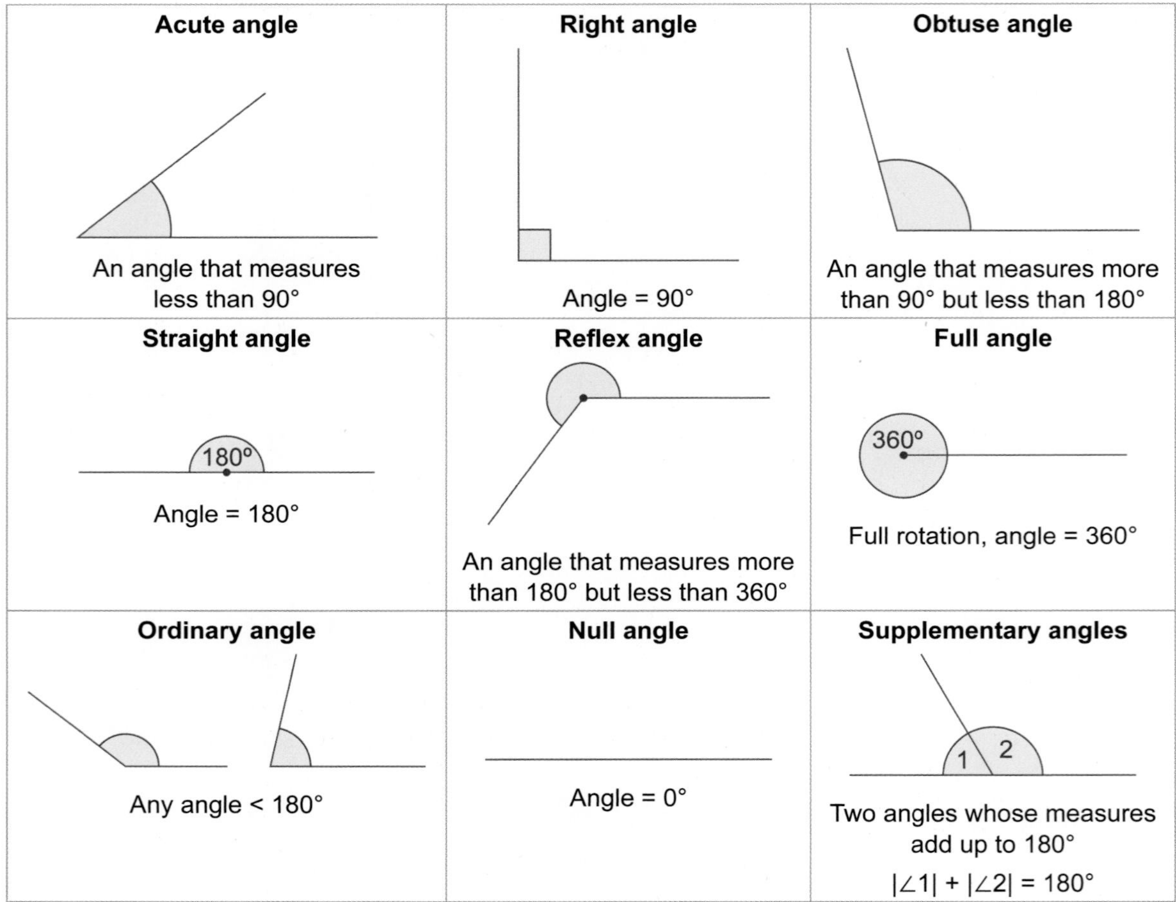

Acute angle
An angle that measures less than 90°
Right angle
Angle = 90°
Obtuse angle
An angle that measures more than 90° but less than 180°
Straight angle
180°
Angle = 180°
Reflex angle
An angle that measures more than 180° but less than 360°
Full angle
360°
Full rotation, angle = 360°
Ordinary angle
Any angle < 180°
Null angle
Angle = 0°
Supplementary angles
1
2
Two angles whose measures add up to 180°
|∠1| + |∠2| = 180°

Supplementary angles do not need to be beside or adjacent to each other.

For example, the two angles shown are supplementary.

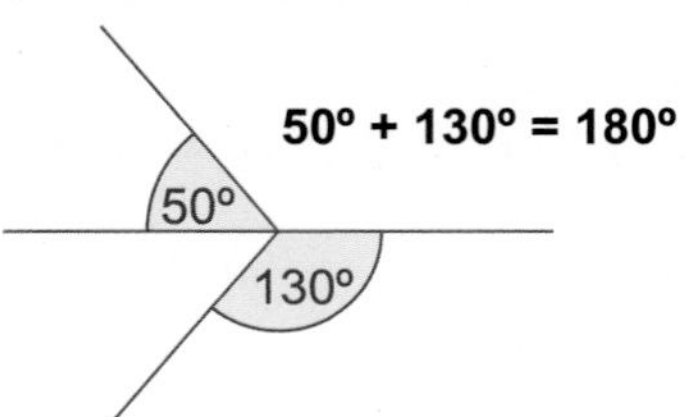

Measuring Angles

Angles on our course are usually measured in degrees or radians.

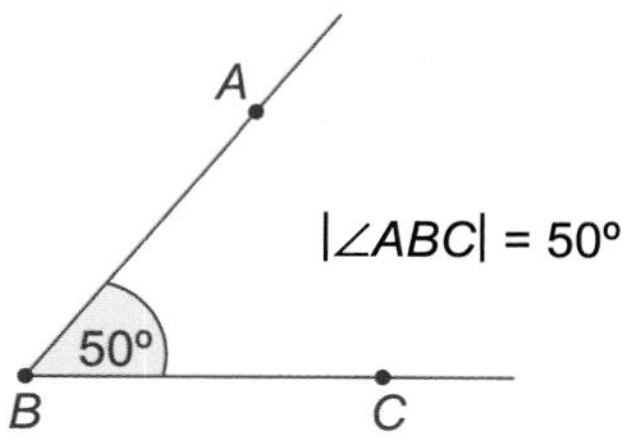

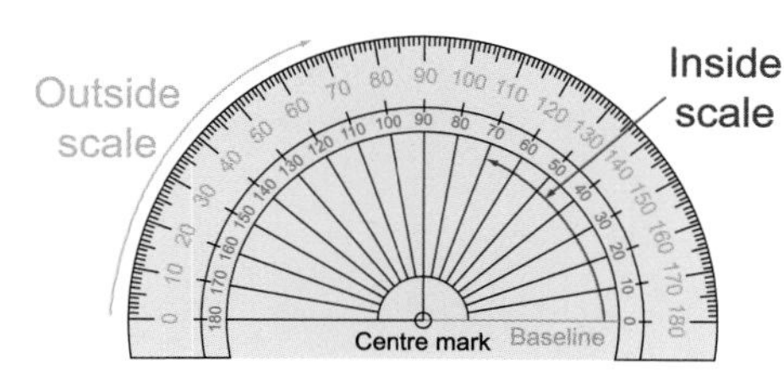

We use a protractor to measure angles accurately.
A protractor has two scales, a centre point and a baseline.

5.4 AXIOMS

An axiom is a statement which we accept **without any proof**. Knowing axioms is essential to understanding geometry and proving geometry theorems.

Axiom 1 (Two Points Axiom)

There is exactly one line through any two given points.

We can draw only one line through the points A and B.

Axiom 2 (Ruler Axiom)

The properties of the distance between points.

1. Distance is never a negative number.
2. $|AB| = |BA|$.
3. If C lies on AB, between A and B, then $|AB| = |AC| + |CB|$.

4. Given any ray from the point X and a distance $d \geqslant 0$, there is exactly one point Y on the ray whose distance from X is d. This property means that we can mark off a distance of, say, 4 cm on a ray from a point X and call this point Y.
   The length of the line segment $[XY]$ will also be 4 cm.

X 4 cm Y

Axiom 3 (Protractor Axiom)

The properties of the degree measure of an angle.

The number of degrees in an angle is always a number between 0 and 360. This axiom has the following properties:

1. A straight angle has 180°.

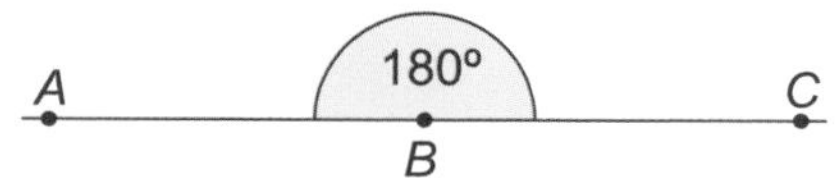

All the angles at a point add up to 360°.

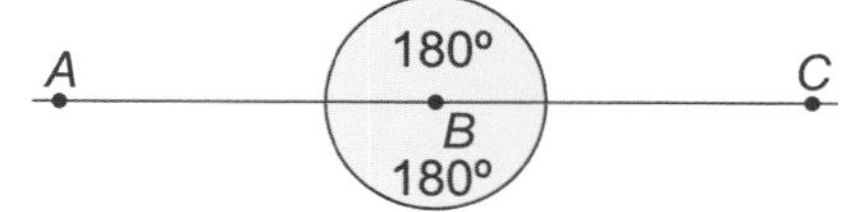

2. Given a ray [*AB* and a number between 0 and 180, there is exactly one ray from *A*, on each side of the line *AB*, that makes an (ordinary) angle having *d* degrees with the ray [*AB*.

   This property of the protractor axiom means that there is, for example, only one 60° angle on each side of the line *AB*.

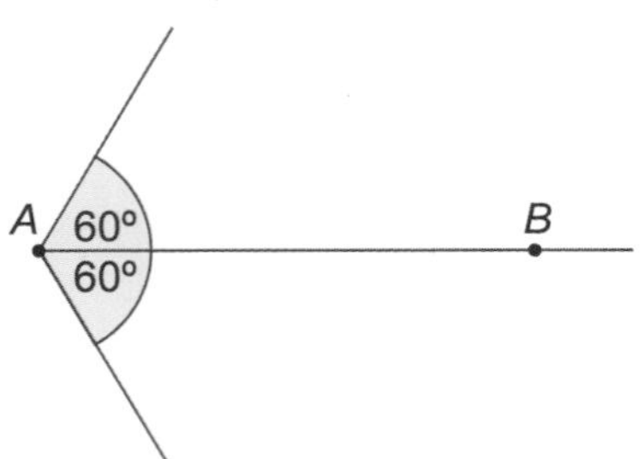

3. If an angle is divided into two smaller angles, then these two angles add up to the original angle.

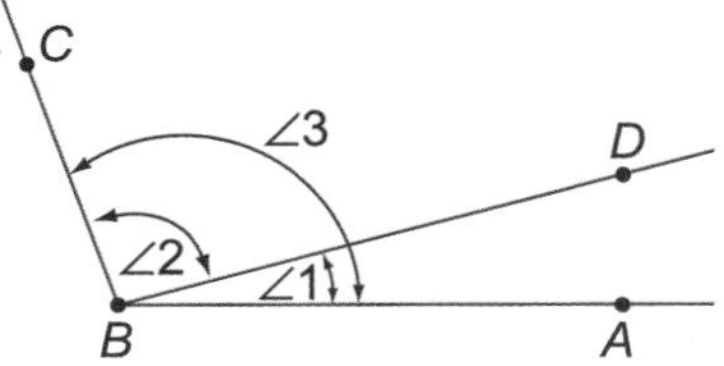

$|\angle 1| + |\angle 2| = |\angle 3|$

Axiom 5 (Axiom of Parallels)

Given any line *l* and a point *P*, there is exactly one line through *P* that is parallel to *l*.

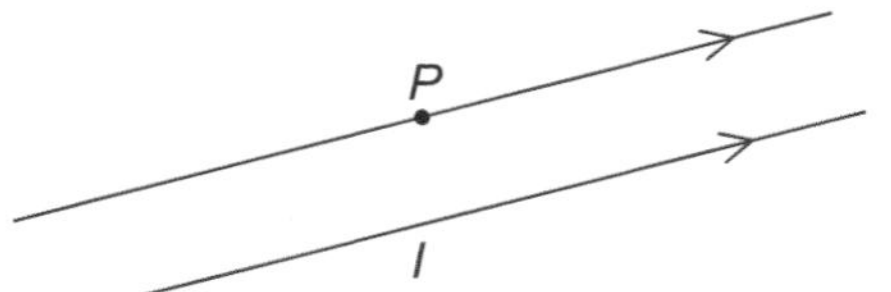

Only one line can be drawn through the point *P* that is parallel to the line *l*.

5.5 BASIC THEOREM TERMS

When dealing with theorems, there are some terms that we need to understand.

A **theorem** is a rule that has been proved by following a certain number of logical steps or by using a previous theorem or axiom that you already know.

For example:

Theorem 17

A diagonal of a parallelogram bisects the area.

An **axiom** is a rule or statement that we accept without any proof.

For example:

Axiom 1 (Two Points Axiom)

There is exactly one line through any two given points.

A **corollary** is a statement that follows readily from a previous theorem.

For example:

Corollary 3

Each angle in a semicircle is a right angle.

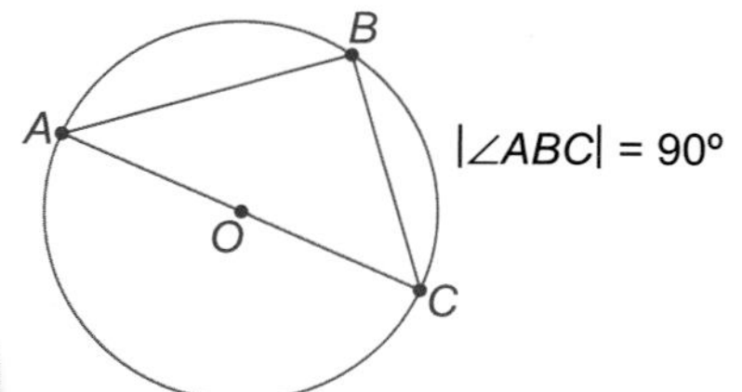

The **converse** of a theorem is the reverse of the theorem.

A theorem is a mathematical statement that can be proved.

Statement: In an isosceles triangle the angles opposite the equal sides are equal.

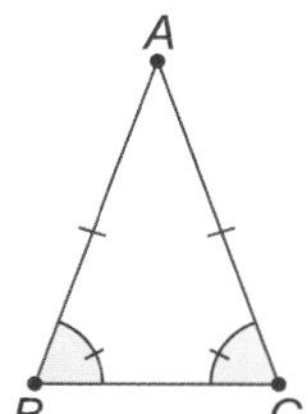

The converse of a theorem is made by switching the statement around.

Converse: If two angles are equal in a triangle, then the triangle is isosceles.

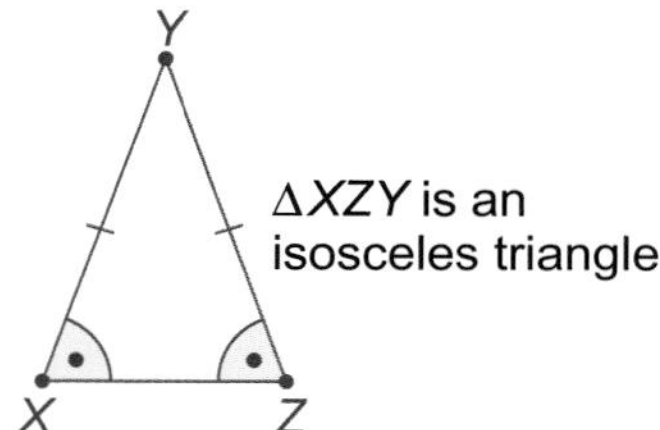

A converse of a statement may not be true.

Example: **Statement** – In a square, opposite sides are equal in length (True).

Converse – If opposite sides are equal in length, then it is a square (False).

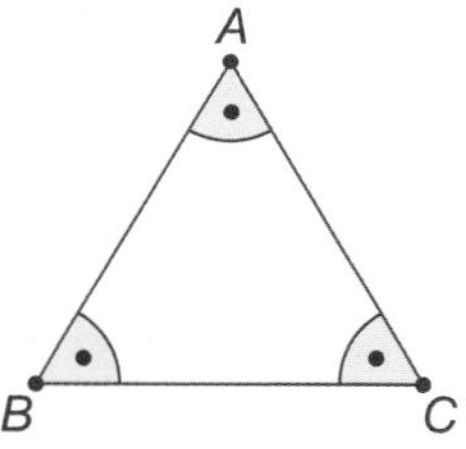

Implies is a term we use in a proof when we can write down a fact we have proved from our previous statements. The symbol for implies is ⇒.

The angles of a triangle ABC are all equal.

⇒ Triangle ABC is an equilateral triangle.

Proofs

When asked for a proof, we may use the following series of steps:

A **proof** is a series of logical steps which we use to prove a theorem.

Theorem: If asked to prove a certain theorem, write down its title.

Given: Write down the information that has been given in the question. Also draw any diagrams that have been used in the question.

To prove: Write down what you need to prove. It helps to know the properties of what you are trying to prove. If we needed to prove that something was a square, we would need to know the properties of a square.

Construction: You may need extra lines or angles to help you to prove the theorem. Construct these lines or angles and label them clearly.

Proof: Write down one reason or statement per line which will go towards proving what you have been asked to prove.

When writing down statements in the proof section, we must always try to give a reason for the statement, whether we have been given this information or whether we have used a theorem.

Statement	Reason
$\lvert\angle A\rvert = \lvert\angle B\rvert$	Isosceles triangle

We always finish by writing **Q.E.D.**

Q.E.D. stands for the Latin phrase *Quod erat demonstrandum*, which means 'what was to be proved'. It signals the end of the proof.

An example of a proof could be written as follows.

Theorem 4

The angles in any triangle add up to 180°.

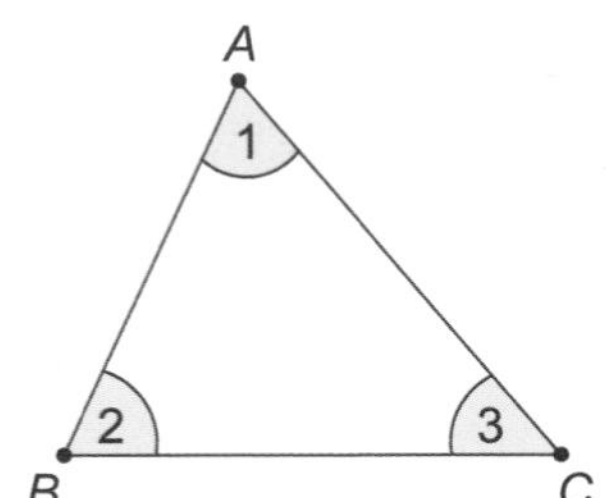

Given: A triangle with angles 1, 2 and 3.

To prove: $\lvert\angle 1\rvert + \lvert\angle 2\rvert + \lvert\angle 3\rvert = 180°$.

Construction: Draw a line through *A*, parallel to *BC*. Label angles 4 and 5.

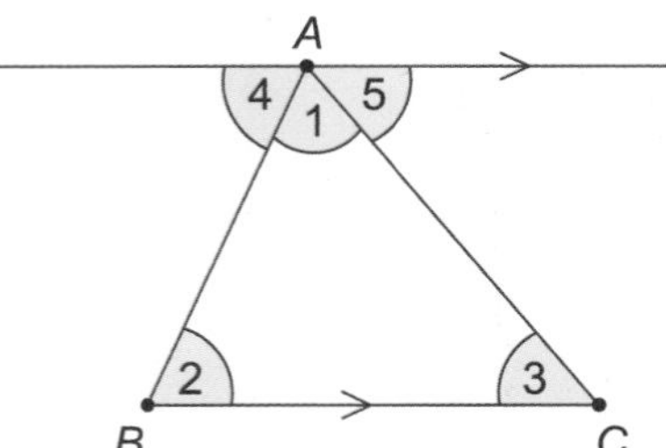

Proof:

Statement	Reason
$\lvert\angle 1\rvert + \lvert\angle 4\rvert + \lvert\angle 5\rvert = 180°$	Straight angle
$\lvert\angle 4\rvert = \lvert\angle 2\rvert$	Alternate
$\lvert\angle 5\rvert = \lvert\angle 3\rvert$	Alternate
$\therefore \lvert\angle 1\rvert + \lvert\angle 2\rvert + \lvert\angle 3\rvert = 180°$	
Q.E.D.	

Worked Example 5.1

Without measuring, solve for *x* in the following diagram.

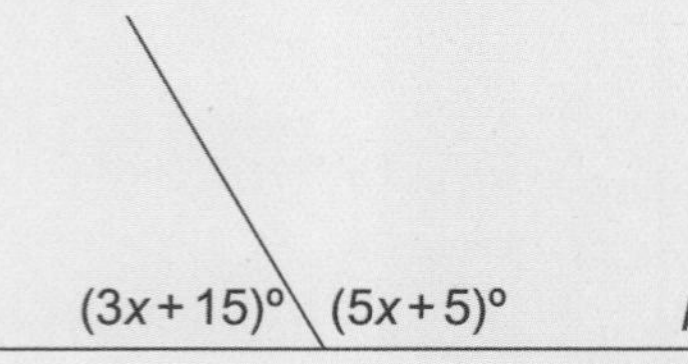

Solution

$$\text{Straight angle} = 180°$$
$$\Rightarrow 3x + 15 + 5x + 5 = 180°$$
$$8x + 20 = 180°$$
$$8x = 160°$$
$$x = 20°$$

Exercise 5.1

1. On a plane, plot the points *A*, *B*, *C*, *D*, *E*, *F*, *G* and *H*. Using these points, draw:

(i) A line *AB*

(ii) A line segment [*DE*]

(iii) A line segment [*FH*]

(iv) A ray *CD*]

(v) A ray [*FG*

(vi) A line parallel to *AB* and passing through the point *E*

(vii) A line perpendicular to *AC* and passing through the point *B*

Hence:

(viii) State, using an axiom, why $\lvert AB\rvert$ and $\lvert BA\rvert$ are equal.

(ix) Find $\lvert EF\rvert$. Explain why you cannot measure the line *EF*.

2. (a) On a plane, plot the points P and Q.

(i) How many lines can be drawn through the point P?

(ii) Draw a line through the points P and Q. How many lines can be drawn through the points P and Q?

(b) (i) Draw a line segment $[RS]$ where $|RS| = 10$ cm.

(ii) Mark any point on the line segment $[RS]$ and label as the point X.

(iii) Show that $|RX| + |SX| = |RS|$.

3. Explain each of the following terms used to describe angles. Construct an example of each angle, giving the measure of the angle.

(i) Obtuse angle (iv) Straight angle

(ii) Ordinary angle (v) Reflex angle

(iii) Acute angle (vi) Full angle

4. Use a protractor to draw the following angles:

(i) 35° (iii) 235° (v) 350°

(ii) 165° (iv) 180°

5. (a) Write down in your own words an explanation for the following terms. Use diagrams and give an example in each case.

(i) Theorem (ii) Axiom (iii) Corollary (iv) Proof (v) Converse

(b) Complete the following table. One has been done for you.

Statement	True/False	Converse	True/False
If the two angles add up to 180°, then they are supplementary.	True	If the two angles are supplementary, then they add to 180°.	True
If a triangle has a 90° angle, it is a right-angled triangle.			
If $x > 10$, then $x = 11$.			
If this month is January, then next month is February.			
If a polygon has four sides, it is a square.			
If it is a car, then it will have four wheels.			
If a woman is from Galway, then she is Irish.			

6. Solve for x in each of the following diagrams. Hence, find the measure of each of the unknown angles.

(i)

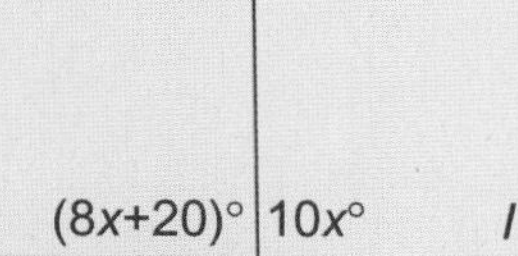

(ii)

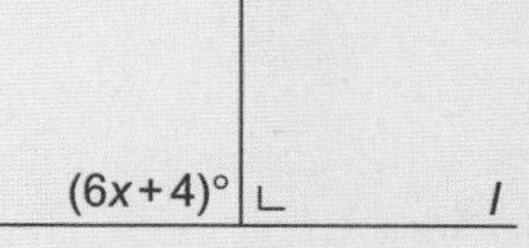

(iii)

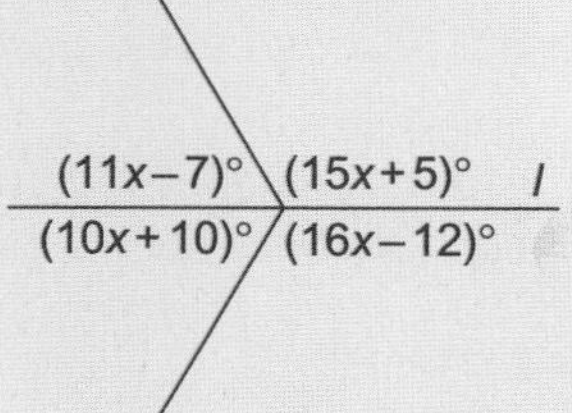

(iv)

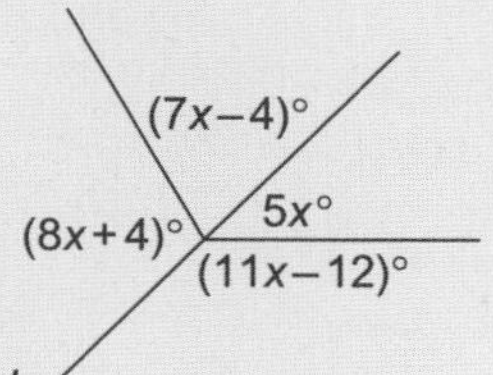

(v)

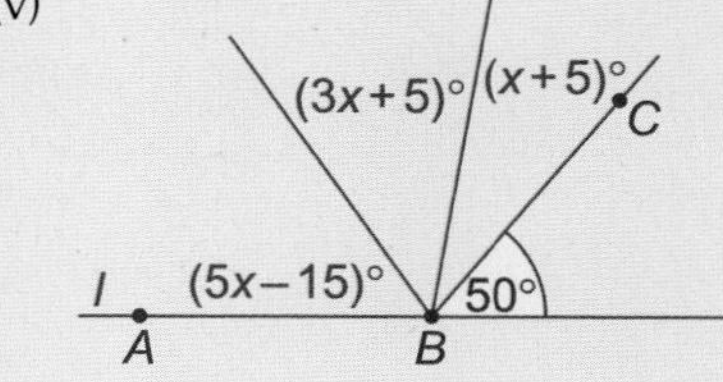

(vi)

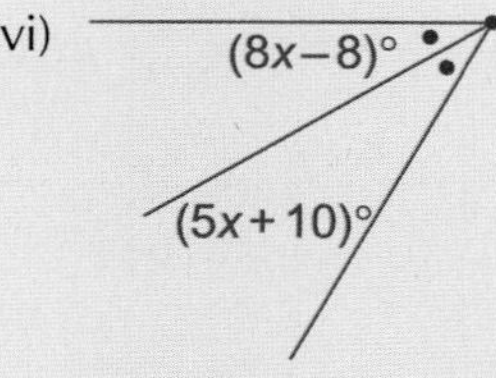

5.6 ANGLES AND LINES

In the previous section, we looked at the different types of concepts and axioms from our geometry course. We can now investigate certain properties, rules or theorems associated with various geometrical shapes.

Let us begin by investigating the relationships between angles and certain lines.

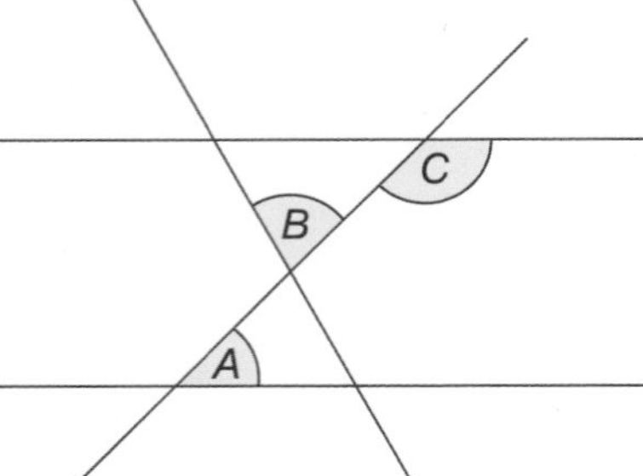

ACTIVITY 5.1

From Activity 5.1, we can state the following theorem:

Theorem 1

Vertically opposite angles are equal in measure.

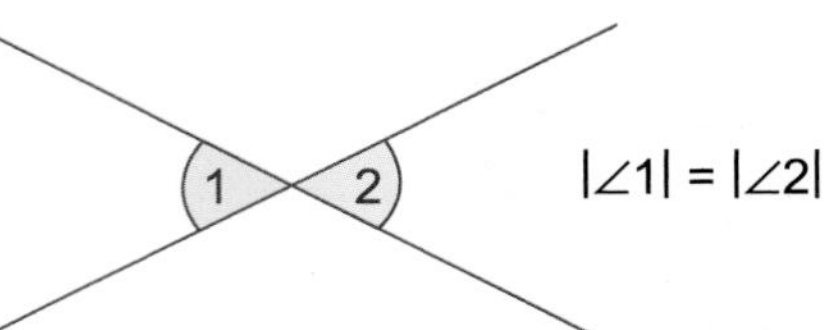

$|\angle 1| = |\angle 2|$

Vertically opposite angles are angles which have the same vertex and are directly opposite each other.

To spot vertically opposite angles, we look for the **X shape**.

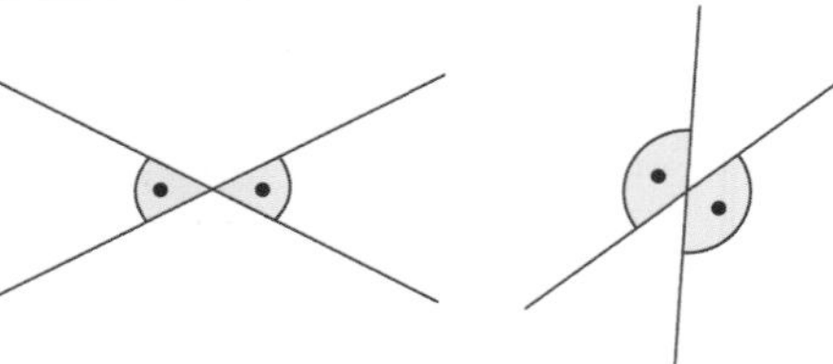

When a line cuts across two or more other lines, certain angles are formed.

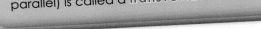

A line which cuts two or more lines (usually parallel) is called a **transversal**.

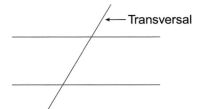

Transversal

Theorem 3

If a transversal makes equal alternate angles on two lines then the lines are parallel (and converse).

l

m

A

B

$|\angle A| = |\angle B|$
$\Rightarrow l \parallel m$

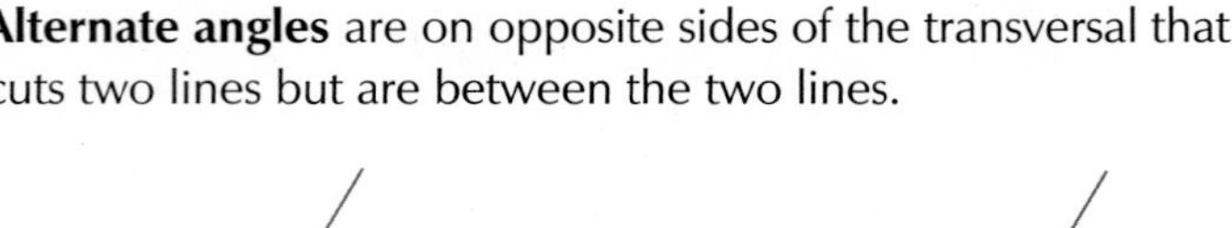

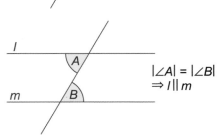

Alternate angles are on opposite sides of the transversal that cuts two lines but are between the two lines.

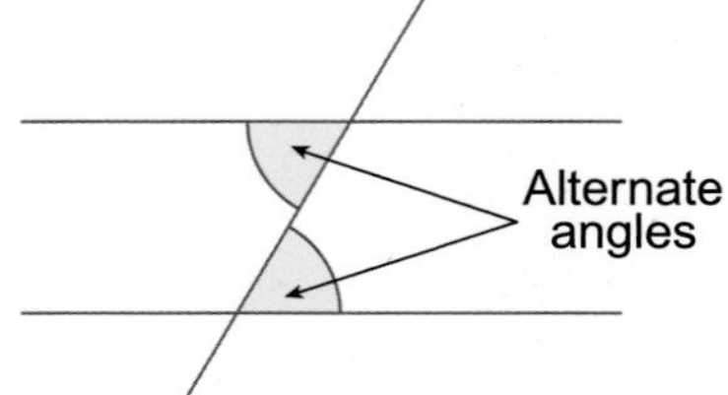

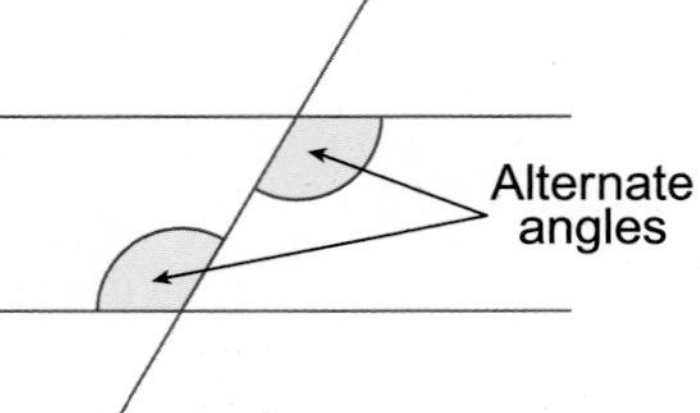

Remember to look for the **Z shape**.

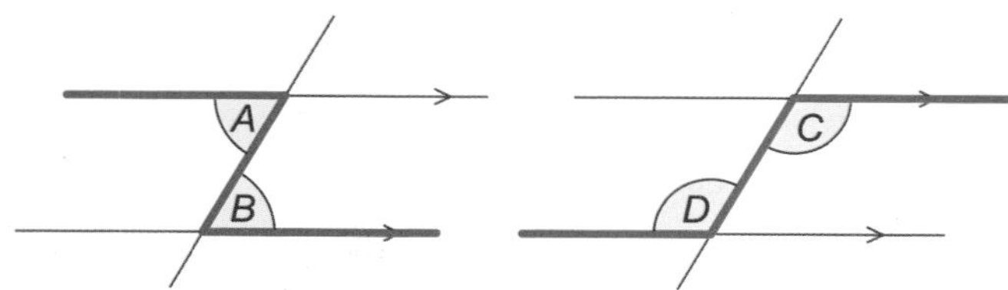

Theorem 5

Two lines are parallel if, and only if, for any transversal, the corresponding angles are equal.

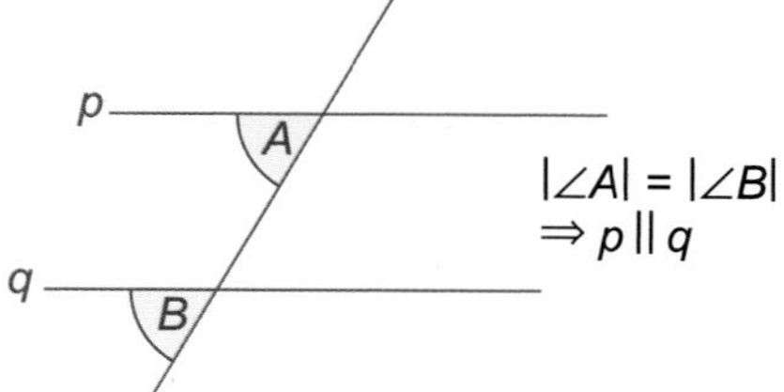

Corresponding angles are on same side of the transversal that cuts two lines. One angle is between the lines, and the other angle is outside the lines.

Remember to look for the **F shape**.

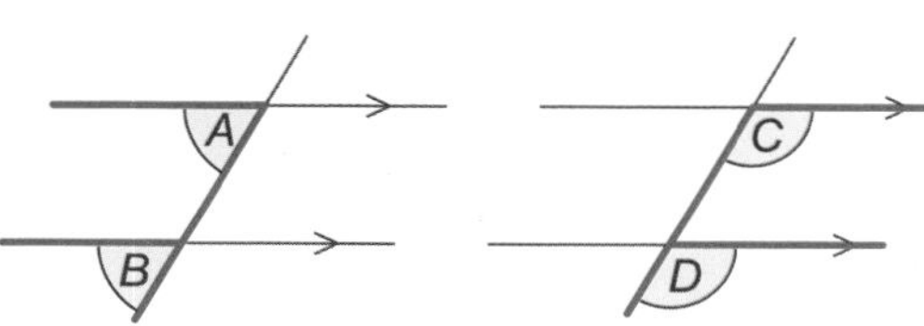

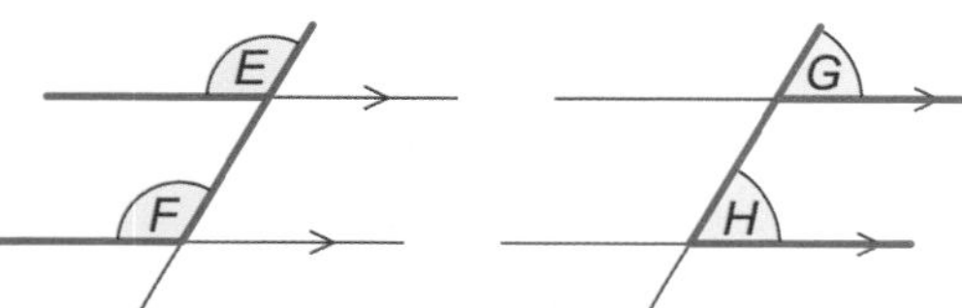

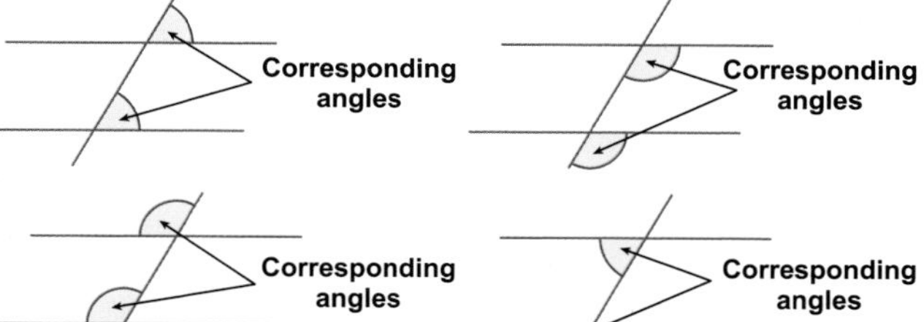

Interior angles between two parallel lines add up to 180°.

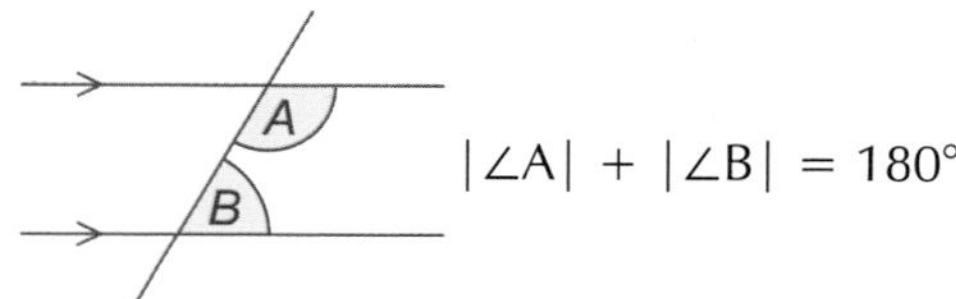

Worked Example 5.2

Without measuring, find the value of $|\angle A|$, $|\angle B|$, $|\angle C|$ and $|\angle D|$.

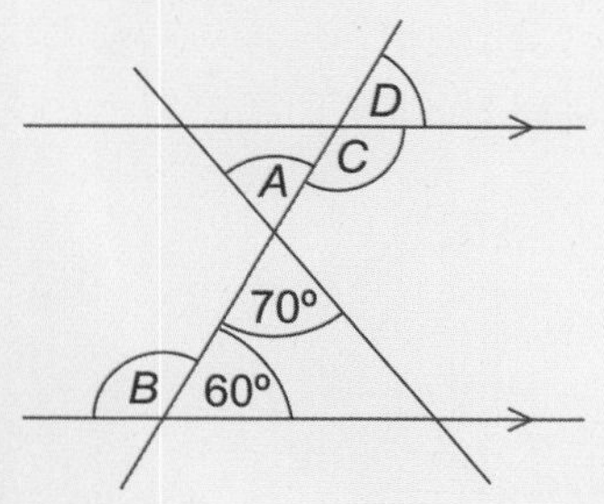

Solution

$|\angle A| = 70°$ (vertically opposite)

$|\angle B| = 180° - 60°$ (straight angle)

$\Rightarrow |\angle B| = 120°$

$|\angle C| = 120°$ (alternate angle to B)

$|\angle D| = 60°$ (corresponding angle)

Remember: Most questions have more than one way in which to find the measure of the required angle.

Exercise 5.2

1. Classify each of the following pairs of angles using the diagram below:

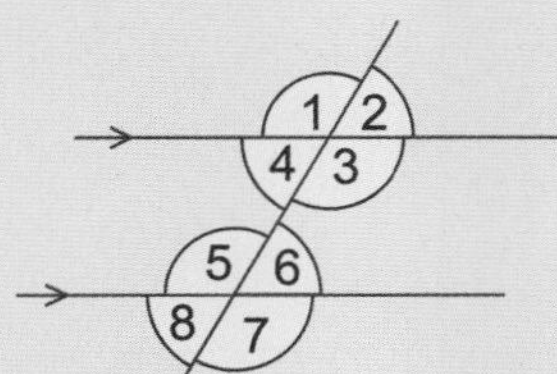

(i)	∠1 and ∠2	Supplementary
(ii)	∠3 and ∠7	
(iii)	∠4 and ∠8	
(iv)	∠4 and ∠2	
(v)	∠1 and ∠5	

2. In the diagram below, list:

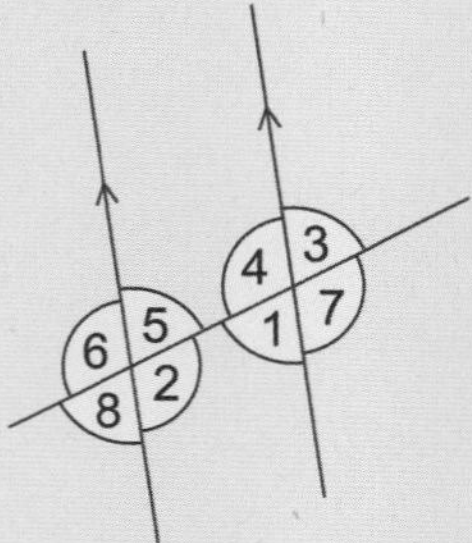

(i) Two pairs of corresponding angles

(ii) Two pairs of alternate angles

(iii) Two pairs of vertically opposite angles

3. Find the measure of each of the unknown angles marked in each of the following diagrams. Make sure to show all your work and give a reason for your answer.

(i)

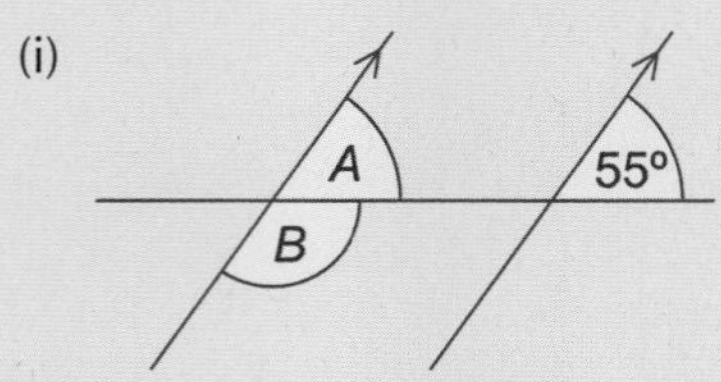

(ii)

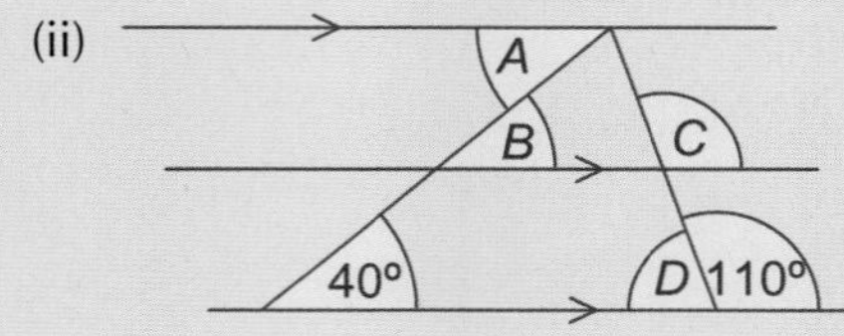

(iii)

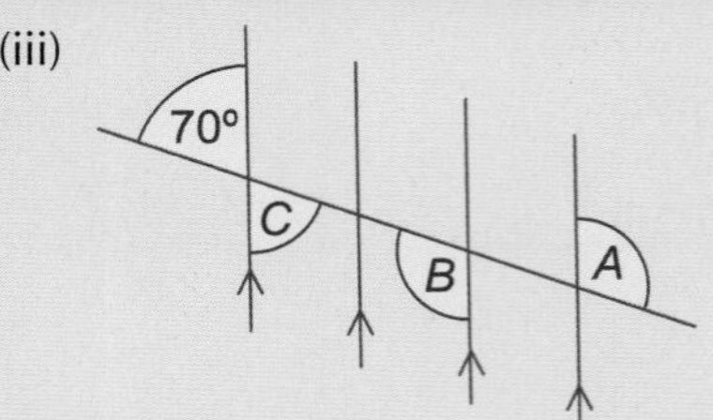

(iv)

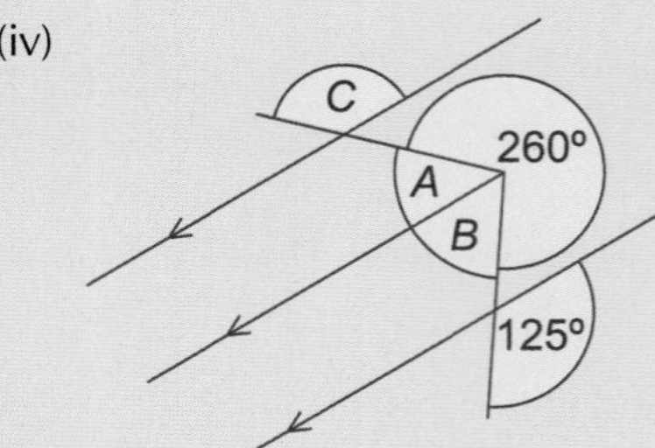

(v)

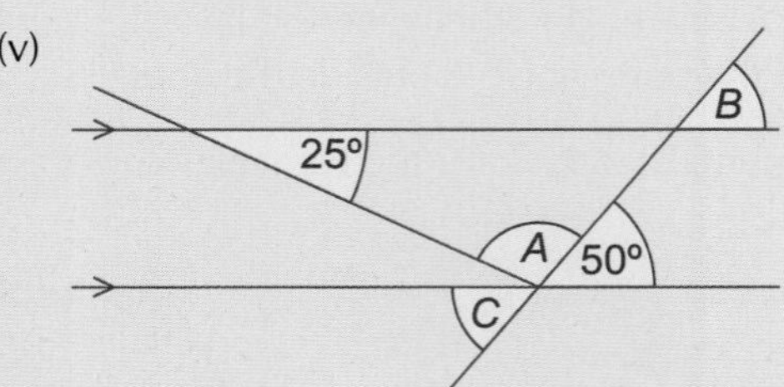

(vi)

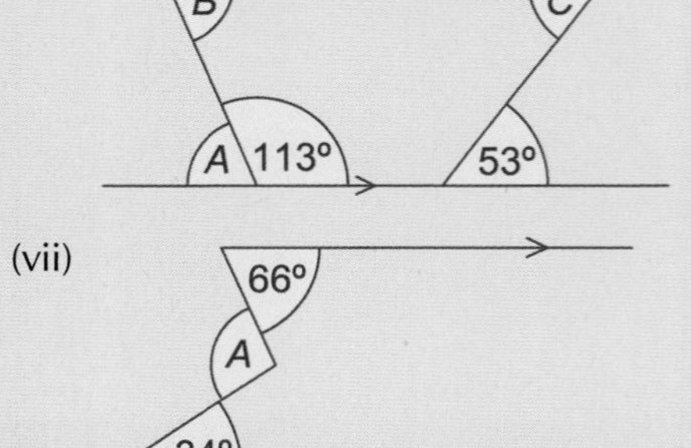

(vii)

66°

A

34°

4. Find the measure of the unknown variable in each of the following diagrams.

(i)

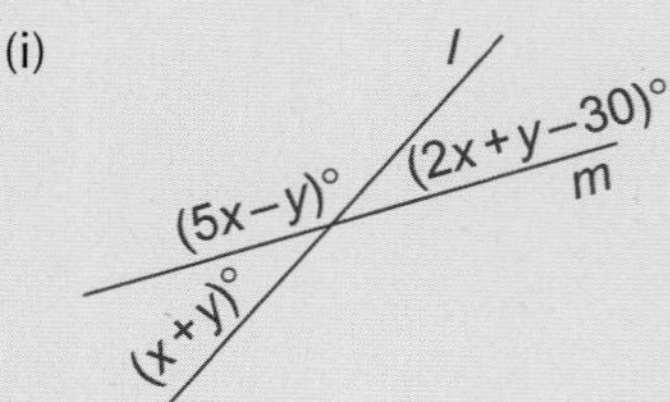

(ii)

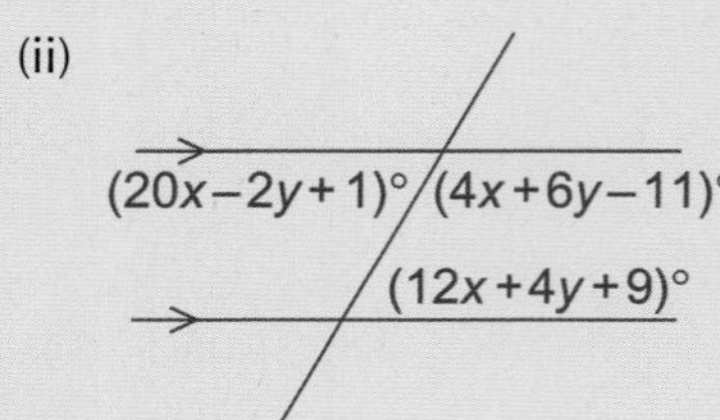

5.7 ANGLES IN TRIANGLES

When investigating triangles, we must first be aware of the different types of triangles and the notation used to describe them.

Equilateral	Isosceles	Scalene
60°, 60°, 60°		
All sides the same length	Two sides the same length	No sides the same length
All angles the same size (60°)	Two angles the same size	No angles the same size

We can now investigate some theorems associated with triangles.

From Activity 5.2, we can state the following theorems:

Theorem 2

In an isosceles triangle the angles opposite the equal sides are equal in measure. Conversely, if two angles are equal in measure, then the triangle is isosceles.

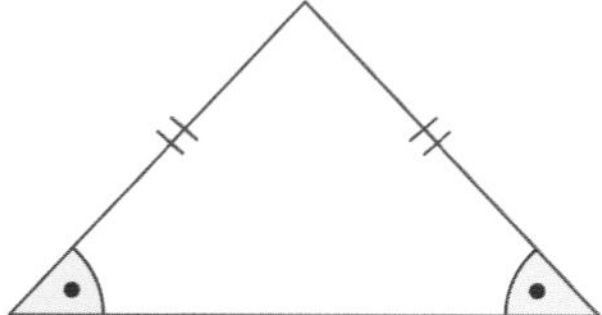

Theorem 4

The angles in any triangle add to 180°.

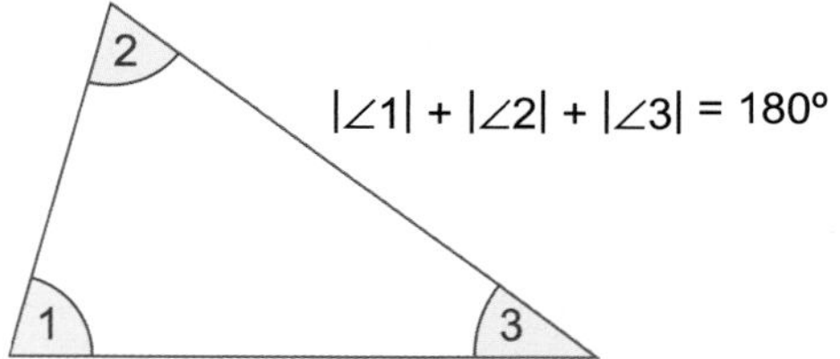

Theorem 6

Each exterior angle of a triangle is equal to the sum of the interior opposite angles.

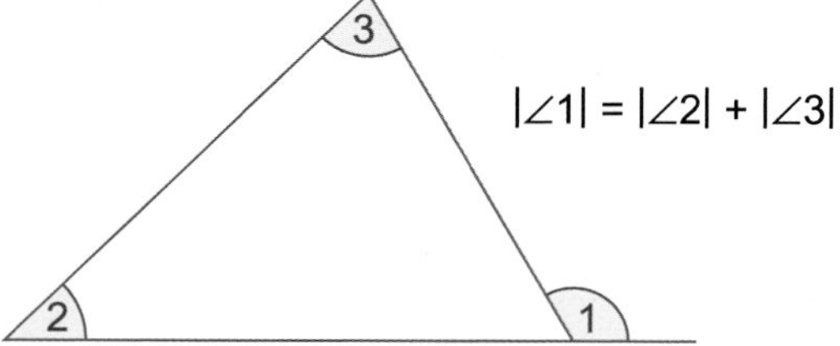

An **exterior angle** of a triangle is the angle between one side of the triangle and the extension of an adjacent side.

Worked Example 5.3

Find, without measuring the angles:

(i) $|\angle A|$

(ii) $|\angle B|$

(iii) $|\angle C|$

(iv) $|\angle D|$

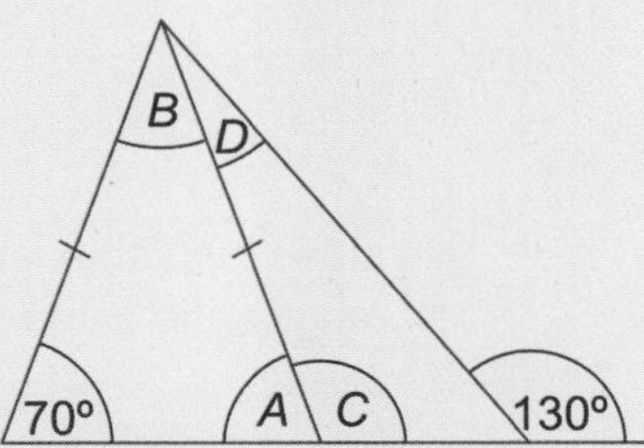

Solution

(i) $|\angle A| = 70°$ (isosceles triangle)

(ii) $|\angle B| + |\angle A| + 70° = 180°$ (angles in a triangle)

$\Rightarrow |\angle B| + 70° + 70° = 180°$

$|\angle B| = 180° - 70° - 70°$

$\therefore\ |\angle B| = 40°$

(iii) $|\angle C| = 180° - 70°$ (straight angle)

$|\angle C| = 110°$

(iv) $|\angle C| + |\angle D| = 130°$ (exterior angle)

$110° + |\angle D| = 130°$

$|\angle D| = 20°$

Exercise 5.3

1. Find the size of each of the unknown angles marked in the following diagrams. Make sure to show all your work and give a reason for your answer.

(i)

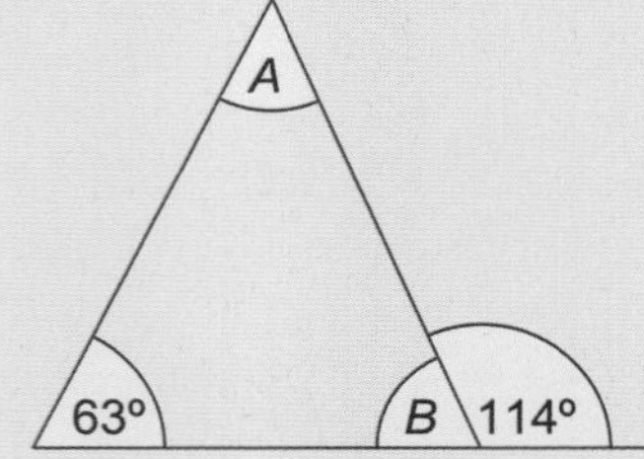

(ii)

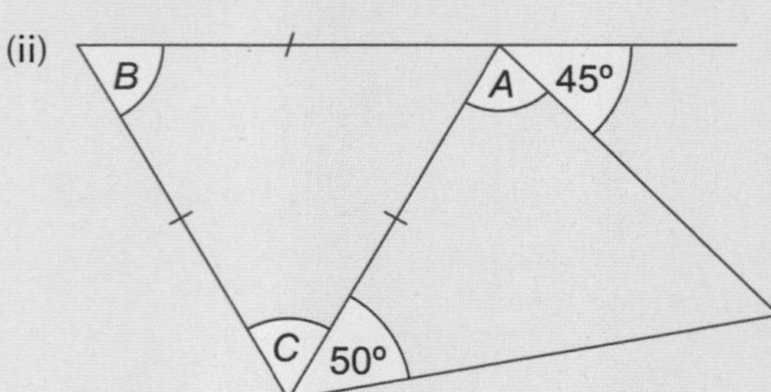

(iii)

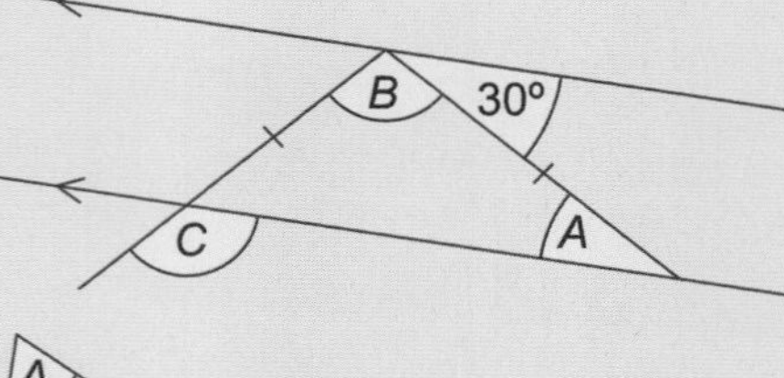

(iv)

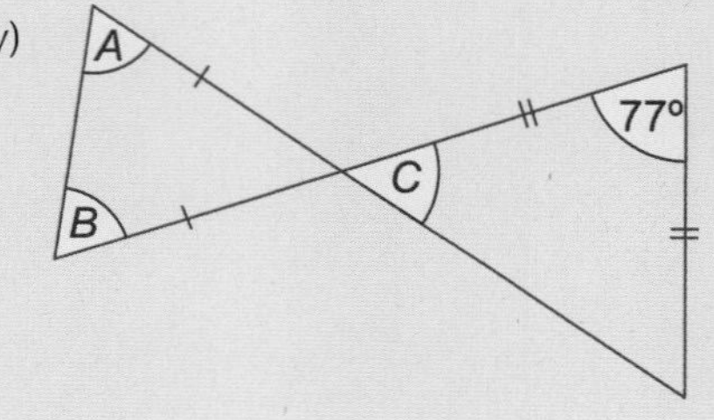

(v)

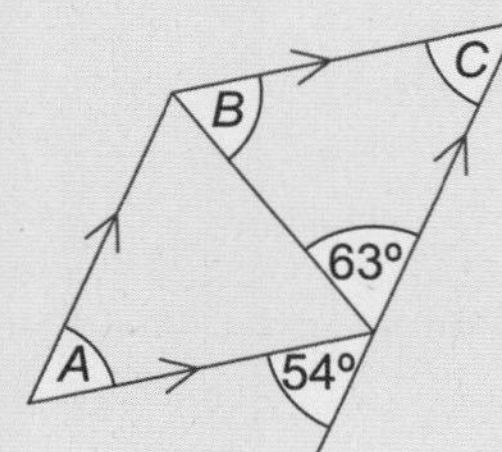

(vi)

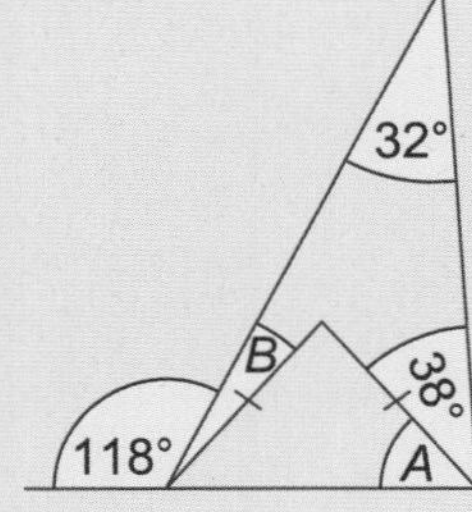

(vii)

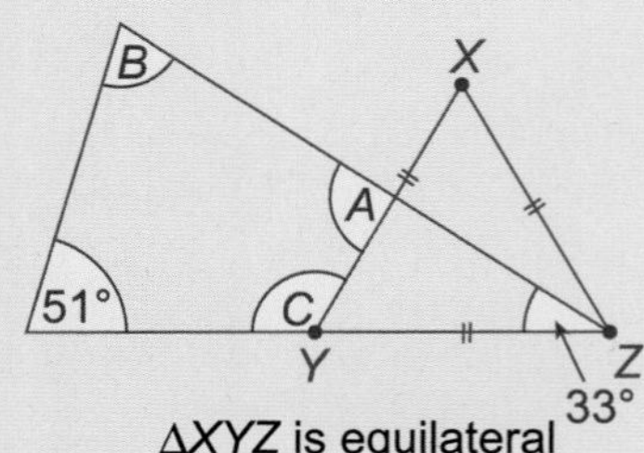

2. Find the measure of the unknown variable in each of the following diagrams.

(i)

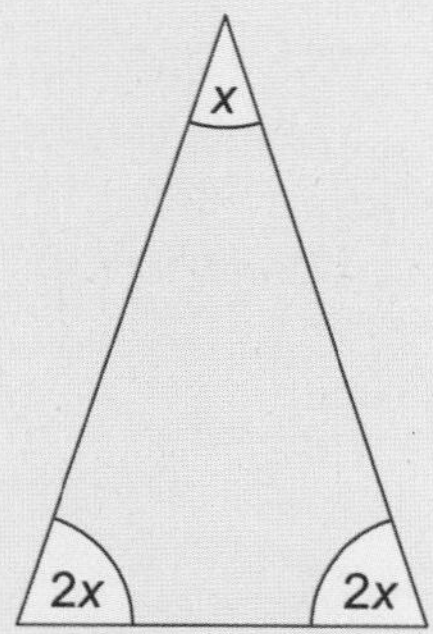

(ii)

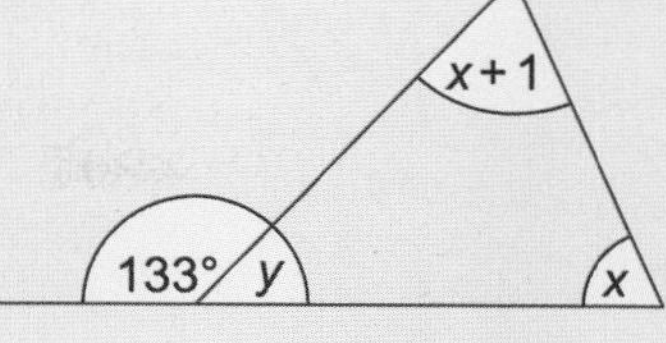

(iii)

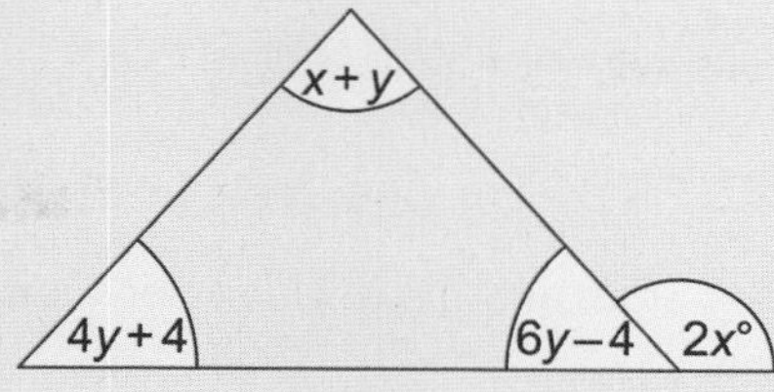

3. Prove that $|\angle B| = 2|\angle A|$, given that PR is a straight line.

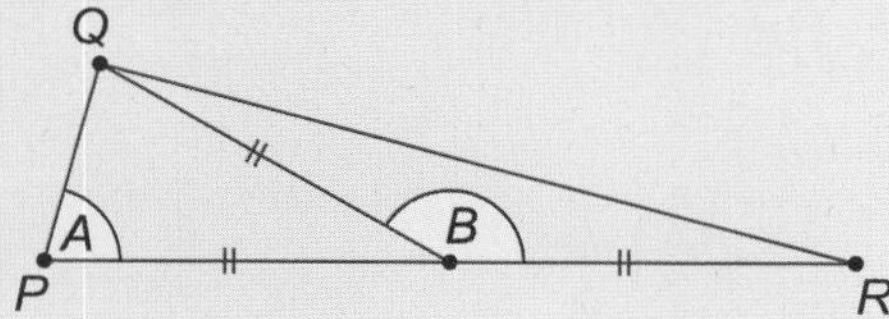

5.8 CONGRUENT TRIANGLES

If two triangles are identical to each other, they can also be described as being **congruent**.

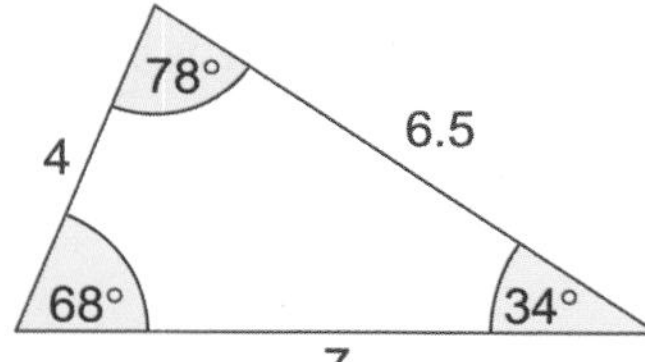

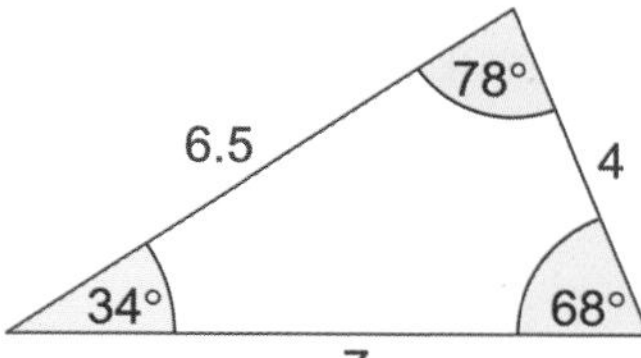

There are four different methods or cases to show that two triangles are congruent. These methods are listed in Axiom 4:

Axiom 4

Congruent triangles (SAS, ASA, SSS and RHS).

Congruent triangles are triangles where all the corresponding sides and interior angles are equal in measure.

Congruent Triangles: Side, Side, Side (SSS)

SSS means **Side, Side, Side.**

ΔABC is congruent to ΔDEF **or** $\Delta ABC \equiv \Delta DEF$.

The side lengths in ΔABC are the same as the side lengths in ΔDEF.

The symbol ≡ is a shorthand way of describing two triangles as congruent, e.g. $\Delta ABC \equiv \Delta DEF$.

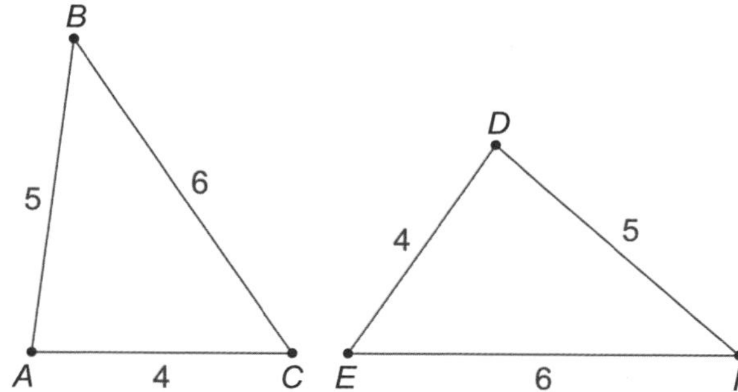

Congruent Triangles: Side, Angle, Side (SAS)

SAS means **Side, Angle, Side**

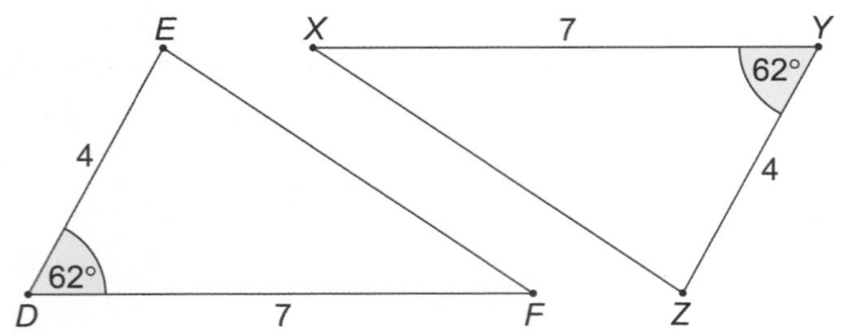

ΔDEF is congruent to ΔXYZ **or** $\Delta DEF \equiv \Delta XYZ$.

Two sides and the angle in between them are equal.

The in-between angle can also be called the **included** angle.

Congruent Triangles: Angle, Side, Angle (ASA)

ΔPQR is congruent to ΔMNO **or** $\Delta PQR \equiv \Delta MNO$.

Two angles and the corresponding side are equal.

ASA means **Angle, Side, Angle.**

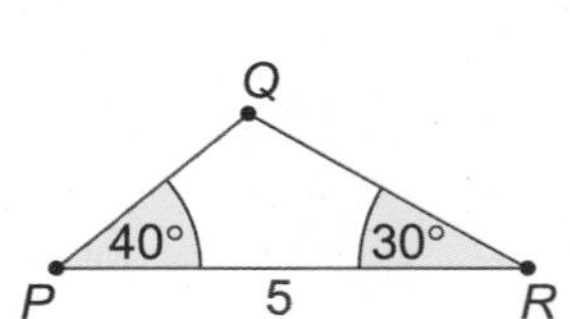

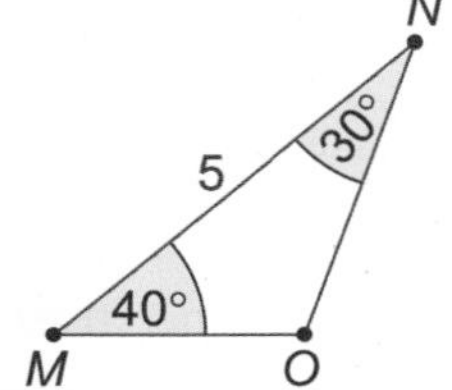

Usually, the corresponding side is the side in between the vertices of the two given angles.

Congruent Triangles: Right Angle, Hypotenuse, One Other Side (RHS)

The hypotenuse is the side opposite the right angle; it is also the longest side in the triangle.

ΔRST is congruent to ΔUVW **or** $\Delta RST \equiv \Delta UVW$.

Both of these triangles are right-angled, their hypotenuse is the same length, and they have one other side that is equal.

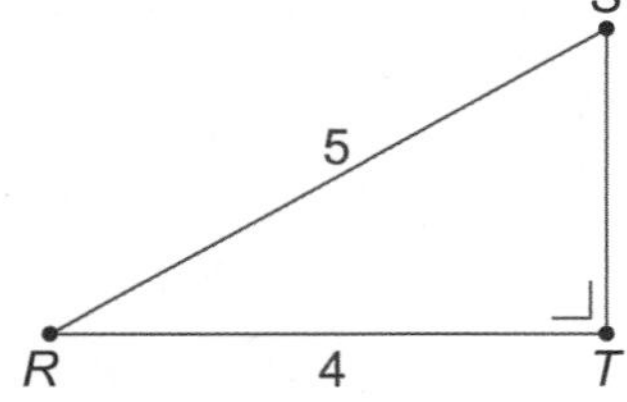

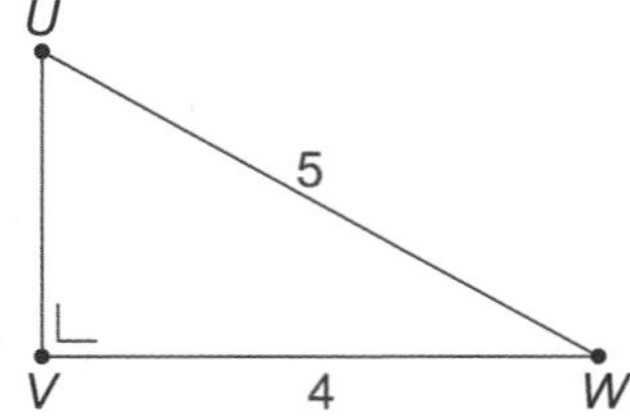

The areas of congruent triangles are equal as well.

Congruent triangles are a good introduction to the method of writing a geometrical proof.

Worked Example 5.4

Prove that the two triangles ABC and DEF are congruent.

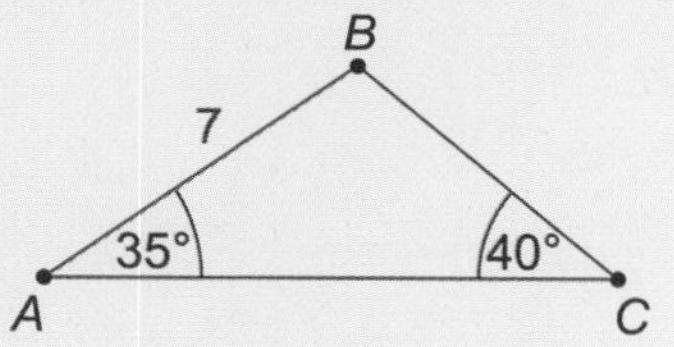

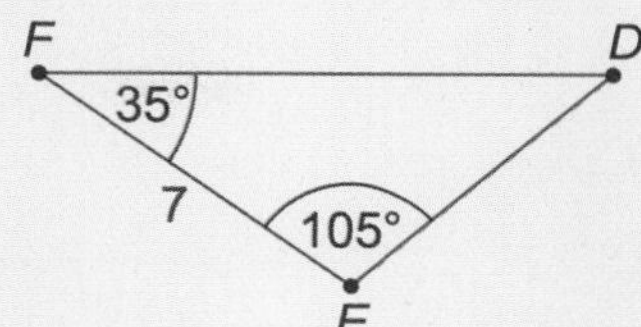

Solution

We must first find $|\angle B|$:

$|\angle B| = 180° - 35° - 40°$ (angles in a triangle)

$|\angle B| = 105°$

Proof:

Statement	Reason
$\|\angle B\| = \|\angle E\|$	As shown
$\|\angle A\| = \|\angle F\|$	Given
$\|AB\| = \|EF\|$	Given
$\Rightarrow \Delta ABC \equiv \Delta DEF$	ASA
Q.E.D.	

Exercise 5.4

1. Prove that the following pairs of triangles are congruent. Explain your answer fully.

(i)

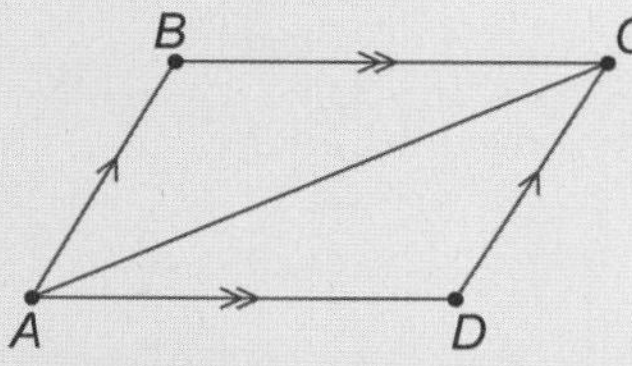

Prove that $\Delta ABC \equiv \Delta ACD$.

(ii)

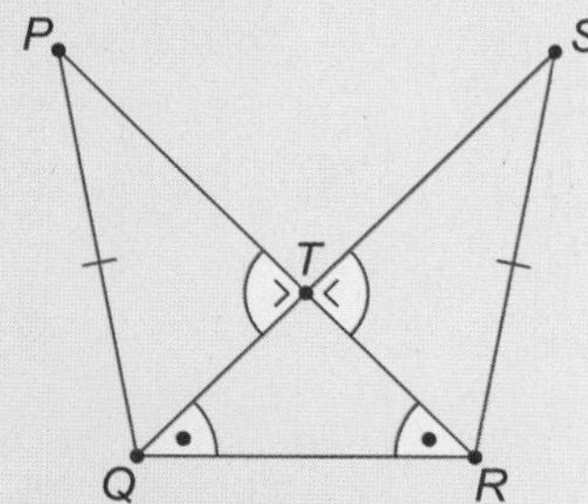

Prove that $\Delta PQT \equiv \Delta RST$.

(iii)

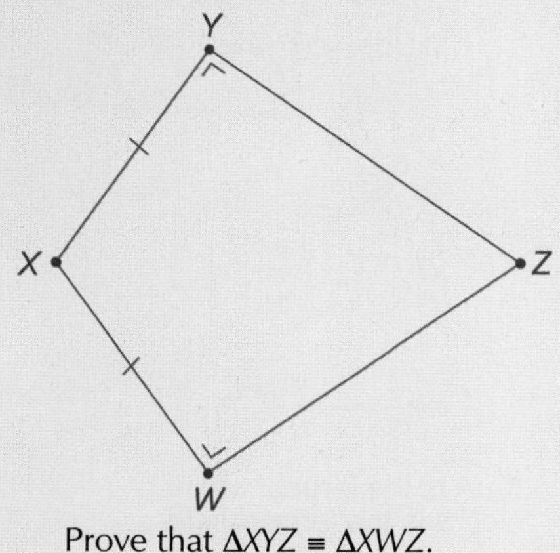

Prove that $\Delta XYZ \equiv \Delta XWZ$.

(iv)

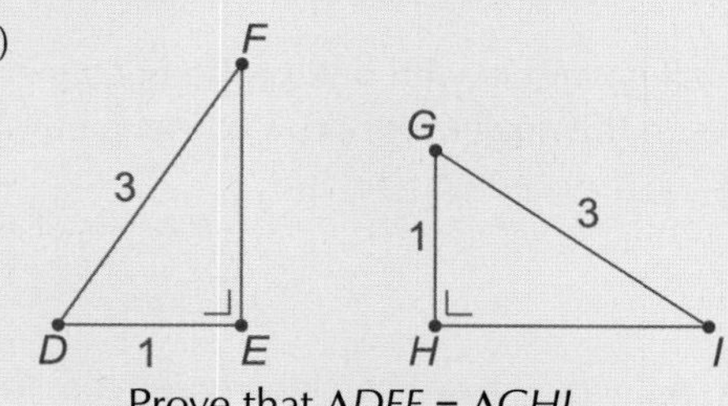

Prove that $\Delta DEF \equiv \Delta GHI$.

(v)

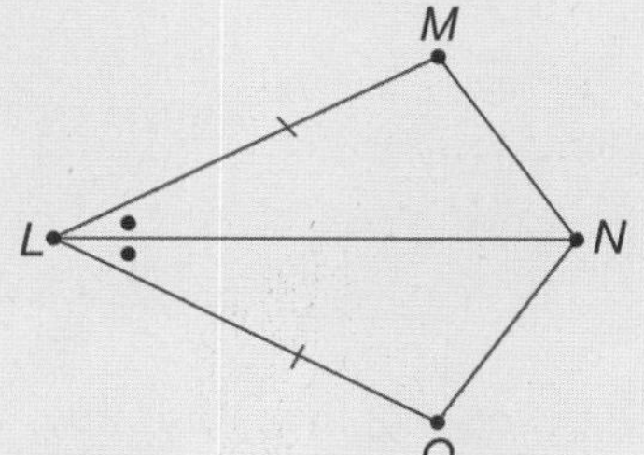

Prove that $\Delta LMN \equiv \Delta LNO$.

(vi)

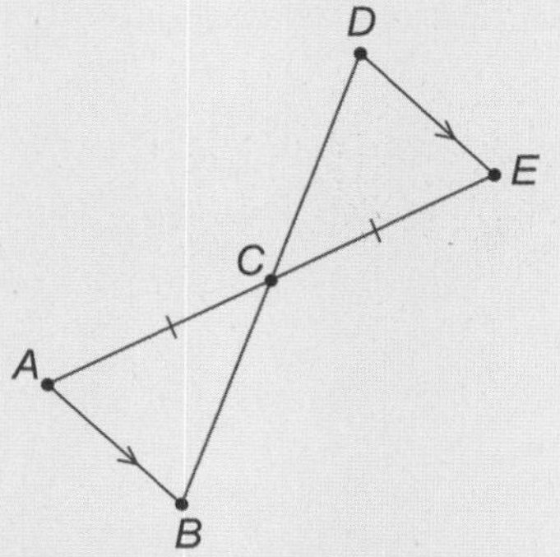

Prove that $\Delta ABC \equiv \Delta CDE$.

(vii)

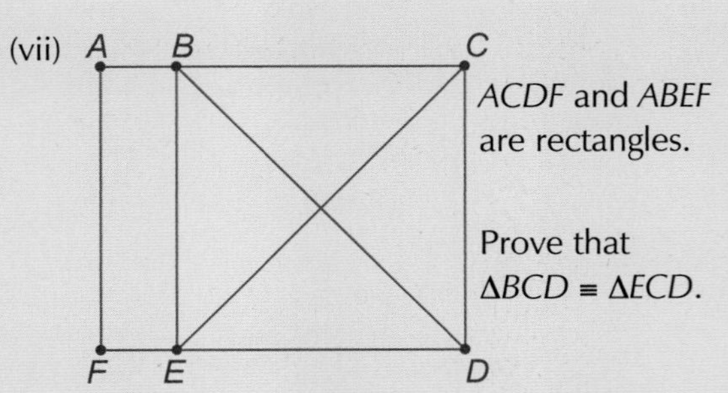

ACDF and *ABEF* are rectangles.

Prove that $\Delta BCD \equiv \Delta ECD$.

(viii)

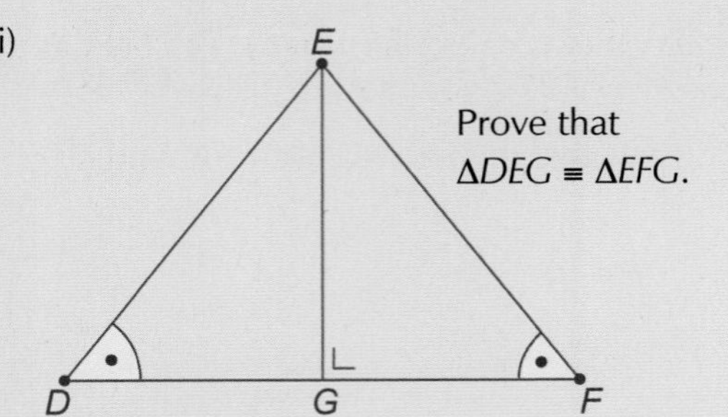

Prove that $\Delta DEG \equiv \Delta EFG$.

2. 'Construction 1: Bisector of an angle' is shown. Prove that $\angle ABC$ is bisected by $[BD$.

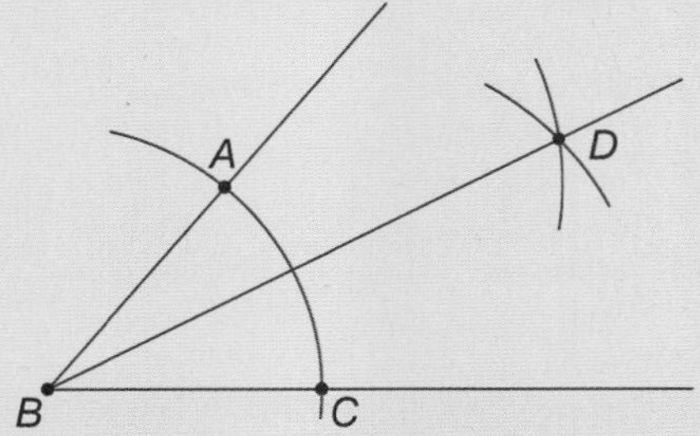

3. In ΔABC, $|\angle BAC| = |\angle BCA|$. Prove that $|AB| = |BC|$.

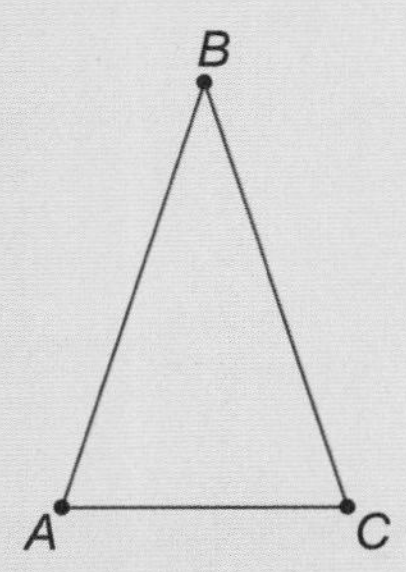

5.9 MORE TRIANGLES

We will now deal with one property concerning the relationship between the angles and sides of triangles.

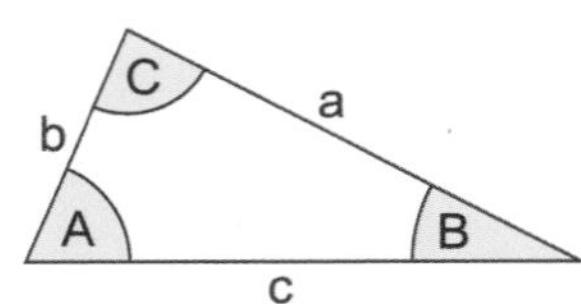

From Activity 5.4, we can clearly see that for any triangle:

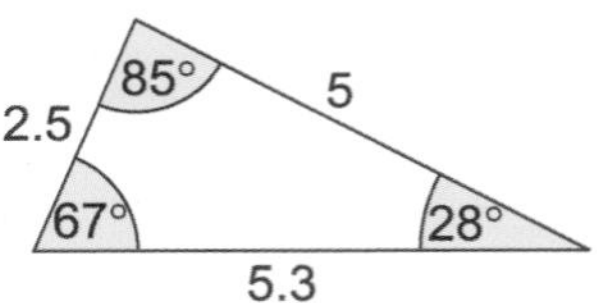

The largest angle is opposite the largest side.

The smallest angle is opposite the smallest side.

The converse (reverse) of this is also true.

The largest side is opposite the largest angle.

The smallest side is opposite the smallest angle.

From our investigations we can state:

Theorem 7

The angle opposite the greater of two sides is greater than the angle opposite the lesser side. Conversely, the side opposite the greater of two angles is greater than the side opposite the lesser angle.

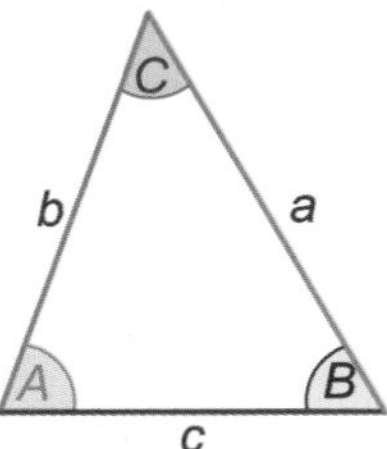

If $\angle A$ is the largest angle, side *a* is the largest side.

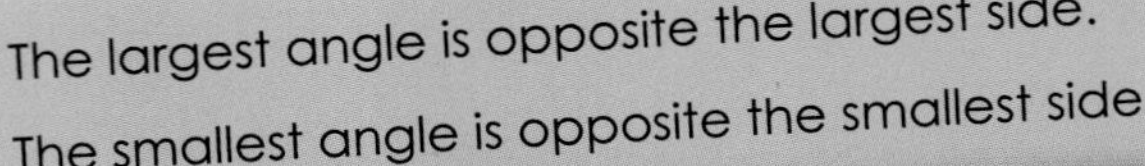

Another property of triangles can help determine if three lengths can form the three sides of a triangle.

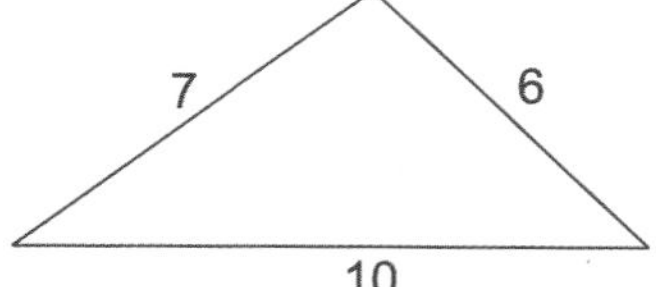

From Activity 5.5 we can see that:

The sum of the lengths of any two sides of a triangle **have to be** greater than the length of the third side.

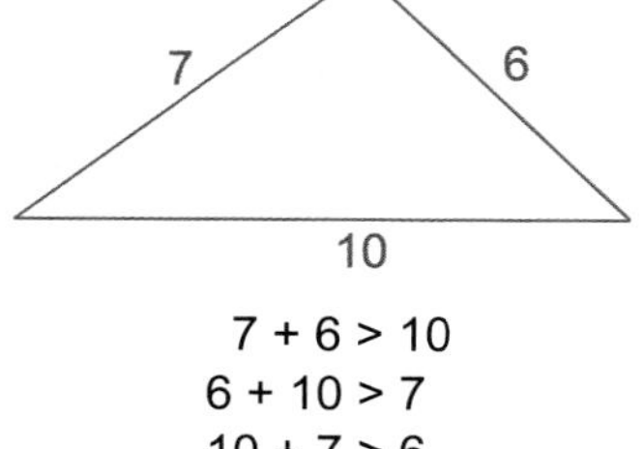

$7 + 6 > 10$
$6 + 10 > 7$
$10 + 7 > 6$

This allows us to state the following theorem:

Theorem 8

Two sides of a triangle are together greater than the third. This theorem is sometimes referred to as the **triangle inequality theorem**.

$a + b > c$
$a + c > b$
$b + c > a$

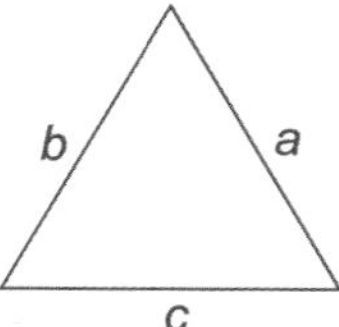

This theorem implies that one side of a triangle must be smaller that the other two sides added together.

Worked Example 5.5

Determine if the following triangles can be constructed.

(i) 9, 4 and 3 cm

(ii) 4, 8 and 11 cm

Solution

(i) Sides of 9, 4 and 3 cm

It is a good idea to draw out a table and to start with the smaller sides first.

3 + 4 = 7	7 is not > 9	∴ Triangle can't be constructed.

(ii) Sides of 4, 8 and 11 cm

The two sides must add to a value greater than (and not equal to) the other side.

4 + 8 = 12	12 > 11	∴ Triangle can be constructed.
8 + 11 = 19	19 > 4	
4 + 11 = 15	15 > 8	

Sometimes, we might be asked to find the range of values that a side of a triangle could have, when the other two sides are given.

Worked Example 5.6

The sides of a triangle are 6.1, 7.2 and n, where $n \in N$.

> $n \in N$ means that n is a natural number which is any whole number greater than 0.

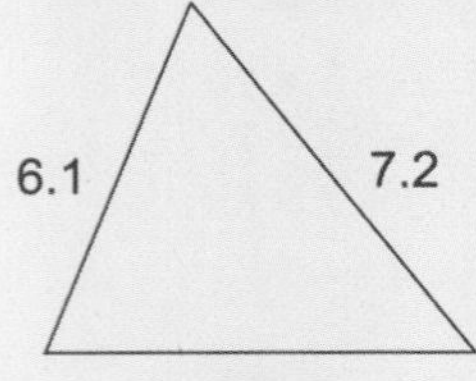

Find:

(i) The minimum possible value of n

(ii) The maximum (largest) possible value of n

(iii) The range of possible values of n

Solution

(i) The minimum possible value of n

n and the smallest side given, when added together, must be greater than the given larger side.

$n + 6.1 > 7.2$

$n > 7.2 - 6.1$

> Minimum possible value of triangle side $>$ Largest side given – smallest side given.

$\therefore n > 1.1$

As $n \in N$, the minimum value of n is the next natural number greater than 1.1.

$\therefore n = 2$

(ii) The maximum possible value of n

The two sides given, when added together, must be greater than n. This means that n must be smaller than the sum of the two sides.

$n < 7.2 + 6.1$

> Maximum possible value of triangle side $<$ Sum of other two sides.

$\therefore n < 13.3$

As $n \in N$, the largest value of n is the next natural number less than 13.3.

$\therefore n = 13$

(iii) The range of the possible values of n

Minimum possible value of triangle side is $n = 2$.

Maximum possible value of triangle side is $n = 13$.

$\therefore 2 \leqslant n \leqslant 13, n \in N$

> When writing a range of values for the sides of the triangle, we usually write it in the form min $\leqslant n \leqslant$ max.

Exercise 5.5

1. In each of the following polygons, **either**:

   (a) Identify the smallest and largest angles (if sides given).

   OR

   (b) Identify the smallest and largest sides (if angles given).

   (i)

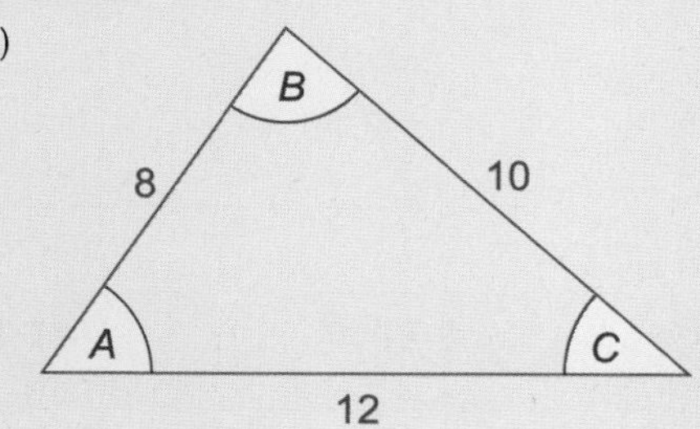

   (ii)

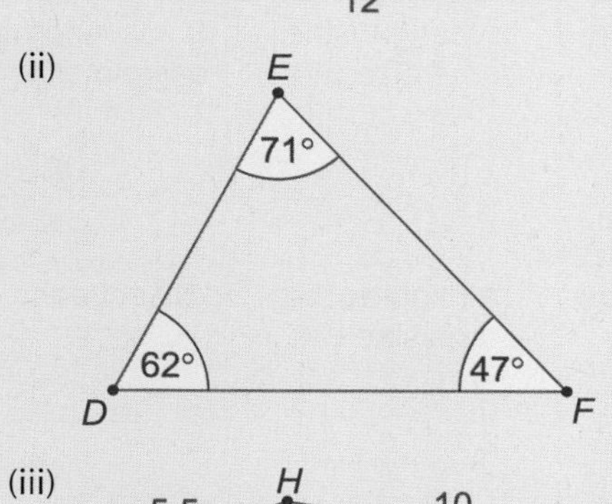

   (iii)

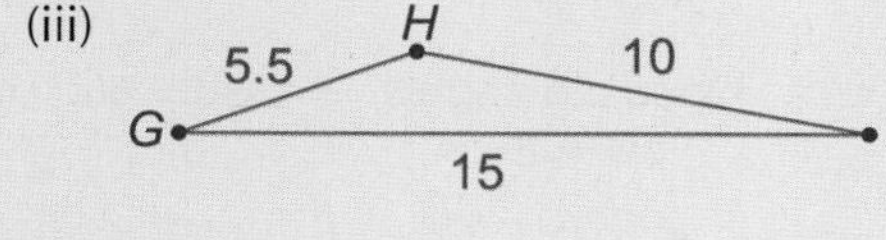

   (iv)

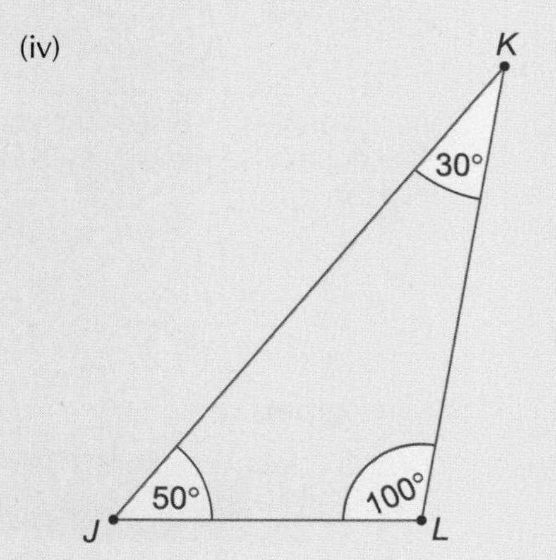

   (v)

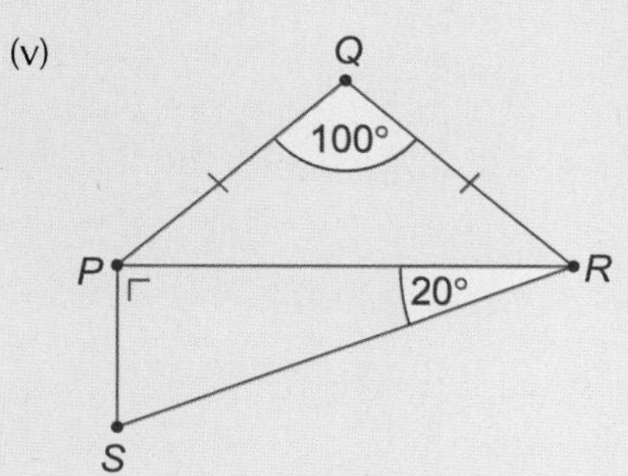

2. Explain, in each case, if it is possible to construct triangles with sides of the following lengths:

   (i) 2, 3, 6

   (ii) 40, 50, 15

   (iii) 8, 9, 10

   (iv) 6, 3, 3

   (v) 3, 4, 4

   (vi) $x + 1, x, x - 3$, where $x \geqslant 5, x \in N$

3. The sides of a triangle are of lengths 4, 10 and n, where $n \in N$. What is the:

   (i) Smallest possible value of n

   (ii) Largest possible value of n

   (iii) Range of the possible values of n

4. The sides of a triangle are of lengths 2.9, 11.4 and a, where $a \in N$. What is the:

   (i) Smallest possible value of a

   (ii) Largest possible value of a

   (iii) Range of the possible values of a

5. The sides of a triangle are of lengths 4, 12.3 and b, where $b \in N$. What is the:

   (i) Smallest possible value of b

   (ii) Largest possible value of b

   (iii) Range of the possible values of b

6. The sides of a scalene triangle are of lengths 4, d and c, where $d, c \in N$, and d and c are less than 7.

   (i) List the side lengths of all possible triangles.

   (ii) Which triangle has the smallest angle?

   (iii) Which triangle has the largest angle?

7. The side lengths of a quadrilateral are 5, 8, 10 and c, where $c \in N$. Find all the possible values of c.

5.10 PARALLELOGRAMS

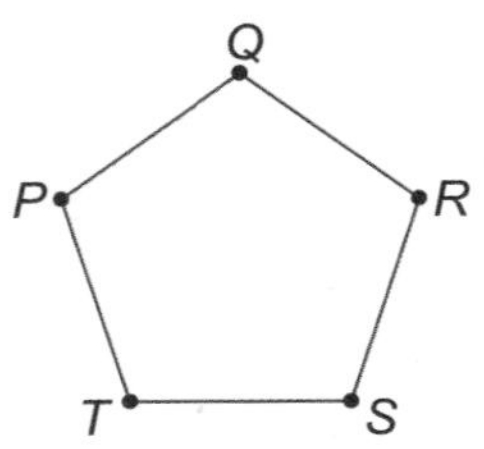

A **polygon** is a closed shape (without gaps or openings) with straight sides. A polygon has at least three sides.

A **regular polygon** has equal sides and equal angles.

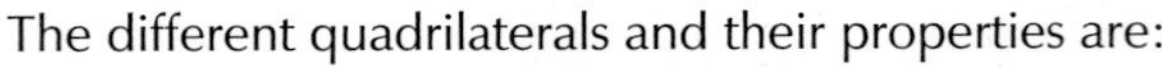

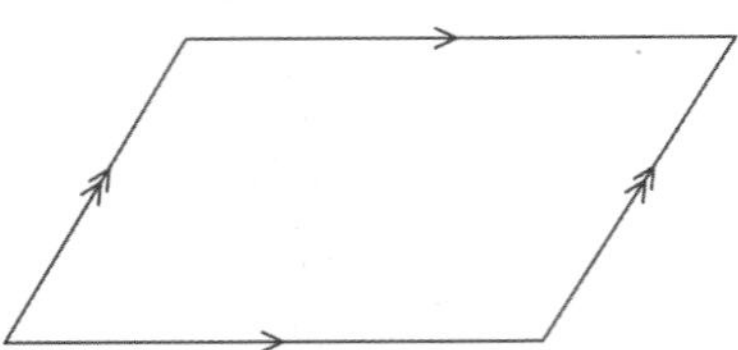

One type of **polygon** commonly encountered is the parallelogram.

A **parallelogram** is a quadrilateral (four-sided polygon) with some special properties.

The different quadrilaterals and their properties are:

Type of quadrilateral	Sides	Parallel sides	Angles	Diagonals
Square	Four equal sides	Opposite sides are parallel	All angles the same size (90°)	Bisect each other – angle of 90° formed
Rectangle	Opposite sides are equal	Opposite sides are parallel	All angles the same size (90°)	Bisect each other
Parallelogram	Opposite sides are equal	Opposite sides are parallel	Opposite angles are equal	Bisect each other
Rhombus	Four equal sides	Opposite sides are parallel	Opposite angles are equal	Bisect each other – angle of 90° formed

A square, rectangle and rhombus could all be described as being **parallelograms**.

We can now investigate specific theorems related to parallelograms.

From Activity 5.6, we can state the following theorems:

Theorem 9

In a parallelogram, opposite sides are equal and opposite angles are equal.

Conversely, if the opposite angles or sides of a quadrilateral are equal, then it is a parallelogram.

A **parallelogram** is a quadrilateral that has two pairs of parallel sides.

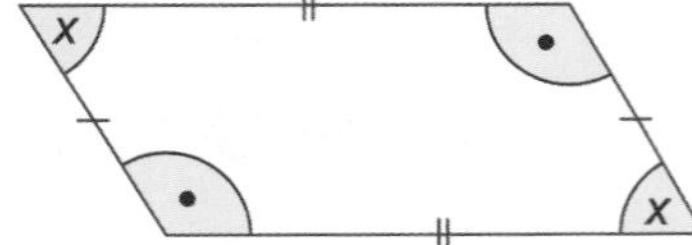

Corollary 1

A diagonal divides a parallelogram into two congruent triangles.

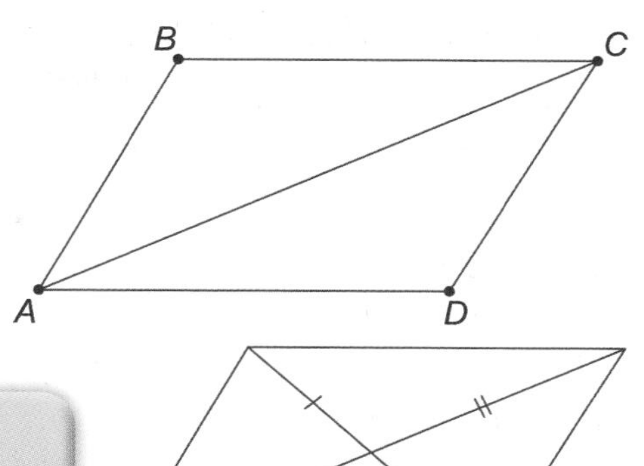

$\Delta ABC \equiv \Delta ADC$ (SAS)

Theorem 10

The diagonals of a parallelogram bisect each other.

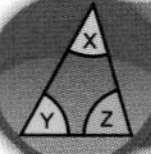

Worked Example 5.7

In the following parallelogram, find:

(i) $|\angle 1|$ (ii) $|\angle 2|$ (iii) $|\angle 3|$

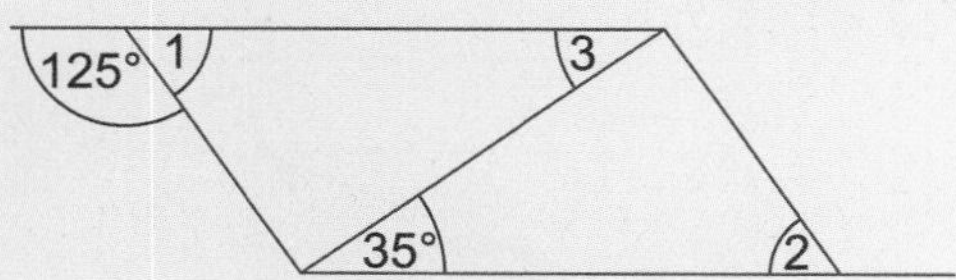

Solution

(i) $|\angle 1| = 180° - 125°$ (straight angle)

$\therefore |\angle 1| = 55°$

(ii) $\angle 2$ is opposite $\angle 1$

$\therefore |\angle 2| = 55°$

(iii) $|\angle 3| = 35°$ (alternate angle)

Exercise 5.6

1. Find the measure of the missing angles in each of the parallelograms. Show as much work as possible.

(i)

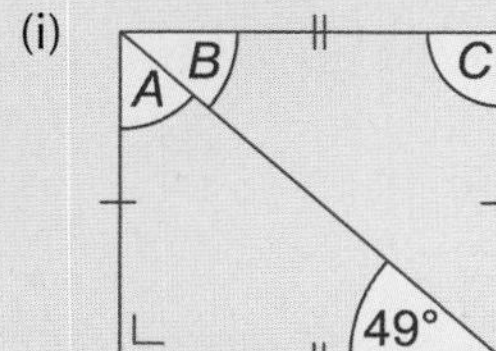

(ii)

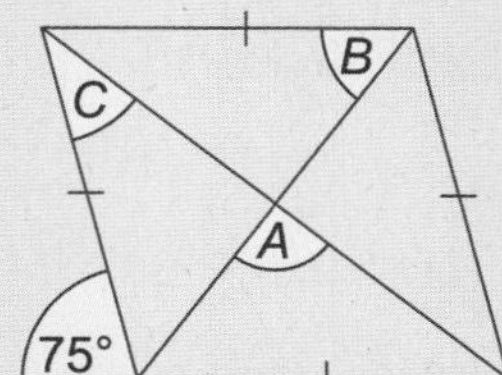

(iii)

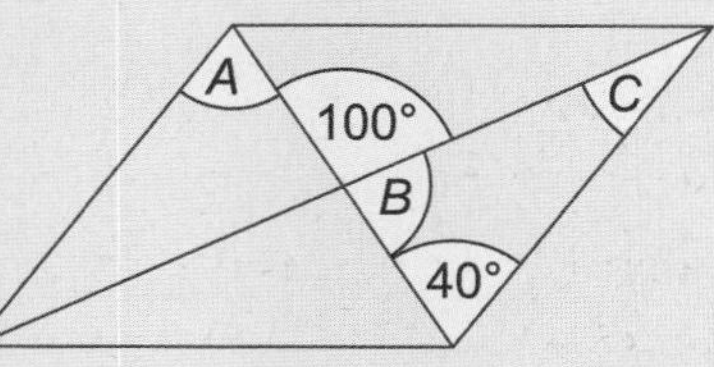

(iv)

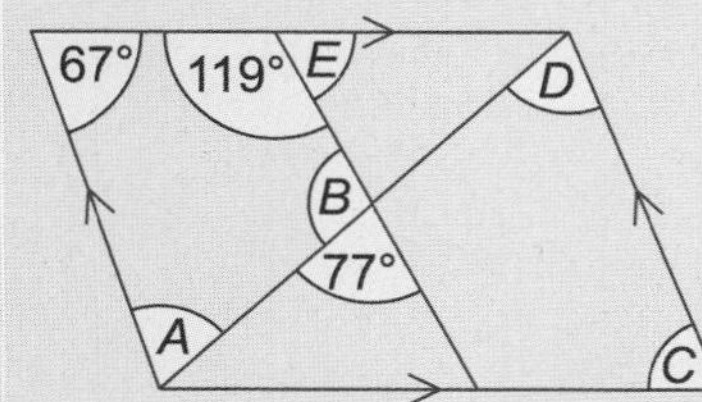

(v)

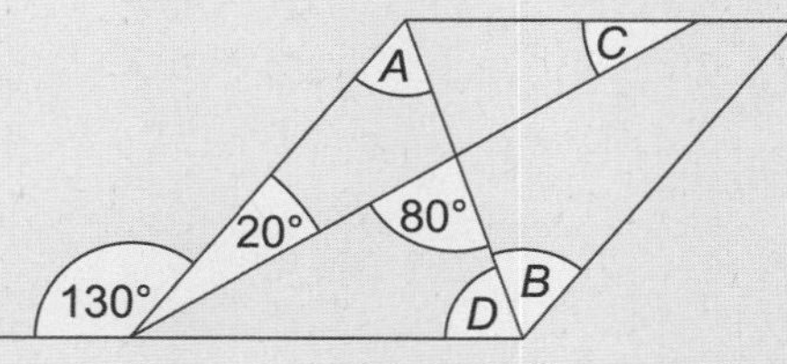

2. Find the value of x and y in each of the following parallelograms.

(i)

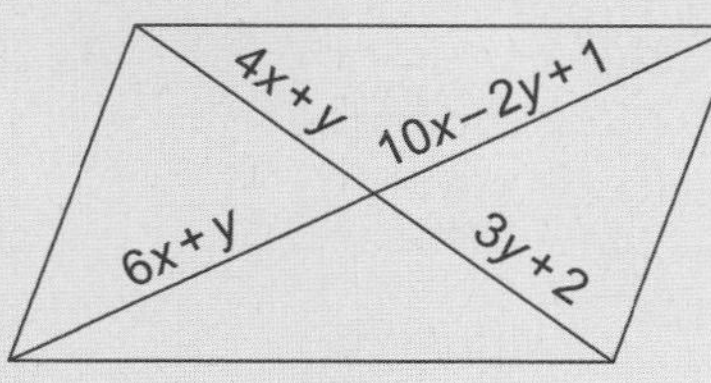

(ii)

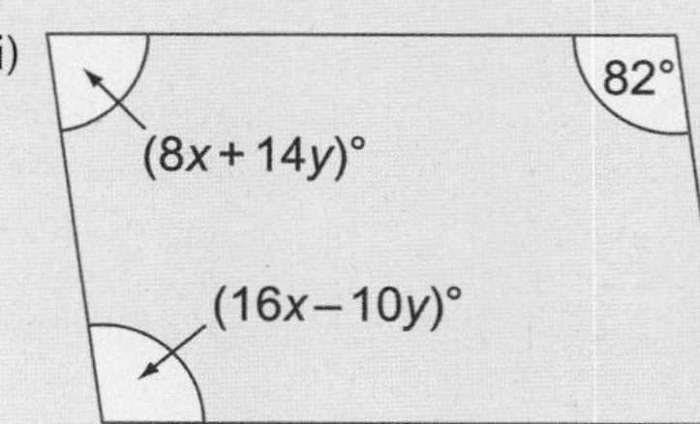

3. In the following diagram, *ABCD* is a parallelogram.

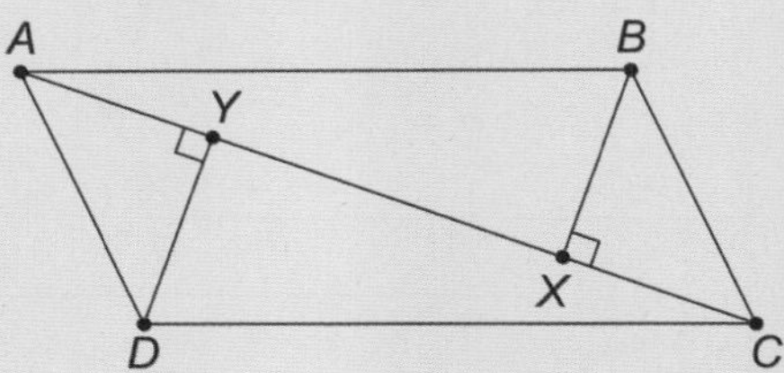

(i) Show that ΔABX is congruent to ΔCYD

(ii) Show that $|AY| = |XC|$.

4. 'Construction 2: Perpendicular bisector of a line segment' is shown. Prove that *AB* is perpendicular to *CD*.

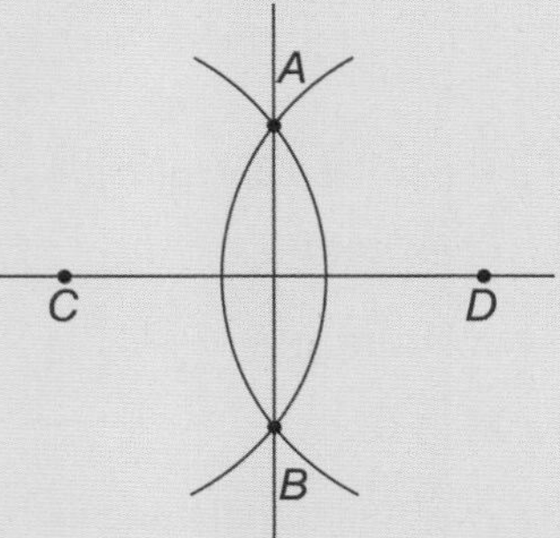

5. *ABCD* is a parallelogram. In the triangle *DCE*, $|DC| = |CE|$.

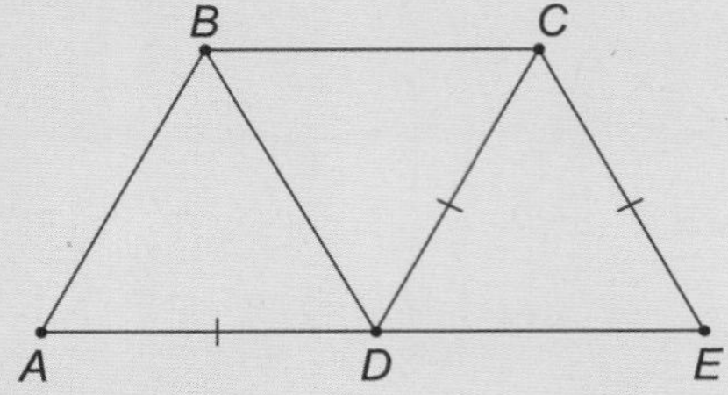

(i) What type of triangle is *DCE*?

(ii) Explain, using a theorem, why $|\angle BAD|$ is equal to $|\angle BCD|$.

(iii) Is $\Delta ABD \equiv \Delta DCE$? State reasons for your answer.

(iv) Show that *ADCB* is a rhombus.

6. In the following diagram, *DEFG* is a parallelogram.

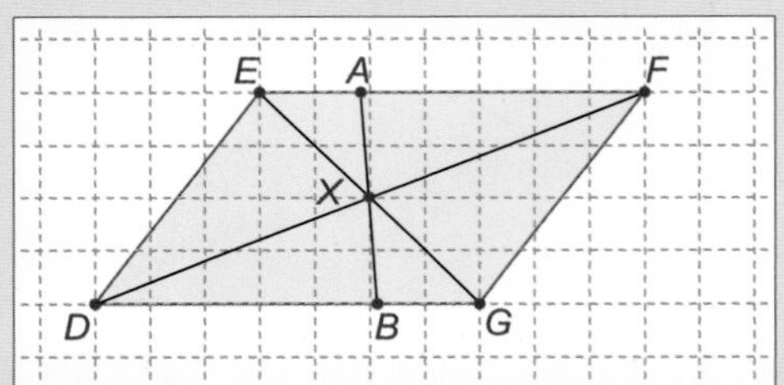

Show that $|AX| = |BX|$.

5.11 PARALLEL LINES AND TRIANGLES

We will now consider:

(a) what happens when three parallel lines intersect a transversal, and specifically,

(b) what happens when that transversal is cut into two equal segments.

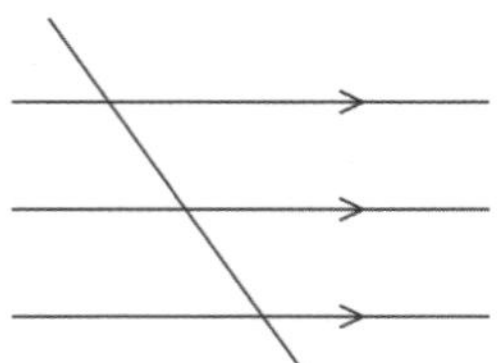

From our investigations, we can determine that:

If a transversal is cut into two equal parts by three parallel lines, then any other transversal drawn between these parallel lines will also be cut into two equal parts.

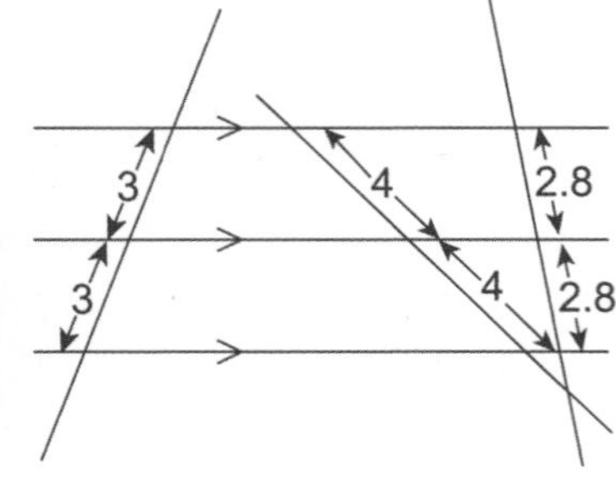

We can now state this as a theorem.

Theorem 11

If three parallel lines cut off equal segments on some transversal line, then they will cut off equal segments on any other transversal.

It is also evident from our investigations that when a line is parallel to one side of a triangle, it divides another side of the triangle in a certain ratio.

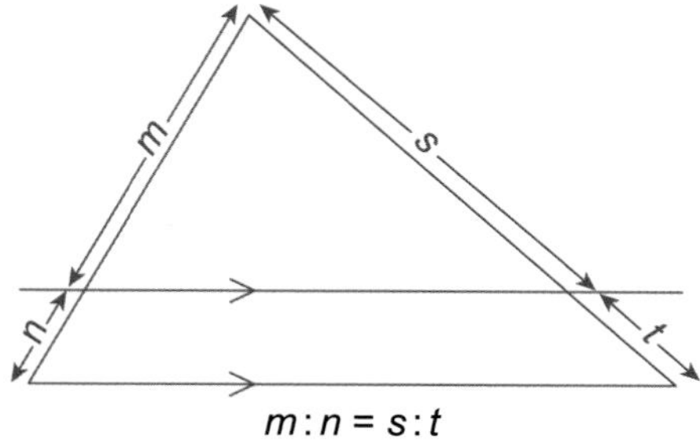

A line that is parallel to one side of a triangle cuts the other two sides of the triangle in the same ratio. This ratio is often referred to as $m : n$.

Consider the triangle shown on the right:

If the ratio $|AX|:|XB|$ is equal to 3 : 2, then the ratio $|AY|:|YC|$ is also 3 : 2.

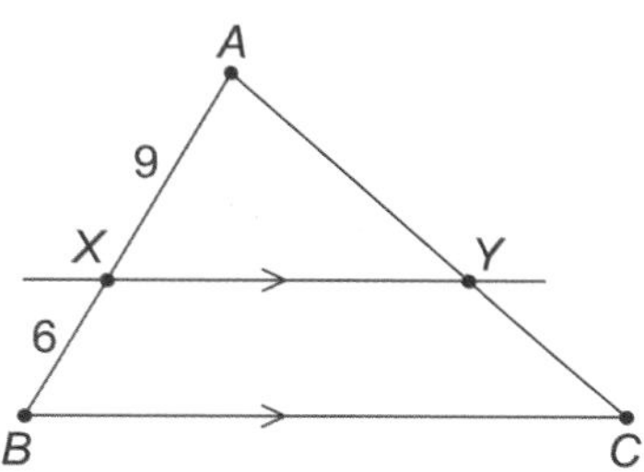

This can be written more formally as:

Theorem 12

Let ABC be a triangle. If a line l is parallel to BC and cuts $[AB]$ in the ratio $m : n$, then it also cuts $[AC]$ in the same ratio.

Ratios can be written as fractions. So, this theorem can also be written as:

FORMULA

$$\frac{|AX|}{|XB|} = \frac{|AY|}{|YC|} \quad \text{or} \quad \frac{\text{Top length}}{\text{Bottom length}} = \frac{\text{Top length}}{\text{Bottom length}}$$

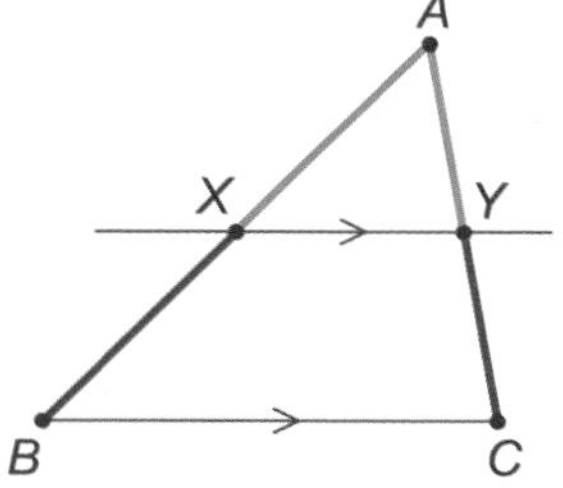

It is important to realise that all of these ratios can be inverted or turned upside down:

FORMULA

$$\frac{|XB|}{|AX|} = \frac{|YC|}{|AY|} \quad \text{or} \quad \frac{\text{Bottom length}}{\text{Top length}} = \frac{\text{Bottom length}}{\text{Top length}}$$

This theorem by itself cannot be used to find the length of the triangle side which is parallel to the intersecting line.

The theorem means that the following is also true:

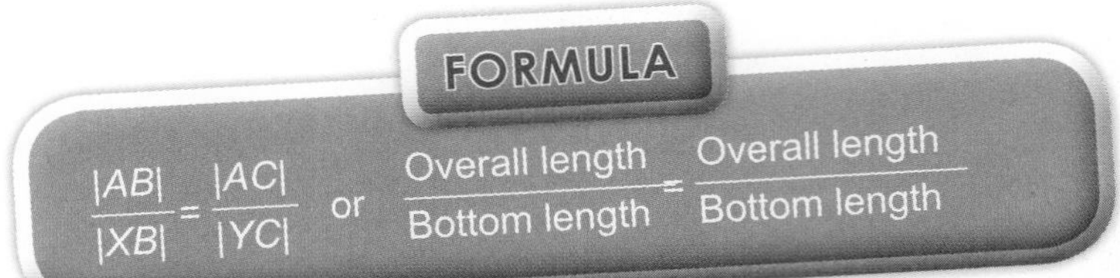

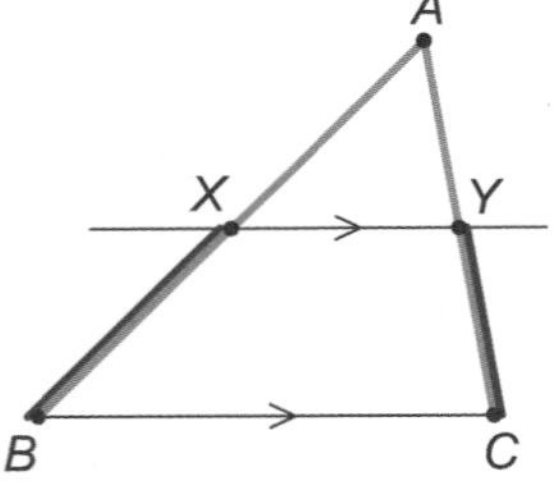

And:

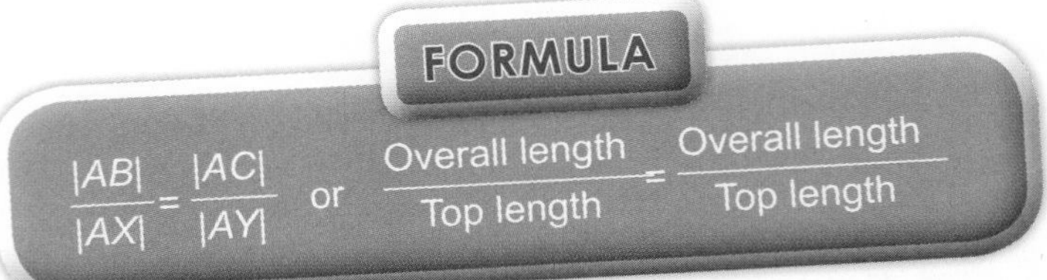

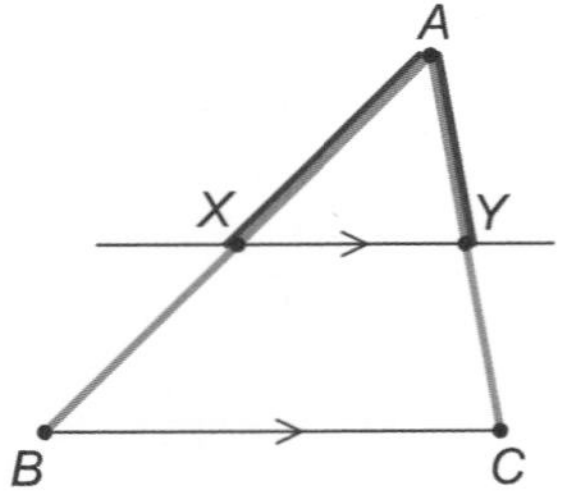

The converse of Theorem 12 can be used to show that two lines are parallel:

If a line cuts two sides of a triangle in the same ratio, then the line is parallel to the side not cut by the line.

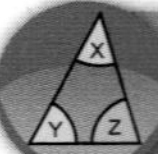

Worked Example 5.8

Find the value of x.

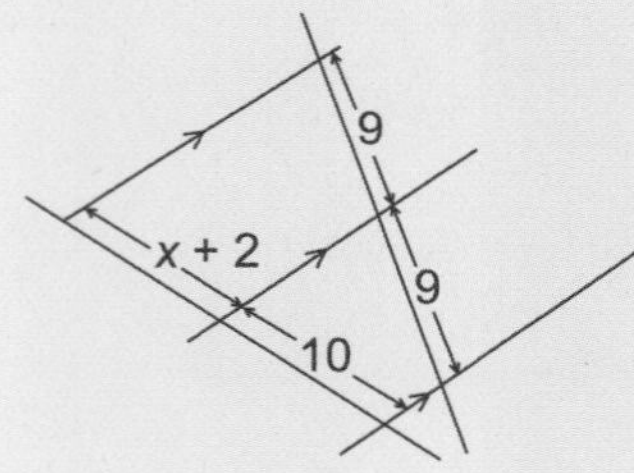

Solution

We can see that the transversal is cut into even parts. Therefore, all the other transversals will be cut into equal parts as well.

To find x:

$$x + 2 = 10$$
$$x = 8$$

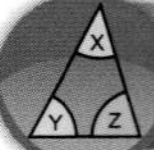

Worked Example 5.9

Find the length of x, given that $DE \parallel BC$.

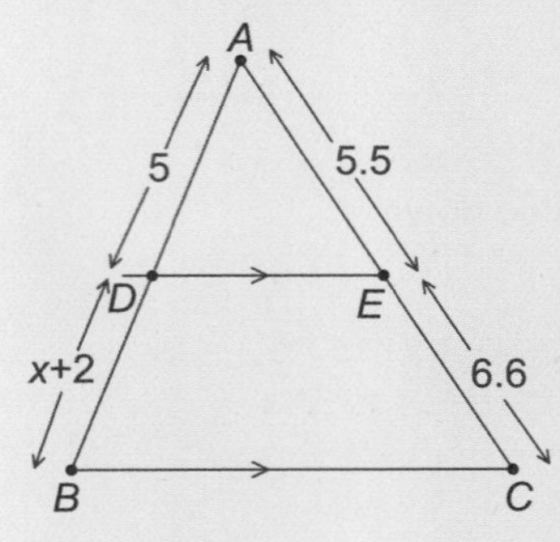

Solution

We will use $|BD|$ to find x, so we must identify which ratio we are using.

We start with the side we are looking for when writing the ratio, as this makes our calculations much easier.

$$\frac{\text{Bottom length}}{\text{Top length}} = \frac{\text{Bottom length}}{\text{Top length}}$$

$$\frac{x + 2}{5} = \frac{6.6}{5.5}$$

Cross-multiply:

$$5.5(x + 2) = 5(6.6)$$
$$5.5x + 11 = 33$$
$$5.5x = 22$$
$$\therefore x = 4$$

Exercise 5.7

1. In each of the following diagrams, find the value of x and y.

(i)

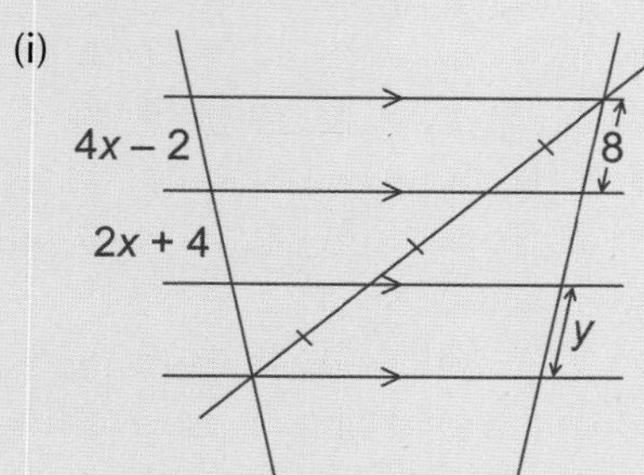

(ii)

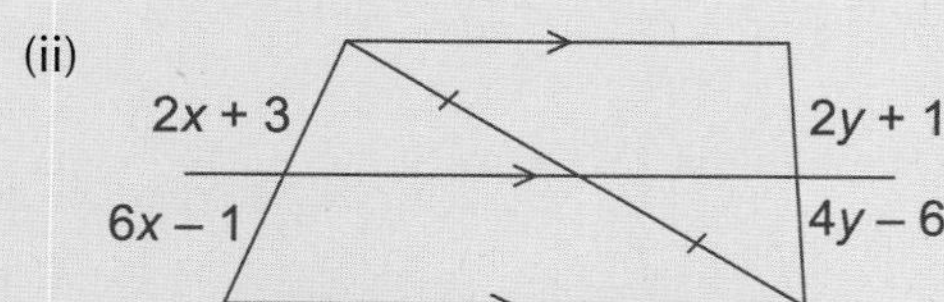

(iii)

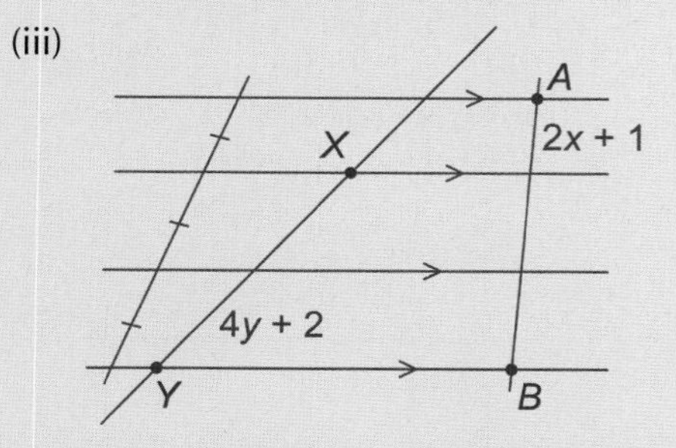

$|AB| = 15$ cm and $|XY| = 12$ cm

2. In the triangle ABC, $PQ \parallel BC$.

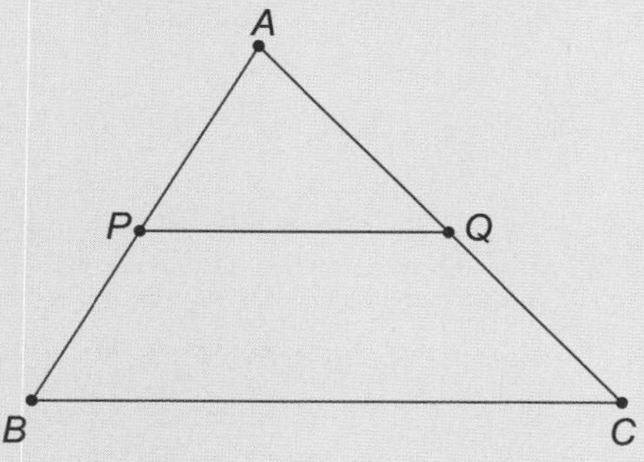

(i) If $\frac{|AP|}{|PB|} = \frac{2}{5}$, then $\frac{|AQ|}{|QC|} =$ ——

(ii) If $\frac{|AP|}{|PB|} = \frac{1}{3}$, then $\frac{|AP|}{|AB|} =$ ——

(iii) If $\frac{|AC|}{|QC|} = \frac{4}{3}$, then $\frac{|AB|}{|AP|} =$ ——

(iv) If $\frac{|AQ|}{|AC|} = \frac{3}{7}$, then $\frac{|AP|}{|AB|} =$ ——

3. Find the value of x in each case.

(i)

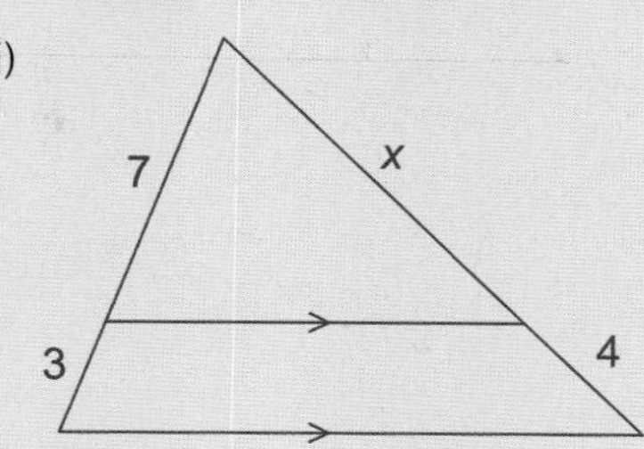

(ii)

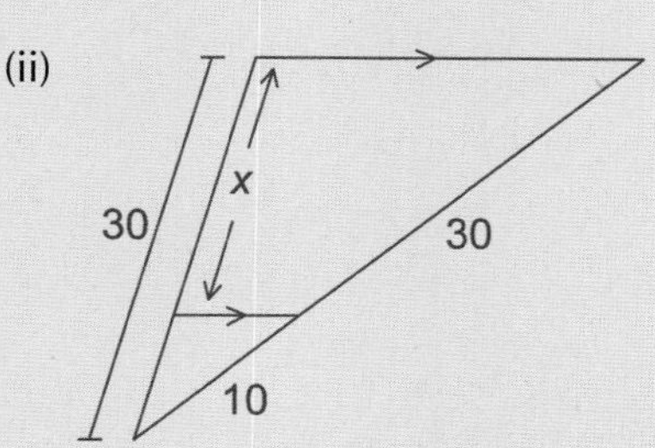

(iii)

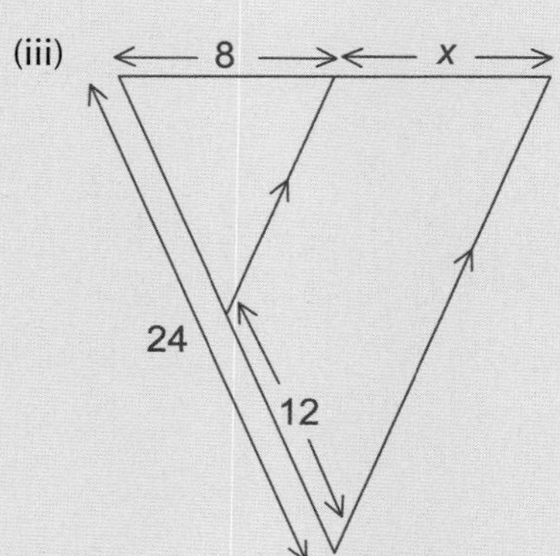

(iv)

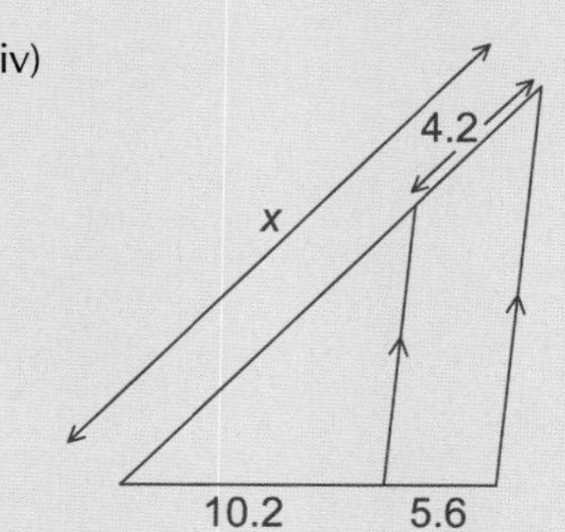

4. Find the value of y in each case.

(i)

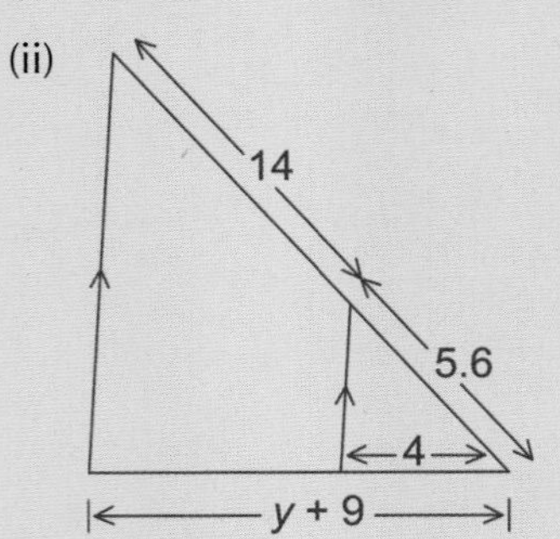

(ii)

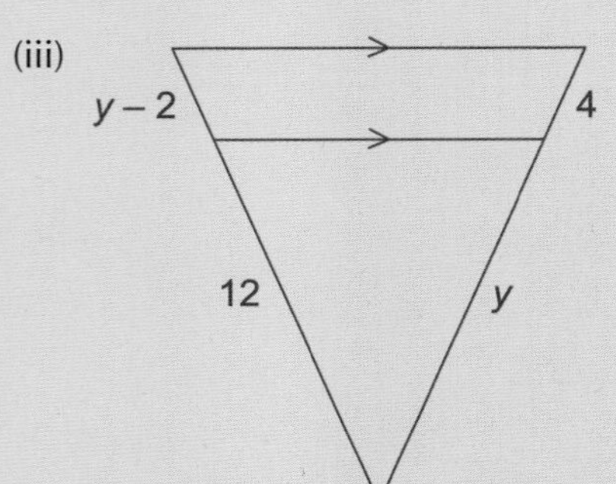

(iii)

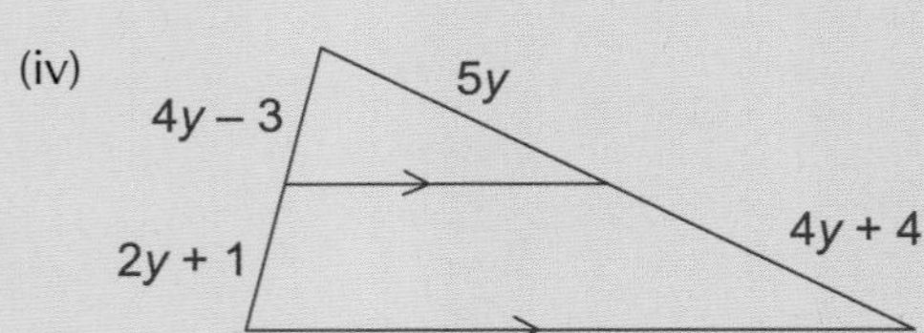

(iv)

5. In the diagram, $ST \parallel QR$.

$|PS| : |PQ| = 3 : 5$.

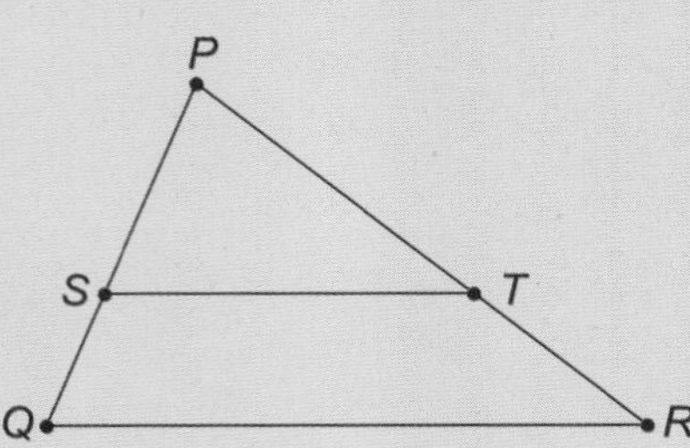

Find the following ratios:

(i) $|PT| : |PR|$
(ii) $|PS| : |SQ|$
(iii) $|PR| : |TR|$

6. In the diagram, $XZ \parallel AB$.

Also, $|XC| : |AX| = 4 : 3$.

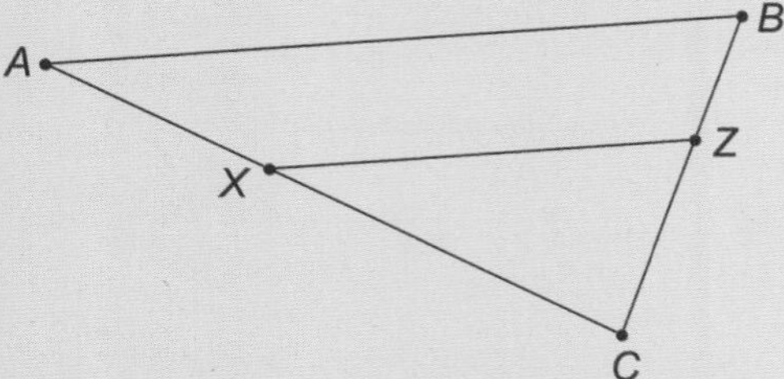

Write down the following ratios:

(i) $\frac{|XA|}{|AC|}$ (ii) $\frac{|BZ|}{|BC|}$ (iii) $\frac{|BC|}{|CZ|}$

7. Investigate if $XY \parallel PR$.

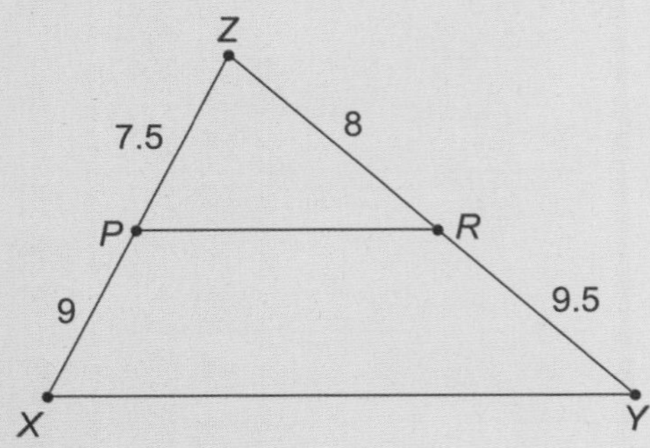

8. Investigate if $AB \parallel DE$.

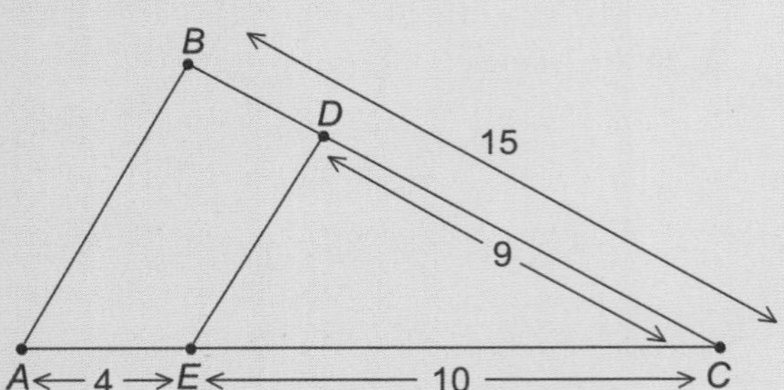

9. In the triangle PQR, $AB \parallel CD \parallel QR$.

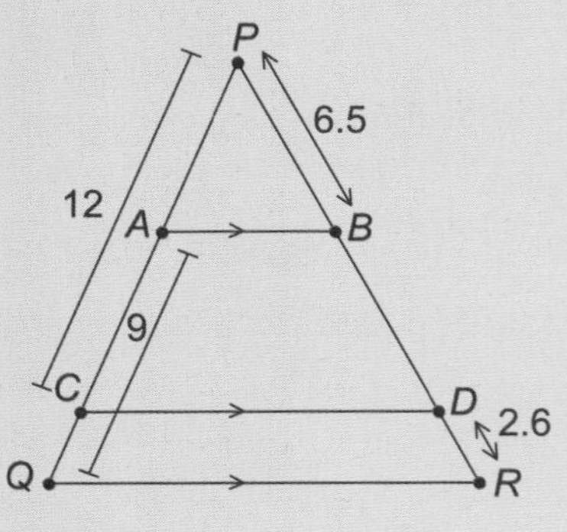

Find:

(i) $|BD|$ (ii) $|AC|$ (iii) $|CQ|$

10. Consider the triangles XYZ and AYB.

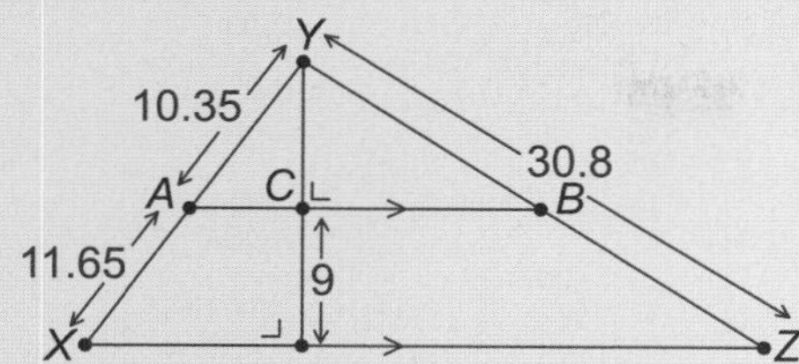

Find:

(i) $|BZ|$

(ii) $|YC|$ correct to nearest whole number

(iii) $|XZ|$ correct to two decimal places

Revision Exercises

1. (a) Consider the following diagram.

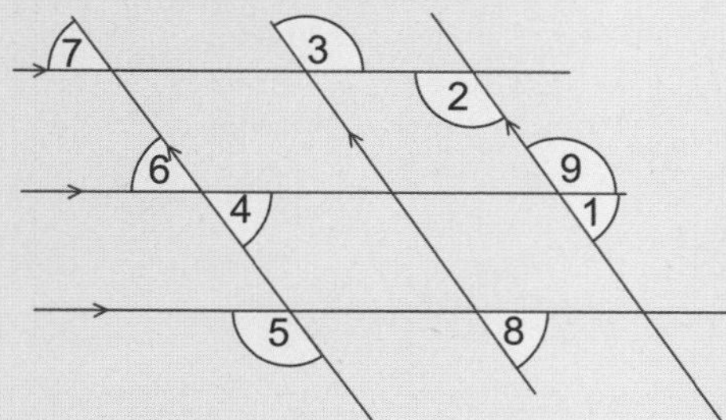

If $|\angle 1| = 63°$, find the measure of all the angles numbered.

(i) $|\angle 2|$
(ii) $|\angle 3|$
(iii) $|\angle 4|$
(iv) $|\angle 5|$
(v) $|\angle 6|$
(vi) $|\angle 7|$
(vii) $|\angle 8|$
(viii) $|\angle 9|$

(b) Consider $ABCD$ and the rhombus $CEFG$.

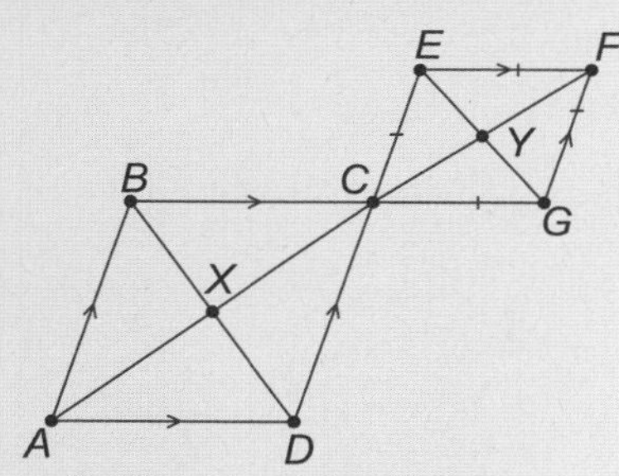

If $|\angle BAC| = 34°$, find:

(i) $|\angle CEF|$
(ii) $|\angle BCD|$
(iii) $|\angle BCA|$
(iv) $|\angle DAC|$
(v) $|\angle CGE|$
(vi) $|\angle BXC|$
(vii) $|\angle EYF|$
(viii) $|\angle DCG|$

2. Consider the following diagram:

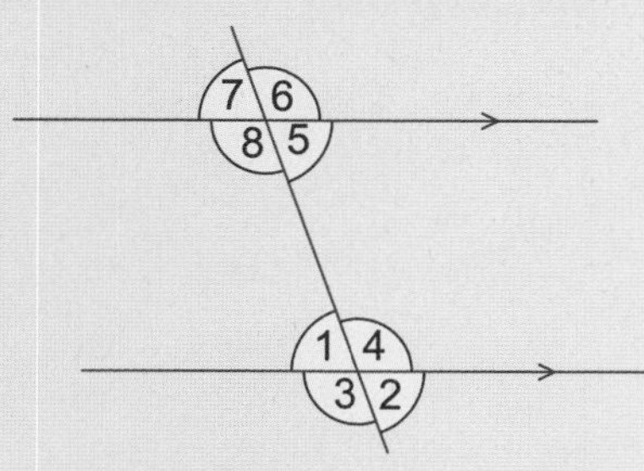

(a) If $|\angle 1| = 70°$, find:

(i) $|\angle 2|$
(ii) $|\angle 4|$
(iii) $|\angle 5|$
(iv) $|\angle 6|$

(b) If $|\angle 4| = (7x + 10)°$ and $|\angle 8| = (8x - 5)°$, find $|\angle 6|$.

3. (a) Consider the following diagram.

$|\angle 2| = (10x + 2y)°$, $|\angle 5| = (5x + 5y)°$ and $|\angle 6| = (15x + 7y)°$

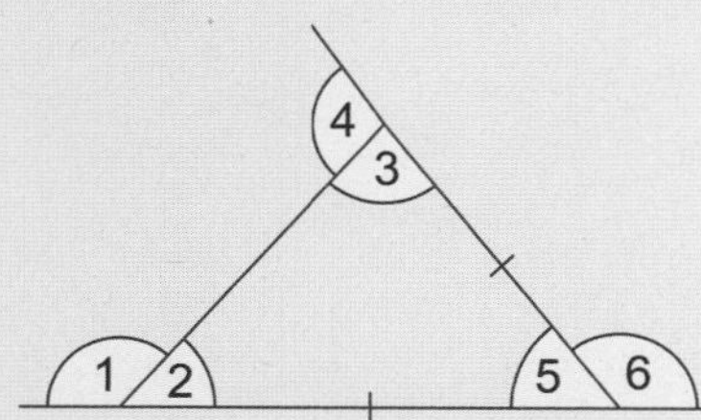

(i) Find the value of x and y.

(ii) Hence, find the measure of each of the listed angles.

(b) The following diagram shows a regular seven-sided polygon (i.e. equal side lengths):

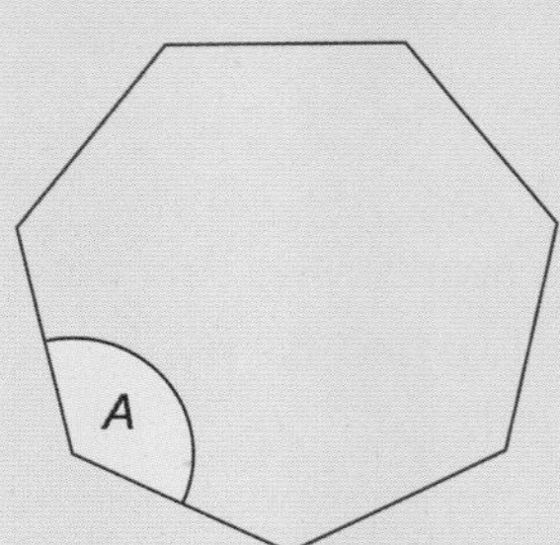

(i) Explain what is meant by the term 'polygon'.

(ii) Show that the sum of the interior angles of any seven-sided polygon is equal to 900°.

(iii) Deduce the measure of angle A, correct to the nearest degree.

(c) A regular n-agon has n sides of equal length.

Explain why the angle at each vertex is $\frac{(n-2)\,180°}{n}$.

4. Consider the parallelogram $ABCD$.

(a) If $|\angle CAD| = 27°$, $|\angle AXB| = 66°$ and $|\angle ACD| = 42°$, find:

(i) $|\angle ABD|$

(ii) $|\angle BXC|$

(iii) $|\angle ADB|$

(iv) $|\angle ACB|$

(b) $|AB| = 4x + 2y + 2$, $|DC| = 7x + \frac{3}{2}y$,
$|BC| = 8x + 4y - 5$ and $|AD| = 4x + 6y - 5$.

(i) Find the value of x and y.

(ii) Hence, find the measure of each of the sides.

5. (a) Prove that the following pairs of triangles are congruent. Explain your answer fully.

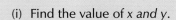

(i)

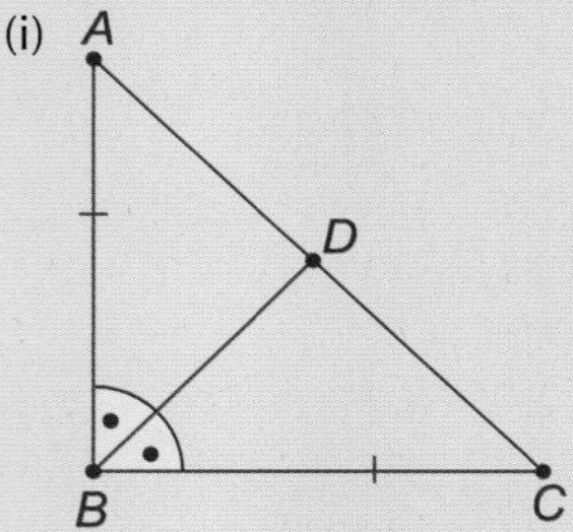

Prove that $\Delta ABD \equiv \Delta BDC$.

(ii)

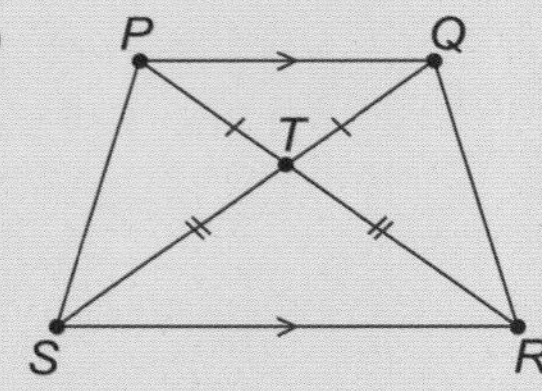

Prove that $\Delta PTS \equiv \Delta QTR$.

(iii)

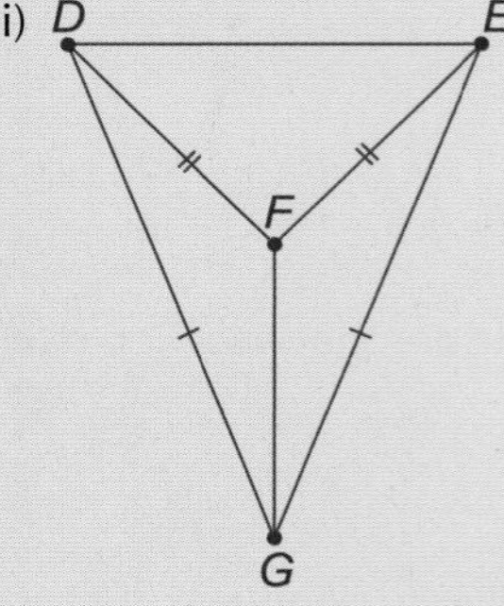

Prove that $\Delta DFG \equiv \Delta EFG$.

(b) In the triangle PQR, $|AP| = |BR|$ and $|AD| = |BD|$.

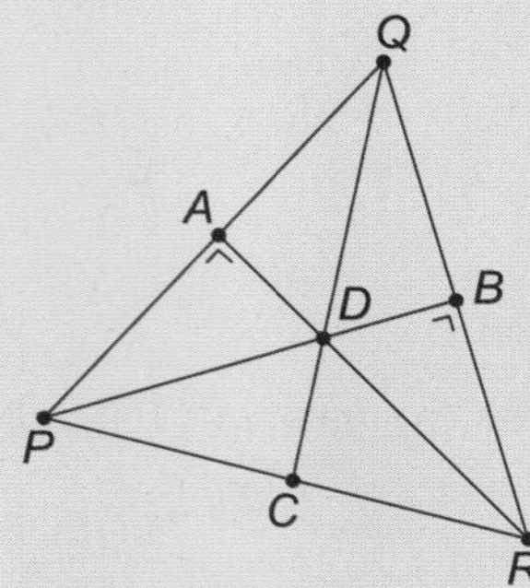

(i) Prove that ΔPQR is an isosceles triangle.

(ii) Show that $|PC| = |CR|$.

6. (a) Two triangular metal frames are joined to form a door part as shown.

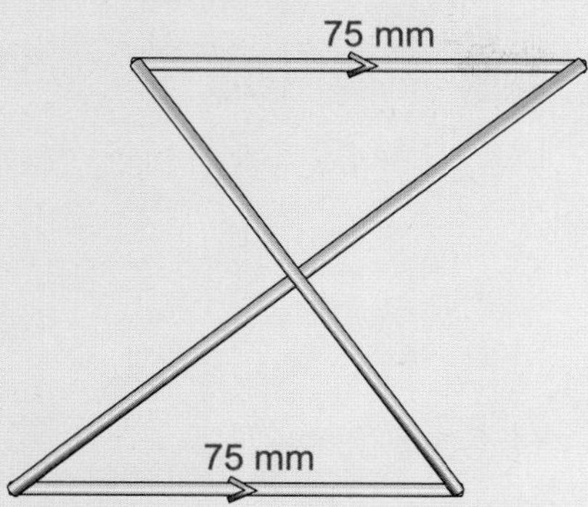

Show that the two triangular metal frames are identical.

(b) A carpenter marks off the two midpoints of two sides of a square wooden panel. He then cuts along the two lines as shown.

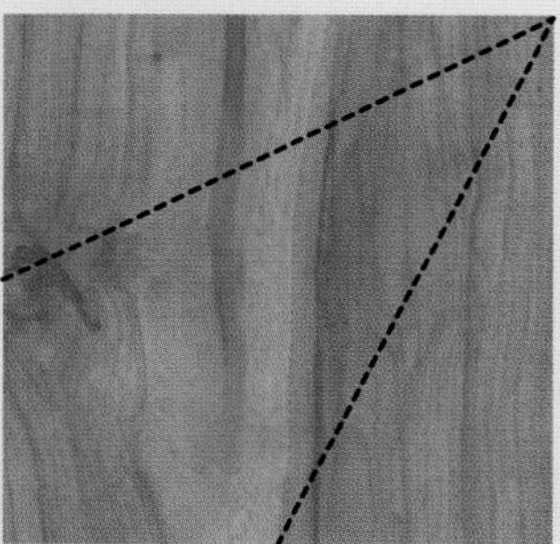

Show that the two cuts are of equal length.

7. (a) Consider the parallelogram $ABCD$.

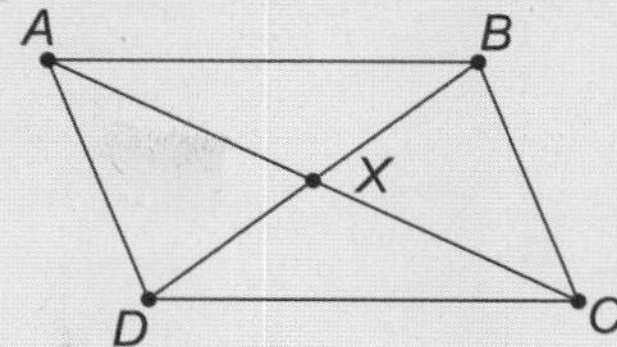

(i) Prove that $\Delta AXD \equiv \Delta BXC$.

(ii) Show that X is the midpoint of $[DB]$.

(b) A blueprint is shown for a part of a table. The part is to be cut from a square piece of wood.

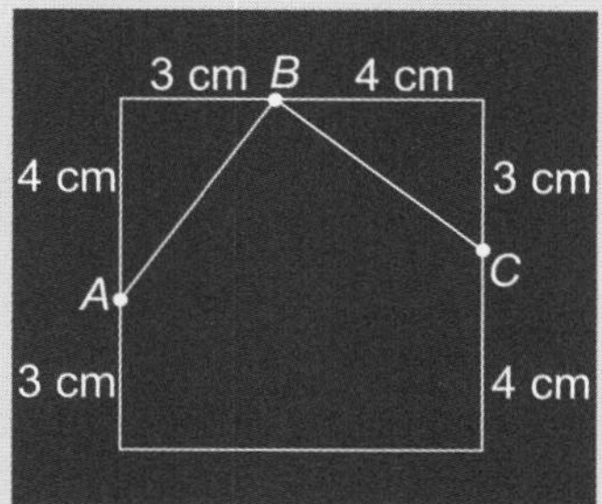

Show that $|\angle ABC| = 90°$.

8. (a) Solve for x in the following triangle:

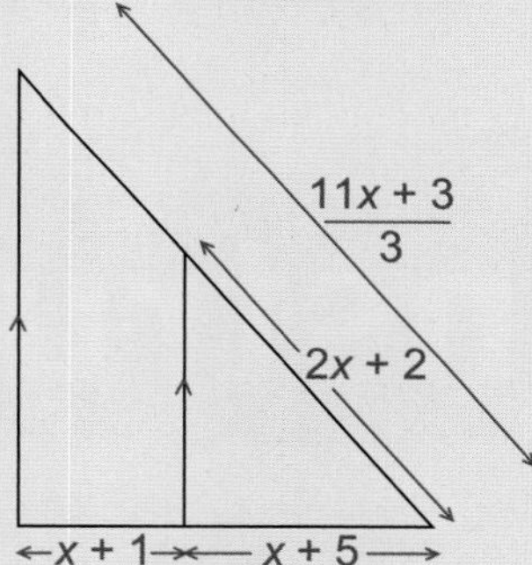

(b) Three roads are all parallel to each other. Ann Street and Bee Street intersect these three roads at junctions P, Q, R, S, T and V as shown on the diagram.

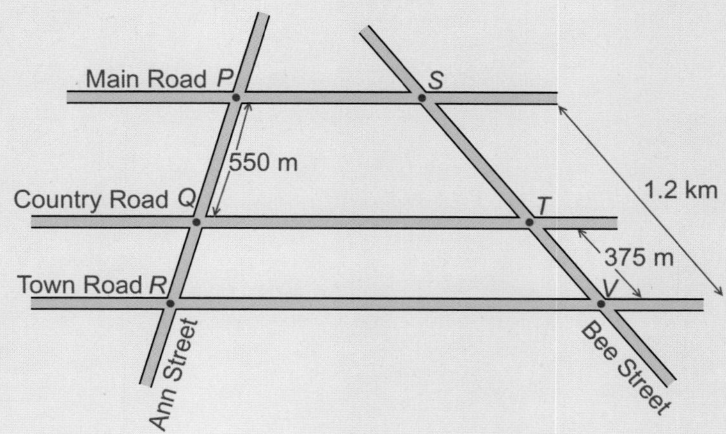

Find the distance between Main Road and Town Road on Ann Street.

6 chapter

Constructions

Learning Outcomes

In this chapter, you will learn to construct the following:

- Constructions as specified on the Junior Certificate Higer Level Syllabus
- Construct the circumcentre and circumcircle of a given triangle, using only a straight edge and a compass
- Construct the incentre and incircle of a given triangle, using only a straight edge and a compass
- An angle of 60°, without using a protractor or a set square
- A tangent to a given circle at a given point on it
- A parallelogram, given the length of the sides and the measure of the angles
- Construct the centroid of a triangle
- Construct the orthocentre of a triangle

6.1 INTRODUCTION

From the design of a new bridge to that of the next video game console, all new ideas, buildings or constructions start off on the drawing board.

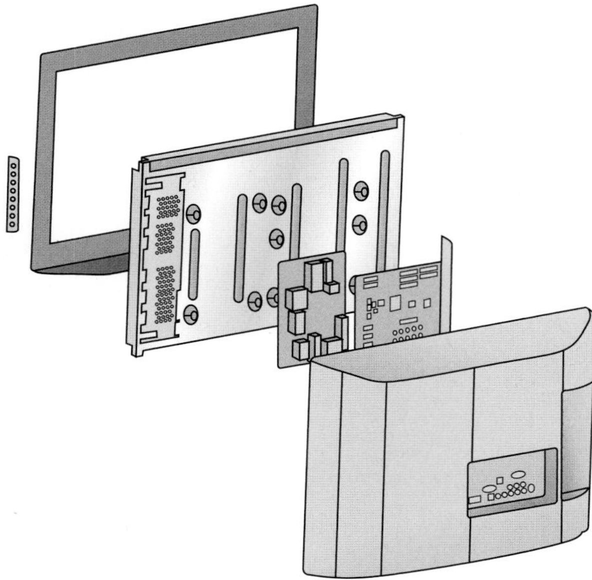

Any engineer, architect or designer will first draw out a new design, and from these drawings a new invention is born.

One only has to remember that the Eiffel tower and the Statue of Liberty (to name a few) were all designed without the aid of computers.

But how do you draw a circle or a triangle accurately? This is where the knowledge and skills of construction play a role.

YOU SHOULD REMEMBER...

- How to draw a line
- How to draw a line segment
- How to draw a ray
- How to measure an angle
- Geometric notation
- Notation used in geometry
- Methods of construction
- The theorem of Pythagoras

KEY WORDS

- **Bisect**
- **Perpendicular bisector**
- **Parallel**
- **Perpendicular**
- **Tangent**
- **SSS**
- **SAS**
- **ASA**
- **RHS**
- **Hypotenuse**
- **Right-angled triangle**
- **Circumcentre**
- **Circumcircle**
- **Incentre**
- **Incircle**
- **Centroid**
- **Orthocentre**

6.2 CONSTRUCTION EQUIPMENT

When doing any construction, accuracy is very important. A mistake of even a few millimetres or half a degree can cause problems. Just ask any engineer!

We use the following equipment when asked to do a construction.

Compass

A compass is used to draw arcs and circles.

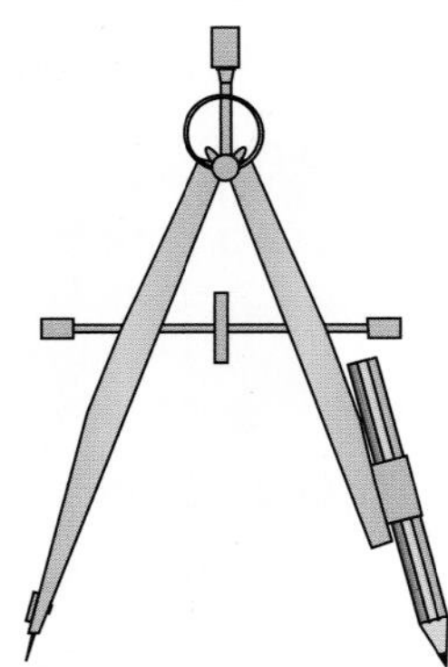

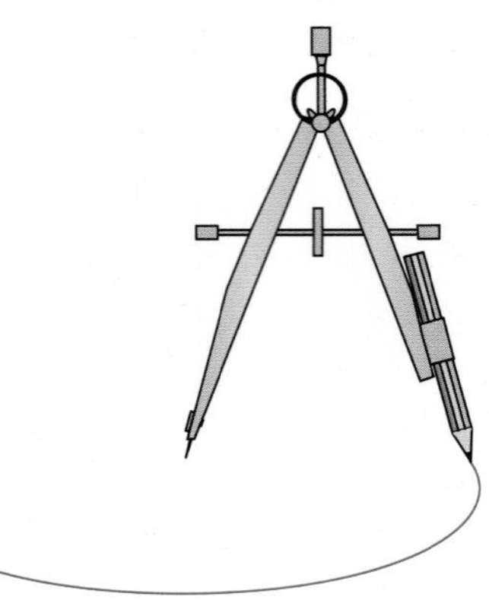

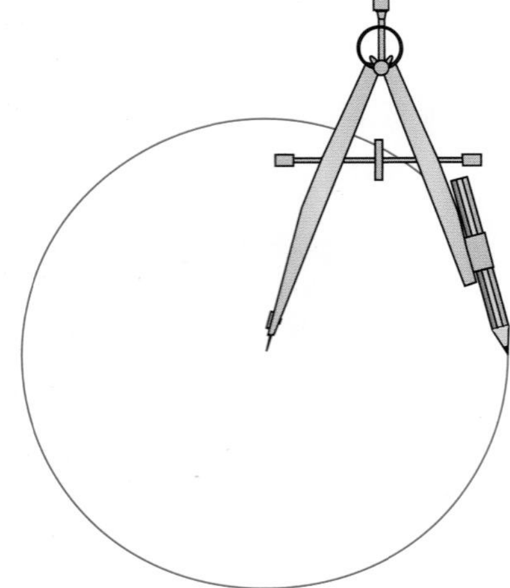

Compass Width

By adjusting the compass width, we can change the size of the arcs or circles that we draw.

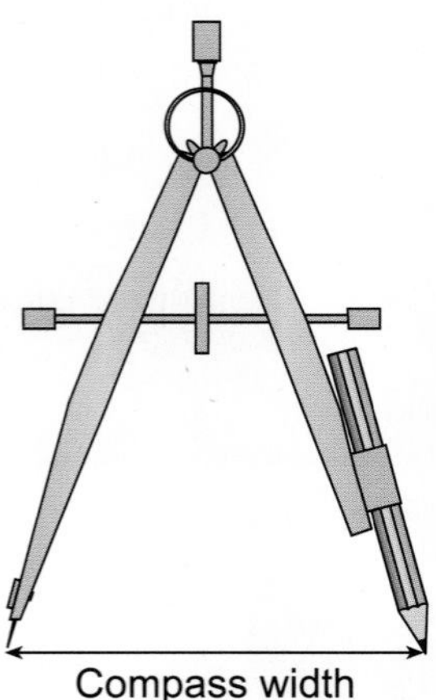

Protractor

The protractor is used to construct and measure angles.

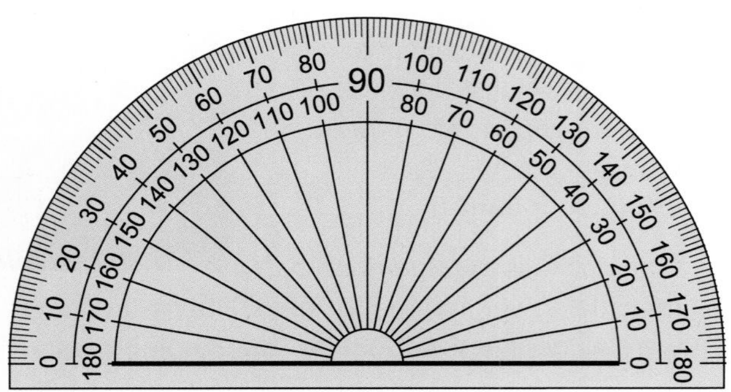

Straight Edge

A straight edge is a tool which is used to draw a straight line. It has no markings, so it cannot be used for measuring lines. In practice, we just use the ruler found in the construction set.

Ruler

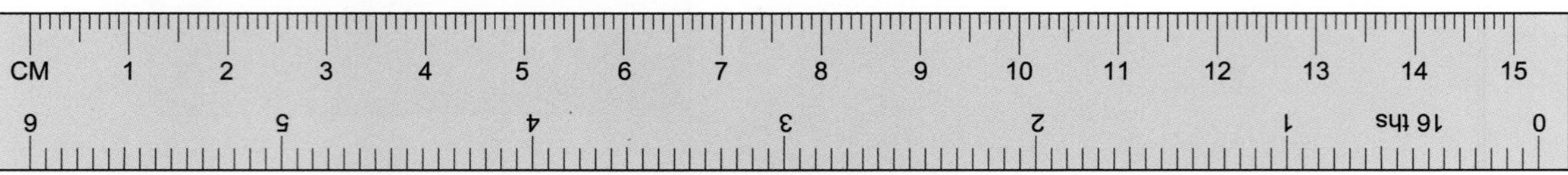

A ruler is used to construct line segments of certain lengths.

Set Square

We can use set squares to draw lines and certain angles. Two set squares are used:

- The 45° set square, which has the angles 45°, 45° and 90°
- The 30° or 60° set square, which has the angles 30°, 60° and 90°

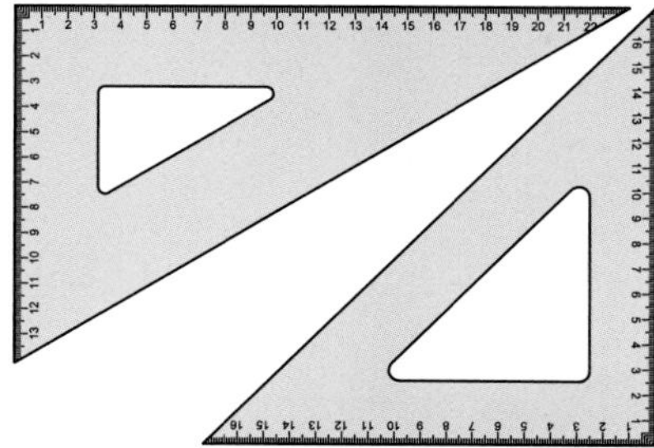

Pencil

Ensure that your pencil has a sharp point and NEVER rub out any lines, arcs, etc. that you have used in your constructions. These construction lines are very important, as they show that you have followed the correct method.

6.3

Note: The following constructions are specified for Junior Certificate Higher Level and should also be known at Leaving Certificate Higher Level.

CONSTRUCTION 1

A Bisector of Any Given Angle Using Only a Compass and a Straight Edge

Worked Example 6.1

Construct the **bisector** of $\angle ABC$.

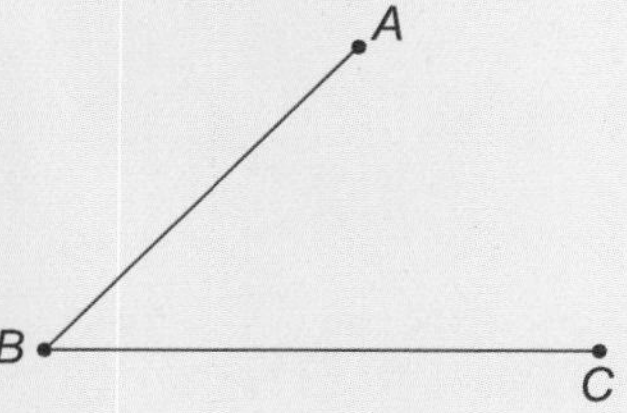

To bisect is to cut into two equal parts. The bisector is the line that cuts an angle in two.

Solution

1 Place the compass point on the angle's **vertex** *B*.

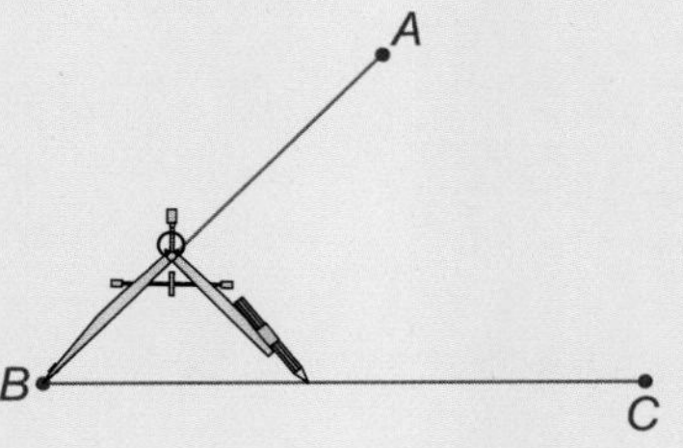

The vertex of an angle is the point where the two rays (or arms) of an angle meet.

2 Draw an arc of the same width across each ray of the angle. Label *X*, *Y*.

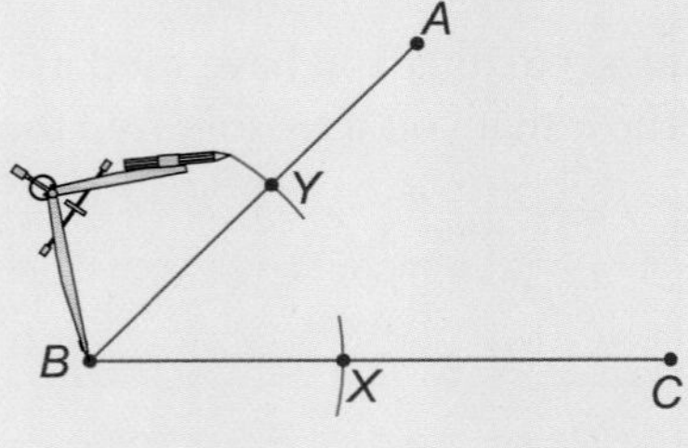

3 Place the compass on the point *X* and draw an arc.

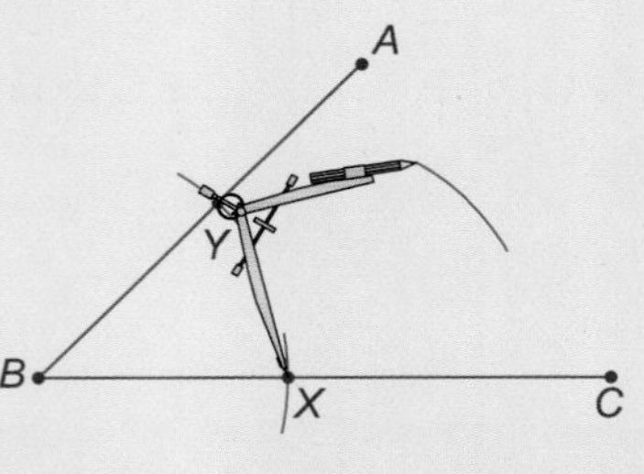

4 Without changing the compass width, place the compass on the point *Y* and draw an overlapping arc.

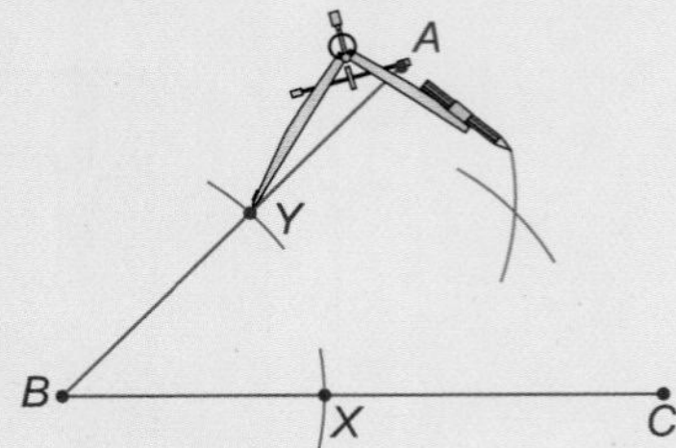

5 Mark the point where the two arcs intersect.

Using a straight edge, draw a line from this point to the vertex *B*.

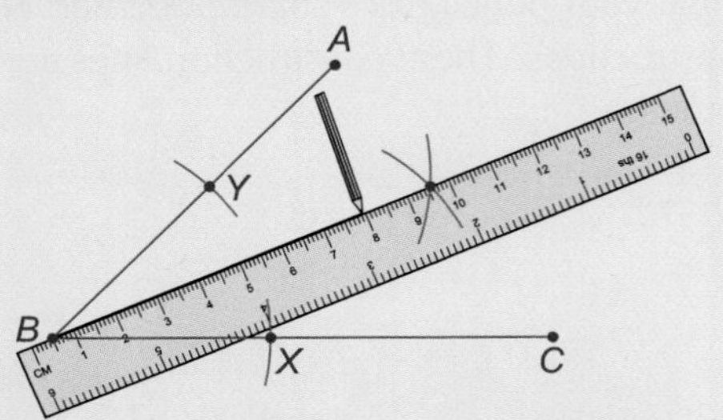

6 This line is the bisector of the angle *ABC*.

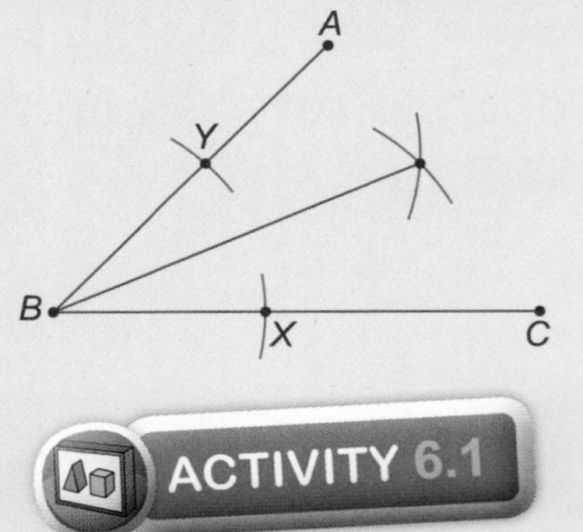

ACTIVITY 6.1

CONSTRUCTION 2

A Perpendicular Bisector of a Line Segment, Using Only a Compass and a Straight Edge

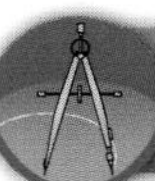

Worked Example 6.2

Construct the **perpendicular bisector** of the line segment $[AB]$, where $|AB| = 3.6$ cm.

A 3.6 cm B

A **perpendicular bisector** cuts the line segment into two equal parts and meets the line segment at an angle of 90°.

Solution

1 Place the compass point on *A*.

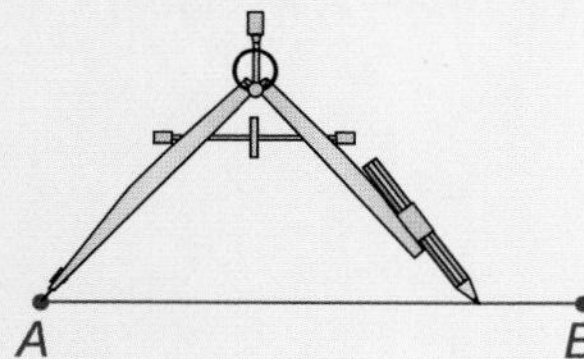

2 Set the compass width to **more than half** the length of [*AB*] and draw an arc.

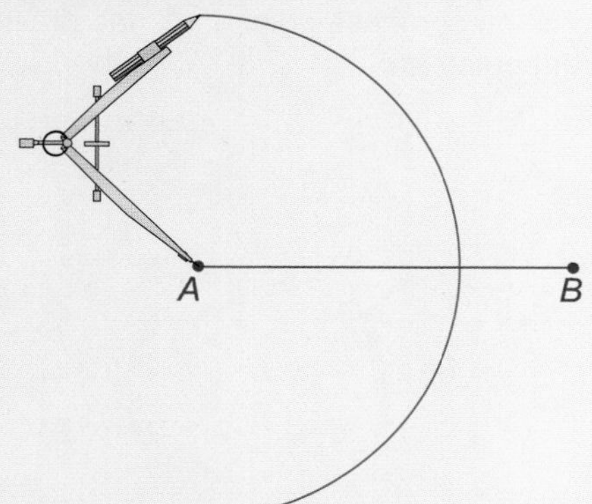

3 Without changing the compass width, place the compass point on *B* and draw an arc.

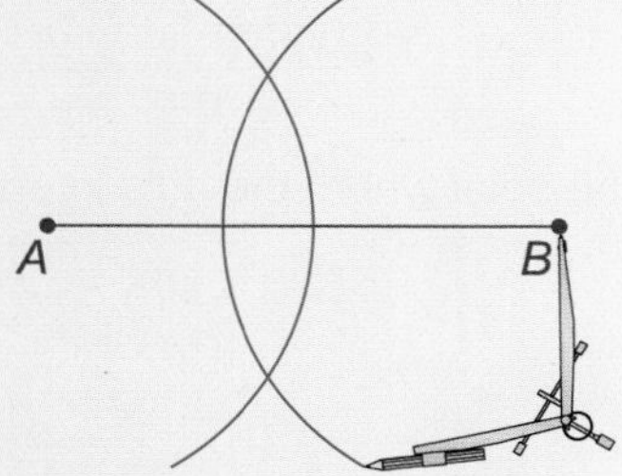

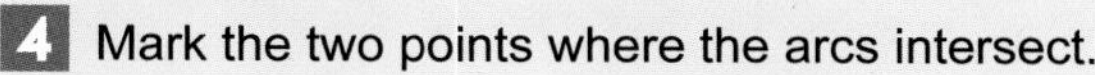

4 Mark the two points where the arcs intersect.

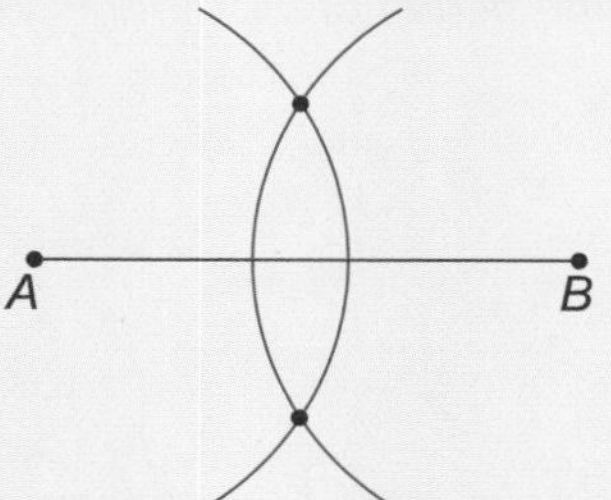

5 Using a straight edge, draw a line through these two points.

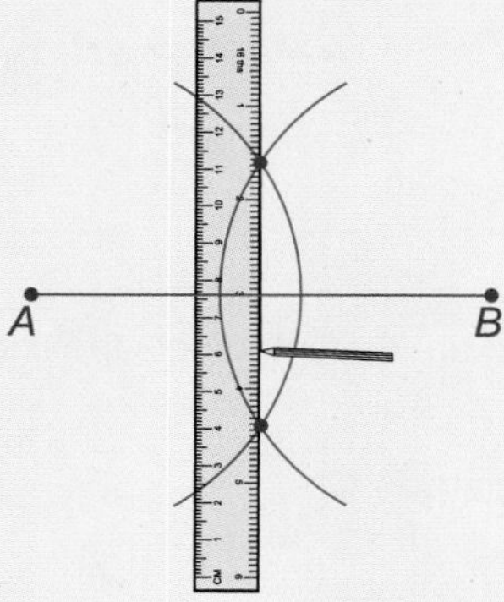

6 This line is the perpendicular bisector of the line segment [*AB*].

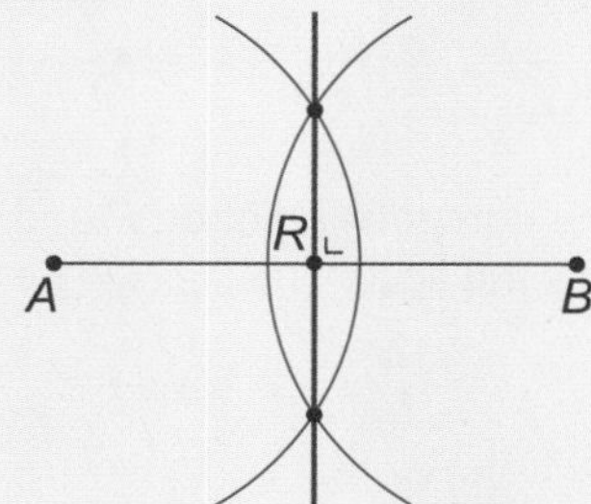

Constructing the perpendicular bisector of a line segment also finds the **midpoint** of the line segment. In the example above, *R* is the midpoint of [*AB*].

CONSTRUCTION 3

A Line Perpendicular to a Given Line *l*, Passing Through a Given Point Not on *l*

Two methods are shown, **both of which must be known**.

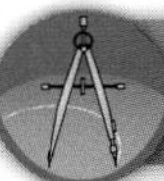

Worked Example 6.3

Construct a line perpendicular to the line *l*, passing through the point *A* not on the line *l*.

A

l

Solution Using a Compass and Straight Edge

1 Place the compass point on *A*.

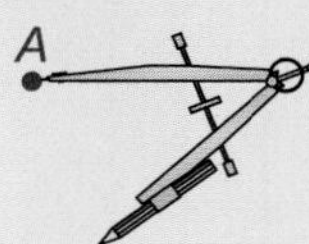

2 Draw an arc that intersects the line *l* at two points.

Label them *P*, *Q*.

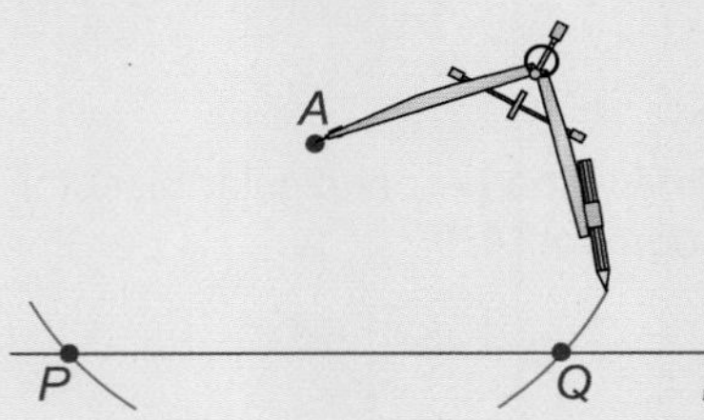

3 Place the compass point on *P* and draw an arc below the line.

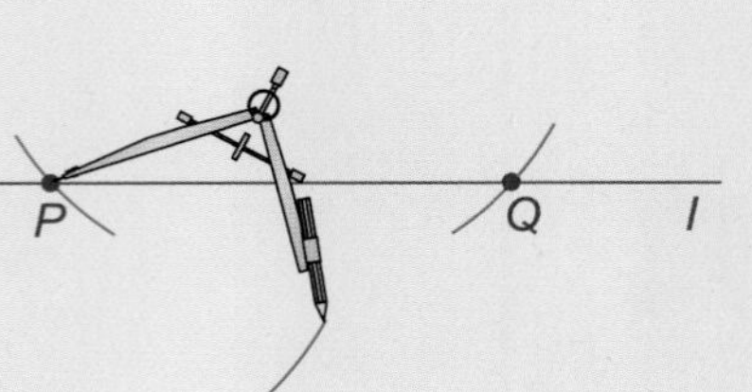

4 Without changing the compass width, place the compass point on *Q* and draw an overlapping arc.

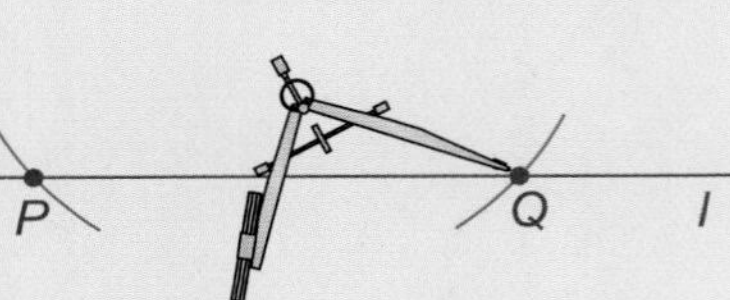

5 Mark the point where the arcs intersect.

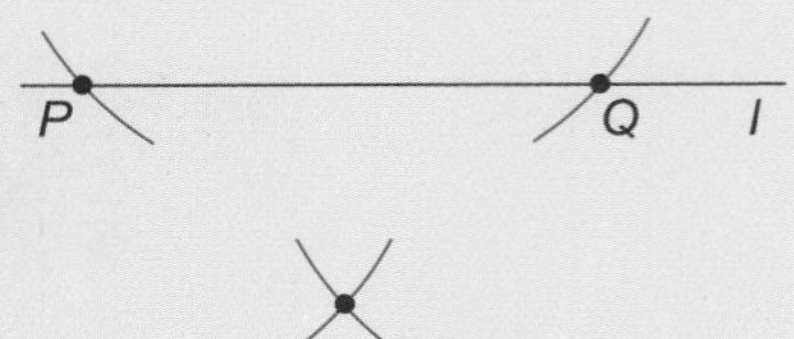

6 Using a straight edge, draw a line through this point and the point A.

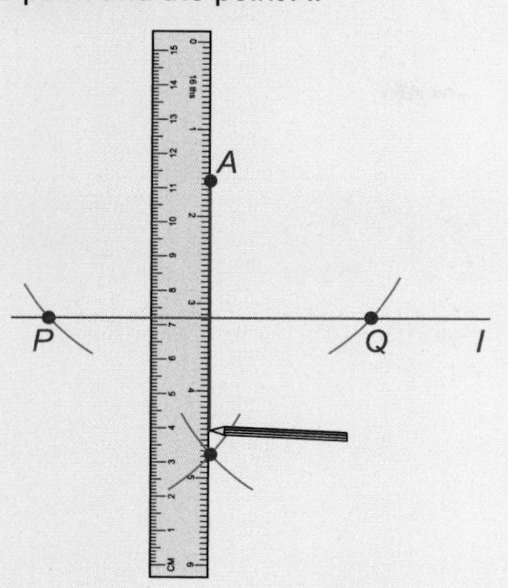

7 This line is perpendicular to the line l and passes through the point A.

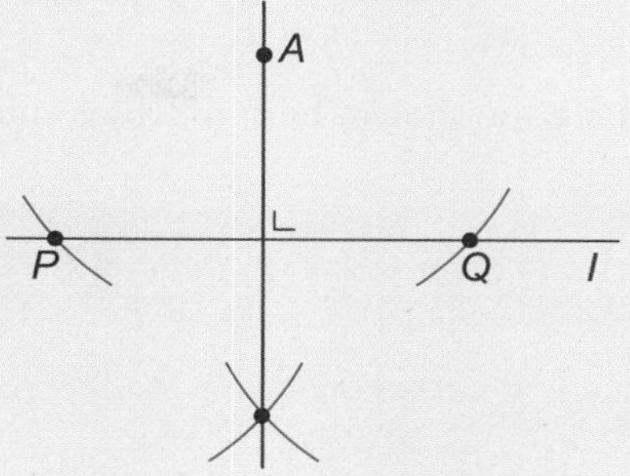

Solution Using a Set Square

1 Line up one side of the right angle of the set square at point A.

Line up the other side of the right angle of the set square on the line l.

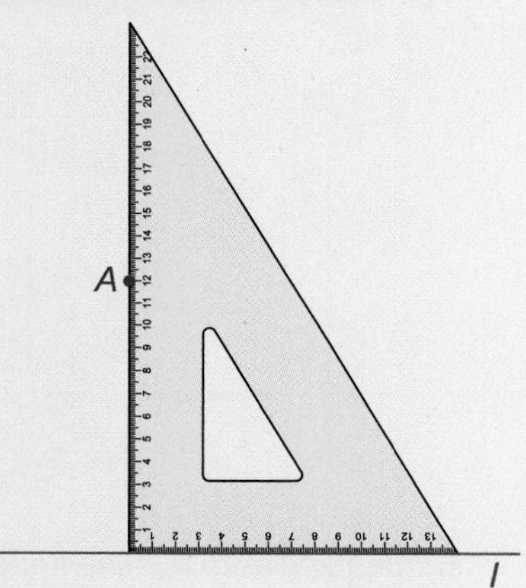

3 This line is perpendicular to the line l and passes through the point A.

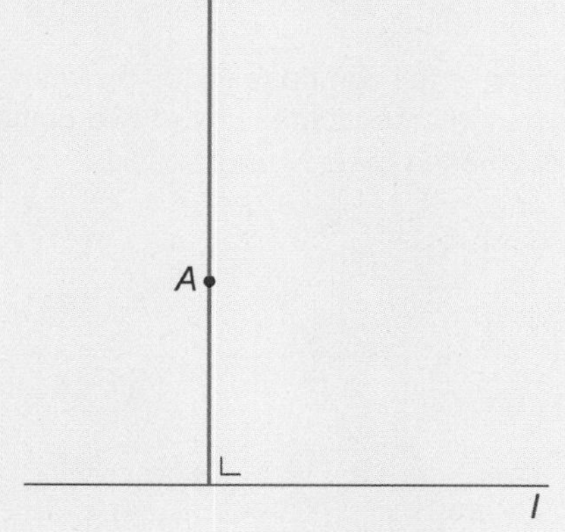

2 Draw a line from the line l through the point A.

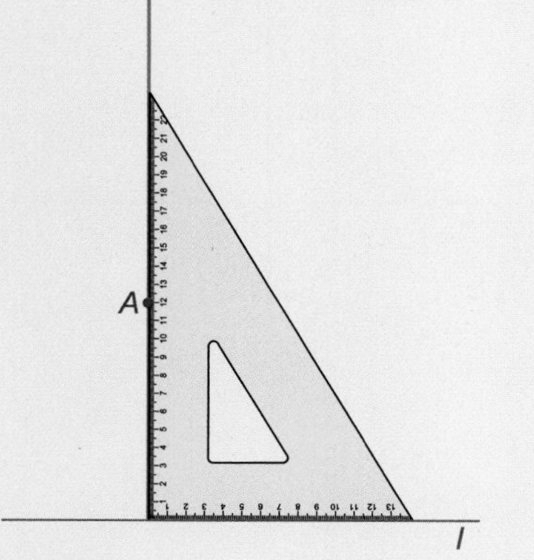

CONSTRUCTION 4

A Line Perpendicular to a Given Line *l*, Passing Through a Given Point on *l*

Two methods are shown, **both of which must be known**.

Worked Example 6.4

Construct a line perpendicular to the line *l*, passing through the point *B* on the line *l*.

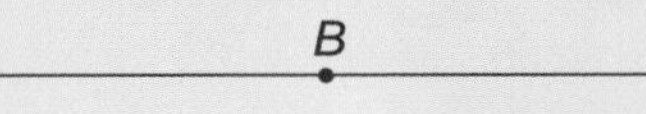

Solution Using a Compass and a Straight Edge

1 Place the compass point on the point *B*.

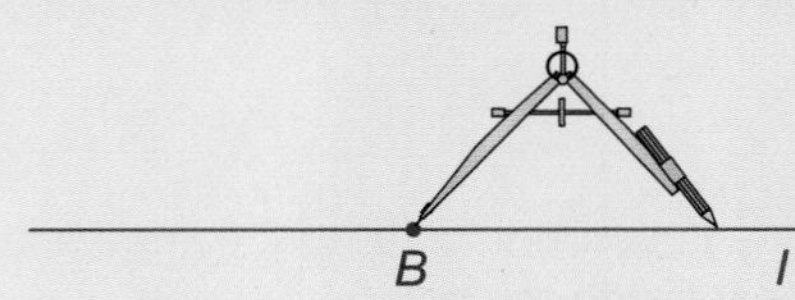

2 Using a small compass width, draw an arc that intersects the line *l* at two points. Label these points *R* and *S*.

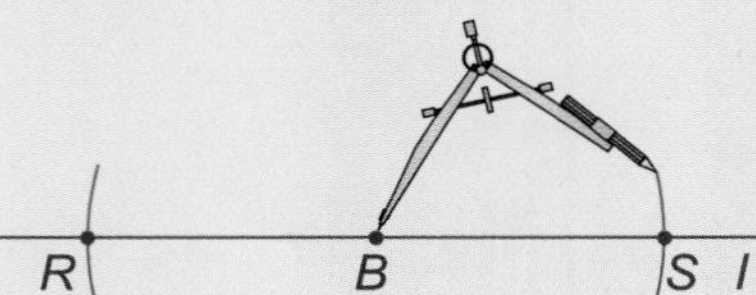

3 Increase the compass width, place the compass point on *R*, and draw an arc.

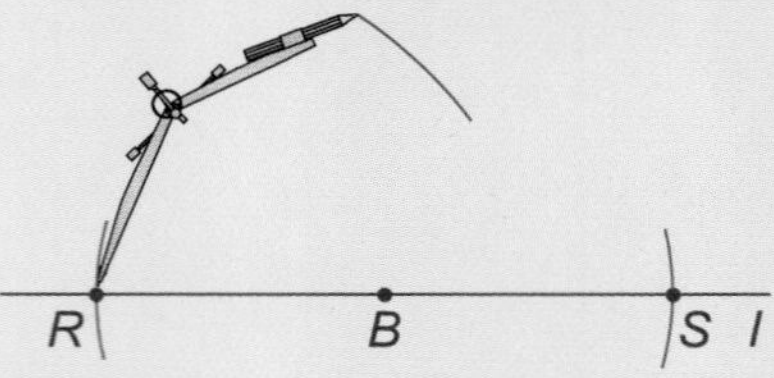

4 Without changing the compass width, place the compass point on *S* and draw an overlapping arc.

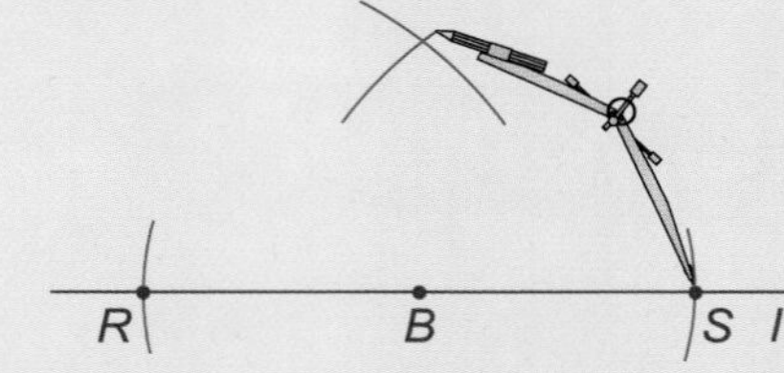

5 Mark the point where the arcs intersect.

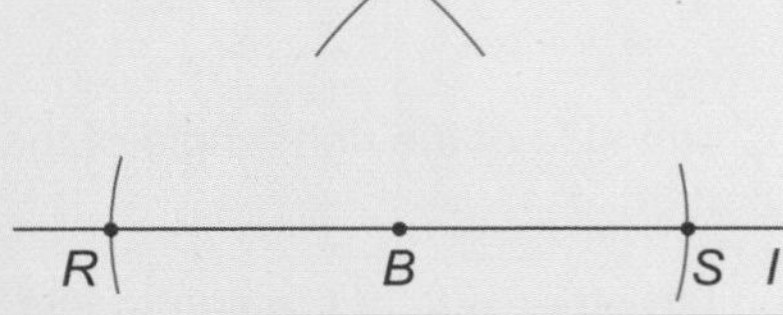

6 Using a straight edge, draw a line through this point and the point *B*.

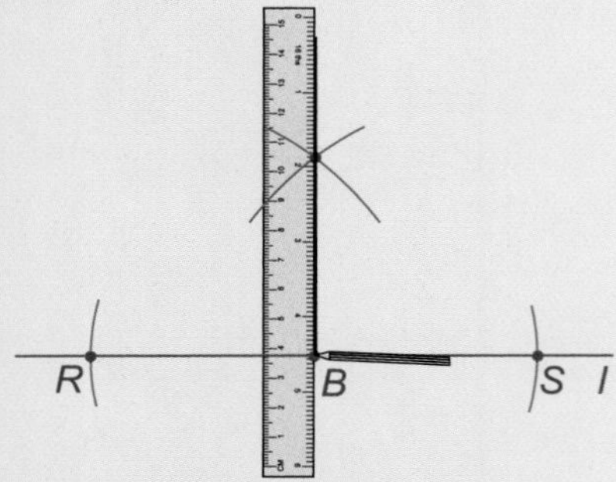

7 This line is perpendicular to the line *l* and passes through the point *B*.

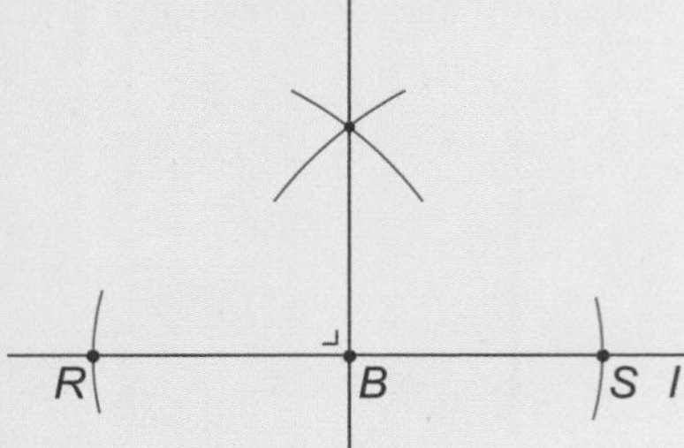

Solution Using a Set Square or Protractor

1 Line up one side of the right angle of the set square at point B and the other side on the line l.

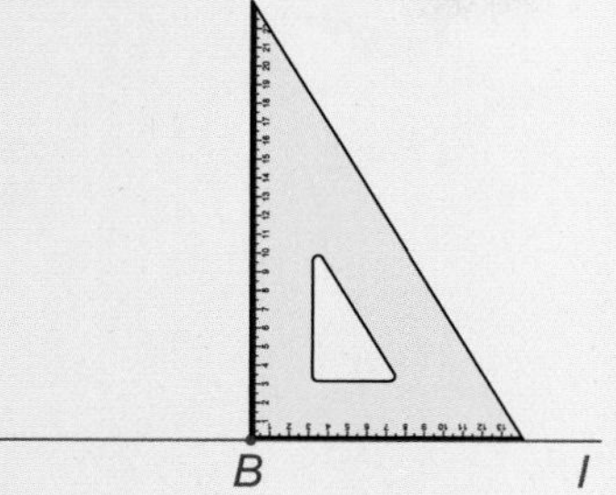

2 Draw a line from the line l through the point B.

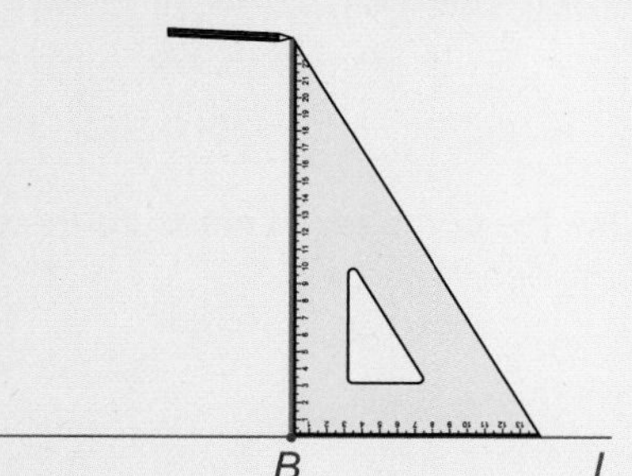

3 This line is perpendicular to the line l and passes through the point B.

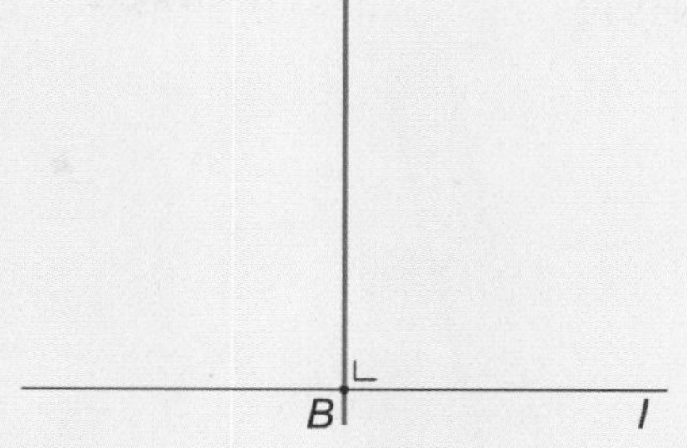

CONSTRUCTION 5

A Line Parallel to a Given Line, Passing Through a Given Point

Two methods are shown, **both of which must be known**.

Worked Example 6.5

Construct a line parallel to the line m, passing through the point C.

C

m

Solution Using a Compass and a Straight Edge

1 Draw a line through the point *C* to the line *m*.

Label the point of intersection of these two lines *D*.

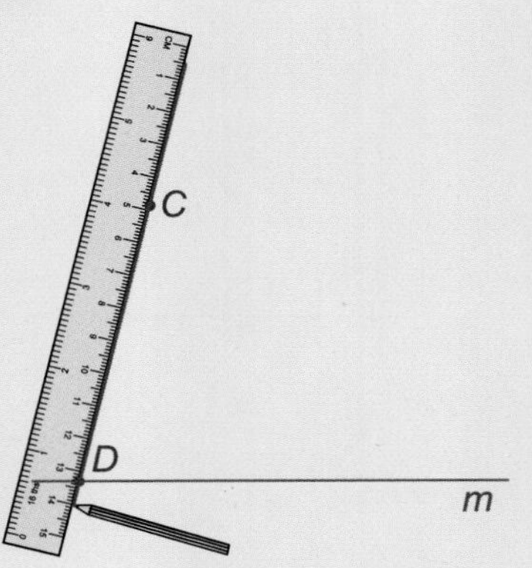

2 Place the compass point on *D*, and draw an arc across both lines.

Ensure that the arc does not go above the point *C*.

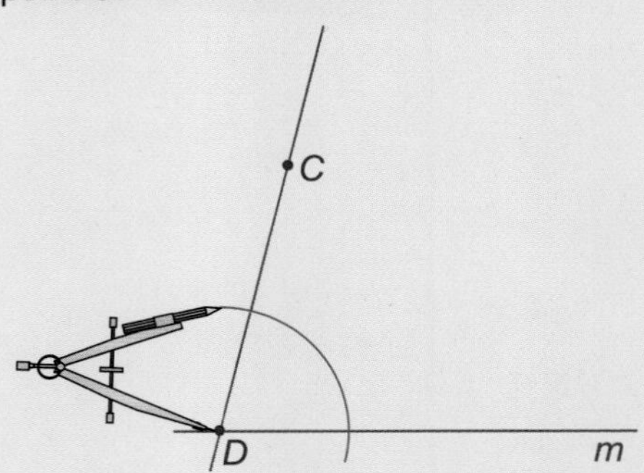

3 Label the points of intersection *X* and *Y*.

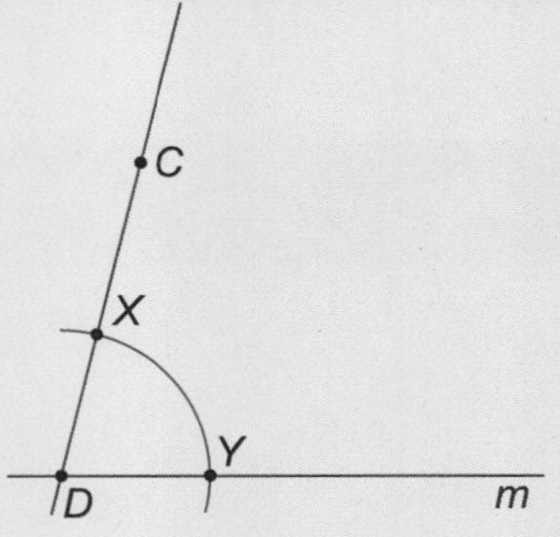

4 Without changing the compass width, place the compass point on *C* and draw an arc.

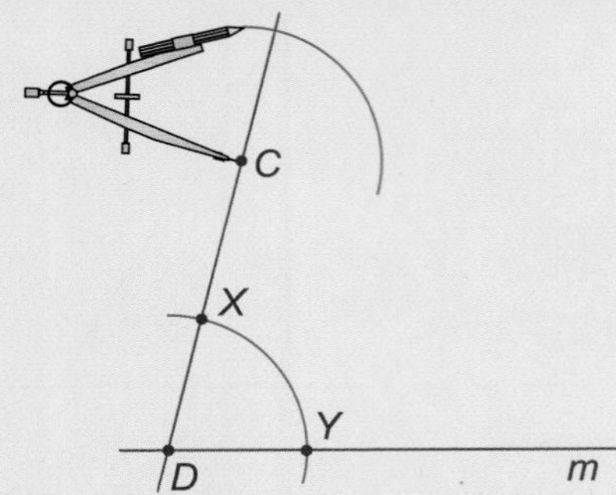

5 Use the compass to measure the distance between *X* and *Y*.

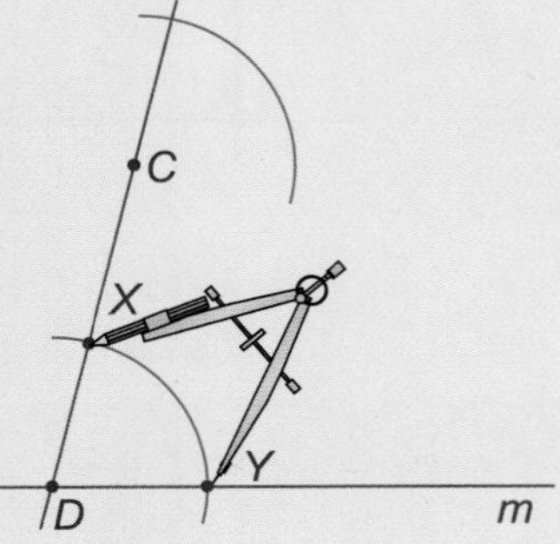

6 Using this compass width, place the compass point where the upper arc and line meet.

Draw a new arc across the upper arc.

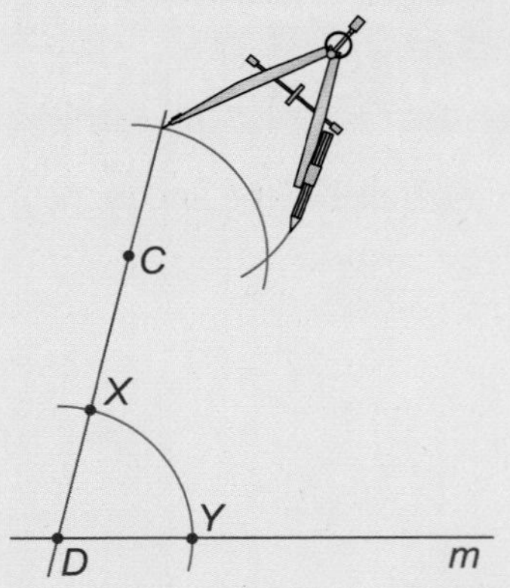

7 Mark the point where the arcs intersect.

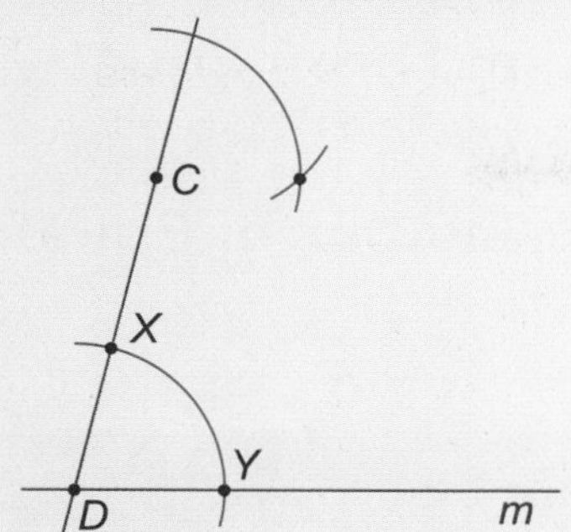

8 Using a straight edge, draw a line from this point through the point C.

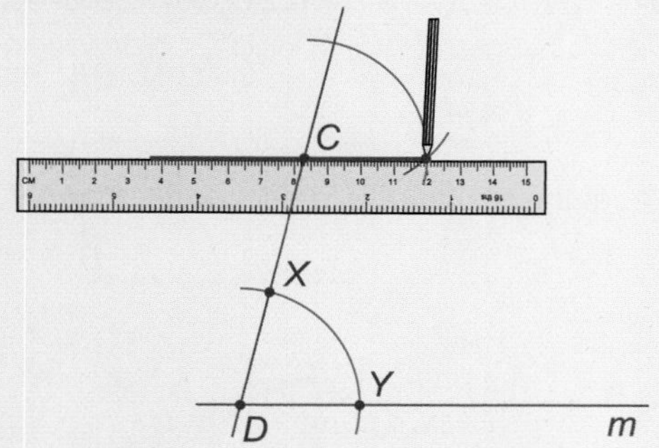

9 This line is parallel to the line m and passes through the point C.

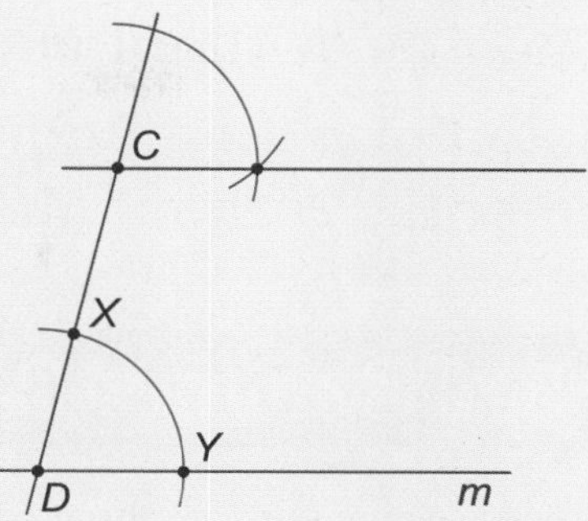

Solution Using a Set Square

1 Using a set square, draw a perpendicular line through the point C to the line m.

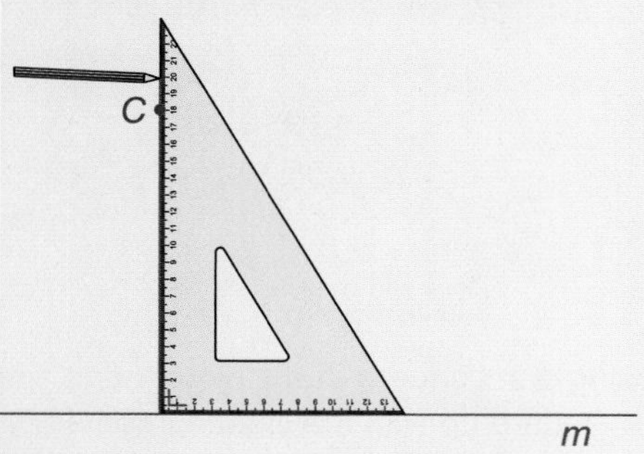

2 Line up one side of the right angle of the set square at point C and the other side on the perpendicular line.

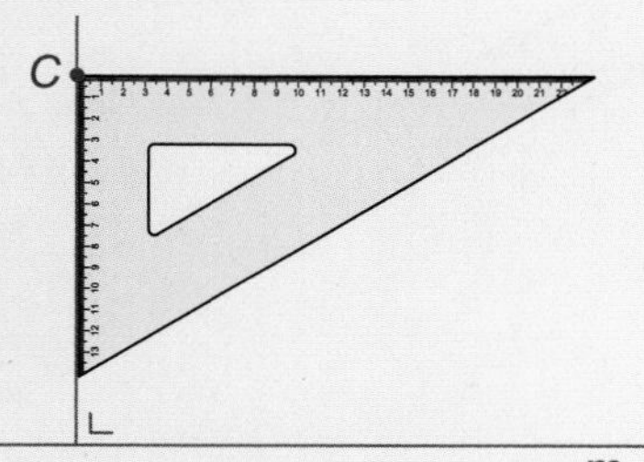

3 Draw a line through the point C.

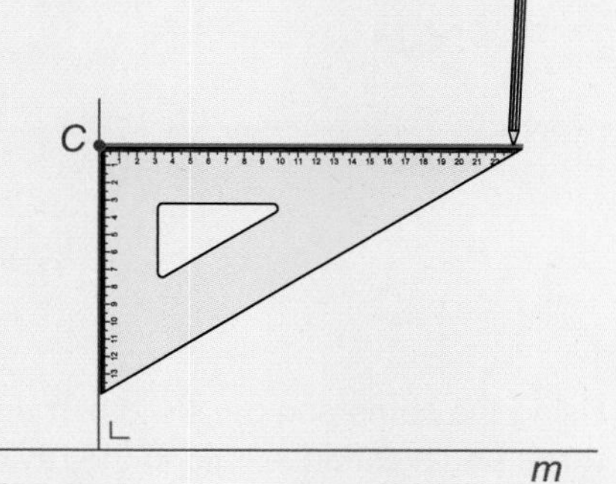

4 This line is parallel to the line m and passes through the point C.

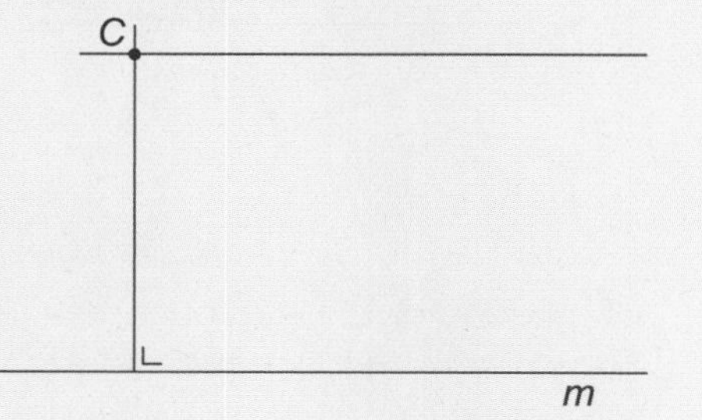

CONSTRUCTIONS 6 AND 7

6: Division of a Line Segment into Two or Three Equal Segments, Without Measuring It

7: Division of a Line Segment into Any Number of Equal Segments, Without Measuring It

Worked Example 6.6

Divide the line segment [*AB*] into **three** equal parts, where $|AB| = 10$ cm.

A ————————— B

> Note: The following method can be used for both Construction 6 and Construction 7.

Solution

1 From point *A* (or *B*), draw a ray at an acute angle to the given line segment.

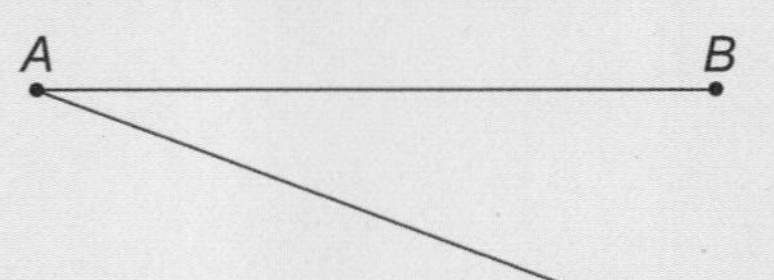

2 Place the compass point on *A*.

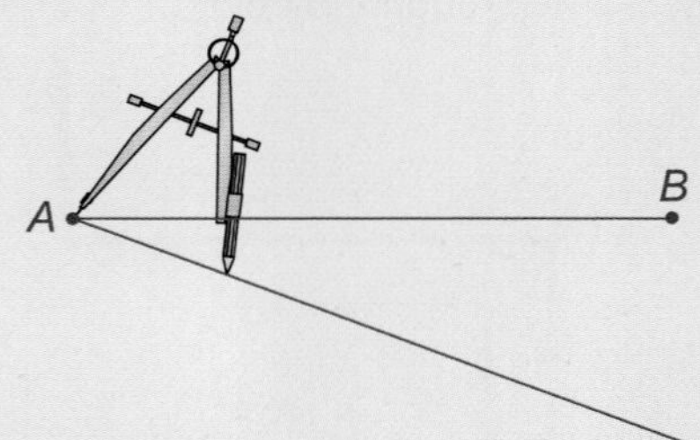

3 Using the same compass width, mark off **three** equal distances along the ray. (Use a small compass width.)

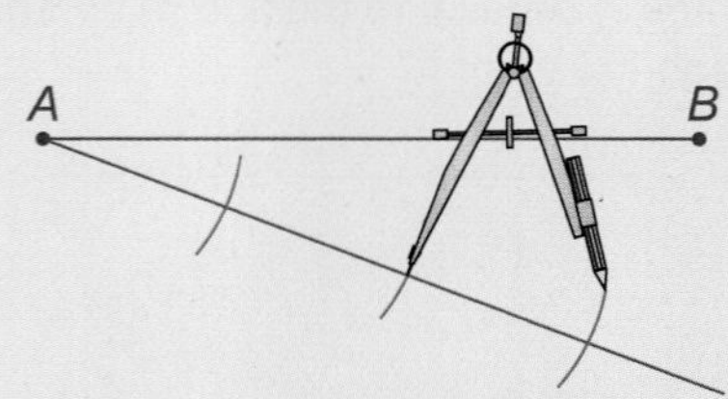

> If asked to divide into four equal parts, mark off four equal distances along the ray, and similarly for any number of equal parts.

4 Label the points of intersection *R*, *S* and *T*.

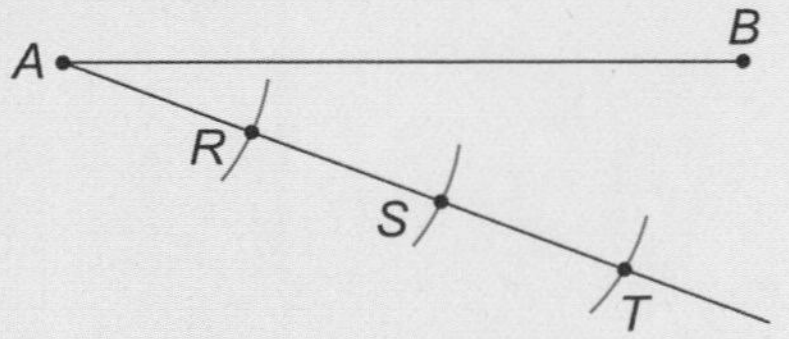

5 Join the last point *T* to the point *B* on the line segment.

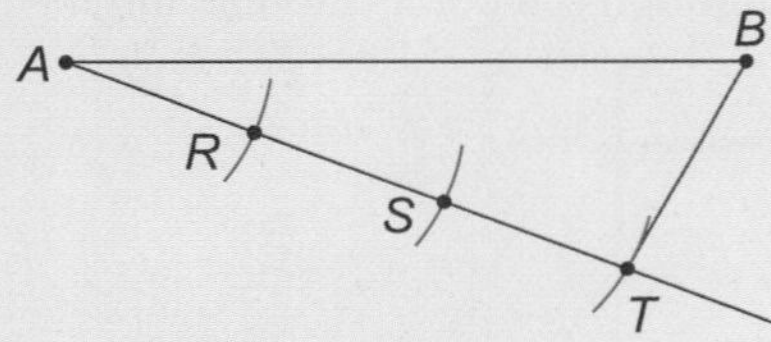

6 Using a set square and straight edge, line the set square up with the line segment [*TB*].

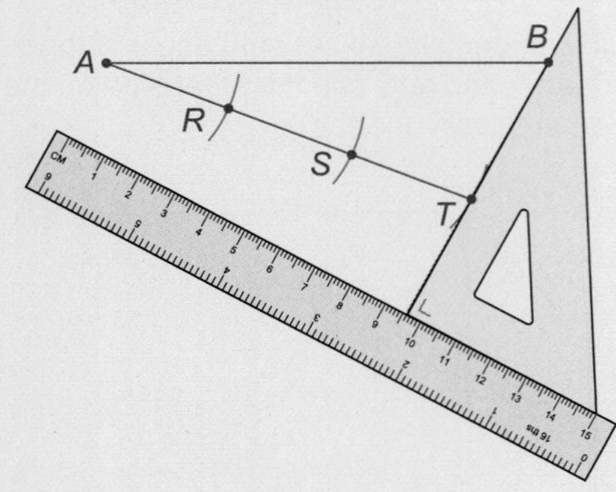

7 Slide the set square along, using the straight edge as a base.

Using the set square, draw a line segment from S and R to the line segment $[AB]$.

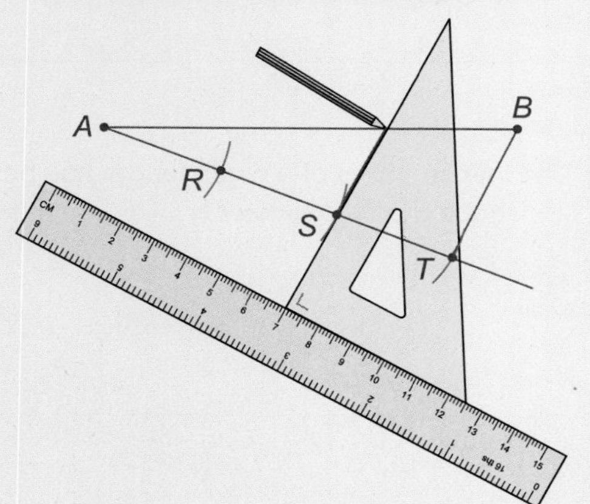

8 Label the points of intersection with the line segment $[AB]$ as points C and D.

The line segment $[AB]$ has now been divided into three equal segments.

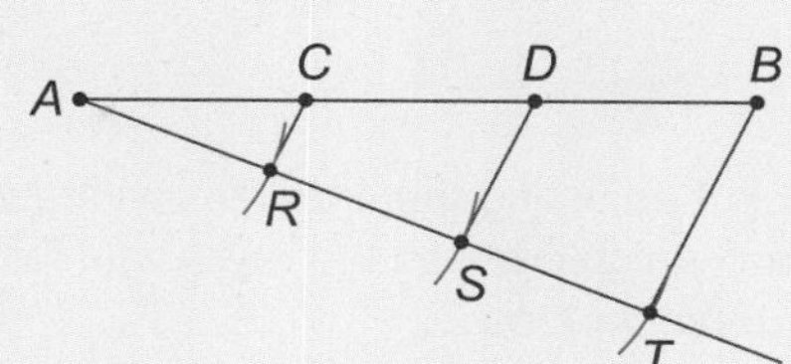

Note: Another method to divide a line segment into two equal parts is to use Construction 2: A perpendicular bisector of a line segment, using only a compass and a straight edge.

CONSTRUCTION 8

A Line Segment of a Given Length on a Given Ray

Worked Example 6.7

Construct a line segment 3 cm in length on the given ray.

X ——————— Y

Solution

1 Using a ruler, draw a line segment $[AB]$ of length 3 cm.

2 Place the compass on the point A. Adjust the compass width until it is at point B, i.e. 3 cm.

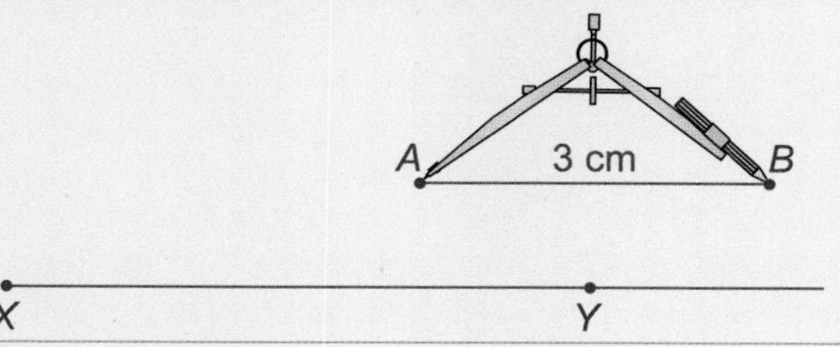

3 Using this compass width, place the compass point on the point X.

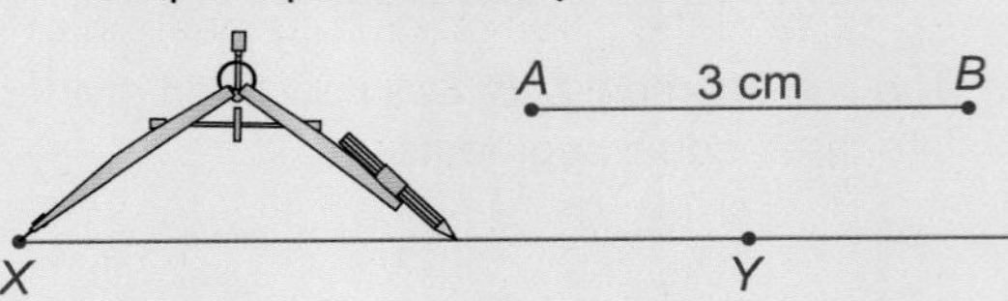

4 Without adjusting the compass width, draw an arc which crosses the ray. Label this point of intersection as Z.

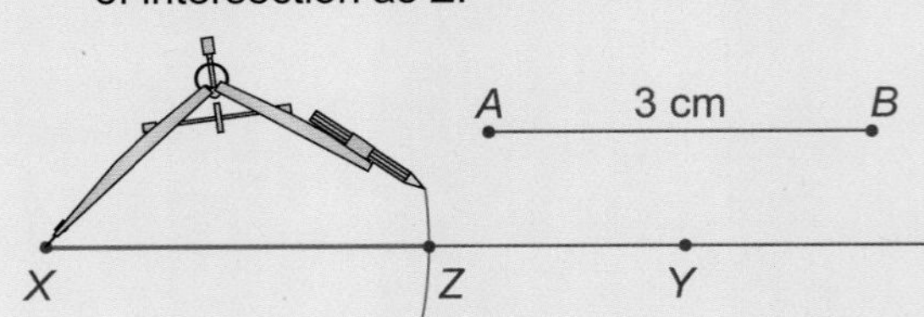

5 Connect X to Z with a straight edge.

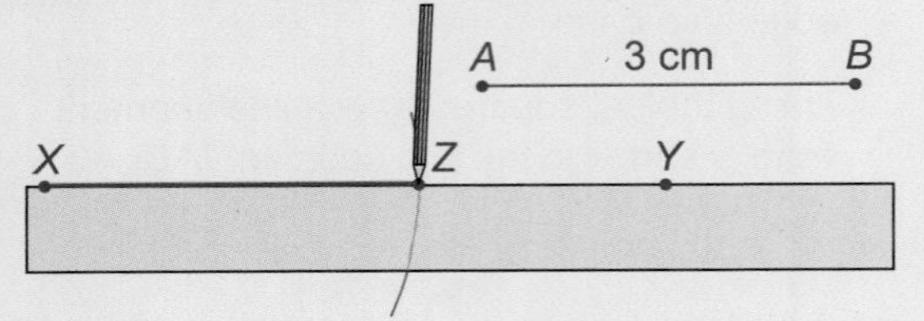

6 The line segment of a given length has been constructed on the given ray.

$|XZ| = 3$ cm

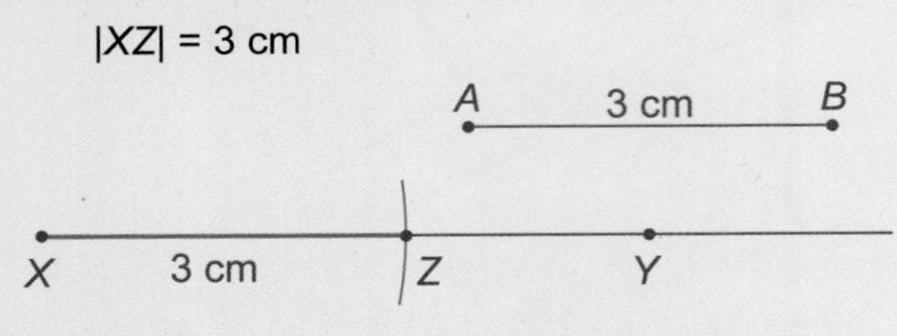

CONSTRUCTION 9

An Angle of a Given Number of Degrees With a Given Ray as One Arm

Worked Example 6.8

Construct an angle of 65° on the ray $[AB$.

Solution

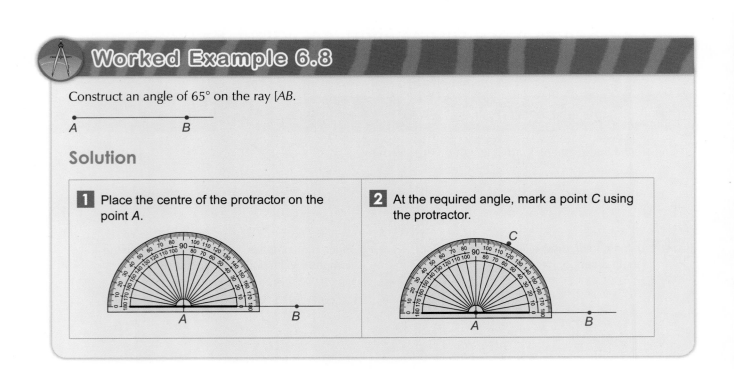

1 Place the centre of the protractor on the point A.

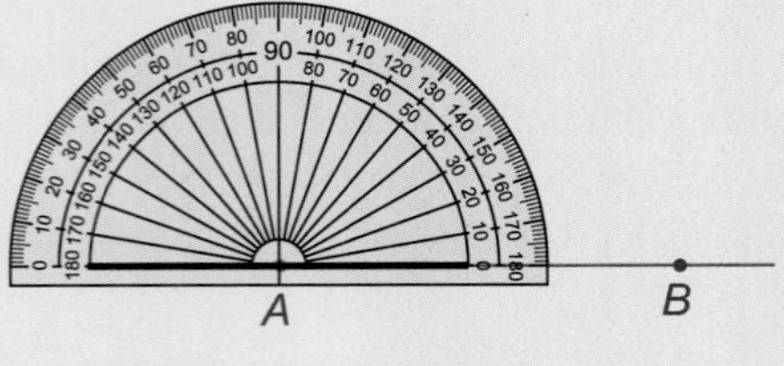

2 At the required angle, mark a point C using the protractor.

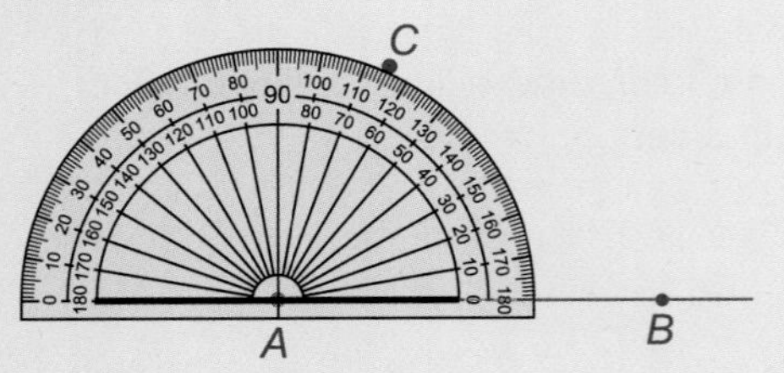

3 Draw a ray from *A* through *C* with a straight edge.

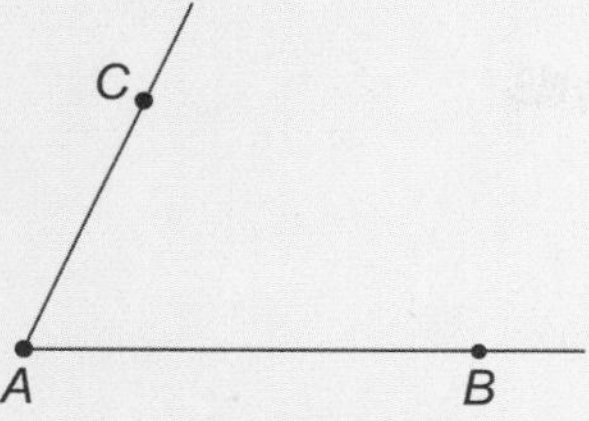

4 Write in the required angle value, i.e. 65°.

An angle of the given length has been constructed on the given ray.

$|\angle BAC| = 65°$.

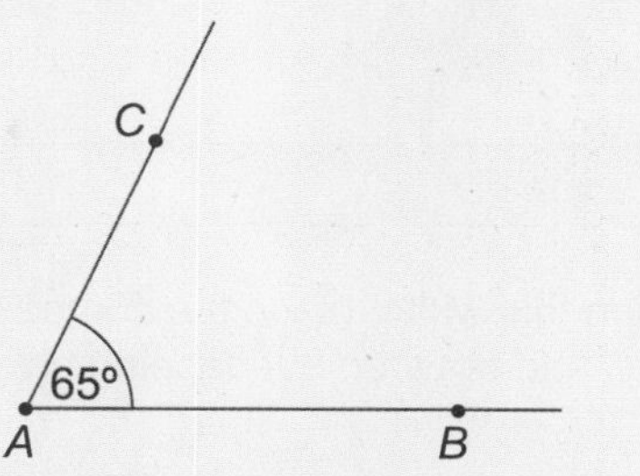

When dealing with more complicated questions, it is always better to draw a rough, labelled sketch before you start your construction.

You should also check that your construction has the same dimensions as given in the question.

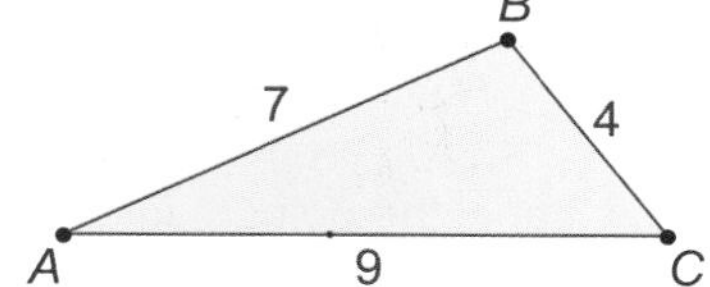

CONSTRUCTION 10

A Triangle, Given the Lengths of Three Sides (SSS)

SSS means **Side, Side, Side**.

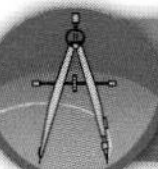

Worked Example 6.9

Construct a triangle *ABC* where $|AB| = 7$ cm, $|BC| = 9$ cm and $|AC| = 5$ cm.

Solution

1 Draw a rough sketch of the construction.

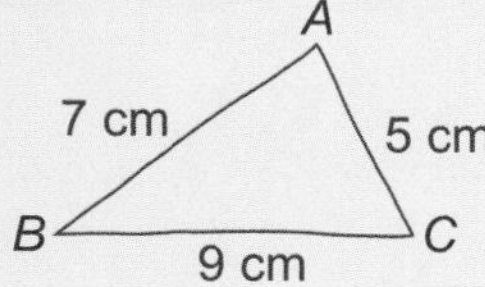

2 Using a ruler, draw the line segment [*BC*]. This will be the base of the triangle, as it is the longest side.

We usually use the longest side as the horizontal base of the triangle.

3 Next, use $|AB| = 7$ cm. Set the compass width to 7 cm.

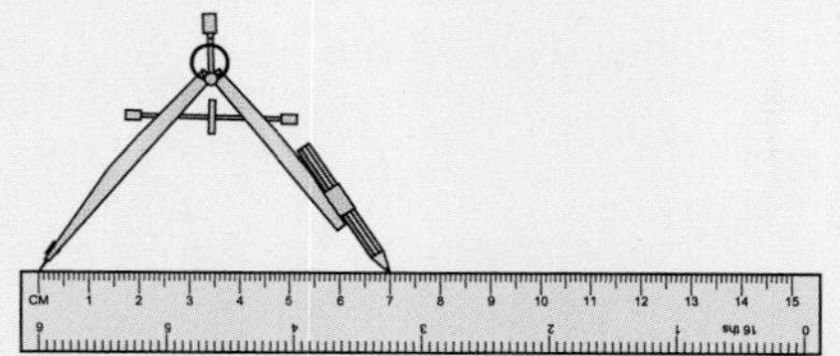

4 Using this width, place the compass point on *B* and draw an arc.

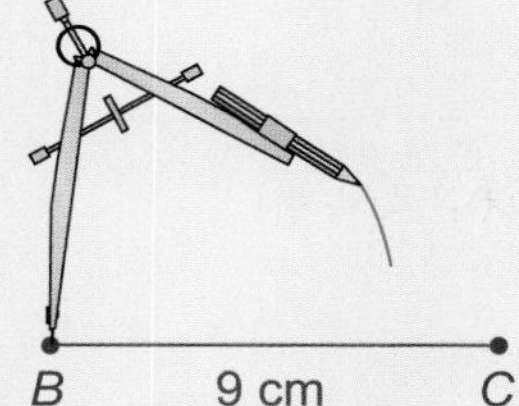

5 Now use |AC| = 5 cm. Set the compass width to 5 cm.

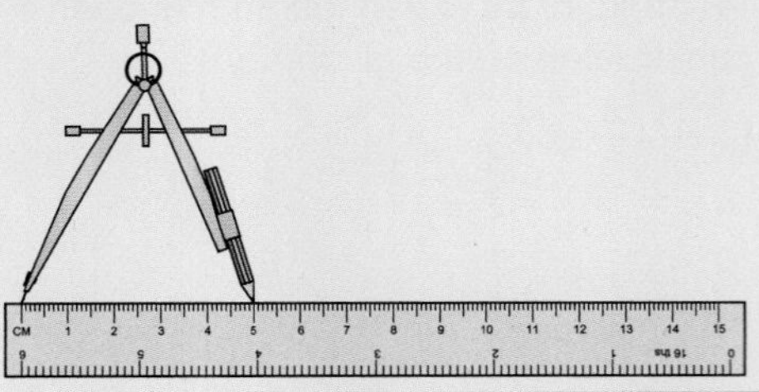

6 Using this width, place the compass point on C and draw an overlapping arc.

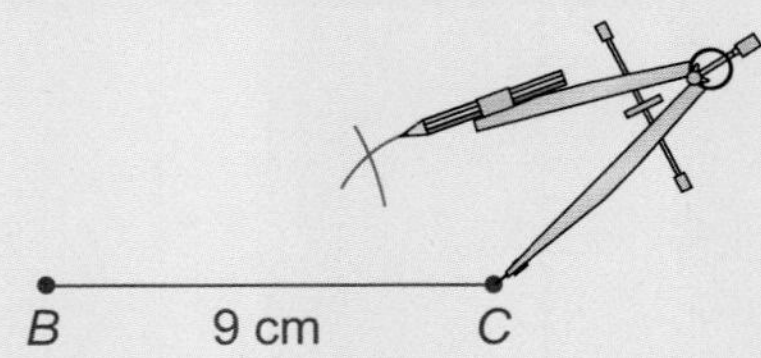

7 Label the point of intersection of the two arcs as point A.

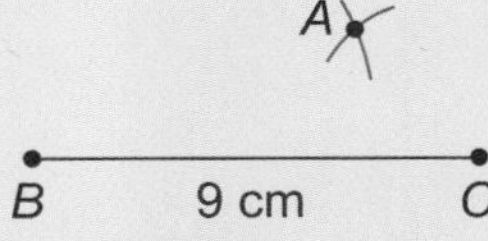

8 Join A to B and A to C.

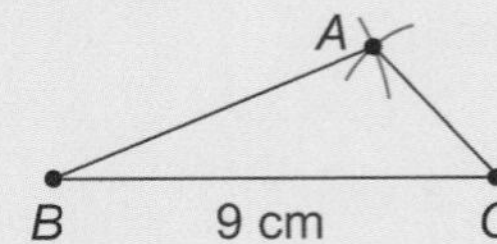

9 Fill in the remaining lengths.

The triangle is now constructed as required.

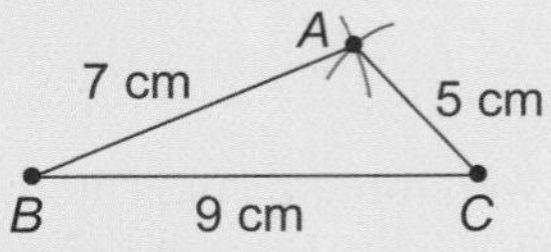

When we have finished the construction, we label all the angles and side lengths that were given in the question.

CONSTRUCTION 11

A Triangle, Given SAS Data (Side, Angle, Side)

SAS means **Side, Angle, Side.**

Worked Example 6.10

Construct a triangle EDF where $|ED| = 10$ cm, $|\angle FED| = 50°$ and $|EF| = 6$ cm.

Solution

1 Draw a rough sketch of the construction, putting the longest side as the base.

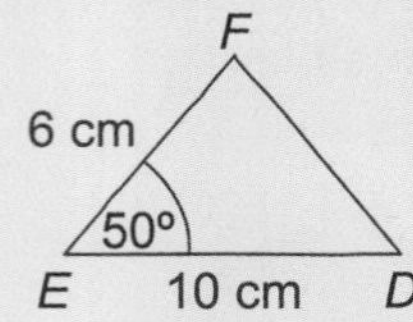

2 Using a ruler, draw the line segment [ED] where |ED| = 10 cm.

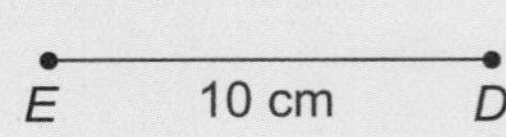

3 Using a protractor, construct an angle of 50° at the point E.

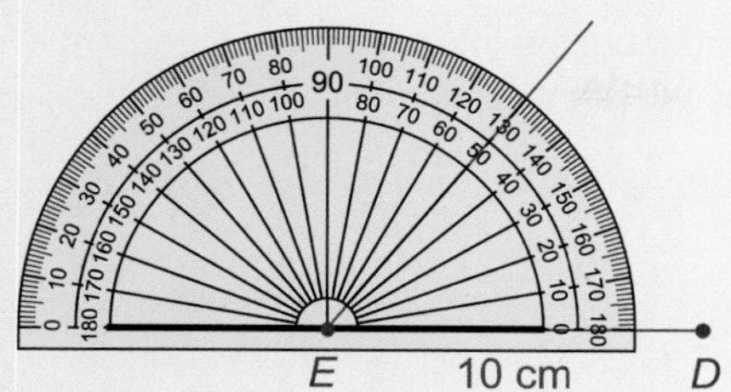

6 Mark and label this intersection as the point F.

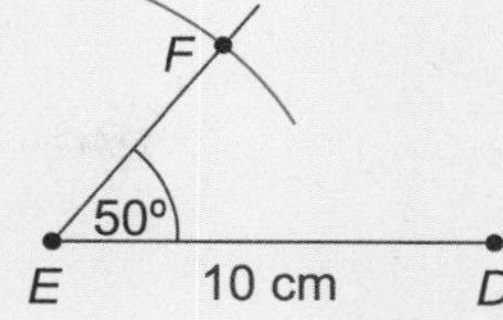

4 Set the compass width to 6 cm.

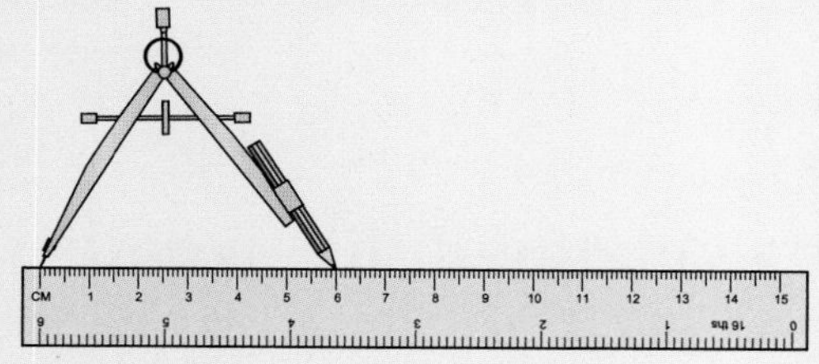

7 Join F to D.

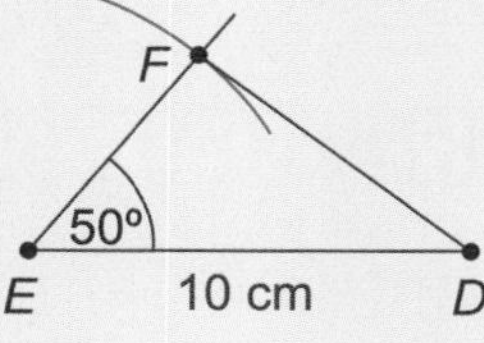

5 Using this width, place the compass point on E and draw an arc on the arm of the angle.

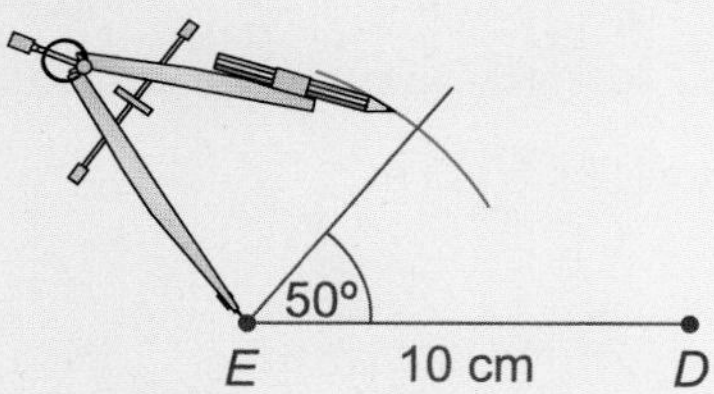

8 Fill in the remaining lengths and the angle.

The triangle is now constructed as required.

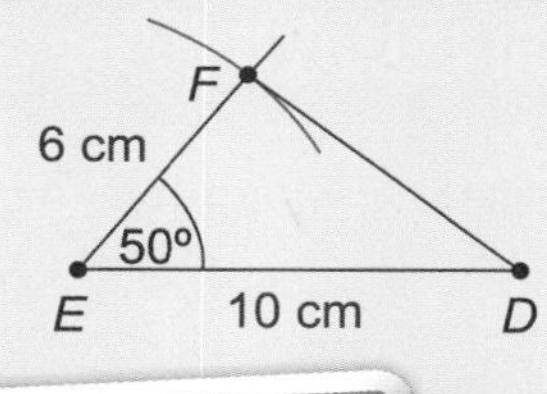

ACTIVITY 6.7

CONSTRUCTION 12

A Triangle, Given Two Angles and the Side Between These Two Angles (ASA)

ASA means **Angle, Side, Angle.**

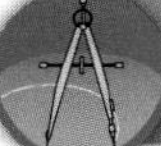

Worked Example 6.11

Construct a triangle ABC where $|AB| = 7$ cm, $|\angle ABC| = 30°$ and $|\angle BAC| = 50°$.

Solution

1 Draw a rough sketch of the construction.

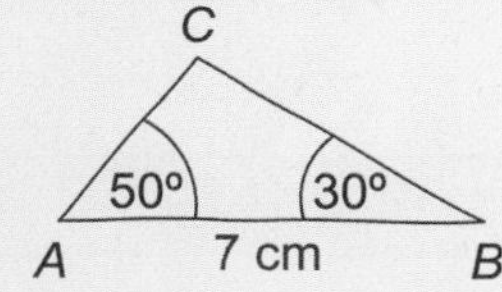

2 Using a ruler, construct a horizontal line segment where $|AB| = 7$ cm.

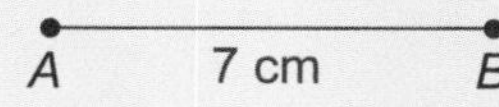

3 Using a protractor, construct an angle of 50° at the point *A*.

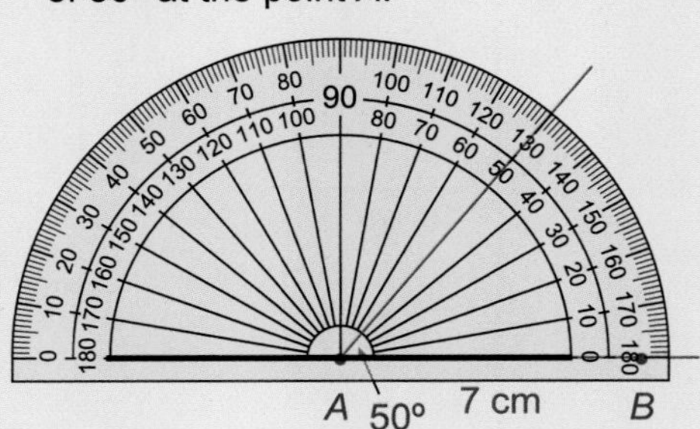

4 Using a protractor, construct an angle of 30° at the point *B*.

Mark and label the intersection of these angles' arms as the point *C*.

The triangle is now constructed as required.

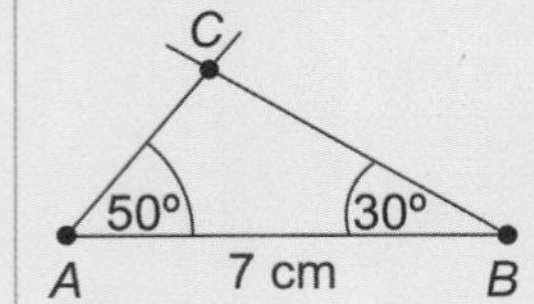

CONSTRUCTION 13

A Right-Angled Triangle, Given the Length of the Hypotenuse and One Other Side

The hypotenuse is always the side opposite the right angle. It is also the longest side.

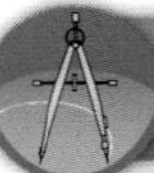

Worked Example 6.12

Construct a triangle *EDF* where $|ED| = 5$ cm, $|\angle EDF| = 90°$ and $|EF| = 8$ cm.

Solution

1 Make a rough sketch of the triangle. It is important to identify where the right angle is and generally not use the hypotenuse as the horizontal line.

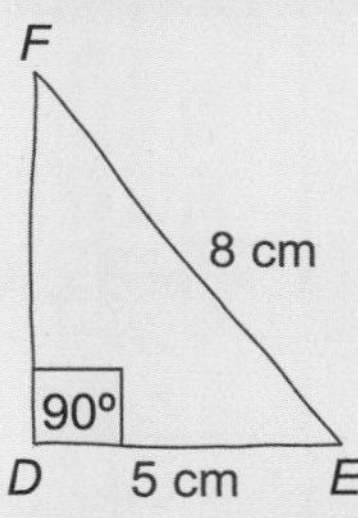

2 Using a ruler, construct the horizontal line segment where $|ED| = 5$ cm.

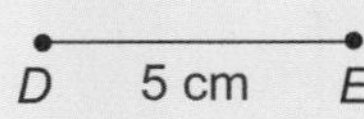

3 Using your protractor or set square, draw an angle of 90° at *D*.

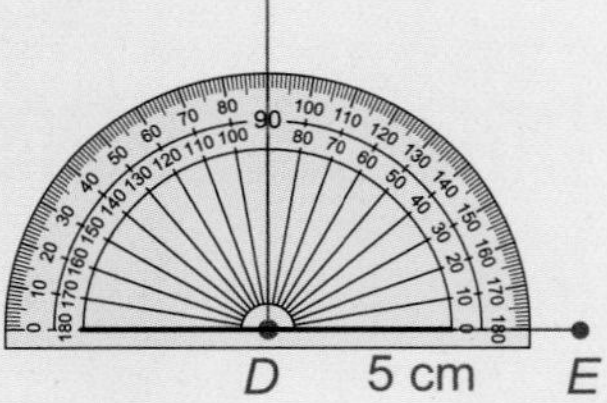

4 Set the compass width to the length of the hypotenuse. $|EF| = 8$ cm.

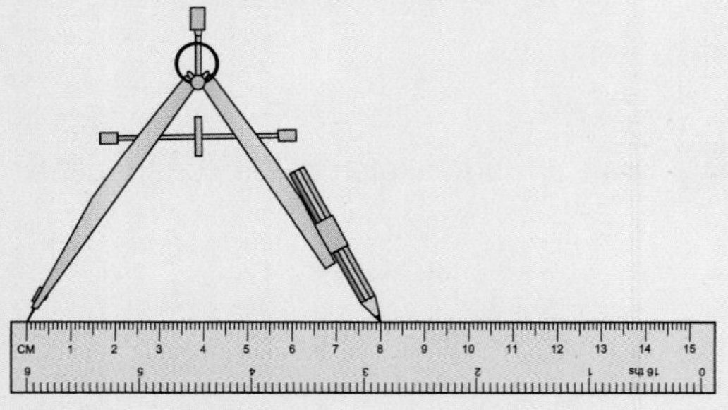

5 Using this width, place the compass point on *E* and draw an arc.

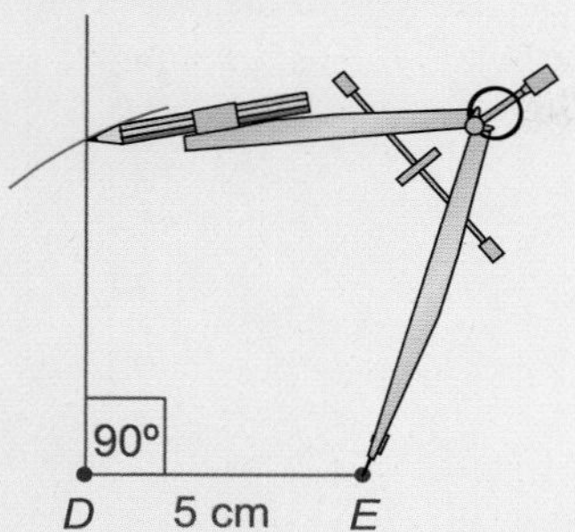

7 Using a ruler, join *F* to *E*.

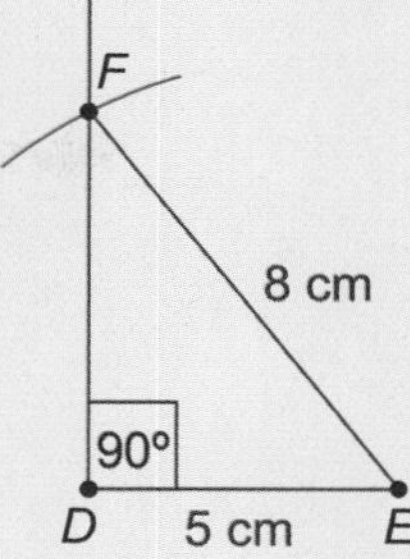

6 Mark and label where the arc meets the vertical line as point *F*.

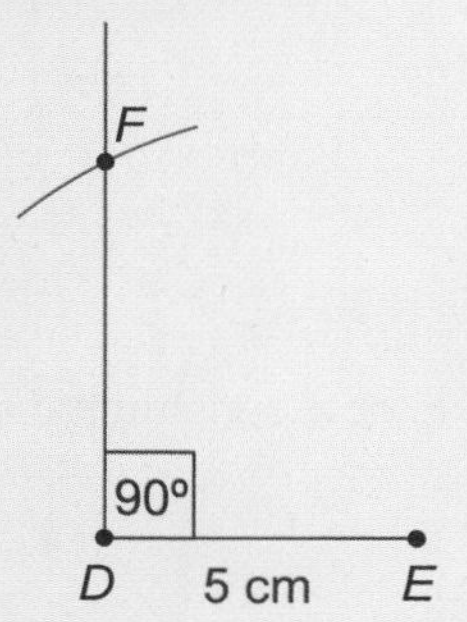

8 The triangle is now drawn as required. Label all given measurements.

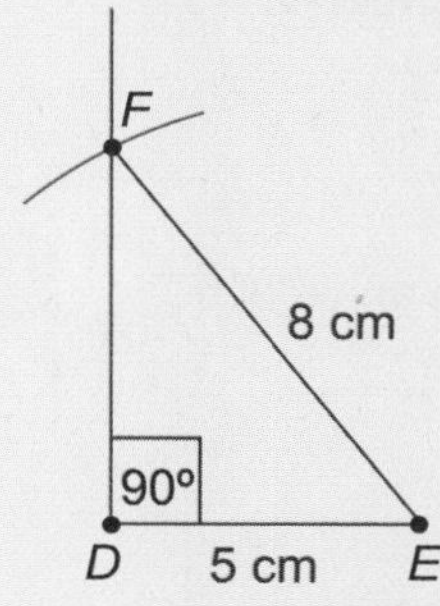

CONSTRUCTION 14

A Right-Angled Triangle, Given One Side and One of the Acute Angles (Several Cases)

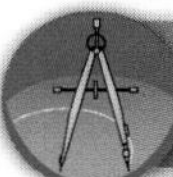

Worked Example 6.13

Construct a triangle *ABC* where $|AB| = 6$ cm, $|\angle ABC| = 90°$ and $|\angle ACB| = 30°$.

Solution

1 Make a rough sketch of the triangle. Identify where the right angle is. Fill in all the angles.

As $|\angle ACB| = 30°$, then $|\angle BAC| = 60°$ (Sum of three angles = 180°)

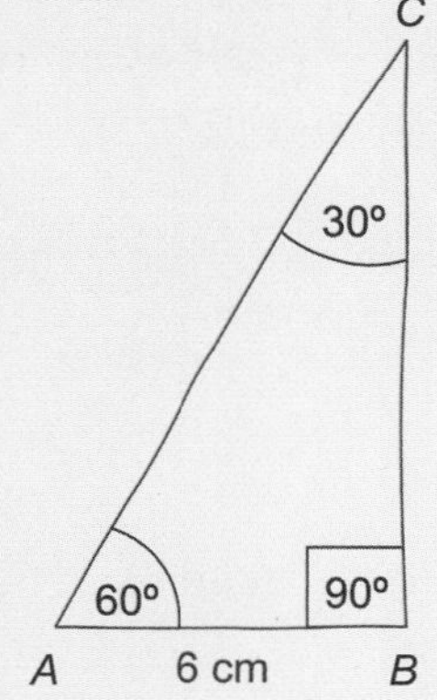

2 Using a ruler, construct the line segment [*AB*] of length 6 cm.

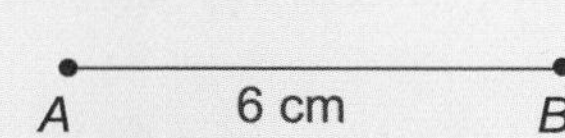

3 Using your protractor or set square, draw an angle of 90° at *B*.

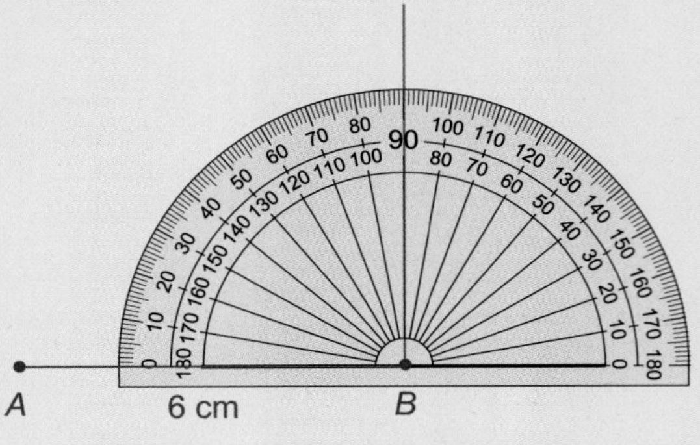

5 Mark and label where this angle's arm meets the right angle's arm as the point *C*.

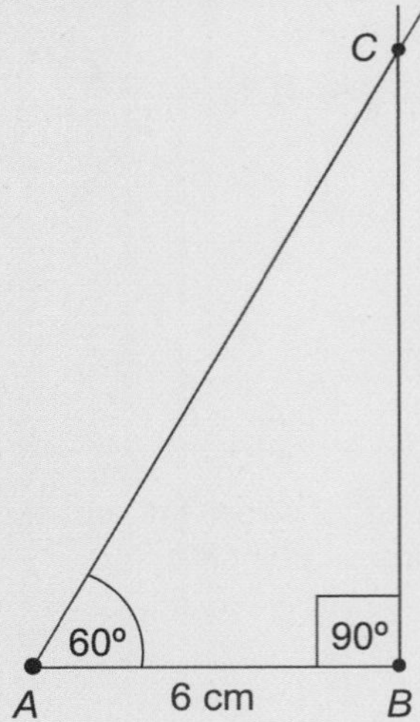

4 Using a protractor, construct an angle of 60° at the point *A*.

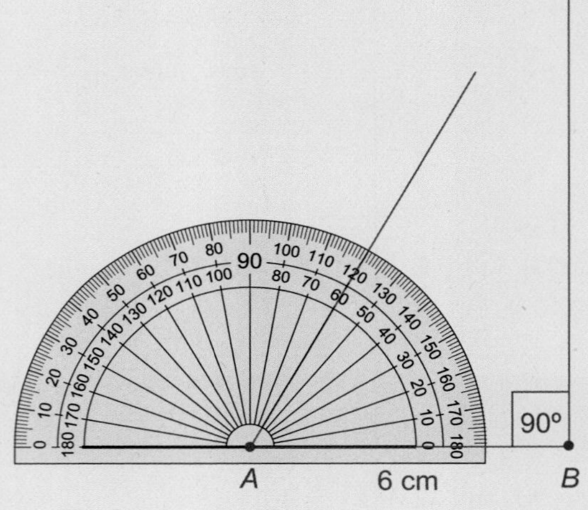

6 Fill in $|\angle ACB| = 30°$.

The triangle is now constructed as required.

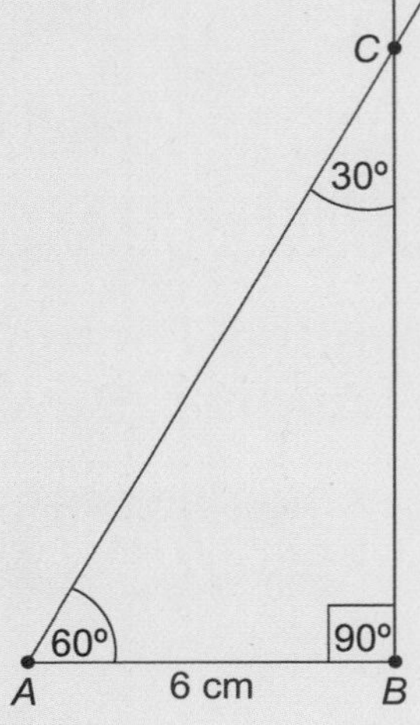

Worked Example 6.14

Construct a triangle *EDF* where $|EF| = 8$ cm, $|\angle EDF| = 90°$ and $|\angle FED| = 50°$.

This triangle is more difficult, as the only side length we are given is the hypotenuse. It is simpler to use the hypotenuse as the base of our triangle.

Solution

1 Make a rough sketch of the triangle. Identify where the right angle is. Fill in all the angles.

$|\angle EFD| = 40^\circ \ (180^\circ - 90^\circ - 50^\circ)$

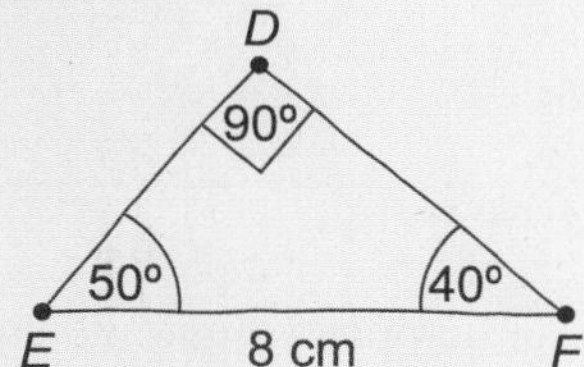

2 Using a ruler, construct the horizontal line segment $[EF]$ where $|EF| = 8$ cm (hypotenuse).

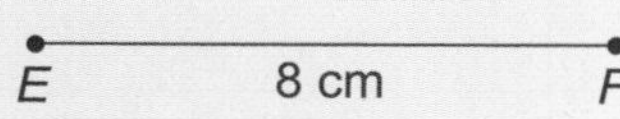

3 Using a protractor, construct an angle of 50° at the point E.

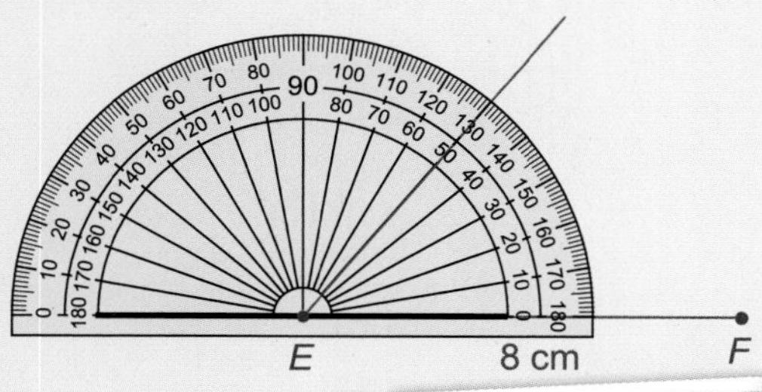

4 Using a protractor, construct an angle of 40° at the point F.

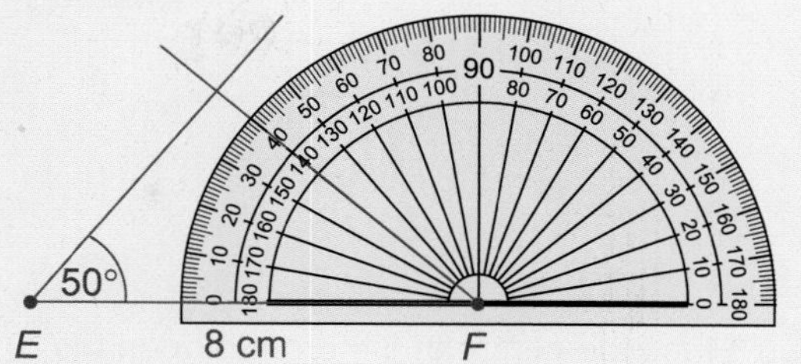

5 Mark and label where the arms of these two angles meet as point D.

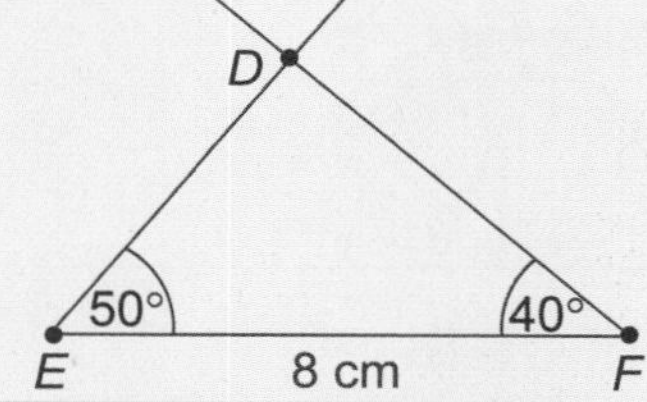

6 Fill in the remaining lengths and angles.

The triangle is now constructed as required.

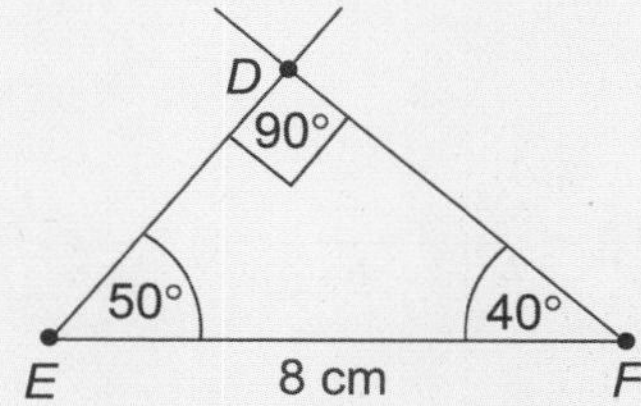

ACTIVITY 6.9

CONSTRUCTION 15

A Rectangle, Given Side Lengths

Worked Example 6.15

Construct a rectangle $ABCD$, where $|AB| = 9$ cm and $|BC| = 4$ cm.

Solution

1 Make a rough sketch of the rectangle.

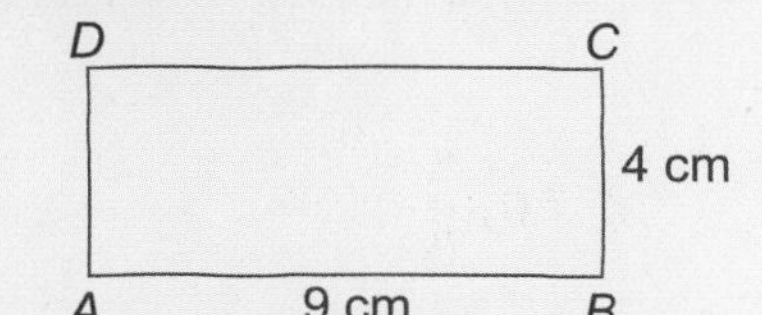

2 Draw a line l.

3 Construct the line segment $[AB]$ where $|AB| = 9$ cm.

4 Place the centre of the protractor on the point A and draw a 90° angle.

You could also use a set square here.

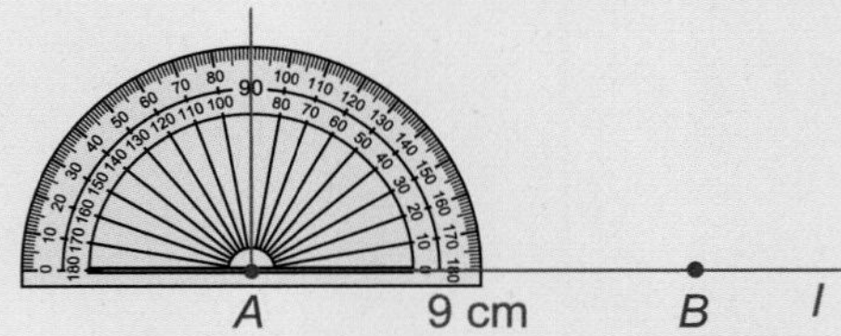

5 Using your compass, mark a point on this line at the given distance from A (4 cm).

Label this point D.

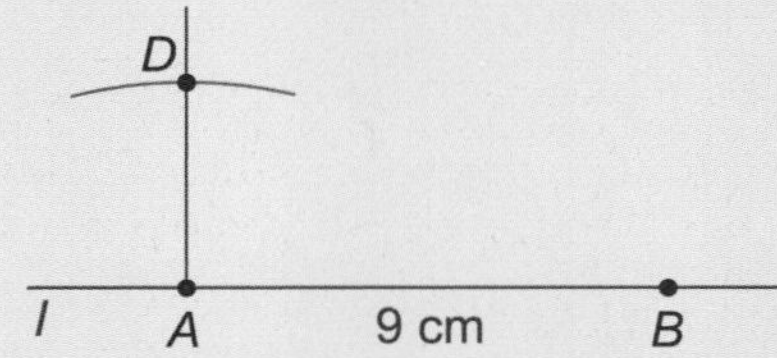

6 Place the centre of the protractor on the point B and draw a 90° angle.

You could also use a set square here.

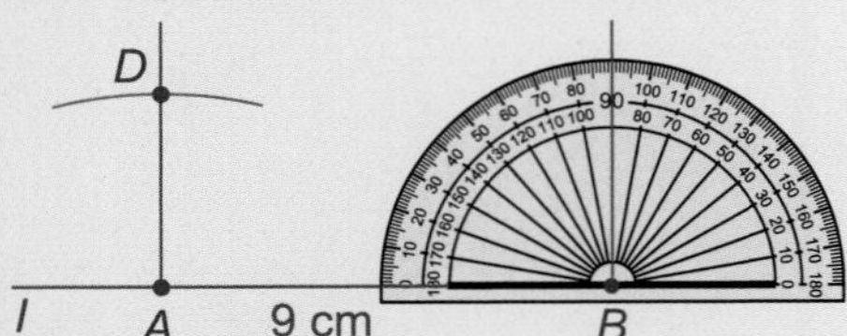

7 Using your compass, mark a point on this line at the given distance from B (4 cm).

Label this point C.

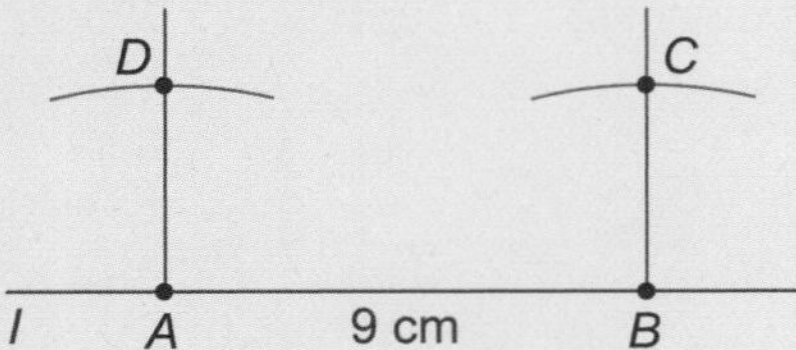

8 Join C to D. Label all given measurements.

The rectangle $ABCD$ is now drawn.

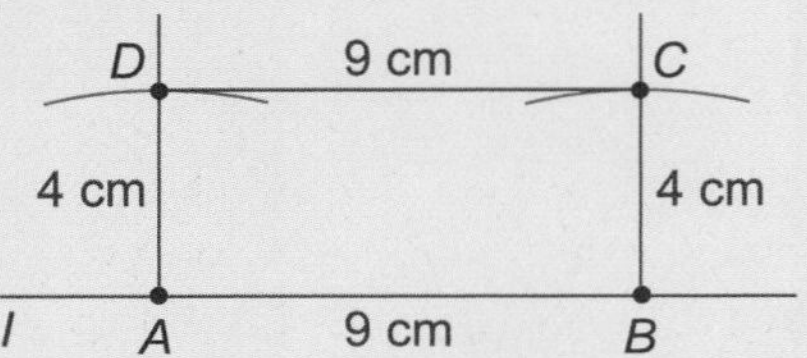

Exercise 6.1

1. Construct the following angles in your copybook. Bisect the indicated angles, **using only a compass and a straight edge**. Remember that you can check your construction with a protractor.

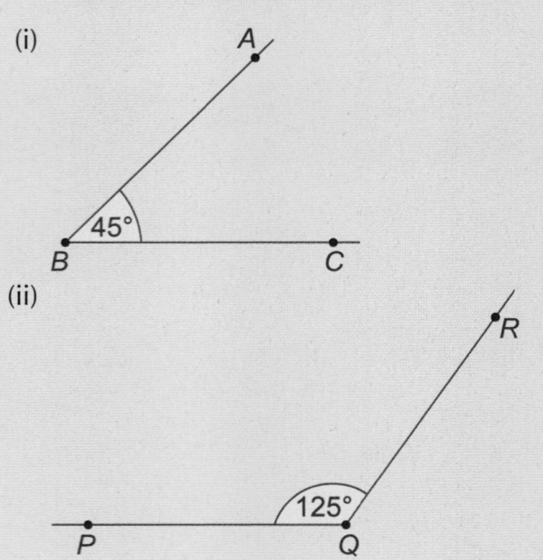

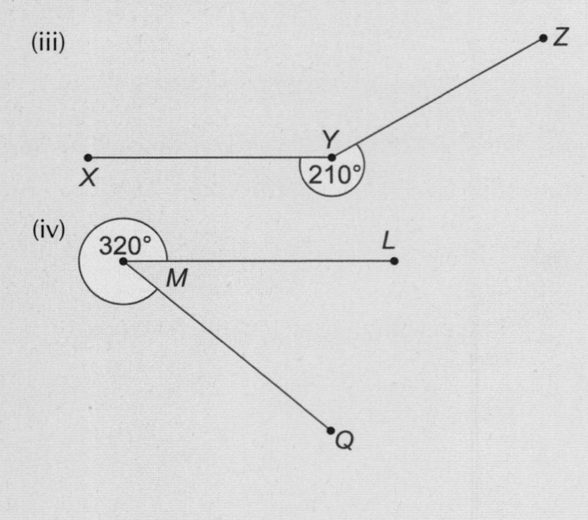

2. (i) Draw a triangle ABC **using a straight edge only** (make the triangle reasonably big).
   (ii) Bisect all three angles of the triangle.
   (iii) Mark where the three bisectors meet. What do you notice?

3. Construct the following line segments in your copybook. Construct the perpendicular bisector of each line segment, **using only a compass and a straight edge.** Remember that you can check your construction with a protractor (or set square) and a ruler.

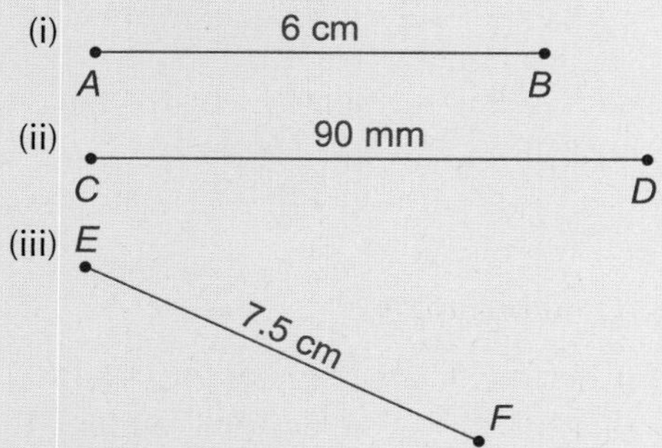

4. Draw a line segment $[CD]$ of length 100 mm. Construct a line that is equidistant from C and D but not parallel to CD.

5. Draw a triangle using a straight edge only (ensure that the triangle is not too small). Label the vertices of the triangle DEF.
   (i) Construct the perpendicular bisectors of all three sides.
   (ii) Mark the point where all three bisectors meet. Label as the point O.
   (iii) Measure $|OD|$, $|OE|$ and $|OF|$. What do you notice?
   (iv) Draw a circle with centre O and with radius length $= |OD|$.

6. Copy the following figures into your copybook. Construct a line perpendicular to the given line passing through the given point, **using only a compass and a straight edge.**

(i) • C

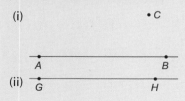

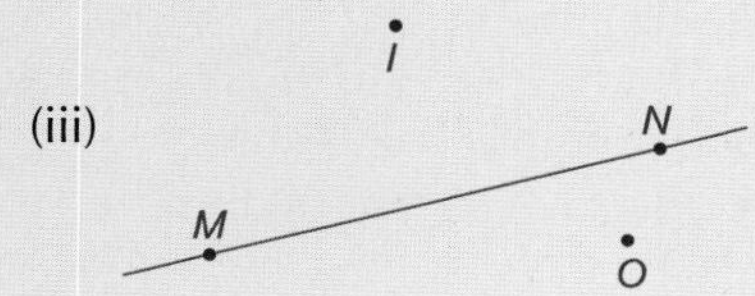

7. Copy the following figures into your copybook. Construct a line perpendicular to the given line passing through the given points, **using a set square.**

(i) A B l

(ii) •C m D

8. (i) Draw a circle of radius 7 cm. Mark the centre of the circle as O.
   (ii) Draw any chord $[XY]$ in the circle (make sure the chord does not pass through the centre O).
   (iii) Construct a line perpendicular to the chord passing through the centre point O, **using only a compass and a straight edge.**
   (iv) What do you notice about this perpendicular line and the chord $[XY]$?

9. Copy the following lines into your copybook. In each case, construct a line perpendicular to the given line passing through the given point, **using only a compass and a straight edge.**

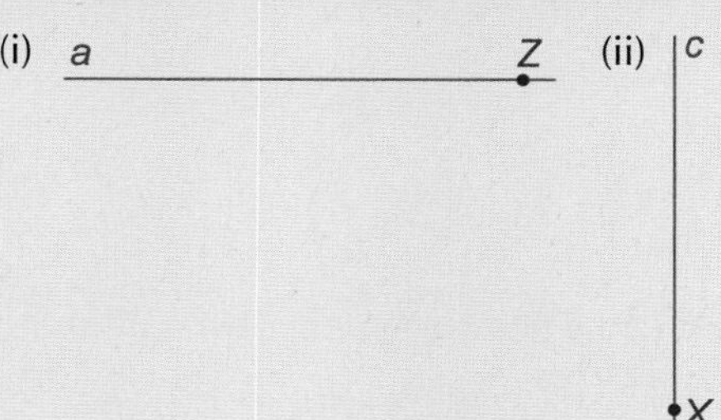

10. Construct the line segment $[PQ]$ where $|PQ| = 12$ cm.
   (i) Mark a point R on the line segment $[QR]$, such that $|QR| = 30$ mm.
   (ii) Using a compass, construct a line perpendicular to the line segment $[PQ]$ through the point R.
   (iii) Mark a point S on the line segment $[PQ]$, such that $|PS| = 40$ mm.
   (iv) Using a protractor, construct a line perpendicular to the line segment $[PQ]$ through the point S.
   (v) Construct the square $SRUV$ where $|RU| = 5$ cm.

11. Copy the following figures into your copybook. In each case, construct a line parallel to the given line passing through the given point, **using only a compass and a straight edge**.

(i) 

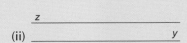

(ii) 

(iii) B

C

x

12. Copy the following figure into your copybook. In each case, construct a line parallel to the given line passing through the given point, **using a set square**.

Note that in each part, two points are given.

(i) F

G

13. (i) Draw a line segment [AB] such that $|AB| = 8$ cm.

(ii) Construct the angle ABC such that $|\angle ABC| = 120°$ and $|BC| = 5$ cm.

(iii) Construct a line through C parallel to AB.

(iv) Construct a line through A parallel to BC.

(v) What is the resulting four-sided figure called?

(vi) Confirm this by listing the measurements of angles and line segments from your construction.

14. Draw a line segment [CD] of length 5 cm. Divide this line segment into three equal segments without measuring it.

15. Draw a line segment [EF] of length 15 cm. Divide this line segment into five equal segments without measuring it.

16. Draw a line segment [UV] of length 135 mm. Divide this line segment into six equal parts without measuring it.

17. (i) Draw a line segment [AB] where $|AB| = 12$ cm. Divide this line segment into four equal parts without measuring it.

(ii) Using only a compass and a straight edge, divide [AB] into eight equal segments.

18. Construct a line segment of length 4 cm on the ray [AB.

19. (i) Draw a line AB.

(ii) Construct a line segment [AC] such that $|AC| = 4$ cm and A, C and B are collinear.

(iii) Mark a point X above the line AB.

(iv) Draw a line parallel to the line AB through the point X.

(v) Construct the line segment [XD] where $|XD| = |AC|$ and $XD \parallel AB$.

20. Construct the following angles with the given ray as one arm of the angle.

(i) A B $|\angle ABC| = 60°$

(ii) 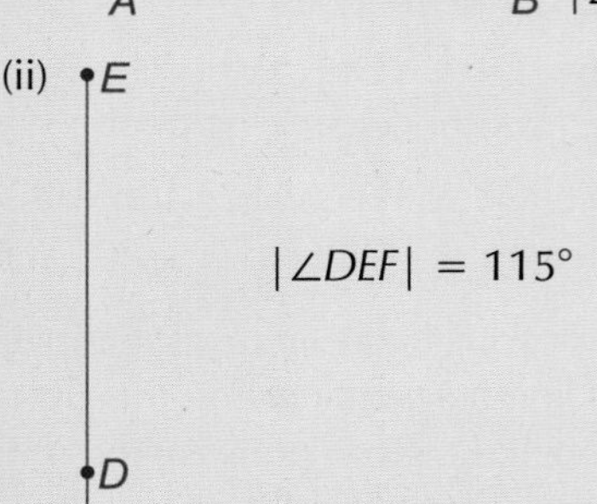

$|\angle DEF| = 115°$

(iii) 

$|\angle GHI| = 295°$

Construct the following triangles:

21. Triangle DEF where $|DE| = 80$ mm, $|EF| = 90$ mm and $|DF| = 100$ mm.

22. Triangle MNO where $|MO| = 11$ cm, $|NO| = 7$ cm and $|MN| = 5$ cm.

23. A triangle GHI where $|GI| = 6$ cm, $|HI| = 4$ cm and $|\angle GIH| = 30°$.

24. A triangle XYZ where $|XY| = 6$ cm, $|XZ| = \frac{4}{3}|XY|$ and $XY \perp XZ$.

25. A triangle DEF where $|\angle EDF| = 110°$, $|\angle EFD| = 20°$ and $|DF| = 6$ cm.

26. A triangle JKL where $|\angle KJL| = 50°$, $|\angle KLJ| = |\angle KJL|$ and $|JL| = 8$ cm.

27. A triangle DEF where $|FE| = 8$ cm, $|\angle FED| = 90°$ and $|FD| = 9$ cm.

28. A triangle TUS where $|ST| = 4\sqrt{2}$ cm, $|SU| = 4$ cm and $|\angle TUS| = 90°$.

29. A triangle DEF where $|\angle DEF| = 90°$, $|\angle EDF| = 35°$ and $|EF| = 7$ cm.

30. A triangle GHI where $|\angle HGI| = 15°$, $|\angle GHI| = 90°$ and $|GI| = 8$ cm.

31. A triangle MNO where $|\angle MON| = 90°$, $|\angle NMO| = 65°$ and $|MN| = 11$ cm.

32. Construct the rectangle $EFGH$ where $|EF| = 55$ mm and $|FG| = 65$ mm.

33. Construct the square $IJKL$ where $|IJ| = 8$ cm.

34. Construct the square $QRST$ where $|QR|^2 + |RS|^2 = 200$ cm^2.

35. Construct the rectangle $UVWX$ where $|UV|$ is twice $|VW|$ and the area of the rectangle $UVWX$ is 50 cm^2.

36. A cable 15 m long joins the top of a vertical mobile mast 12 m high as shown on the diagram.

(i) Construct the triangle shown in the diagram, using an appropriate scale.

(ii) Find the horizontal distance between the cable and the mast, using a ruler.

(iii) What other method could you use to find this horizontal distance?

(iv) Using the method named in part (iii), find the horizontal distance.

Comment on the accuracy of the two methods used.

37. Two offices are 10 km away from each other as shown.

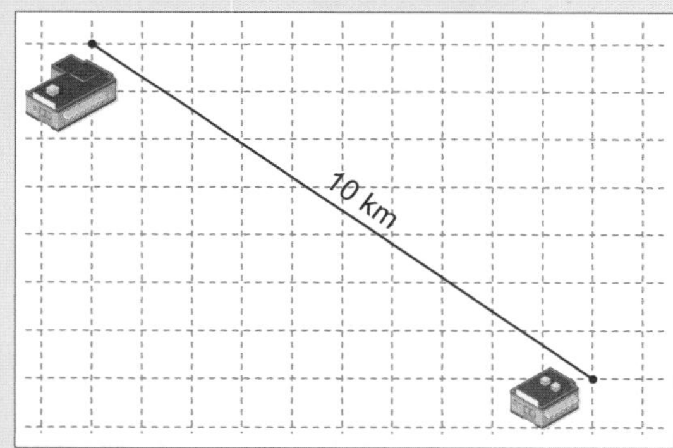

A road is to be built that is equidistant from each office. Show this road on a diagram. (Use a scale of 1 cm = 1 km.)

38. The management of a local sports complex wants to paint an out of bounds line on the walls around the court for indoor football. The line must be parallel to the gym floor and be 2.5 m above the ground.

Construct the out of bounds line using an appropriate scale.

39. Two new lanes are to be built that link the two schools shown to the road. The lanes must link to the road by the shortest distance possible.

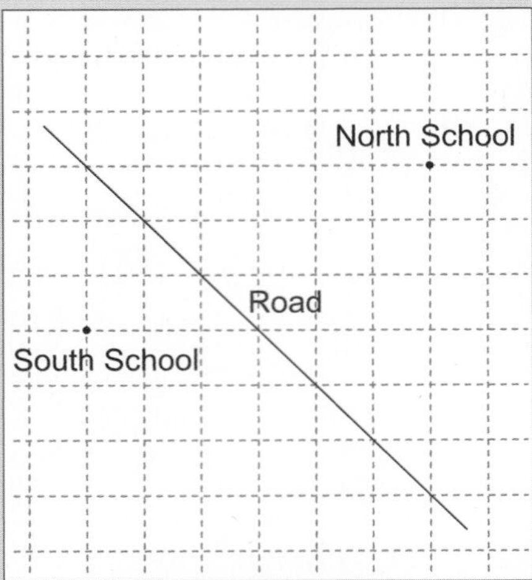

Show on a diagram the possible location of the two lanes.

6.4

The following constructions were not studied at Junior Certificate Higher Level but must be known at Leaving Certificate Higher Level.

CONSTRUCTION 16

The Circumcentre and Circumcircle of a Given Triangle, Using Only a Straight Edge and a Compass

Worked Example 6.16

Construct the circumcentre and circumcircle of the triangle *ABC*.

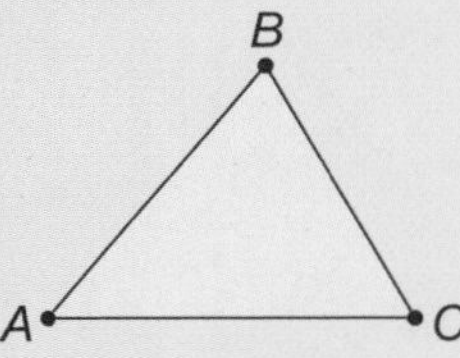

Solution

1 Construct the perpendicular bisector of [*AC*].

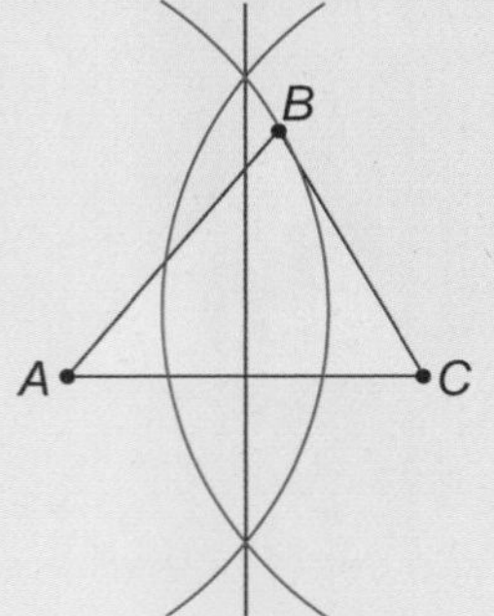

2 Construct the perpendicular bisector of any other side of the triangle – in this case the side [*BC*].

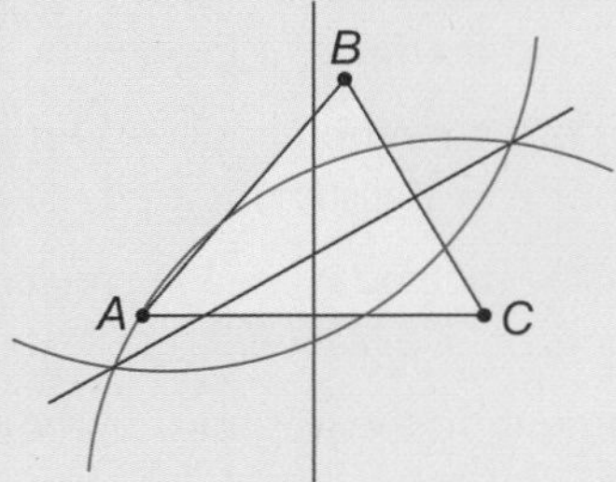

3 Mark the point of intersection of the perpendicular bisectors and label as point O.

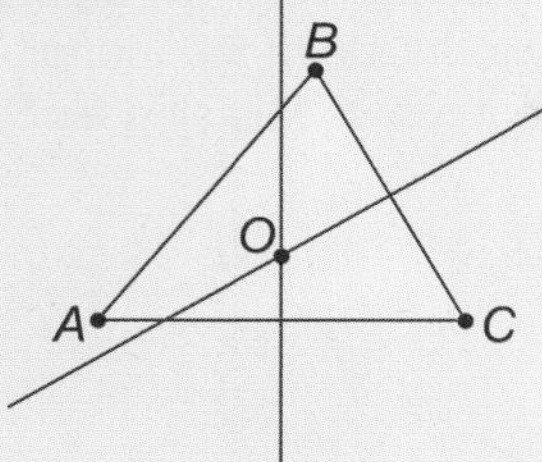

4 Point O is the **circumcentre** of the triangle ABC.

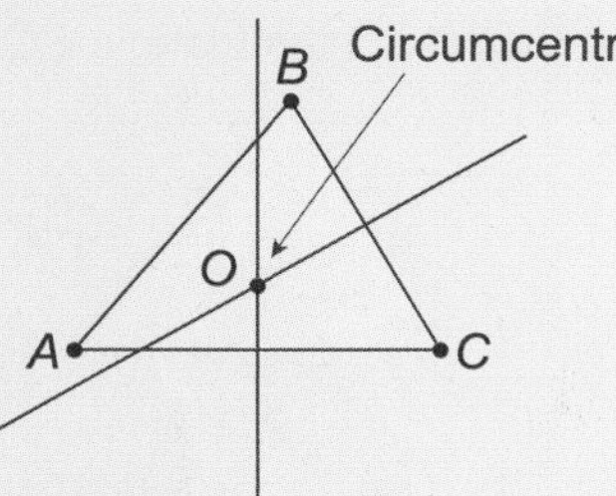

The circumcentre is the point where a triangle's three perpendicular bisectors meet.

5 Place the compass point on O and draw a circle of radius length $|OA|$.

This circle is the **circumcircle** of the triangle ABC.

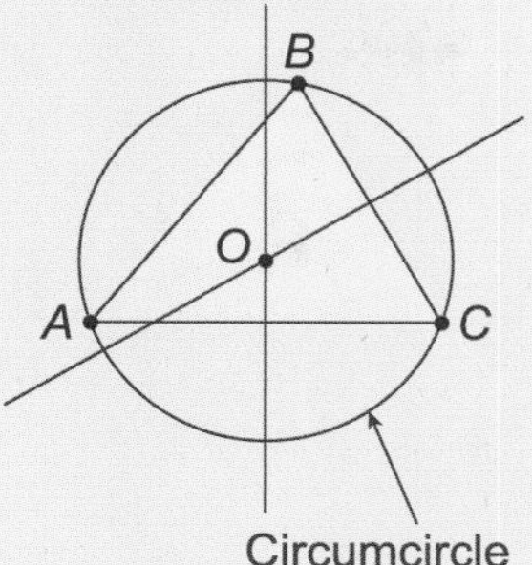

The circumcircle of a triangle is a circle that passes through all three vertices of the triangle.

6 $|AO| = |BO| = |CO|$

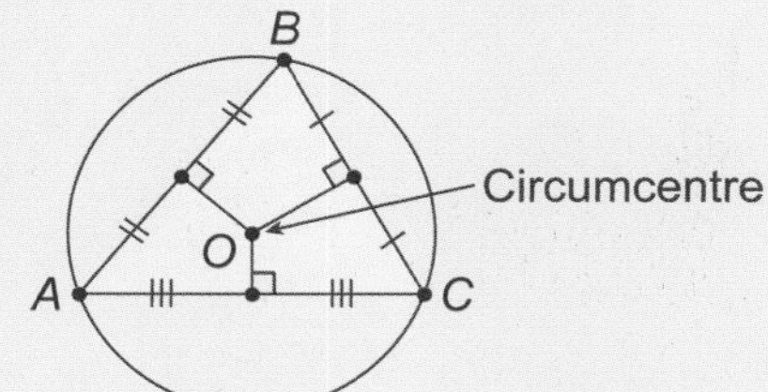

CONSTRUCTION 17

Incentre and Incircle of a Given Triangle, Using Only a Straight Edge and a Compass

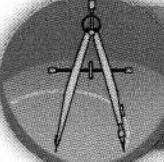

Worked Example 6.17

Construct the incentre and incircle of the triangle PQR.

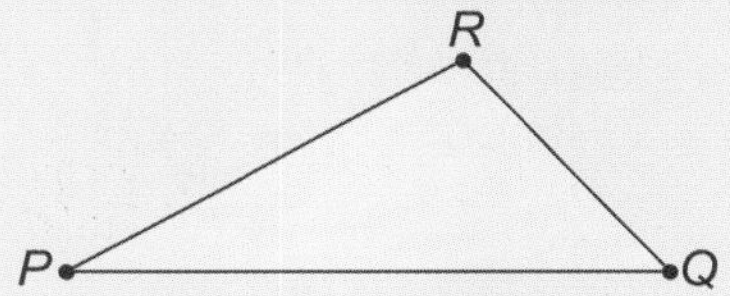

Solution

1 Construct the bisector of the angle *PQR*.

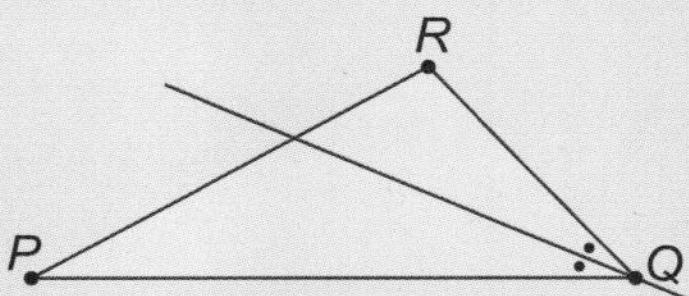

2 Construct the bisector of any other angle in the triangle, e.g. ∠*RPQ*.

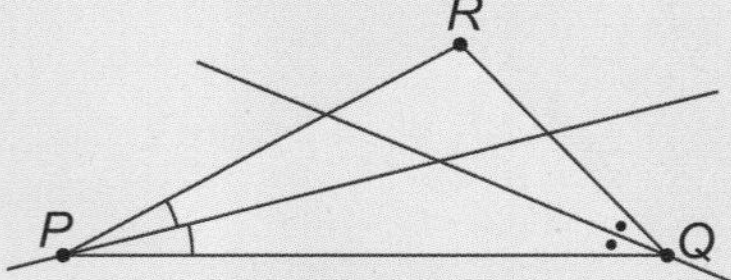

3 Mark the point of intersection of the angle bisectors, and label as point *O*.

Point *O* is the **incentre** of the triangle *PQR*.

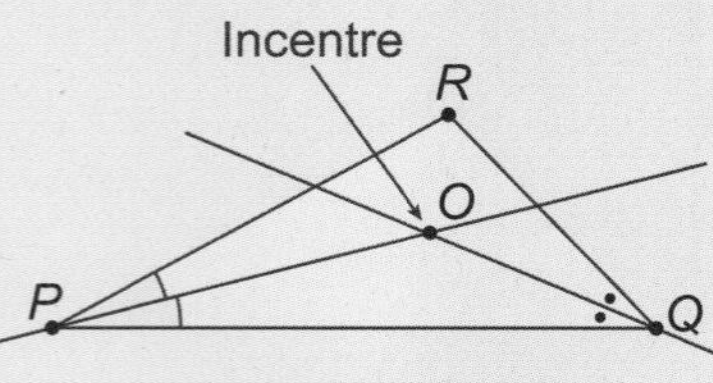

The incentre is the point where a triangle's three angle bisectors meet.

4 Using your set square, draw a perpendicular line from *O* to a side of the triangle. Label the point where it meets this side as *S*.

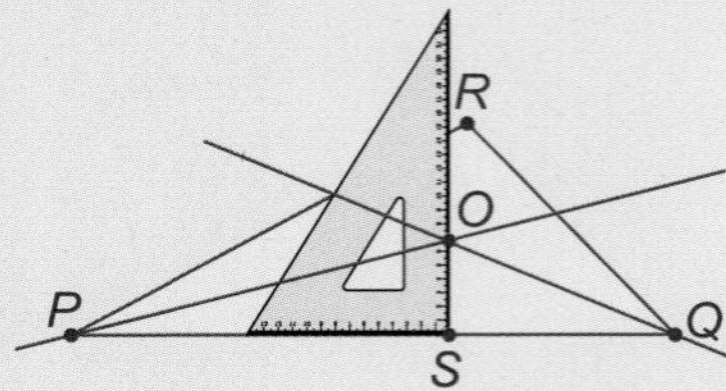

5 Place the compass point on *O* and the pencil on *S*, and draw a circle. This circle should touch all three sides of the triangle.

This is the **incircle** of the triangle *PQR*.

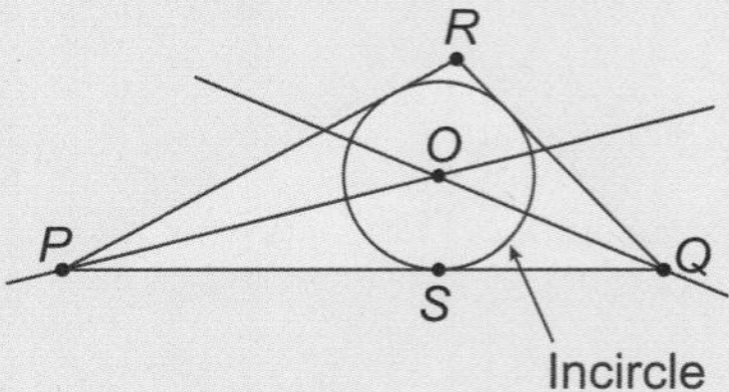

The incircle of a triangle is the largest circle that will fit inside the triangle. Each of the triangle's three sides is a tangent to the circle.

6 $|OS| = |OT| = |OU|$

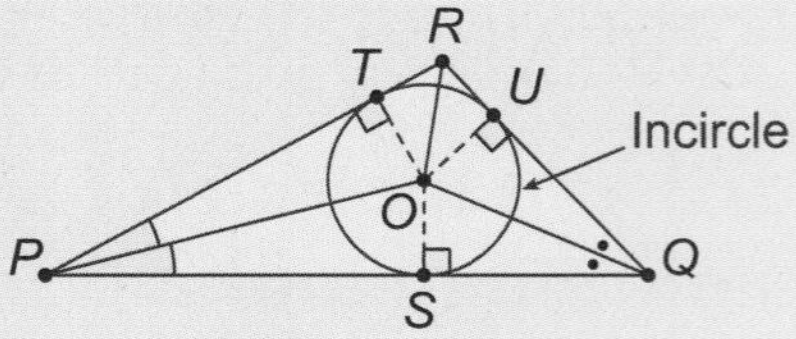

CONSTRUCTION 18

An Angle of 60° Without Using a Protractor or a Set Square

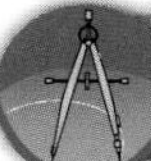

Worked Example 6.18

Construct an angle of 60° without using a protractor or a set square.

Solution

1 Draw a line segment [AB].

2 Place the compass point at A, and draw an arc of radius length $|AB|$.

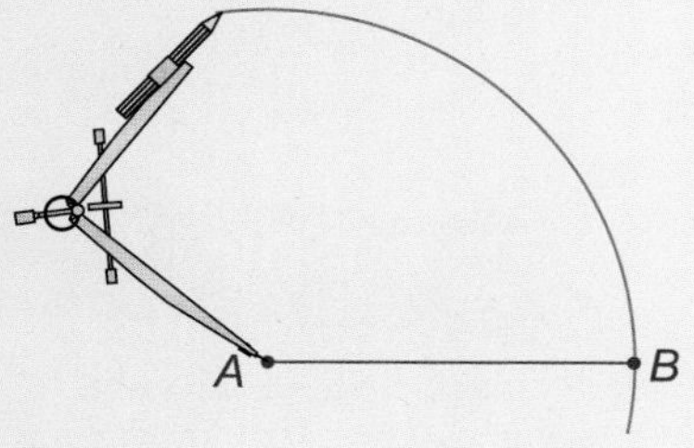

3 Place the compass point at B, and draw an arc of radius length $|AB|$.

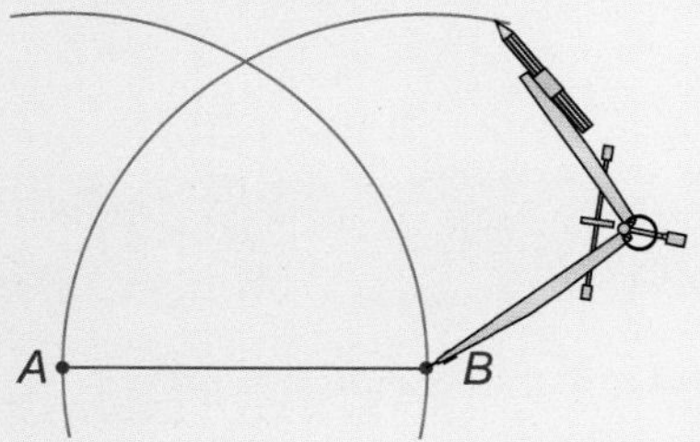

4 Mark the point of intersection of the arcs and label as point C.

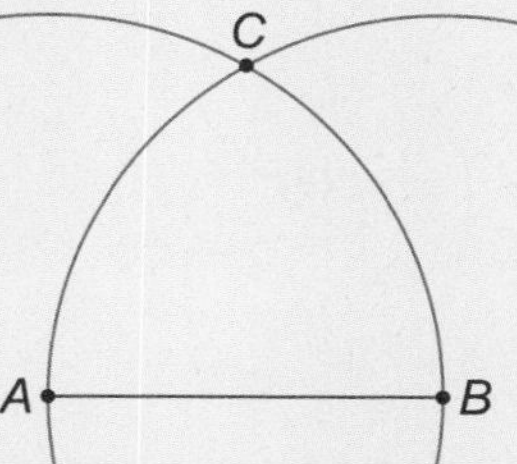

5 Join C to A. Label $|\angle CAB|$ as 60°.

(Note: $|\angle CAB| = 60°$, as ΔABC is equilateral and all angles are therefore 60°.)

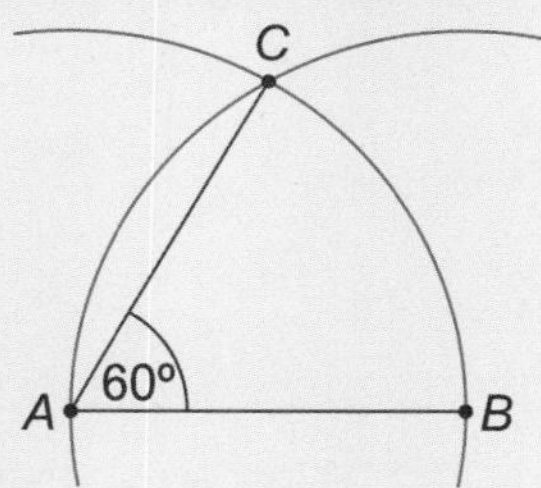

CONSTRUCTION 19

A Tangent to a Given Circle at a Given Point on It

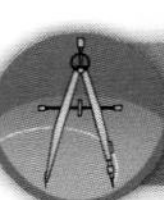

Worked Example 6.19

Construct a **tangent** to the given circle at the point A.

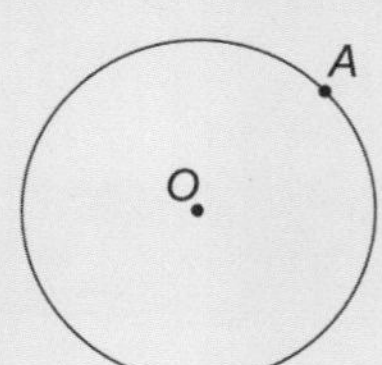

A **tangent** is a line that touches the circle at a single point.

Solution

1 Draw a ray from the centre O of the circle through the given point A.

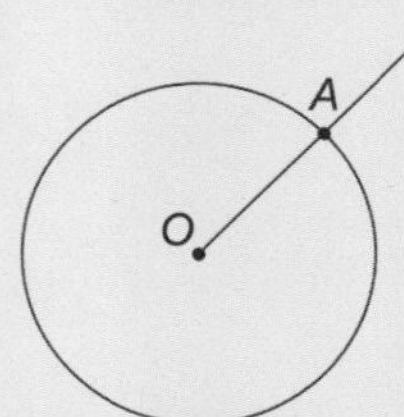

2 Construct a line perpendicular to the ray $[OA$ through the point A.

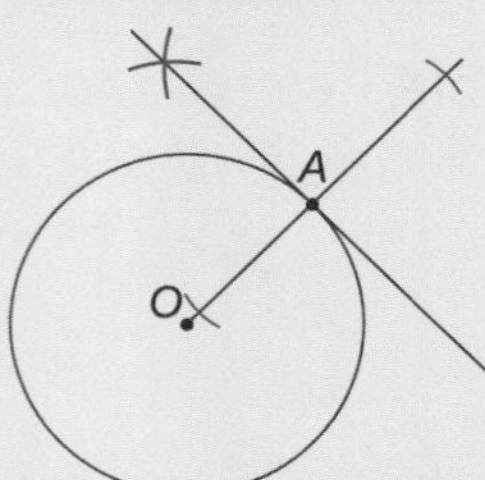

3 This is the tangent to the circle.

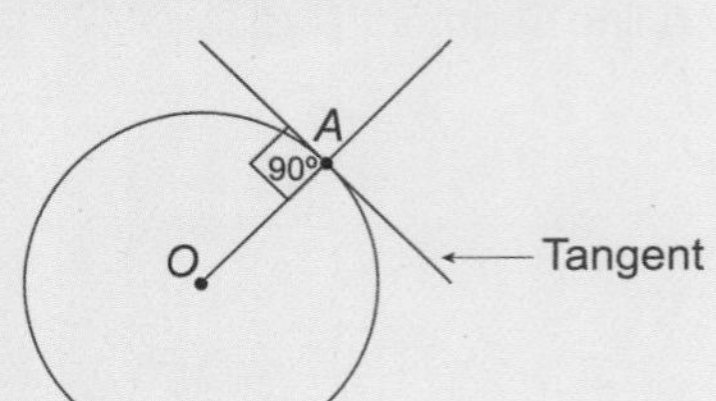

CONSTRUCTION 20

A Parallelogram, Given the Length of the Sides and the Measure of the Angles

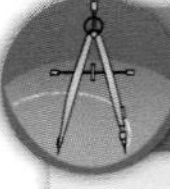

Worked Example 6.20

Construct a parallelogram $ABCD$ where $|AB| = 7$ cm, $|BC| = 4$ cm and $|\angle ABC| = 60°$.

Solution

1 Draw a rough sketch of the parallelogram.

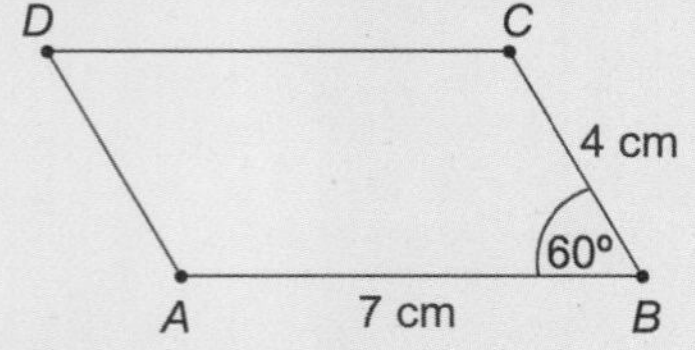

2 Construct the line segment $[AB]$ where $|AB| = 7$ cm.

A 7 cm B

3 At point *B*, construct an angle of 60°, using the line segment [*AB*] as one arm of the angle.

Use your protractor for this angle.

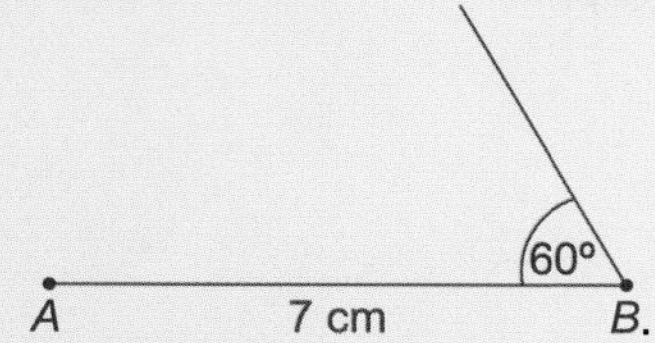

4 Mark the point *C* on this angle such that |*BC*| = 4 cm.

Use your compass (or ruler) for this measurement.

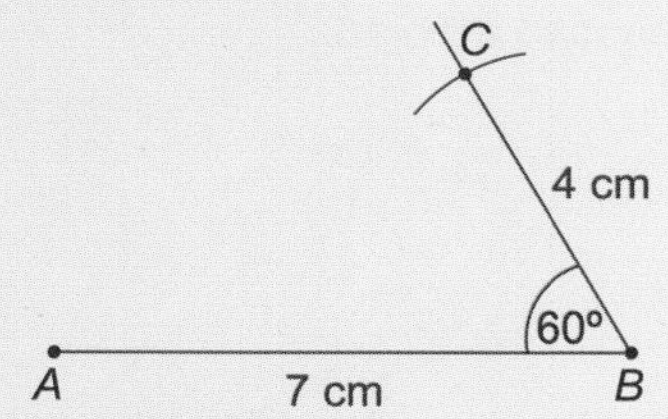

5 At point *A*, construct a ray parallel to *BC*.

Use your protractor to measure the correct angle.

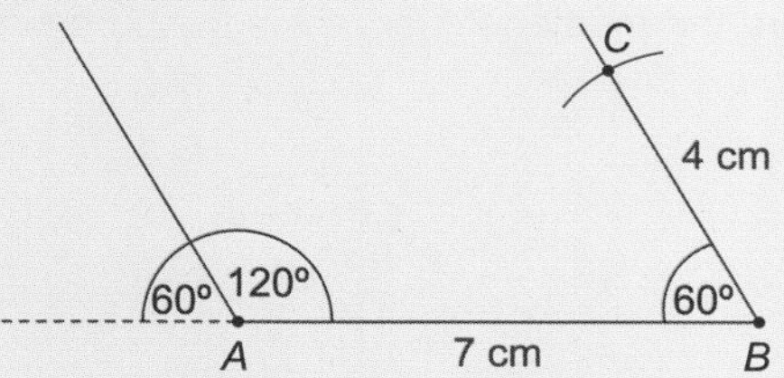

6 Mark the point *D* on this ray such that |*AD*| = 4 cm.

Use your compass (or ruler) for this measurement.

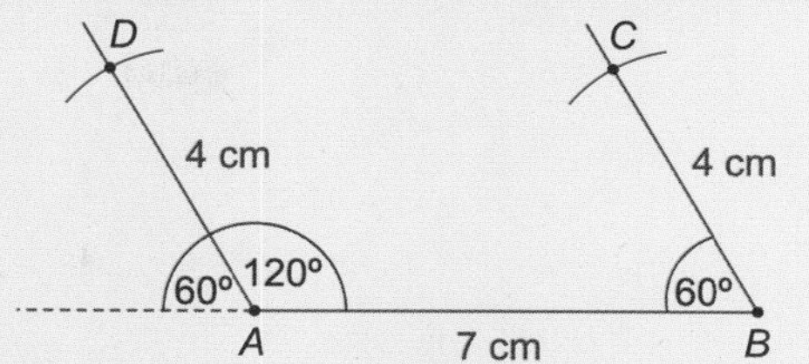

7 Using a ruler, join *C* to *D*.

Label all given measurements.

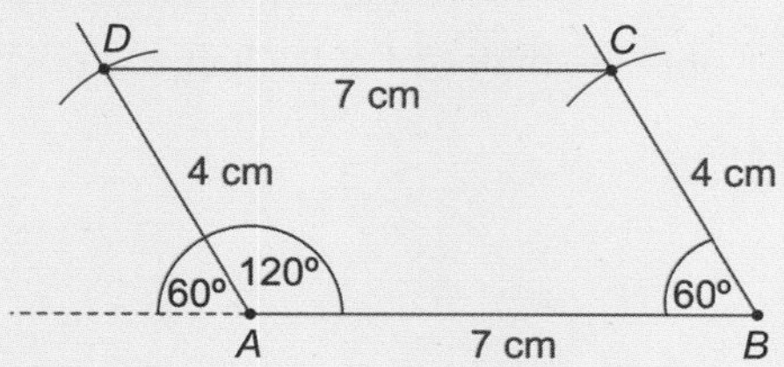

CONSTRUCTION 21

The Centroid of a Triangle

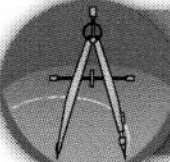

Worked Example 6.21

Construct the centroid of the triangle *PQR*.

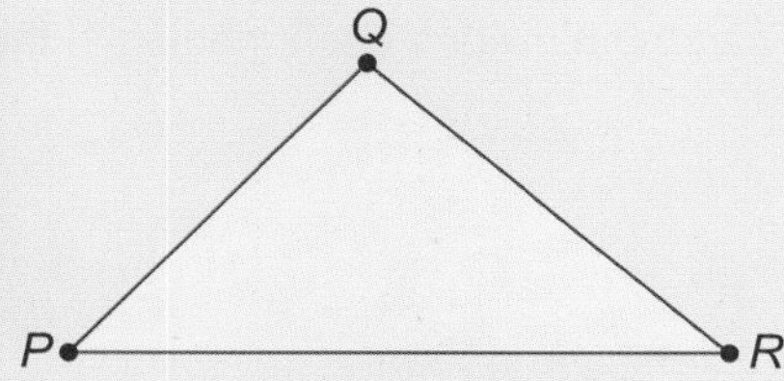

Solution

1 Construct the perpendicular bisector of the side [*PQ*].

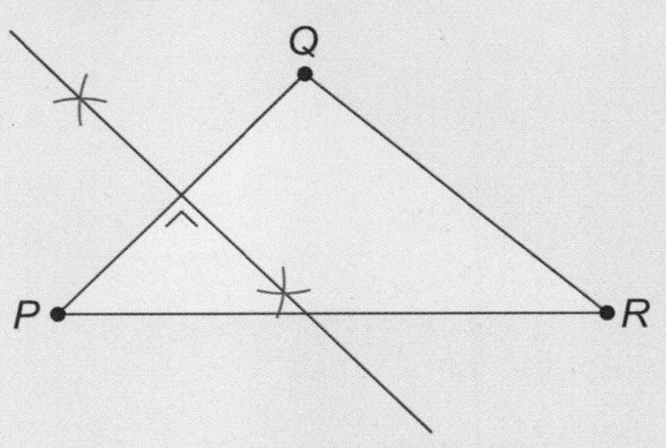

5 Construct the perpendicular bisector of [*PR*] and label the midpoint *Y*.

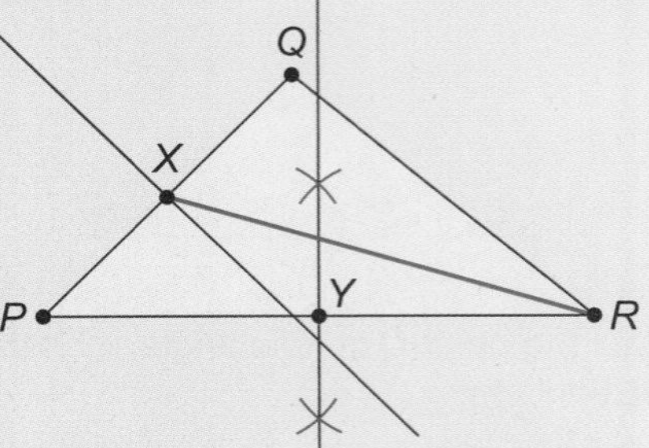

2 Label the midpoint of [*PQ*] as the point *X*.

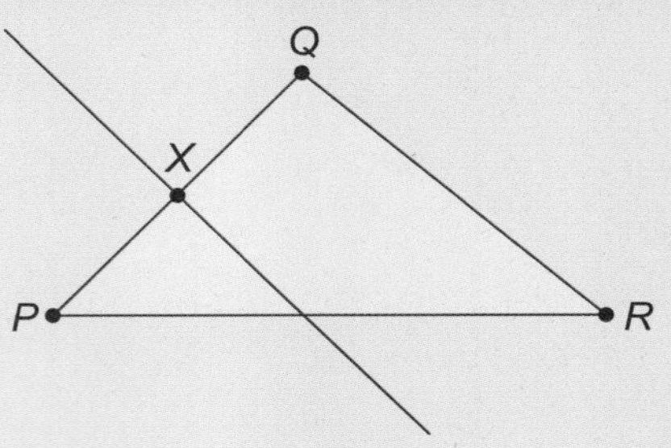

6 Using a straight edge, join *Y* to the opposite vertex, *Q*.

This is a second median.

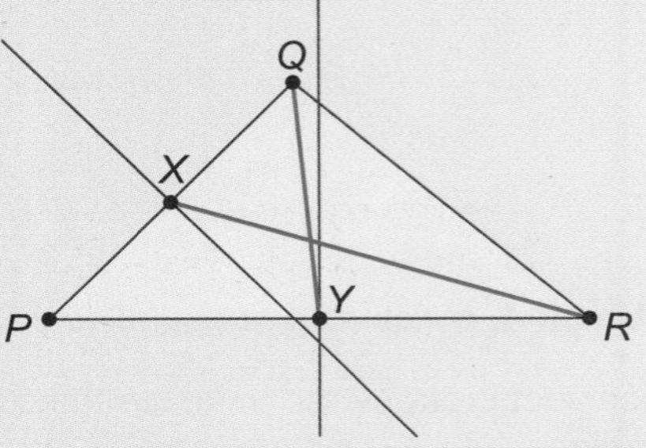

3 Using a straight edge, draw a line from *X* to *R*, the opposite vertex of the triangle.

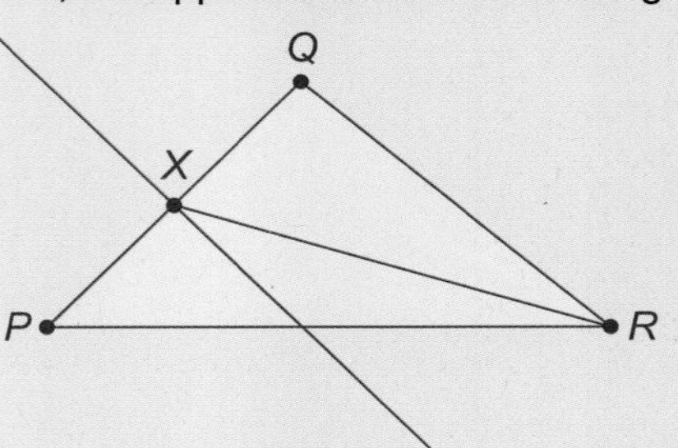

7 Where the medians intersect is the centroid of the triangle *PQR*.

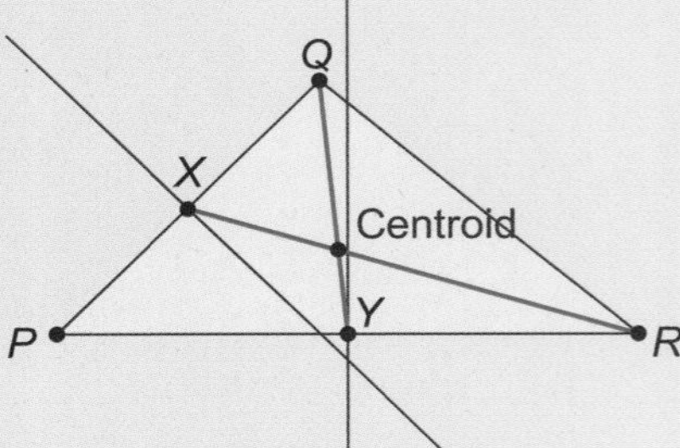

4 This line is a **median** of the triangle *PQR*.

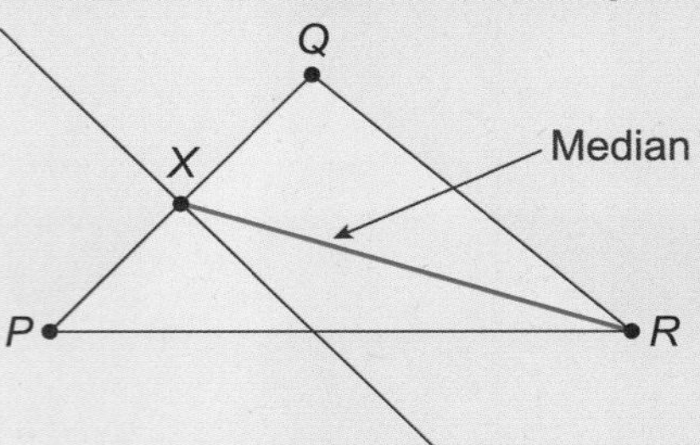

The **centroid** is the triangle's balance point or centre of gravity, i.e. the point where the three medians of the triangle meet.

A **median** of a triangle is a segment that goes from one of the triangle's vertices to the midpoint of the opposite side.

8 The centroid of a triangle divides each median in the ratio 2:1.

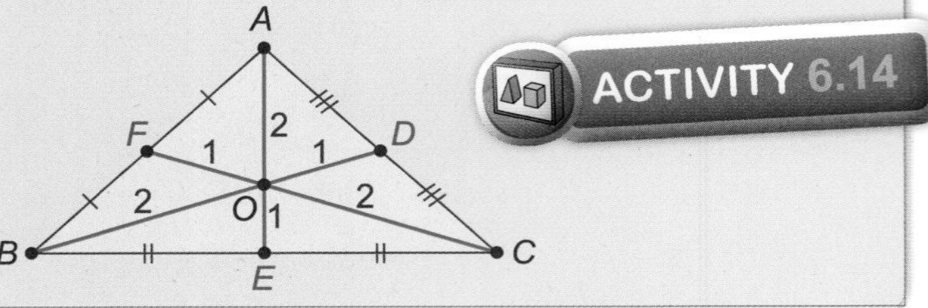

CONSTRUCTION 22

The Orthocentre of a Triangle

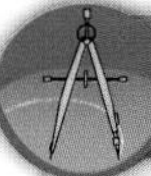

Worked Example 6.22

Construct the orthocentre of the triangle *ABC*.

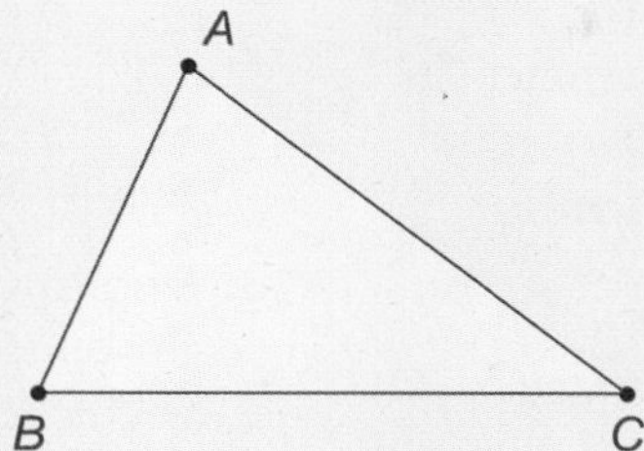

Solution

1 Construct a line perpendicular to [*BC*], passing through the opposite vertex *A*.

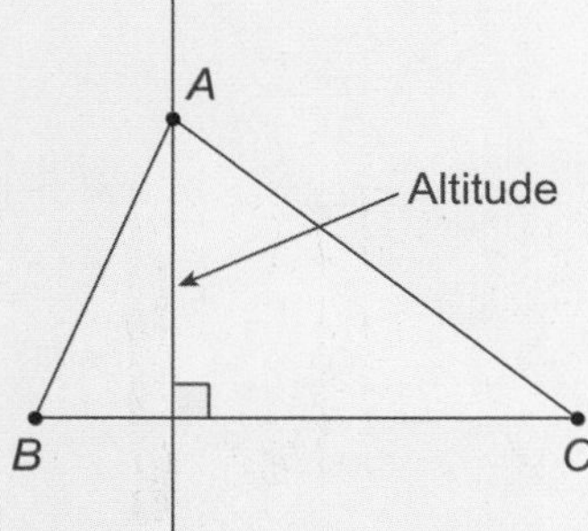

An **altitude** is a segment drawn from a vertex of a triangle to its opposite side such that it forms a right angle with the opposite side.

2 Construct a line perpendicular to [*AC*], passing through the opposite vertex *B*.

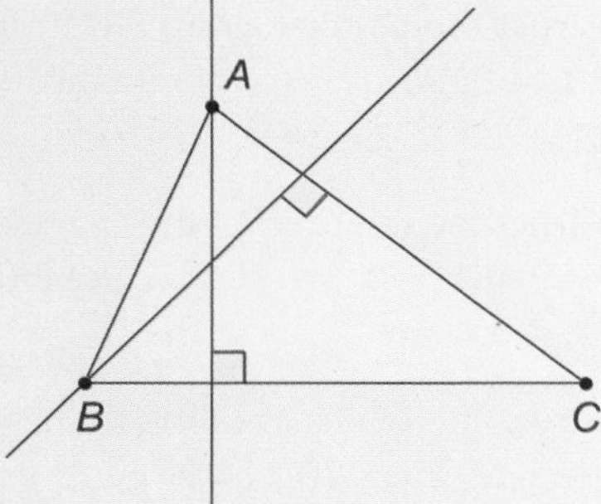

3 Mark the point where these two altitudes meet as the point *O*.

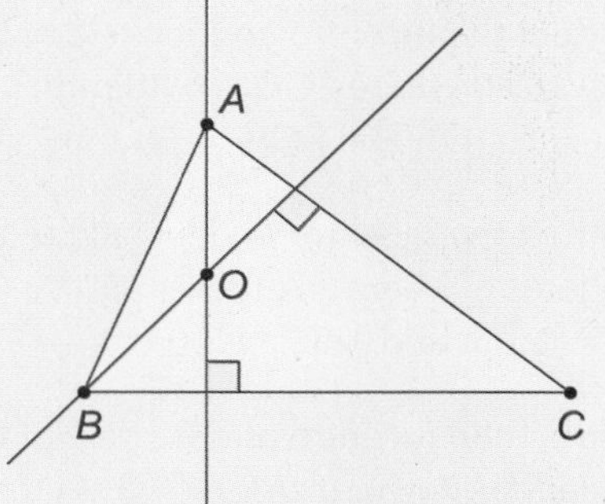

4 *O* is the **orthocentre** of the triangle *ABC*.

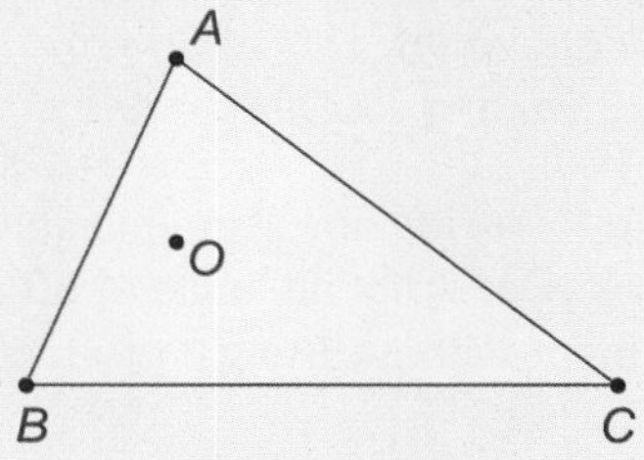

The **orthocentre** is the point where the altitudes of a triangle intersect.

Exercise 6.2

1. Construct the circumcentre and circumcircle of the triangle ABC where $|AB| = 4$ cm, $|BC| = 5.5$ cm and $|AC| = 7.5$ cm.

2. Construct the circumcentre and circumcircle of the triangle GHI where $|\angle HIG| = 35°$, $|\angle GHI| = 100°$ and $|IH| = 9$ cm.

3. Construct the circumcentre and circumcircle of the triangle MNO where $|\angle MON| = 90°$, $|\angle OMN| = 25°$ and $|MO| = 8.5$ cm.

4. (i) Construct a right-angled triangle, an acute triangle and an obtuse triangle.
   (ii) Construct the circumcentre of each triangle.
   (iii) Compare the position of the circumcentre for each type of triangle. What do you notice?

5. Construct the incentre and incircle of the triangle GHI where $|GH| = 80$ mm, $|HI| = 70$ mm and $|GI| = 55$ mm.

6. Construct the incentre and incircle of the triangle ABC where $|\angle ABC| = 90°$, $|AB| = 6$ cm and $|AC| = 10$ cm.

7. Construct the incentre and incircle of the triangle MNO where $|MO| = 5.7$ cm, $|ON| = 10.2$ cm and $|\angle MON| = 95°$.

8. Construct the incentre and incircle of the triangle PQR where $|PQ| = 9$ cm, $|PR| = 7$ cm and $|\angle QPR| = 90°$.

9. Copy the following line segments into your copybook. Construct an angle of 60° on each line segment without using a protractor or set square.

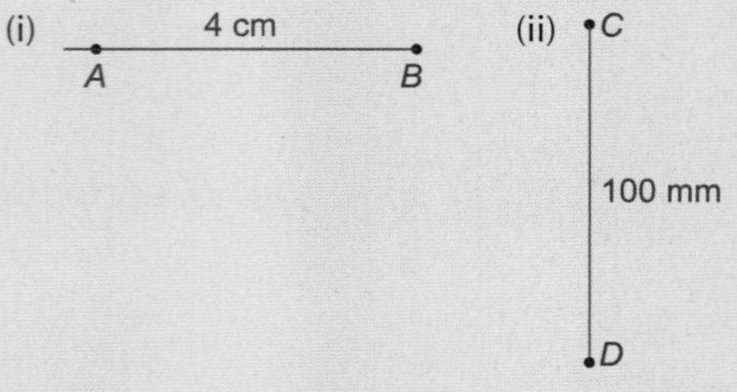

10. (i) Construct an equilateral triangle of side length 8 cm using only a ruler and a compass.
    (ii) Hence, **using only a compass and a straight edge**, construct an equilateral triangle of side length 4 cm.

11. Using only a compass and a straight edge, construct an angle of 30°. Explain how you constructed this angle.

12. Construct a circle of radius 60 mm, and construct a tangent to this circle at any point on the circle.

13. Construct the following circles with centre O in your copybook, and construct a tangent to each circle at the given point:

(i) $|OA| = 3$ cm

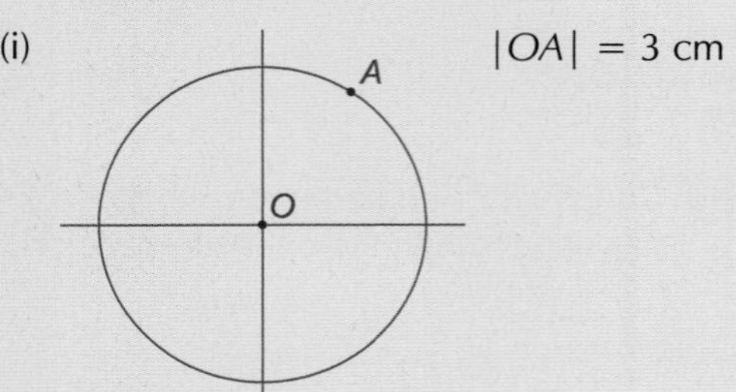

(ii) $|OC| = 4.5$ cm

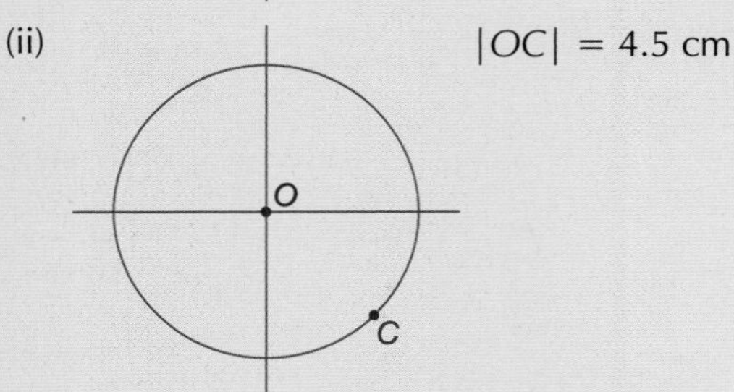

14. Construct the parallelogram $ABCD$ where $|AB| = 7$ cm, $|BC| = 4$ cm and $|\angle ABC| = 105°$.

15. Construct the parallelogram $EFGH$ where $|EF| = 5$ cm, $|FG| = 8$ cm and $|\angle EFG| = 150°$.

16. Construct the rhombus $MNOP$ where $|MN| = 8.4$ cm and $|\angle OMN| = 30°$.

17. Construct the parallelogram $UVWX$ where $|UW| = 8$ cm, $|UV| = 5$ cm and $|\angle UVW| = 75°$.

18. Construct the centroid of the triangle ABC where $|AB| = 8$ cm, $|BC| = 5.2$ cm and $|AC| = 9.4$ cm.

19. Construct the centroid of the triangle DEF where $|\angle EDF| = 20°$, $|DE| = 10$ cm and $|FD| = 6$ cm.

20. Construct the centroid of the triangle TUV where $|TV| = 10.2$ cm, $|\angle UTV| = 36°$ and $|\angle VUT| = 90°$.

21. Construct the centroid of an equilateral triangle PQR where $|PQ| = 70$ mm.

22. Construct the orthocentre of an equilateral triangle ABC where $|AB| = 10$ cm.

23. Construct the orthocentre of an isosceles triangle DEF where $|\angle EDF| = 70°$, $|DE| = 8$ cm and $|FD| = |DE|$.

24. Construct the orthocentre of the triangle TUV where $|TV| = 10$ cm, $|UT| = 7$ cm and $|\angle TUV| = 90°$.

25. (i) Construct a right-angled triangle, an acute triangle and an obtuse triangle.

(ii) Construct the orthocentre of each triangle.

(iii) Compare the position of the orthocentre for each type of triangle.
What do you notice?

26. An architect wished to design a new window and produces a blueprint. The radius length for the arcs EC and DE is equal to $|AB|$.
The centre for the arc EC is D, and the centre for the arc DE is C.

$|AD| = 2$ m and $|AB| = 3$ m.

The architect uses a scale of 1 cm = 40 cm or 1 : 40.

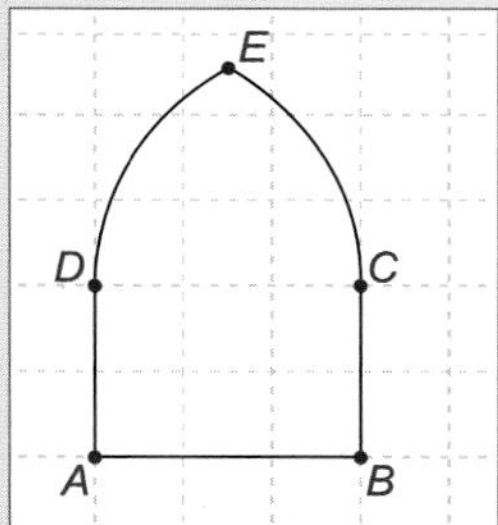

(i) Construct the scaled drawing of this window.

(ii) Find the area of this window.

It is then decided to insert a design of a triangle in the window as shown.

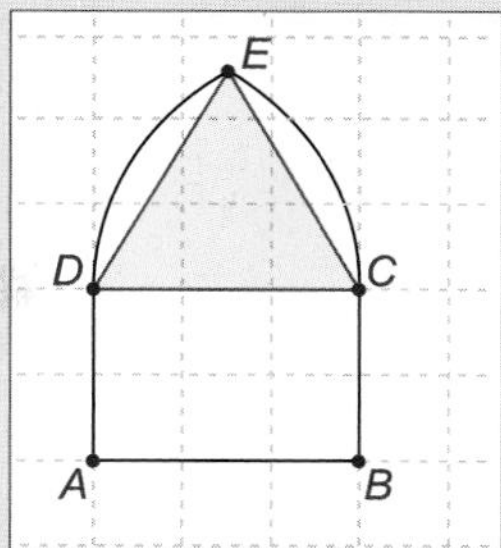

(iii) Prove that the triangle DEC is an equilateral triangle.

27. A scaled diagram of a sail is shown.

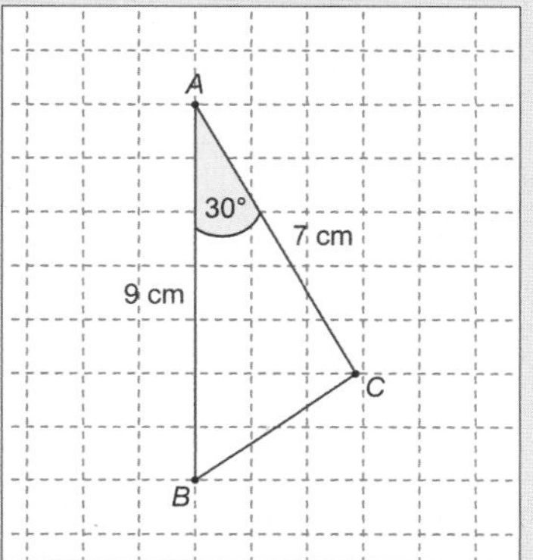

(i) Construct the sail shown.
If the scale used to build the sail is 1: 25, use your construction to find the length of the side of the sail $[BC]$.

(ii) The sail is to be divided up into coloured strips. $|AD| = |DE| = |EB|$ and $|AF| = |FG| = |GC|$. Use your construction to find $|DF|$ and $|EG|$ (scale 1 : 25).

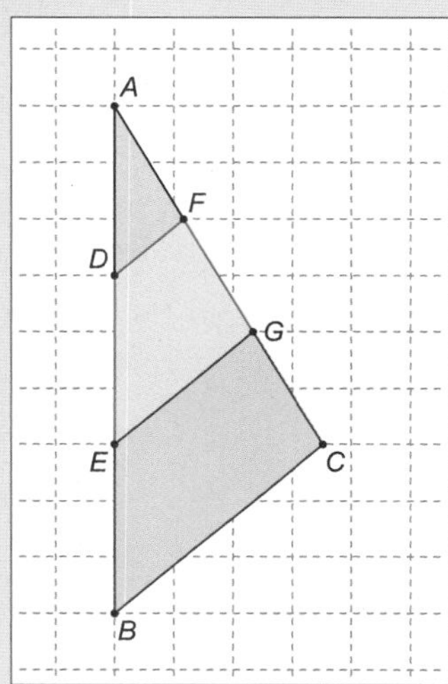

Revision Exercises

1. (i) Draw a line segment [AB] such that $|AB| = 90$ mm.

(ii) Find the midpoint of [AB], and mark as point C.

(iii) Construct a square using [AB] as one of the diagonals.

2. (i) Construct the line segment [XY] such that $|XY| = 12$ cm.

(ii) Divide the line [XY] into five equal parts without measuring it.

(iii) Draw a ray [PQ.

(iv) Construct on the ray [PQ a line segment [PR] such that $|PR| = \frac{2}{3}|XY|$.

3. (i) Draw the line segment [AB] such that $|AB| = 9$ cm.

(ii) Using a compass and a straight edge, construct the angle ABC such that $|\angle ABC| = 60°$.

(iii) Construct an equilateral triangle of side 9 cm.

(iv) Using only a compass and a straight edge, construct an equilateral triangle of side 3 cm. Show clearly how you constructed this triangle.

4. Using only a compass and a straight edge, construct the following angles:

(i) 90° (ii) 45° (iii) 22.5°

5. (i) Construct a triangle ABC where $|AB| = 6$ cm, $|AC| = 8$ cm and $|BC| = 5$ cm.

(ii) Construct the circumcentre of the triangle ABC.

(iii) Explain in your own words what the circumcentre of a triangle is.

(iv) Construct the circumcircle of the triangle ABC.

6. Copy the following diagram onto graph paper.

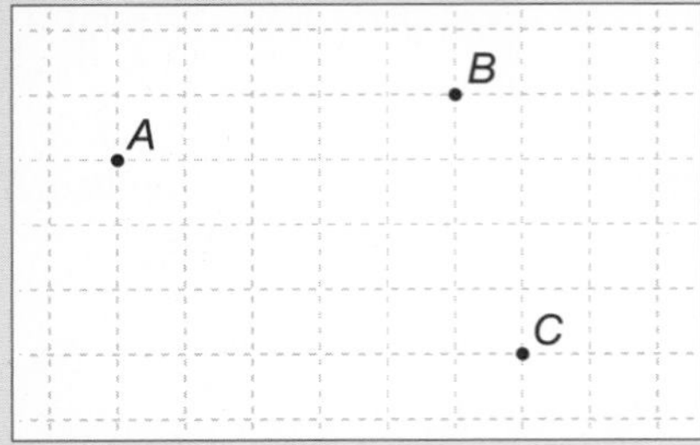

Using only a compass and a straight edge, construct a circle which passes through the points A, B and C.

7. (i) Construct a triangle DEF where $|DF| = 75$ mm, $|\angle EDF| = 62°$ and $|\angle EFD| = 43°$.

(ii) Construct the incentre of the triangle DEF.

(iii) Explain in your own words what the incentre of a triangle is.

(iv) Construct the incircle of the triangle DEF.

8. (i) Construct a triangle GHI where $|GH| = 4$ cm, $|\angle GHI| = 90°$ and $|\angle IGH| = 35°$.

(ii) Find the length of the sides [GI] and [HI] using a ruler.

9. (i) Construct the triangle ABC where $|AB| = 7$ cm, $|AC| = 10$ cm and $|\angle BAC| = 50°$.

(ii) Hence construct the triangle DEF where $|DE| = |AC|$, $|FE| = |BC|$ and $|\angle BCA| = |\angle FED|$.

(iii) Prove that $\Delta ABC \equiv \Delta DEF$.

10. (i) Construct the triangle XYZ where $|XY| = 100$ mm, $|YZ| = 80$ mm and $|XZ| = 60$ mm.

(ii) Show, without measuring, that the triangle XYZ is a right-angled triangle.

11. (i) Construct the triangle JKL where $|JL| = 6$ cm, $|\angle KJL| = 100°$ and $|\angle KLJ| = 25°$.

(ii) Construct the centroid of the triangle JKL.

(iii) Explain in your own words what the centroid of a triangle is.

12. (i) Construct a triangle ABC.
    (ii) Using the constructed triangle ABC, construct a parallelogram $ABCD$ ($ABCD$ is not a rectangle).

13. (i) Construct a triangle PQR where $|PR| = 85$ mm, $|\angle PQR| = 90°$ and $|\angle RPQ| = 40°$.
    (ii) Construct the orthocentre of the triangle PQR.
    (iii) Find the area of the triangle PQR.

14. The perimeter of an equilateral triangle is 12 cm. Using only a compass and a straight edge, construct this equilateral triangle.

15.

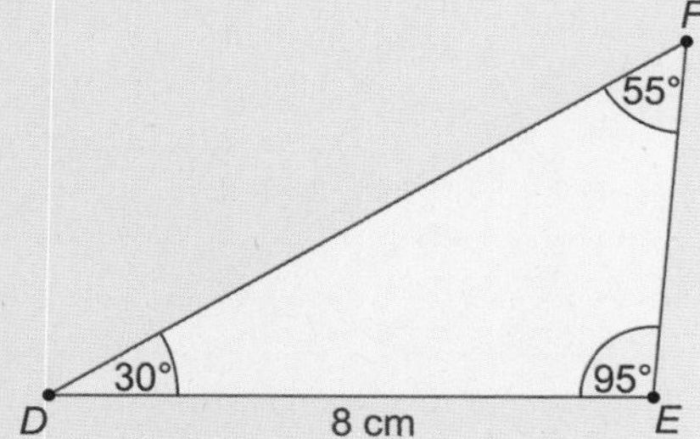

(i) Construct the triangle DEF as shown.
(ii) Draw a line segment $[PR]$ where $|PR| = 12$ cm.
(iii) Construct the triangle PQR which is similar to the triangle DEF.
(iv) Find $|PQ|$ and $|RQ|$.

16. (i) Construct a triangle ABC where $|AB| = 8$ cm, $|\angle ABC| = 30°$ and $|BC| = 7$ cm.
    (ii) Construct a triangle ABD, where the area of ΔABD is half the area of ΔABC.
    (iii) Find $|BD|$.

17.

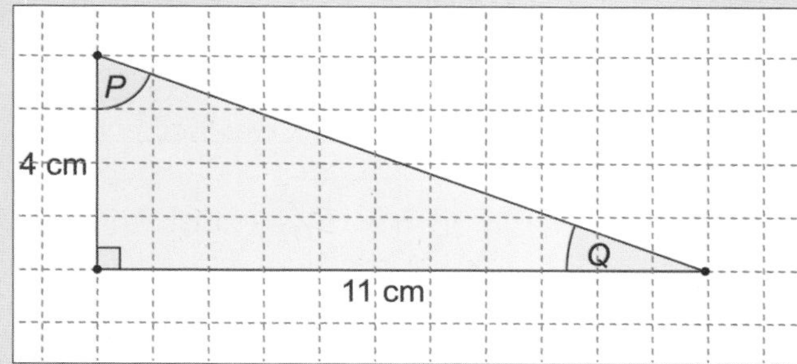

(i) Construct the triangle shown in the diagram.
(ii) Using a protractor, find the measure of angles P and Q.
(iii) Construct the circle that circumscribes the triangle.
(iv) Measure the radius of this circle.
(v) Explain why the centre of this circle is the midpoint of the hypotenuse.

18.

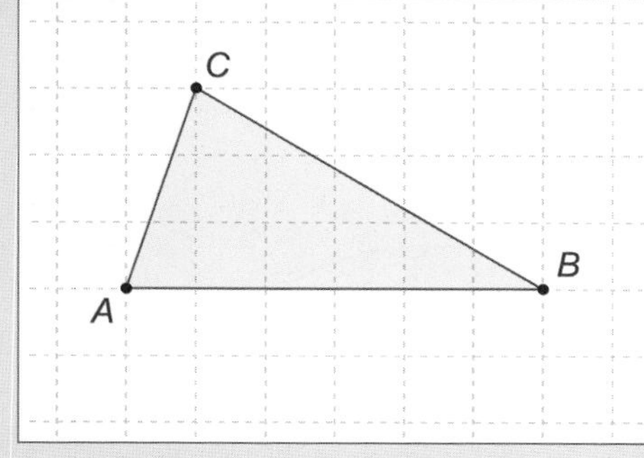

(i) Draw a triangle ABC as shown in the diagram.
(ii) Construct a line perpendicular to AB passing through the point C.
(iii) Measure the perpendicular distance between C and $[AB]$.
(iv) Find the area of the triangle drawn.

19. (i) Draw any quadrilateral using a straight edge. Label the vertices A, B, C and D.
    (ii) Construct the perpendicular bisector of all four sides of the quadrilateral.
    (iii) Starting at $[AB]$, join the midpoint of each side to form a new quadrilateral.
    (iv) What type of quadrilateral is formed?

20. (i) Construct a circle of radius 70 mm.

(ii) Construct two tangents to this circle which are parallel to each other, using only a compass and a straight edge.

21. (i) Construct the parallelogram *ABCD* where $|AB| = 11$ cm, $|BC| = 6$ cm and $|\angle ABC| = 125°$.

(ii) Construct a ray which is equidistant from [*AB*] and [*BC*].

22. The diagram shows four circles inscribed in a rectangle.

The radius of each circle is 35 mm.

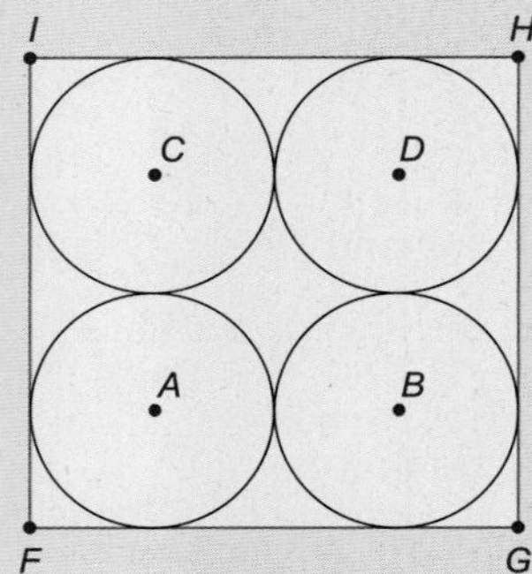

(i) Construct the rectangle *FGHI*.

(ii) Using only a compass and a straight edge, construct the four circles inscribed in the rectangle. Explain how you constructed these four circles.

23. (i) Draw a circle of centre *O* and with diameter length 10 cm.

(ii) Using only a compass and a straight edge, construct the chords [*AB*] and [*CD*] which are parallel to each other as shown in the diagram.

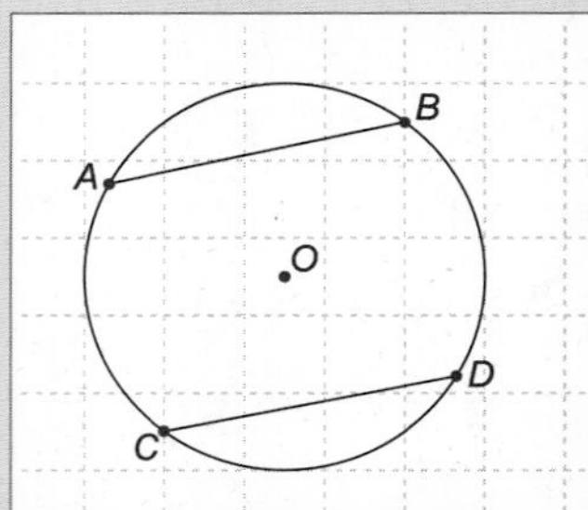

(iii) Construct the perpendicular bisectors of [*AB*] and [*DC*].

(iv) What point do these perpendicular bisectors have in common?

24. Using only a compass and a straight edge, construct the following angles:

(i) 60° (ii) 120° (iii) 30° (iv) 15°

25. An advertising company wants to design a logo of a circle inside an equilateral triangle as shown.

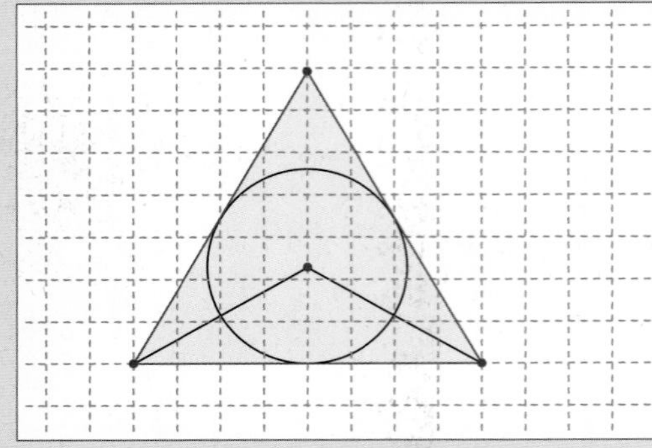

(i) If the equilateral triangle has sides of length 10 cm, construct this logo.

(ii) It is decided to add two further circles each of which has half the radius of the original circle as shown.

Add these circles to your construction.

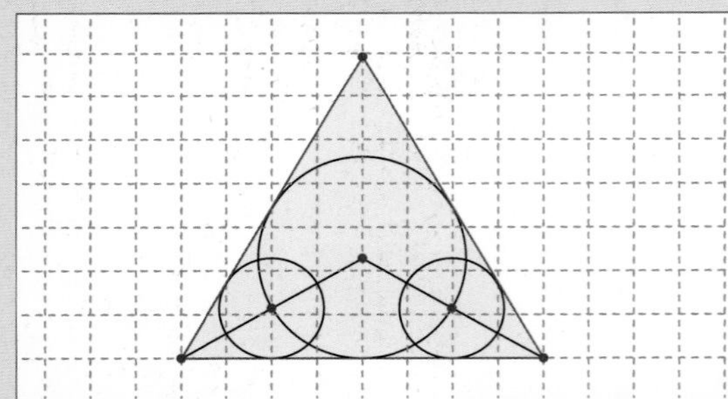

26. Using only a ruler and a compass, construct the shape shown below. ΔDEF is an isosceles triangle. $|DE| = |EF|$.

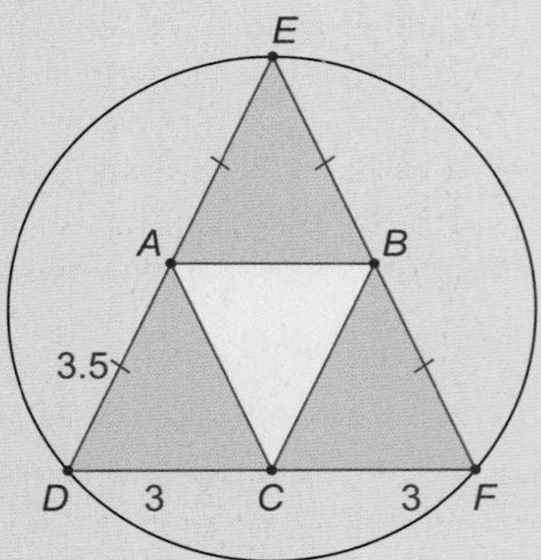

27. A triangle ABC has side lengths of 8 cm, 5 cm and n cm, where $n \in N$.

(i) Construct the largest triangle possible.

(ii) Construct the smallest triangle possible.

28. (i) Construct a circle of radius 5 cm and with centre (0,0) on a Cartesian plane. Make sure that both the x-axis and the y-axis are drawn to the same scale.

(ii) Construct a tangent t to this circle at the point (–3,4).

(iii) Construct another tangent s to the circle which is a parallel to t. Explain the steps you used to construct the tangent s.

(iv) Construct another tangent r to this circle which is perpendicular to t. Explain the steps you used to construct the tangent r.

29. (i) Construct the rectangle $ABCD$ where $|AB| = 50$ mm and $|BC| = 90$ mm, using only a compass and a ruler.

(ii) Construct a square whose area $= n$ cm^2 and perimeter $= n$ cm, $n \in N$.

30. A landscaper is given a design for a lawn. The lawn should be in the shape of a triangle and have dimensions of 7 m, 8 m and 5.5 m.

(i) Construct a scaled drawing of this lawn.

(ii) The landscaper decides that a large circular flower-bed should surround the lawn, with each corner of the lawn touching the circular flower-bed. Construct the largest flower-bed possible into your drawing from part (i).

(iii) Find the area of this flower-bed using the measurements from your construction.

31. (a) (i) Construct an equilateral triangle of sides 10 cm.

(ii) Construct the circumcentre of this triangle.

(iii) Construct the centroid of this triangle.

(iv) Construct the orthocentre of this triangle.

(v) What do you notice?

(b) (i) Construct any triangle. (Make sure the triangle is reasonably large and not an equilateral triangle.)

(ii) Construct the circumcentre of this triangle.

(iii) Construct the centroid of this triangle.

(iv) Construct the orthocentre of this triangle.

(v) Try to draw a line that contains all three points. What do you notice?

This line is called the Euler line and is named after Leonhard Euler (1707–1783), a famous Swiss mathematician and physicist.

- For any triangle that is not equilateral, the Euler line will pass through the circumcentre, the centroid and orthocentre of the triangle.
- However, the incentre lies on the Euler line only for isosceles triangles.

32. (i) Construct the triangle and its incircle as shown in the diagram.

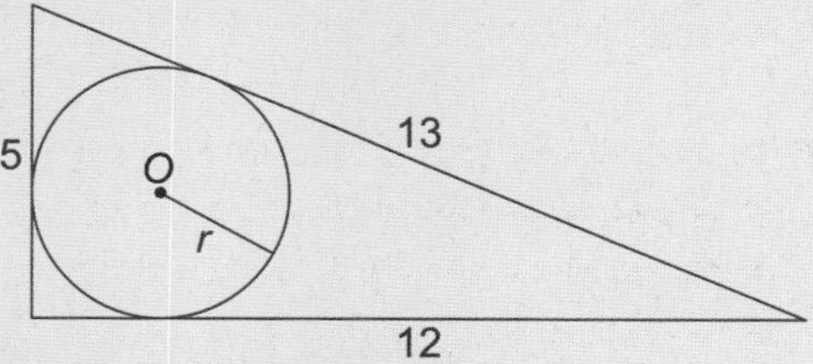

(ii) Prove that the incircle of a right-angled triangle with side lengths of 5 cm, 12 cm and 13 cm has a radius length of 2 cm.

(Note: Measurement from your construction is not a proof.)

7 chapter

Trigonometry

Learning Outcomes

In this chapter you will learn how to:

- Solve right-angled triangles using the theorem of Pythagoras
- Use the trigonometric ratios sin, cos and tan to solve problems
- Define sin x and cos x for all values of x
- Define tan x
- Find trigonometric ratios in surd form for angles 30°, 45° and 60°
- Calculate the area of a triangle
- Use the Sine and Cosine Rules to solve problems
- Calculate the area of a sector of a circle and the length of an arc of a circle
- Graph the trigonometric functions sine, cosine, tangent
- Graph trigonometric functions of type $a \sin n\theta$, $a \cos n\theta$ for $a, n \in N$
- Solve trigonometric equations
- Derive the trigonometric formulae 1, 2, 3, 4, 5, 6, 7, 9
- Apply the trigonometric formulae 1–24

Trigonometry is the study of triangles, their angles, areas and lengths. It is not the work of any one mathematician or nation. Its history dates back thousands of years. Archaelogical evidence dating to 2150 BCE suggests that the ancient Egyptians had a knowledge of trigonometry.

Much of the technology that we use in today's highly developed world would not be possible without trigonometry. There are numerous applications of trigonometry. Astronomers use trigonometry to calculate distances to nearby stars. Engineers use trigonometry to construct bridges and build giant skyscrapers. Seismologists use trigonometry to study earthquakes. Here is a list of just some of the other areas to which trigonometry has been applied: navigation, medical imaging (MRI scans), computer graphics, electrical engineering, biology and economics.

YOU SHOULD REMEMBER...

- The angles in a triangle sum to 180°.
- Angles at the base of an isosceles triangle are equal in measure.
- All angles in an equilateral triangle measure 60°.
- Distance = Speed × Time.

- **Right-angled triangle**
- **Pythagoras' theorem**
- **Opposite, adjacent, hypotenuse**
- **sin, cos, tan**
- **Unit circle**
- **Reference angle**
- **Sine Rule**
- **Cosine Rule**
- **Period**
- **Range**

7.1 RIGHT-ANGLED TRIANGLES AND PYTHAGORAS' THEOREM

Pythagoras, an ancient Greek mathematician, discovered a very famous feature of right-angled triangles. Today, this feature is known as **Pythagoras' theorem**.

In a right-angled triangle, the area of the square on the hypotenuse is equal to the sum of the areas of the squares on the other two sides.

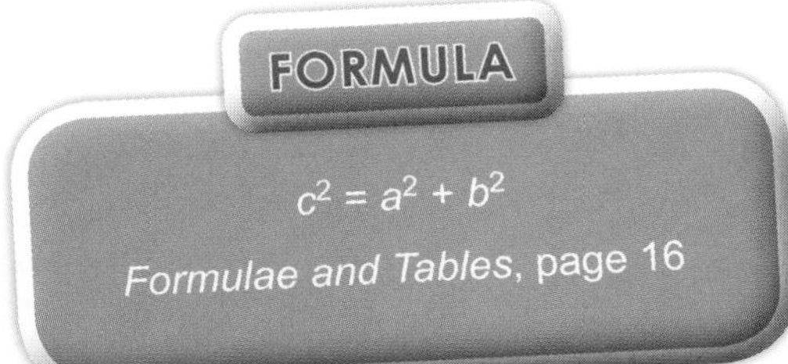

FORMULA
$c^2 = a^2 + b^2$
Formulae and Tables, page 16

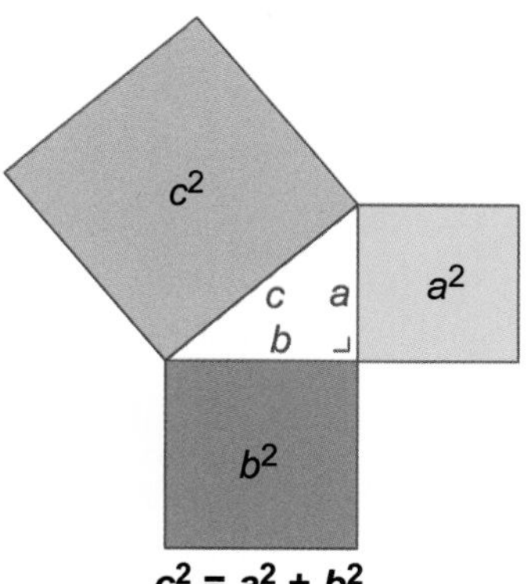

$c^2 = a^2 + b^2$

Worked Example 7.1

Use the theorem of Pythagoras to find the value of x.

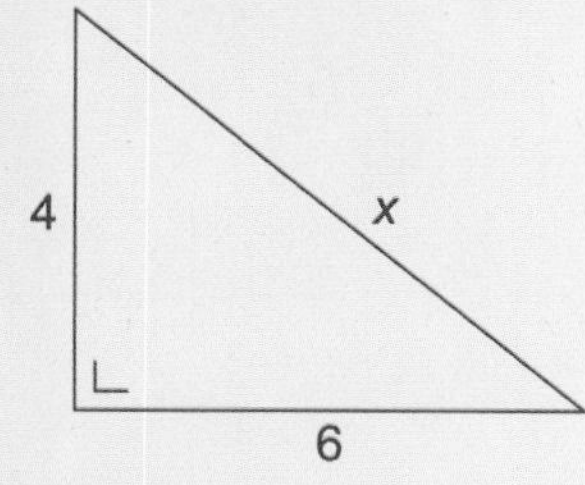

Solution

$x^2 = 4^2 + 6^2$ (Pythagoras)

$x^2 = 16 + 36$

$x^2 = 52$

$x = \sqrt{52} = \sqrt{4}\sqrt{13} = 2\sqrt{13}$

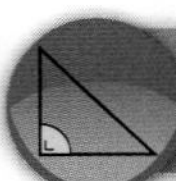

Worked Example 7.2

A mast on a sailing boat is held in place by steel wires called stays. The mast is 12 m tall. The stay is 13 metres long. What is the width of the deck between the base of the mast and the stay?

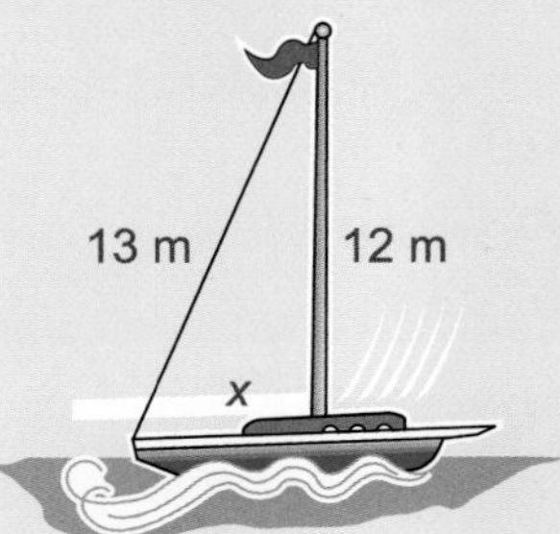

Solution

Let the distance between the base and the stay be x.

$13^2 = 12^2 + x^2$

$169 = 144 + x^2$

$169 - 144 = x^2$

$25 = x^2$

$x = 5$ m

7.2 RIGHT-ANGLED TRIANGLES AND THE TRIGONOMETRIC RATIOS

In a right-angled triangle, we have the following special ratios:

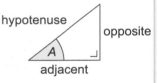

hypotenuse, opposite, A, adjacent

$\sin A = \dfrac{\text{opposite}}{\text{hypotenuse}}$	$\cos A = \dfrac{\text{adjacent}}{\text{hypotenuse}}$	$\tan A = \dfrac{\text{opposite}}{\text{adjacent}}$

These ratios can be found on page 16 of the *Formulae and Tables*.

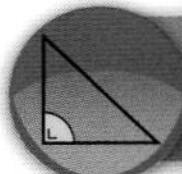

Worked Example 7.3

In the following right-angled triangle, write down the value of each of the following ratios: $\sin A$, $\cos A$ and $\tan A$; also $\sin B$, $\cos B$ and $\tan B$.

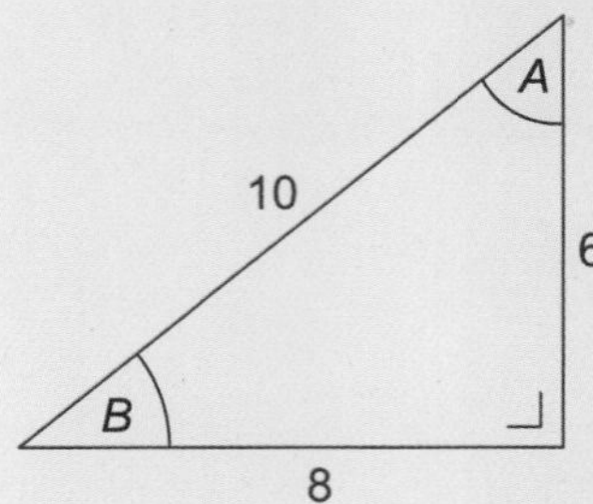

Solution

$\sin A = \dfrac{8}{10} = \dfrac{4}{5}$ $\quad$ $\sin B = \dfrac{6}{10} = \dfrac{3}{5}$

$\cos A = \dfrac{6}{10} = \dfrac{3}{5}$ $\quad$ $\cos B = \dfrac{8}{10} = \dfrac{4}{5}$

$\tan A = \dfrac{8}{6} = \dfrac{4}{3}$ $\quad$ $\tan B = \dfrac{6}{8} = \dfrac{3}{4}$

7.3 CALCULATOR WORK

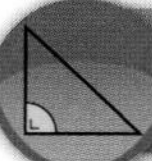

Worked Example 7.4

Use your calculator to find the value of each of the following, correct to four decimal places:

(i) $\sin 32.4°$

(ii) $\cos 45.6°$

(iii) $\tan 22.5°$

Solution

Make sure your calculator is in degree mode.

(i) On the calculator, press:

The answer should be 0.5358 corrected to four decimal places.

(ii)

(iii)

How can we find the measure of the angle A?
From the diagram, we know that:

$\sin A = \frac{11}{61}$

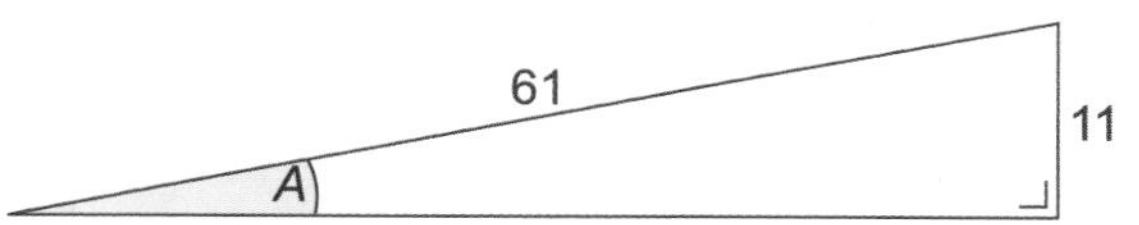

We can now use the calculator to find A.

Key in the following:

This gives an answer of 10.39° (to two decimal places).

This is written as:

$\sin A = \frac{11}{61}$

$\therefore A = \sin^{-1} \frac{11}{61}$

$\therefore A = 10.39°$

Note: Individual calculators may differ from what is shown next.

Worked Example 7.5

Change 35.6° to degrees and minutes.

Solution

Note: On some calculators, D°M'S is replaced with ° ′ ″.

The answer 35° 36′ 0″ is displayed. Therefore, 35.6° = 35° 36′.

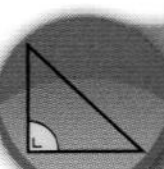

Worked Example 7.6

Change 64° 45′ to degrees.

Solution

64° | D°M′S | 45 | D°M′S | = | 2nd F | D°M′S

The answer 64.75 is displayed.

$\Rightarrow 64° 45' = 64.75°$

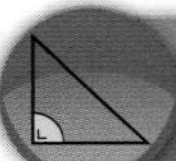

Worked Example 7.7

Use your calculator to find the measure of the angle X, if $\sin X = 0.5469$.

Give your answer correct to the nearest minute.

Solution

$\sin X = 0.5469$

$\Rightarrow X = \sin^{-1} 0.5469$

2nd F | sin | 0.5469 | =

The answer 33.15459885 is displayed.

Now, convert this to the nearest minute:

The answer 33° 9′ 16.556″ is displayed.
This answer, corrected to the nearest minute, is 33° 9′.

Worked Example 7.8

If $\cos A = 0.2183$, then using your calculator, find:

(i) The measure of the angle A to two decimal places

(ii) The measure of the angle A to the nearest minute

Solution

(i) $\cos A = 0.2183$

$\Rightarrow A = \cos^{-1} 0.2183$

Key in the following:

This gives an answer of 77.39° (to two decimal places).

(ii) Key in the following:

This gives the answer 77° 23′ (to the nearest minute).

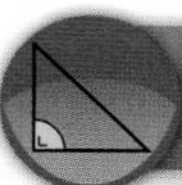

Worked Example 7.9

Consider the triangle ABC. If $AB = 9$ cm and $|\angle ABC| = 50°$, find the remaining two sides of the triangle correct to two decimal places.

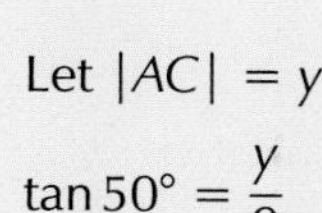

Solution

Let $|BC| = x$.

$\cos 50° = \frac{9}{x}$

$x \cos 50° = 9$ (multiply both sides by x)

$x = \frac{9}{\cos 50°}$ (divide both sides by $\cos 50°$)

$x = 14.00$ (calculate to two decimal places)

$\therefore |BC| = 14.00$ cm

Let $|AC| = y$.

$\tan 50° = \frac{y}{9}$

$9 \tan 50° = y$ (multiply both sides by 9)

$y = 10.7258$

$\therefore |AC| = 10.73$ cm

7.4 USING TRIGONOMETRY TO SOLVE PRACTICAL PROBLEMS

Compass Directions

The diagram below shows the four main compass directions, North, South, East and West.

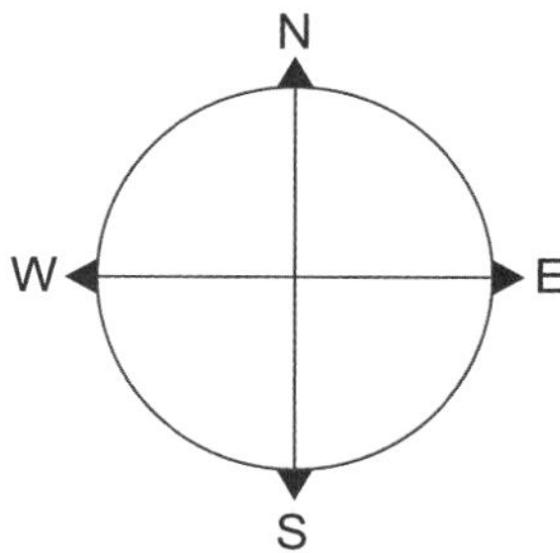

For all other compass directions, we can begin by looking North or South and then turning either East or West through the required number of degrees. This is shown in the diagrams below. One could also begin by looking East or West and then turning North or South through the required angle.

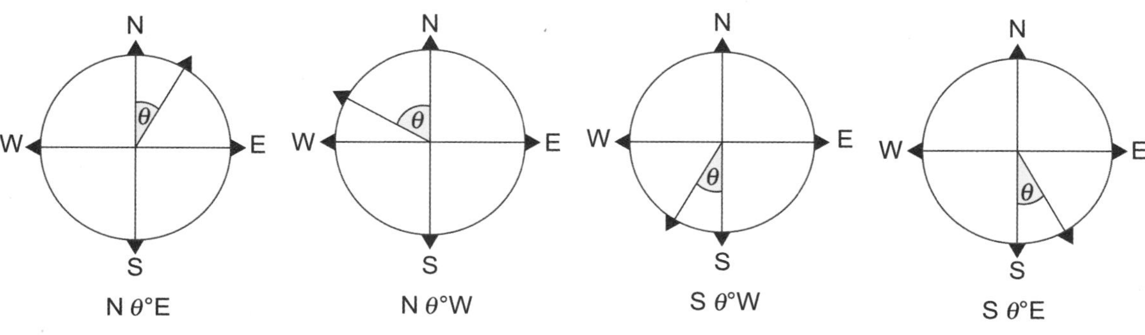

Angles of Elevation and Depression

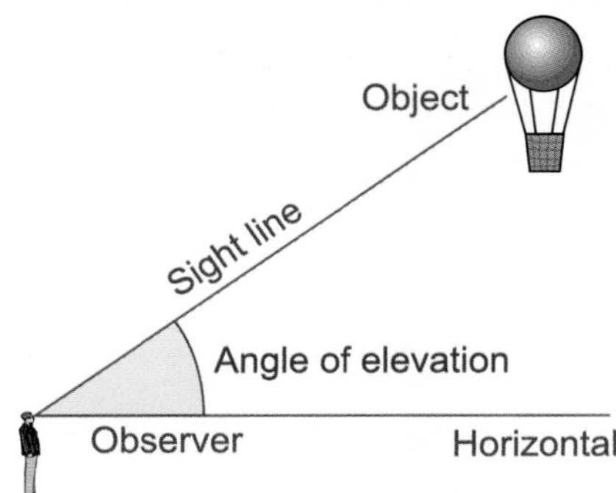

If you look up at a tall building or object, the angle that your line of vision makes with the horizontal is called the **angle of elevation**.

The angle of elevation is the angle above the horizontal.

If you stand on top of a cliff and observe a swimmer out at sea, the angle that your line of vision makes with the horizontal is called the **angle of depression**.

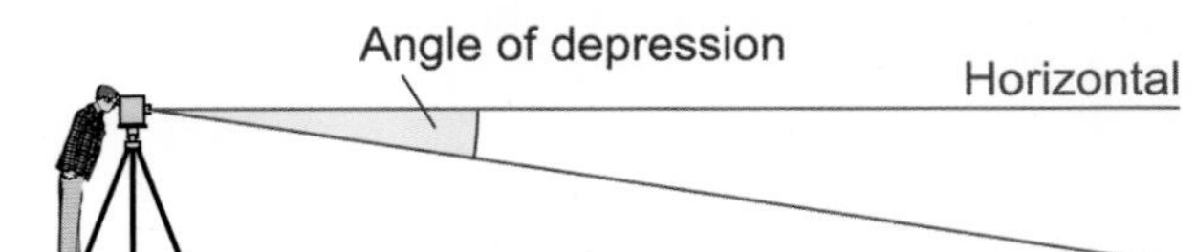

The angle of depression is the angle below the horizontal.

Worked Example 7.10

Ger is out playing golf. As he approaches the ninth tee his friend tells him the hole is 310 m from the tee (A) to the hole (C).

On the first stroke the ball travels a distance of 225 m in the direction N 40° E. Ger then takes his second shot and the ball travels in the direction S 50° E and rolls onto the green and into the hole.

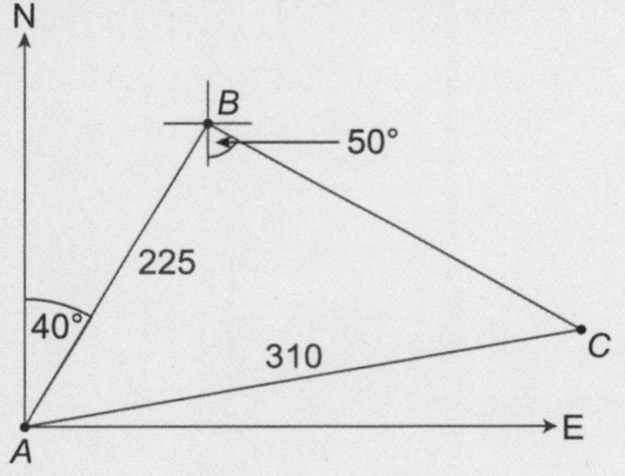

(i) How far did Ger hit the ball on his second shot? Give your answer to the nearest metre.

(ii) Find $|\angle ACB|$ to the nearest degree.

Solution

(i) $|\angle ABC| = 40° + 50° = 90°$

$|AC| = 310$

$|AC|^2 = |AB|^2 + |BC|^2$ (Pythagoras)

$310^2 = 225^2 + |BC|^2$

$|BC|^2 = 45475$

$|BC| = 213.2487$

Ans ≈ 213 m

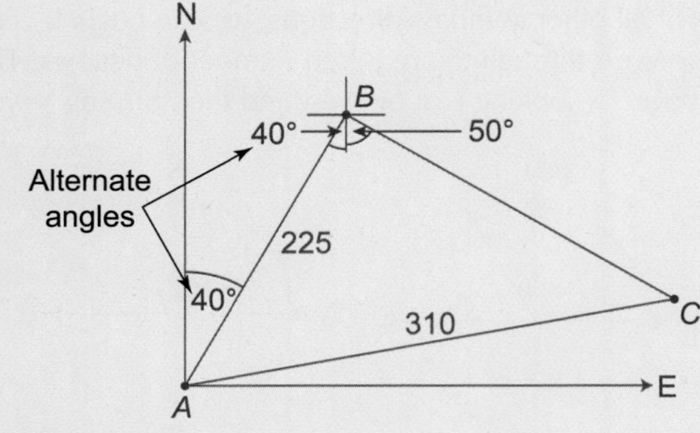

(ii) $\sin|\angle ACB| = \dfrac{225}{310}$

$|\angle ACB| = \sin^{-1}\left(\dfrac{225}{310}\right)$

$|\angle ACB| \approx 47°$

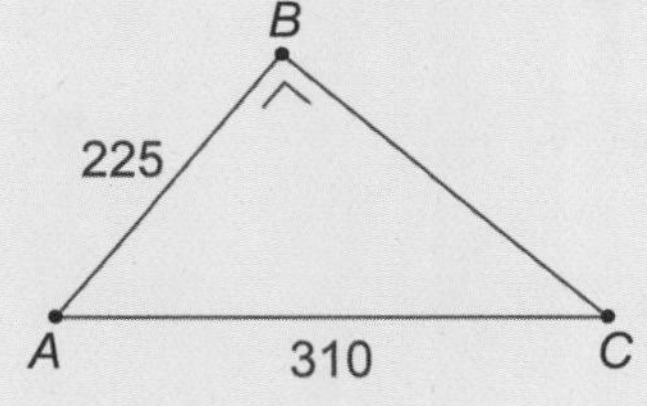

Exercise 7.1

1. Find the value of x in each case:

(i)

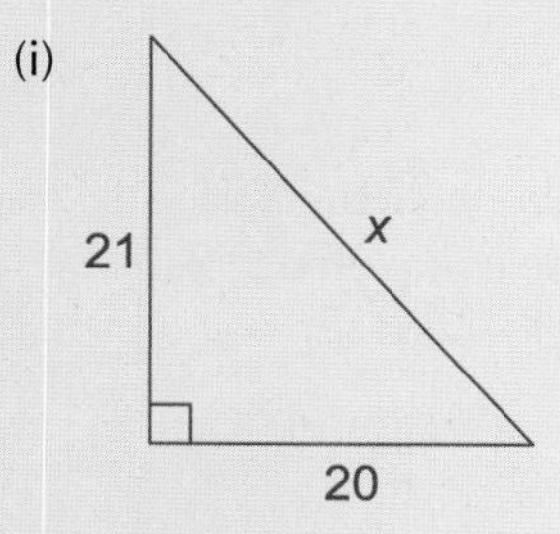

(ii)

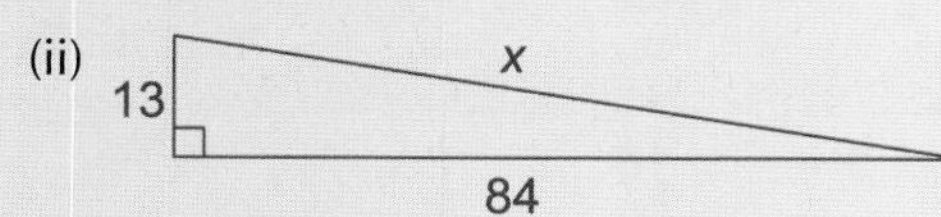

(iii)

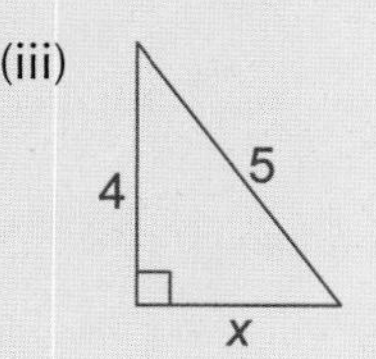

(iv)

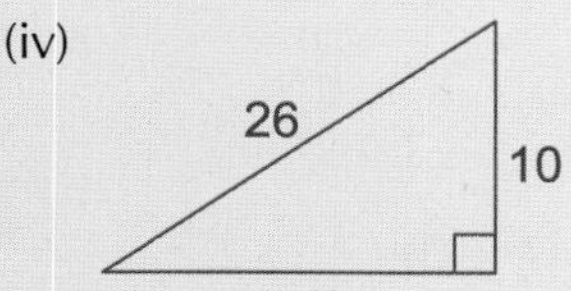

(v)

(vi)

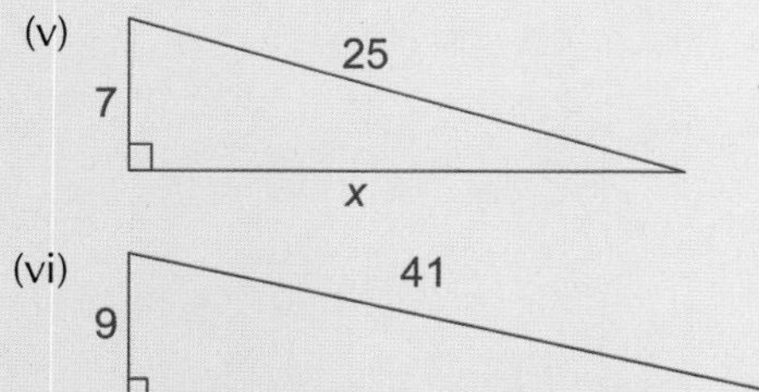

2. Find the value of x in each case (leave your answers in surd form):

(i)

(ii)

(iii)

(iv)

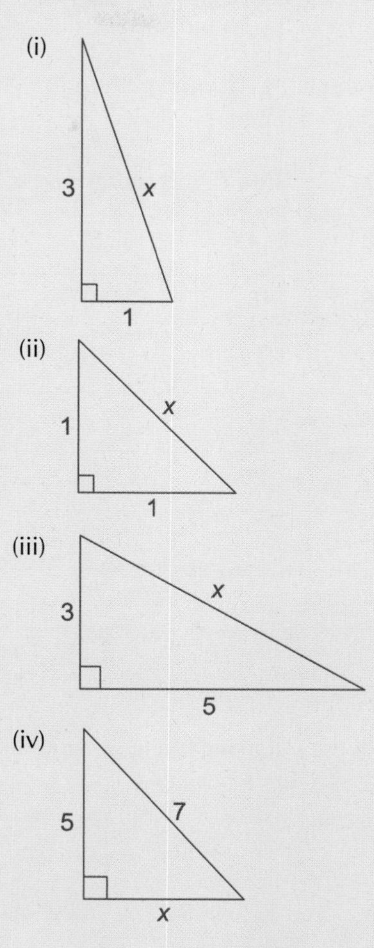

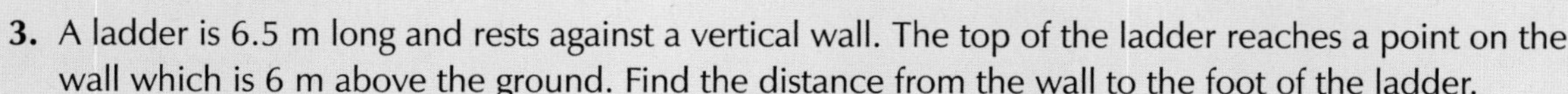

3. A ladder is 6.5 m long and rests against a vertical wall. The top of the ladder reaches a point on the wall which is 6 m above the ground. Find the distance from the wall to the foot of the ladder.

4. Find the value of x and y in each case (diagrams are not drawn to scale):

(i)

(ii)

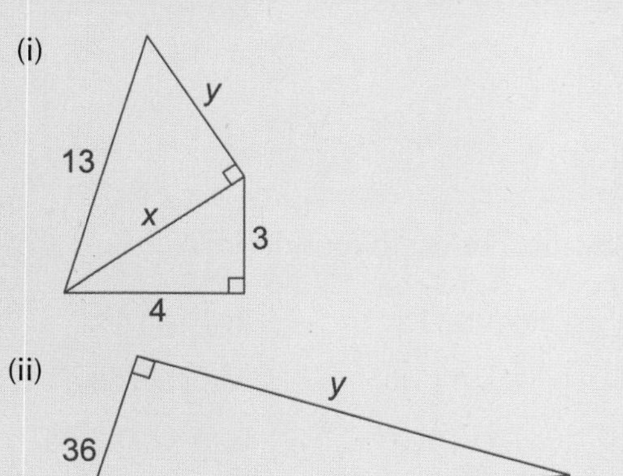

(iii)

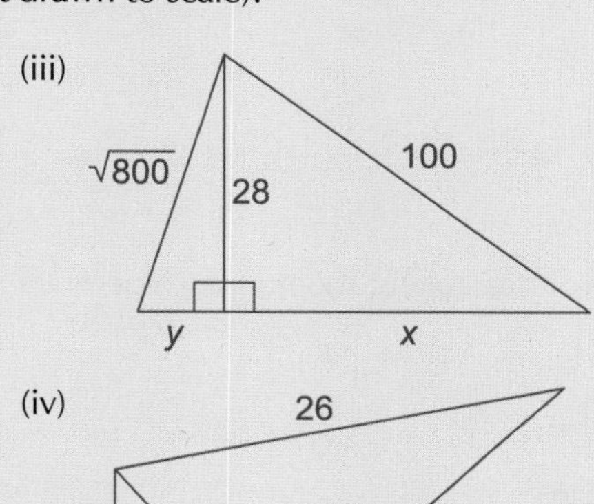

(iv)

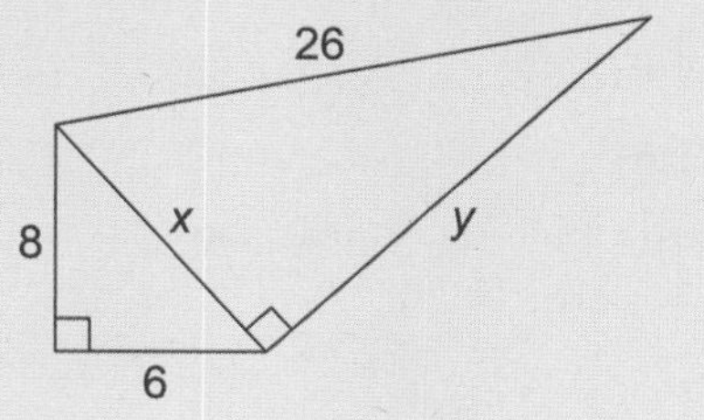

5. The perimeter of a rectangle is 280 cm. The length of the longest side is 80 cm. Find:

(i) The length of the shortest side

(ii) The length of a diagonal of the rectangle

(iii) The area of the rectangle

6. (a) Copy the table. Use the pattern to complete the table.

Side *a*	Side *b*	Hypotenuse *c*
3	4	5
6	8	10
9	12	15
12		
	20	
		30
21		

(b) Using your calculator, check if $a^2 + b^2 = c^2$ for each row of the completed table. Copy the table below and show your results.

a^2	b^2	c^2	$a^2 + b^2 = c^2$ Tick if true
9	16	25	✓
36			

7. For each of the following triangles, write down the values of $\sin A$, $\cos A$ and $\tan A$.

(i)

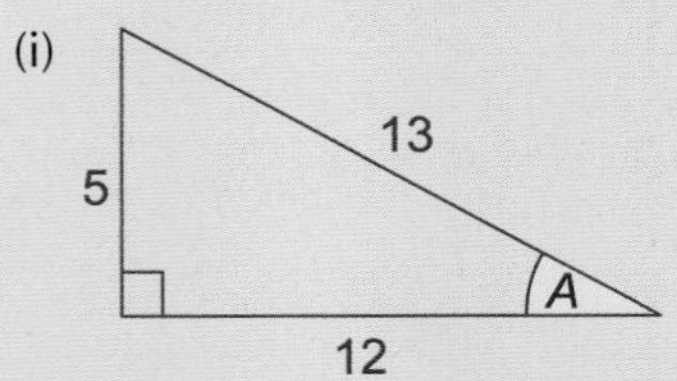

(ii)

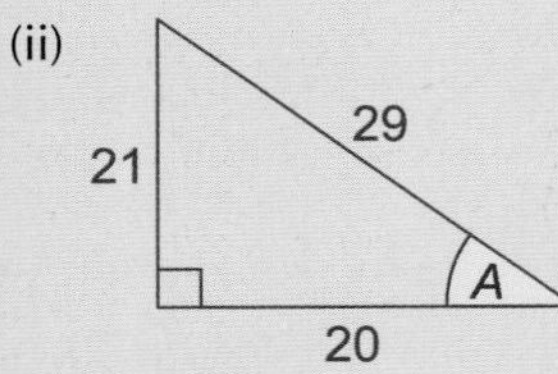

8. For each one of the following triangles, write down the values of $\sin A$, $\cos A$, $\tan A$, $\sin B$, $\cos B$ and $\tan B$:

(i)

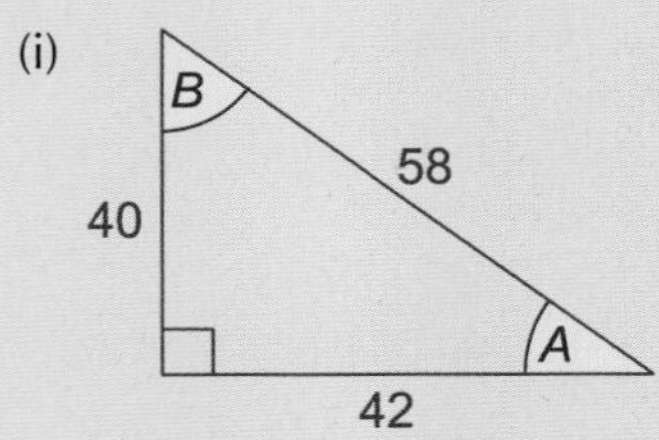

(ii)

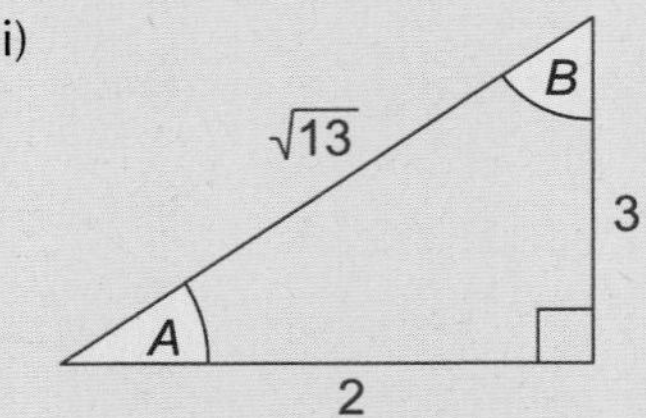

(iii)

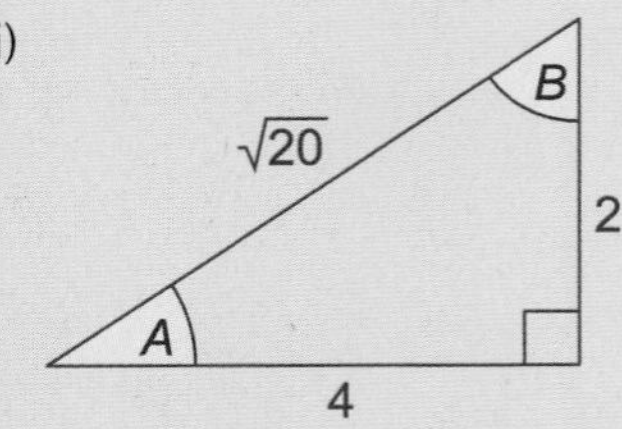

9. Use your calculator to find the value of each of the following, correct to four decimal places:

(i) $\sin 15°$	(v) $\tan 42°$	(ix) $\tan 80°$	(xiii) $\sin 31.4°$	(xvii) $\sin 63.3°$
(ii) $\cos 30°$	(vi) $\cos 85°$	(x) $\tan 25.6°$	(xiv) $\tan 15.8°$	(xviii) $\tan 82.4°$
(iii) $\tan 75°$	(vii) $\tan 12°$	(xi) $\cos 43.8°$	(xv) $\cos 30.9°$	(xix) $\cos 88.24°$
(iv) $\sin 14°$	(viii) $\sin 30°$	(xii) $\sin 79.2°$	(xvi) $\cos 56.7°$	(xx) $\sin 63.16°$

10. Use your calculator to find the measure of the angle A, $0° \leqslant A \leqslant 90°$.
Give your answers to two decimal places.

(i) $\sin A = 0.6192$
(ii) $\cos A = 0.8694$
(iii) $\tan A = 0.3592$
(iv) $\sin A = 0.4375$
(v) $\tan A = 0.3762$
(vi) $\cos A = 0.1246$
(vii) $\tan A = 1.6347$
(viii) $\sin A = 0.7221$
(ix) $\tan A = 2.1375$
(x) $\cos A = 0.4523$
(xi) $\sin A = 0.1436$
(xii) $\tan A = 0.8777$

11. Change each of the following to degrees and minutes. Give your answers to the nearest minute.

(i) 2.5°
(ii) 2.25°
(iii) 2.75°
(iv) 25.4°
(v) 1.2°
(vi) $\frac{1}{3}$ of a degree

12. Change the following to degrees. Give your answers correct to two decimal places.

(i) 2° 31′
(ii) 10° 40′
(iii) 25° 50′
(iv) 70° 22′
(v) 11° 37′
(vi) 33° 33′

13. Use your calculator to find the measure of the angle B, $0° \leqslant B \leqslant 90°$.
Give your answers to the nearest minute.

(i) $\sin B = 0.9701$
(ii) $\cos B = 0.6661$
(iii) $\tan B = 0.9628$
(iv) $\sin B = 0.6635$
(v) $\tan B = 0.3193$
(vi) $\cos B = 0.8925$
(vii) $\tan B = 3.4650$
(viii) $\sin B = 0.2411$
(ix) $\tan B = 0.4080$
(x) $\cos B = 0.5297$
(xi) $\sin B = 0.4321$
(xii) $\cos B = 0.9201$

14. Calculate, to the nearest degree, the value of the angle B.

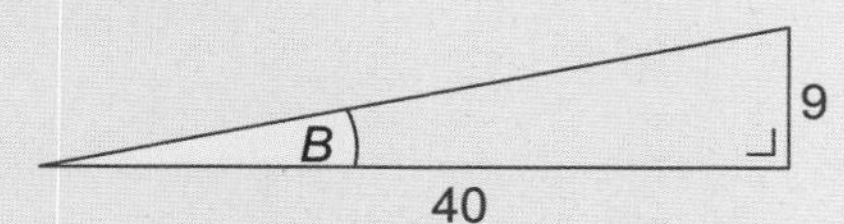

15. Calculate, to the nearest minute, the value of the angle C.

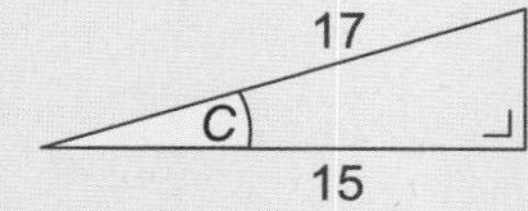

16. Find the value of x in the following triangles (answers to two decimal places where necessary):

(i)

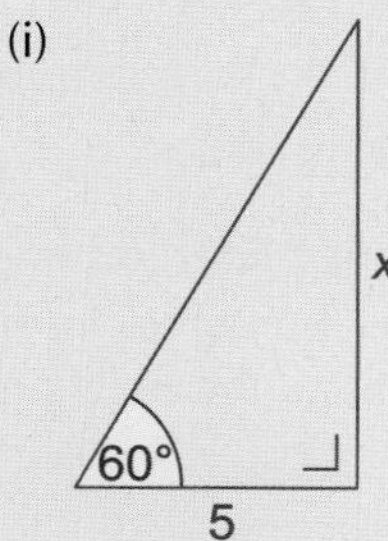

(ii)

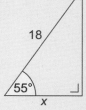

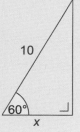

10
60°
x

(iii)

18
55°
x

(iv)

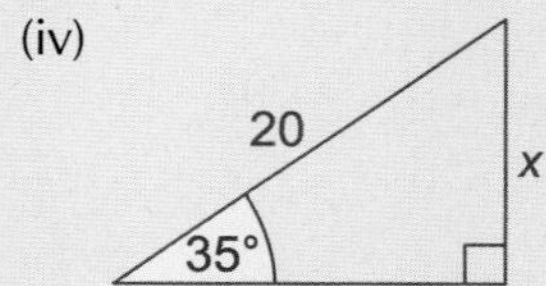

(v)

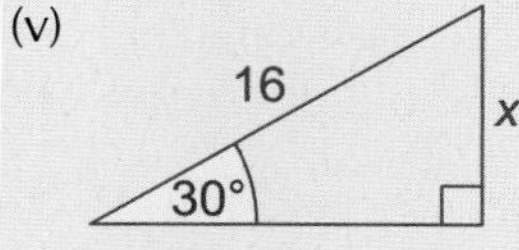

(vi)

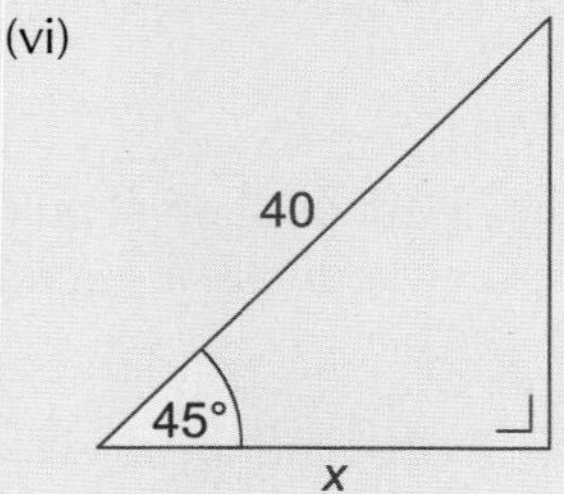

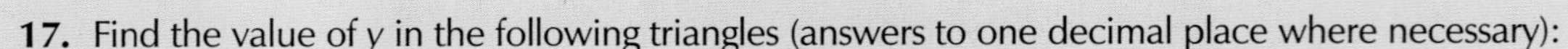

17. Find the value of y in the following triangles (answers to one decimal place where necessary):

(i)

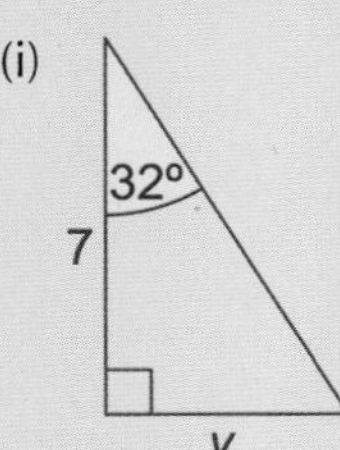

(iii)

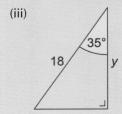

(v)

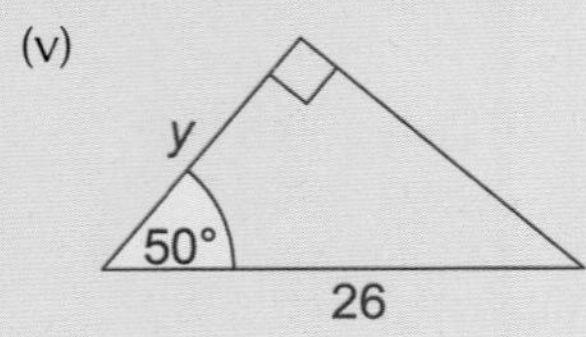

(ii)

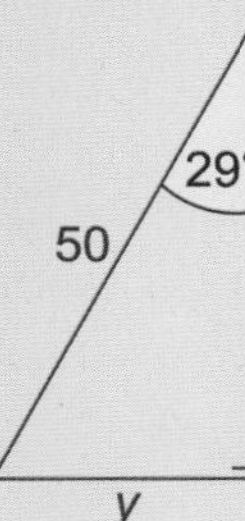

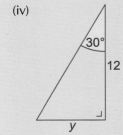

(iv)

(vi)

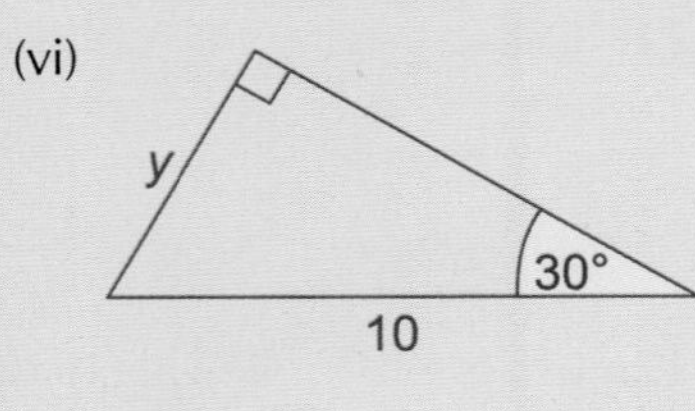

18. Solve for x and y to two decimal places.

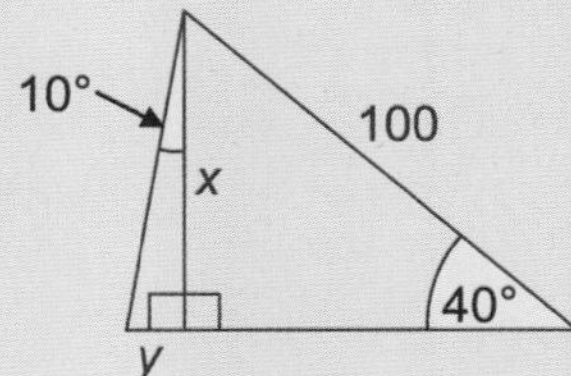

19. Solve for x, y and z to two significant figures.

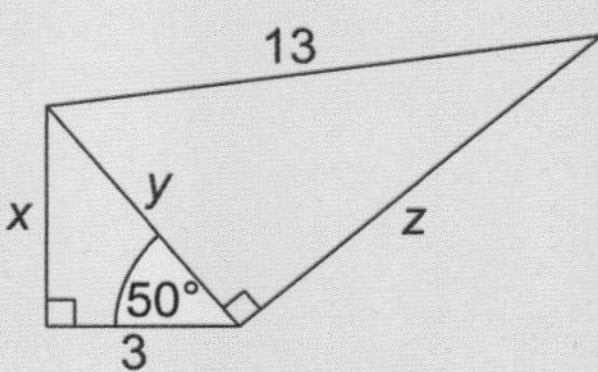

20. A ship leaves a port A and sails a distance of 4 km in the direction N 30° E. The ship then changes direction and sails for a further 6 km in the direction S 60° E to a point C (see diagram).

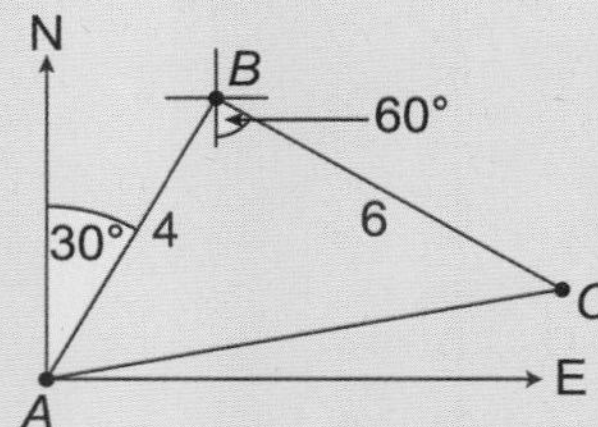

(i) Calculate the distance from the ship's present position at point C to port A. Give your answer to one decimal place.

(ii) Find $|\angle BCA|$, to the nearest degree.

(iii) Hence, find the direction of C **from** A.

21. Two ships A and B leave the same harbour. Ship A travels due west and Ship B travels 67° south of west. After two hours, Ship A has travelled 46 km and is directly north of Ship B.

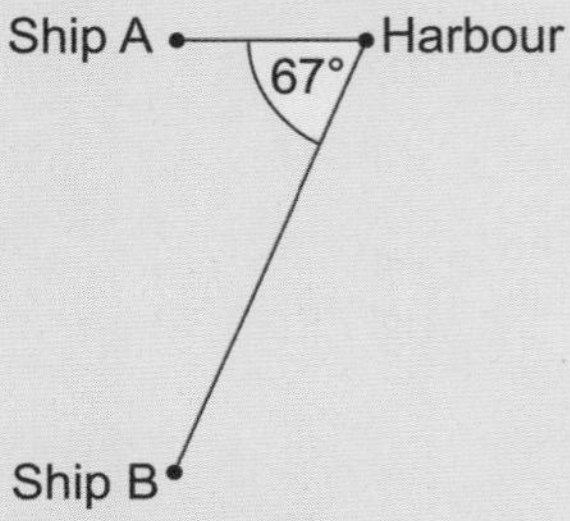

(i) What is the distance (to the nearest km) travelled by Ship B in this time?

(ii) Find the speed (to the nearest km/h) of Ship A.

(iii) Find the speed (to the nearest km/h) of Ship B.

22. The Empire State Building pictured below is one of New York's tallest buildings. Using the information given, calculate the height of the building.

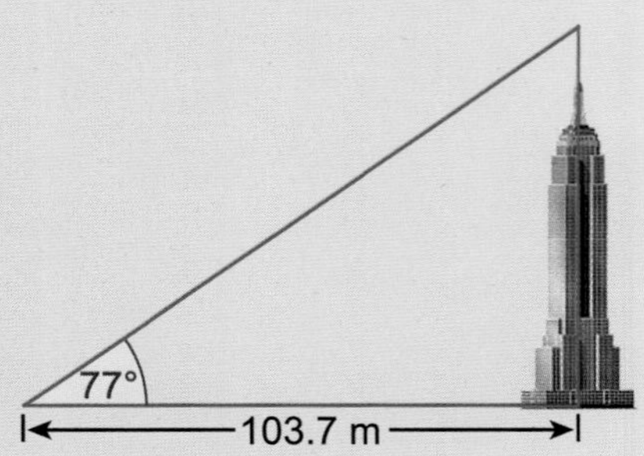

23. John is standing on a cliff top and observes a boat drifting towards the base of the cliff. He decides to call the emergency services and give them the position of the boat. He measures the angle of depression of the boat from the cliff top to be 30°, and he knows the cliff top is 200 m above sea level. How far is the boat from the base of the cliff?

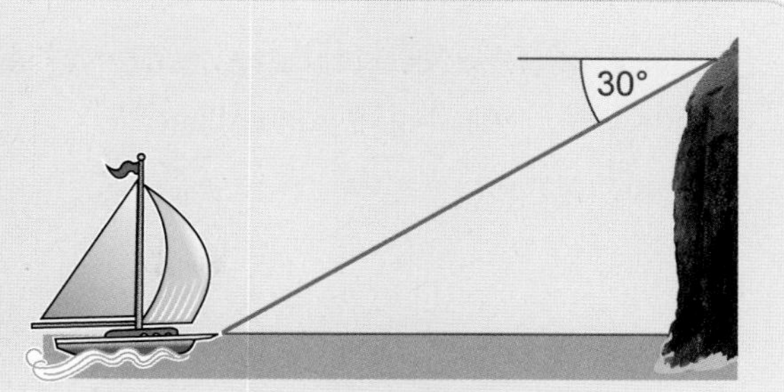

7.5 DEGREES AND RADIANS

There is often more than one way to measure the same thing. For example, it is only since January 2005 that distances on Irish road signs have been given in kilometres – up to then distances were given in miles. Changing the unit of measurement does not change the distance between towns.

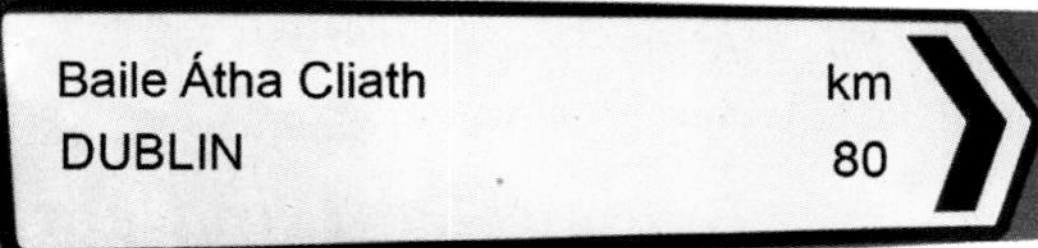

The same applies to angles. Angles can be measured in degrees or in radians. Radian measure is essential in Higher Level mathematics, particularly for calculus.

What is a Radian?

Draw a circle or radius length $r = x$ cm, then mark an arc of length $l = x$ cm on this circle. The angle θ which is created by this arc measures **one radian.**

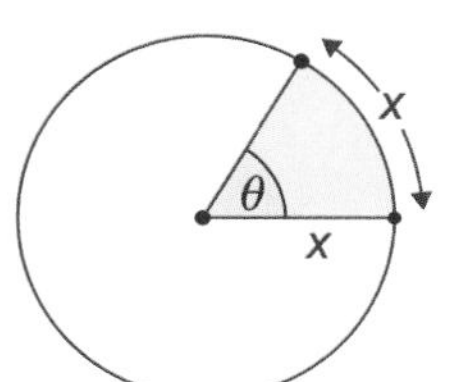

One radian is the measure of the angle at the centre of a circle when the length of the arc is equal to the length of the radius.

If you marked an arc of length $l = 2x$ cm on a circle with radius length $r = x$ cm, the angle θ which is created is **two radians** in measure.

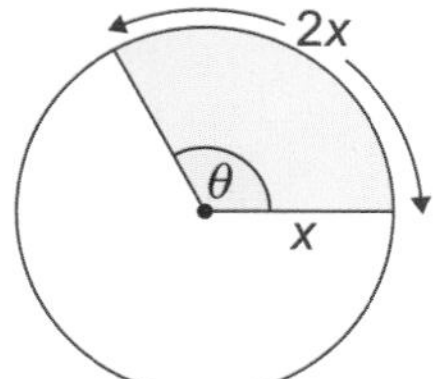

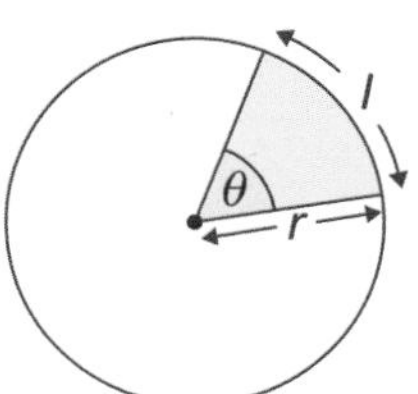

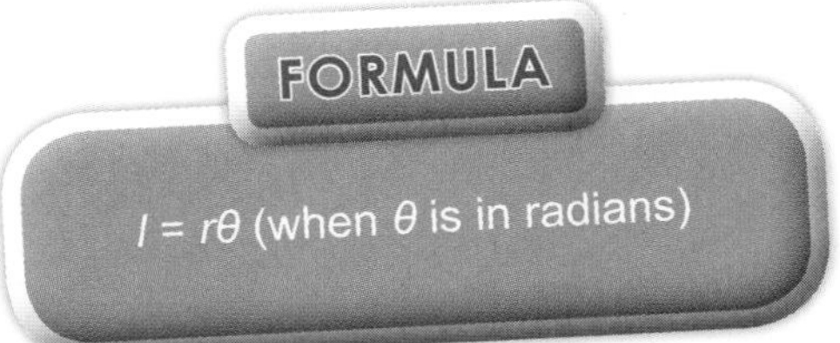

$l = r\theta$ (when θ is in radians)

This formula appears on page 9 of the *Formulae and Tables*.

How Many Radians Are in a Full Rotation?

Formula: $l = r\theta$ (when θ is in radians)

In a full rotation $l = 2\pi r$

$$l = l$$

so $$2\pi r = r\theta$$

$$r\theta = 2\pi r$$

$$\theta = \frac{2\pi r}{r}$$

$$\theta = 2\pi \text{ (radians in a full rotation)}$$

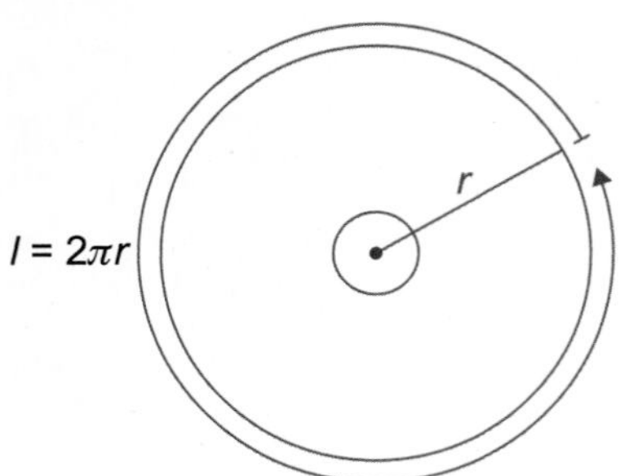

From this, we can say the following:

$$2\pi \text{ radians} = 360° \quad \text{(360° in a full rotation)}$$

$$\pi \text{ radians} = 180°$$

$$1 \text{ radian} = \frac{180°}{\pi} \approx 57.296°$$

$$1° = \frac{\pi}{180} \approx 0.01745 \text{ radians}$$

Formulae and Tables, page 13

Converting Degrees to Radians and Radians to Degrees

The following examples show how we can convert degrees to radians and radians to degrees.

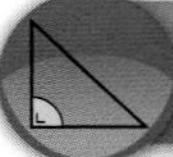

Worked Example 7.11

Convert 135° to radians.

Solution

$$180° = \pi \text{ radians}$$

$$\therefore 1° = \frac{\pi}{180} \text{ radians}$$

$$\therefore 1° \times 135 = \frac{\pi}{180} \times 135 \text{ radians}$$

$$135° = \frac{135\pi}{180} \text{ radians}$$

$$135° = \frac{3\pi}{4} \text{ radians}$$

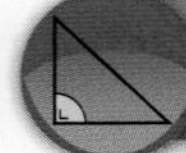

Worked Example 7.12

Convert $\frac{7\pi}{9}$ radians to degrees.

Solution

$$\pi \text{ radians} = 180°$$

$$\frac{7\pi}{9} \text{ radians} = \frac{7(180°)}{9}$$

$$= \frac{1260°}{9}$$

$$\frac{7\pi}{9} \text{ radians} = 140°$$

7.6 ANGLES OF DIFFERENT SIZES

There are many situations where angles measure much more than one rotation.

In a day, the hands on a clock turn through a lot more than 360°. The minute hand on a clock turns through 8640° in one day.

If a breakdancer does 15 spins on his head, he will turn through far more than 360° (2π radians).

Determining the Quadrant in Which an Angle Terminates

The following example shows how to find the quadrant in which an angle terminates.
The x- and y-axes divide the plane into four quadrants.
Angles are measured from the positive sense of the x-axis.

- Positive is an anticlockwise direction.
- Negative is a clockwise direction.

An angle can be of any size, positive or negative.

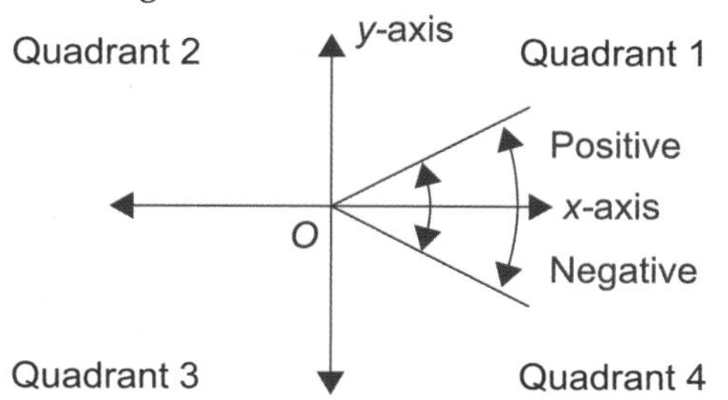

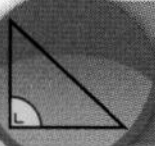

Worked Example 7.13

Dan is a member of a breakdancing club.

During a routine he spins on his head, turning a total of 960°.

(i) In which quadrant would an angle of 960° terminate?

(ii) What is the measure of this angle in radians?

Solution

(i) To answer this question, reduce the angle by as many full rotations as possible.

$960° - 360° = 600°$

$600° - 360° = 240°$

So 960° is two complete rotations plus 240°.

$960° = 360° + 360° + 240°$

This angle would terminate in the third quadrant.

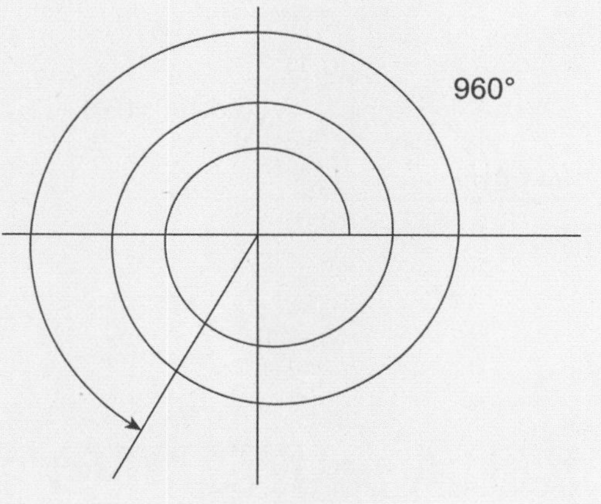

(ii) $180° = \pi$ radians

$1° = \frac{\pi}{180}$ radians

$1° \times 960 = \frac{960\pi}{180}$ radians

$960° = \frac{16\pi}{3}$ radians

Exercise 7.2

1. Copy and complete the table.

Degrees	90°	180°	270°			45°	
Radians		π		2π	$\frac{\pi}{6}$		$\frac{\pi}{3}$

2. Convert the following angles (given in radians) to degrees:

(i) $\frac{\pi}{2}$ rad (ii) $\frac{3\pi}{2}$ rad (iii) $\frac{5\pi}{2}$ (iv) $\frac{4\pi}{3}$ (v) $\frac{5\pi}{4}$ (vi) $\frac{5\pi}{18}$

(vii) 4π (viii) 6π (ix) $\frac{3\pi}{4}$ (x) $\frac{11\pi}{6}$ (xi) $\frac{4\pi}{9}$ (xii) $\frac{4\pi}{5}$

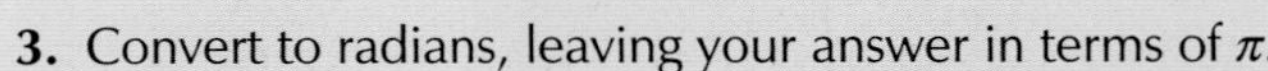

3. Convert to radians, leaving your answer in terms of π.

(i) 90° (ii) 270° (iii) 45° (iv) 15° (v) 540° (vi) 30°

(vii) 432° (viii) 450° (ix) 75° (x) 37.5° (xi) 210° (xii) 980°

4. In which quadrants do these angles terminate?

(i) 110° (ii) $\frac{\pi}{4}$ rads (iii) 50° (iv) 185° (v) $\frac{8\pi}{6}$ rads (vi) $-\frac{5\pi}{6}$ rads

(vii) $-60°$ (viii) $\frac{9\pi}{4}$ rads (ix) 460° (x) 840° (xi) 1010° (xii) $\frac{6\pi}{5}$ rads

7.7 THE UNIT CIRCLE

The unit circle has its centre at (0,0) and has a radius length of 1 unit.

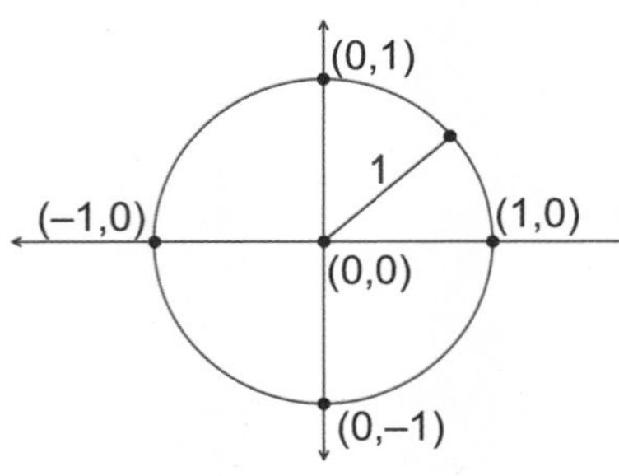

In the previous activities, using the unit circle, we defined the sine, cosine and tangent of an angle.

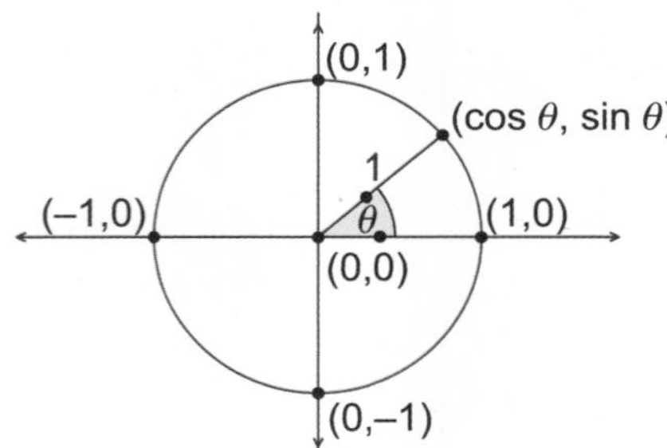

$\cos\theta = x$ co-ordinate
$\sin\theta = y$ co-ordinate
Also, $\tan\theta = \frac{\sin\theta}{\cos\theta}$
All of these definitions are on page 13 of *Formulae and Tables*.

7.8 EVALUATING THE TRIGONOMETRIC RATIOS OF ALL ANGLES BETWEEN 0° AND 360°

Reference Angles

Consider an angle AOB, where $|\angle AOB| = 140°$.

$\angle AOB$ will lie in the second quadrant of the unit circle.

$|\angle AOB| = 140°$
Reference angle
$= 180° - 140°$
$= 40°$

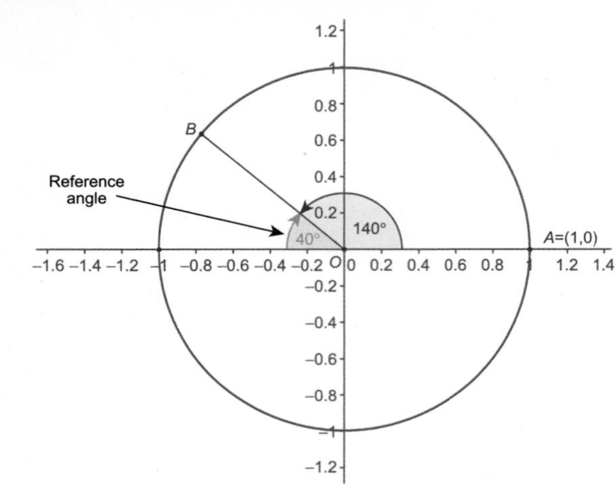

The acute angle formed by the terminal side of $\angle AOB$ (i.e. where the angle ends) and the **x-axis** is called the reference angle of $\angle AOB$. In this case, the reference angle measures 40°.

Here are similar examples for angles that lie in the third and fourth quadrants respectively.

$|\angle AOB| = 250°$

Reference angle

$= 250° - 180°$

$= 70°$

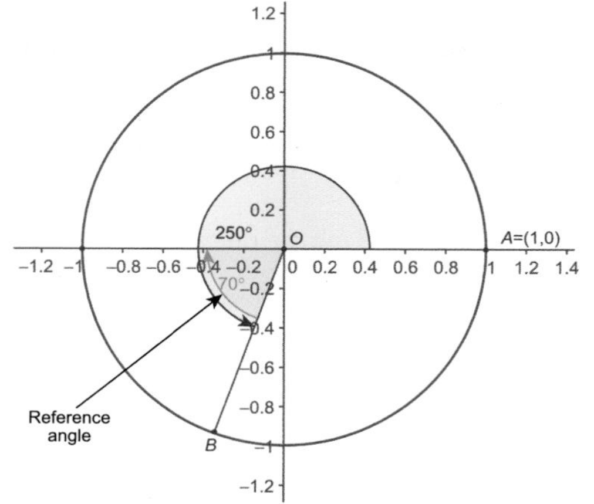

$|\angle AOB| = 330°$

Reference angle

$= 360° - 330°$

$= 30°$

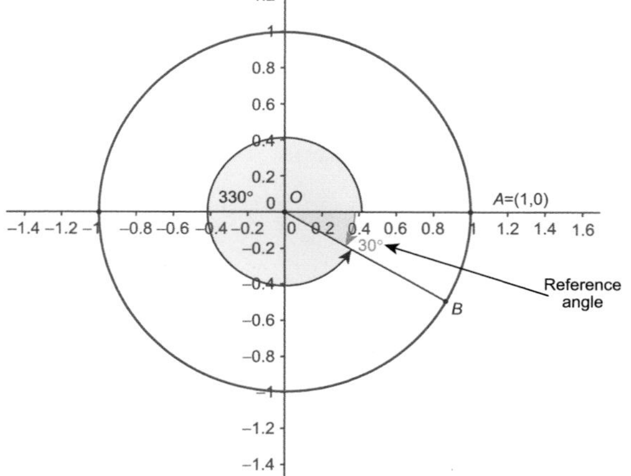

The Sign of the Ratios in Each Quadrant

First Quadrant (0° < θ < 90°)

In the first quadrant, all three ratios are positive.

- $\cos\theta$ is positive, as its value lies on the positive x-axis.
- $\sin\theta$ is positive, as its value lies on the positive y-axis.
- $\tan\theta = \dfrac{\sin\theta}{\cos\theta} = \dfrac{+}{+} = +$ Hence, $\tan\theta$ is positive.

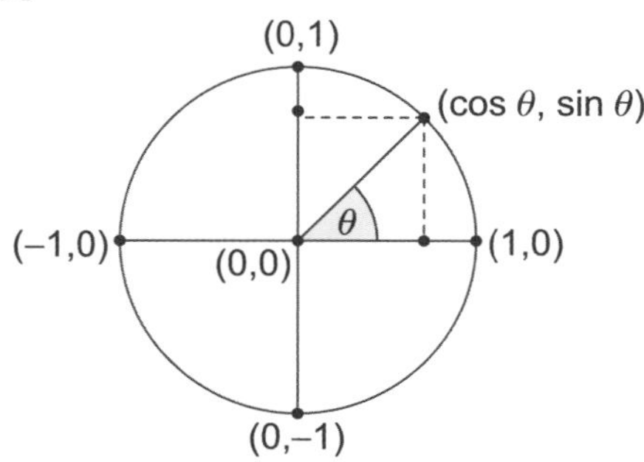

Second Quadrant (90° < θ < 180°)

In the second quadrant, sin is positive; cos and tan are negative.

- $\cos\theta$ is negative, as its value lies on the negative x-axis.
- $\sin\theta$ is positive, as its value lies on the positive y-axis.
- $\tan\theta = \dfrac{\sin\theta}{\cos\theta} = \dfrac{+}{-} = -$ Hence, $\tan\theta$ is negative.

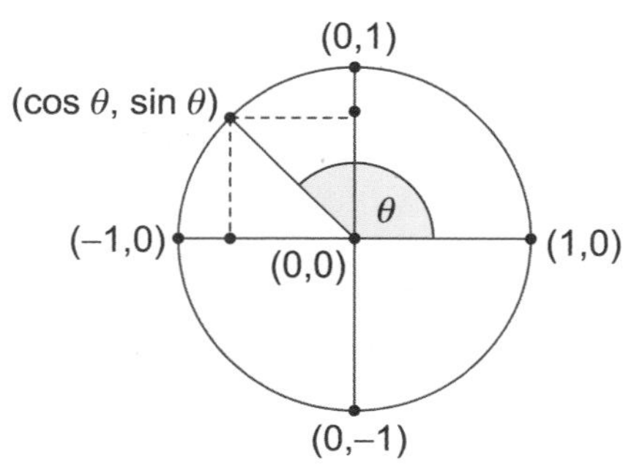

Third Quadrant (180° < θ < 270°)

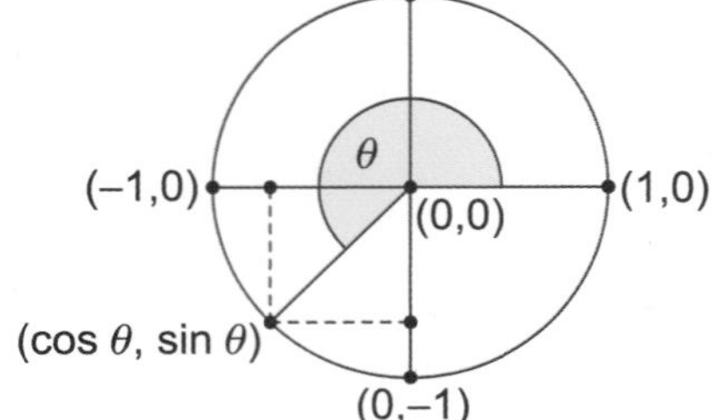

In the third quadrant, tan is positive; sin and cos are negative.

- $\cos\theta$ is negative, as its value lies on the negative x-axis.
- $\sin\theta$ is negative, as its value lies on the negative y-axis.
- $\tan\theta = \dfrac{\sin\theta}{\cos\theta} = \dfrac{-}{-} = +$ Hence, $\tan\theta$ is positive.

Fourth Quadrant (270° < θ < 360°)

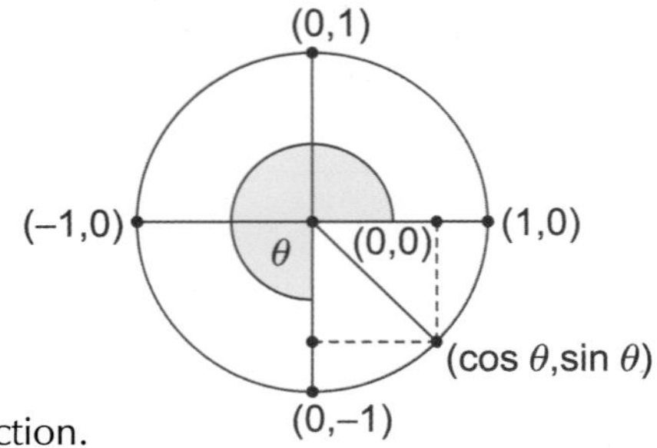

In the fourth quadrant, cos is positive; sin and tan are negative.

- $\cos\theta$ is positive, as its value lies on the positive x-axis.
- $\sin\theta$ is negative, as its value lies on the negative y-axis.
- $\tan\theta = \dfrac{\sin\theta}{\cos\theta} = \dfrac{-}{+} = -$ Hence, $\tan\theta$ is negative.

CAST

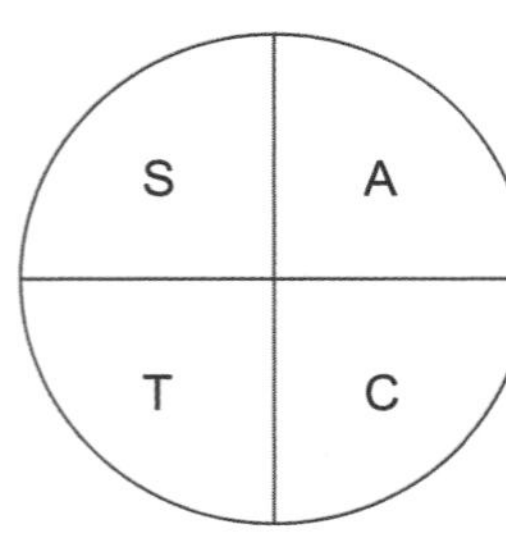

The diagram on the left summarises this section.

(a) In the first quadrant, all (A) are positive.

(b) In the second quadrant, only sin (S) is positive.

(c) In the third quadrant, only tan (T) is positive.

(d) In the fourth quadrant, only cos (C) is positive.

When asked to give an answer in surd form, the sine, cosine and tangent ratios can be read easily for the angles 30°, 45° and 60°.
Example: tan 60° = $\sqrt{3}$ in surd form
tan 60° = 1.7321 in decimal form

See page 13 of *Formulae and Tables.*

Worked Example 7.14

Write in surd form:

(i) cos 225° (ii) tan 330° (iii) sin 135°

Solution

(i) **Step 1**

Draw an angle of 225°.

Step 2

The angle is in the third quadrant, so its cos is negative.

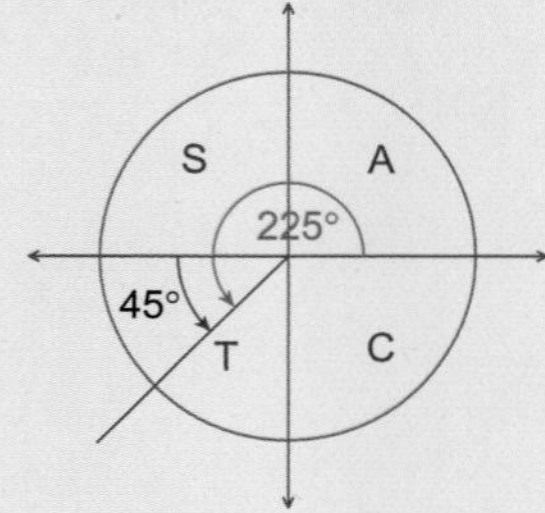

Step 3

The reference angle is 45° (225° – 180°).

$\cos 45° = \dfrac{1}{\sqrt{2}}$

Step 4

$\therefore \cos 225° = -\dfrac{1}{\sqrt{2}}$

(ii) **Step 1**

Draw an angle of 330°.

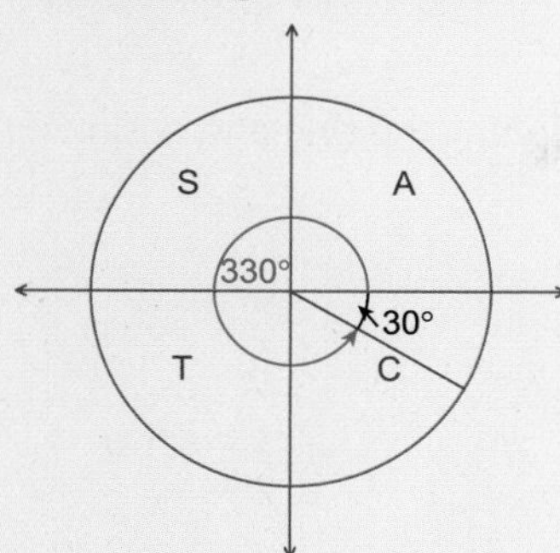

Step 2

The angle is in the fourth quadrant, so its tan is negative.

Step 3

The reference angle is 30° (360° – 330°).

$\tan 30° = \frac{1}{\sqrt{3}}$

Step 4

$\therefore \tan 330° = -\frac{1}{\sqrt{3}}$

(iii) **Step 1**

Draw an angle of 135°.

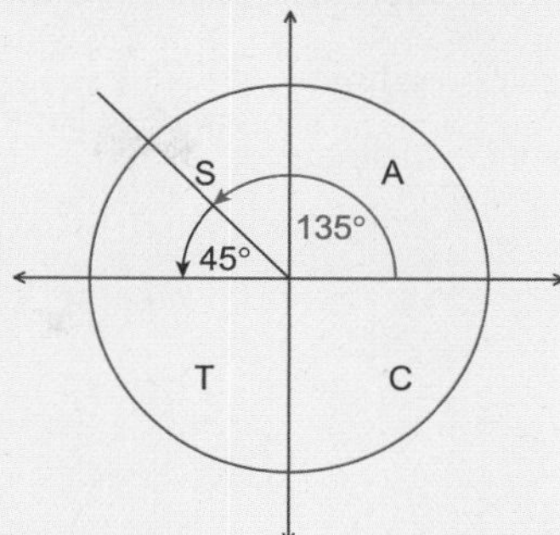

Step 2

The angle is in the second quadrant, so its sine is positive.

Step 3

The reference angle is 45° (180° – 135°).

$\sin 45° = \frac{1}{\sqrt{2}}$

Step 4

$\therefore \sin 135° = \frac{1}{\sqrt{2}}$

Exercise 7.3

1. In the following questions, use the unit circle to find the answer:

(i) cos 270° (vi) cos 180° (xi) cos 360°
(ii) sin 270° (vii) sin 180° (xii) sin 360°
(iii) cos 90° (viii) cos 0° (xiii) tan 360°
(iv) sin 90° (ix) sin 0°
(v) tan 180° (x) tan 0°

(0,1)
(cos θ,sin θ)
(–1,0)
(1,0)
(0,–1)

2. (a) For the following questions, write your answer in surd form:

(i) cos 135° (vi) cos 315°
(ii) sin 150° (vii) sin 120°
(iii) cos 240° (viii) cos 210°
(iv) sin 330° (ix) tan 300°
(v) tan 210° (x) tan 60°

(b) For the following questions, use your calculator and give your answer correct to two decimal places:

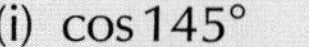

(i) cos 145° (vi) cos 325°
(ii) sin 160° (vii) sin 140°
(iii) cos 230° (viii) cos 230°
(iv) sin 355° (ix) tan 350°
(v) tan 220° (x) tan 160°

3. Write down the values of the following, giving your answer in surd form where appropriate:

(i) sin 405° (iv) $\cos \frac{11\pi}{6}$ (vi) $\cos \frac{9\pi}{2}$
(ii) cos 420° (v) sin 660° (vii) tan 1020°
(iii) tan 960°

7.9 GRAPHING TRIGONOMETRIC FUNCTIONS

We recall from our investigations of the unit circle that:

- $\sin\theta = y$ co-ordinate
- $\cos\theta = x$ co-ordinate

These definitions are used when graphing the sine and cosine functions.

Graphing the Sine Function ($y = \sin\theta$)

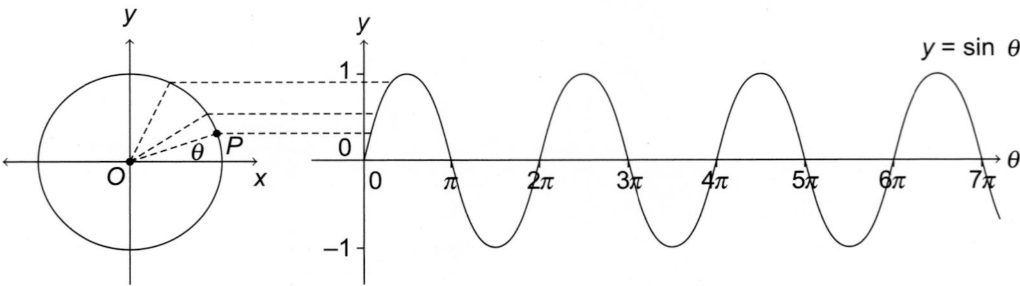

θ	0	$\frac{\pi}{4}$	$\frac{\pi}{2}$	$\frac{3\pi}{4}$	π	$\frac{5\pi}{4}$	$\frac{3\pi}{2}$	$\frac{7\pi}{4}$	2π
$y = \sin\theta$	0	0.7	1	0.7	0	−0.7	−1	−0.7	0

Rotating OP through θ and plotting the y co-ordinate for P for each value of θ gives the sine curve.

- $\sin 0° = 0$, so the curve passes through the origin.
- The maximum value of $\sin\theta$ is 1.
- The minimum value of $\sin\theta$ is −1.
- The graph repeats itself every 2π radians, so it is a **periodic function**.

Period = 2π

Range = $[-1,1]$

Graphing the Cosine Function ($y = \cos\theta$)

Graphing the cosine function can be done in a similar way to the sine function.

N.B. As $\cos\theta = x$ co-ordinate, it is necessary to **rotate the axis in the unit circle by 90°**.

Rotating OP through θ and plotting the x co-ordinate for P for each value of θ gives the cosine curve.

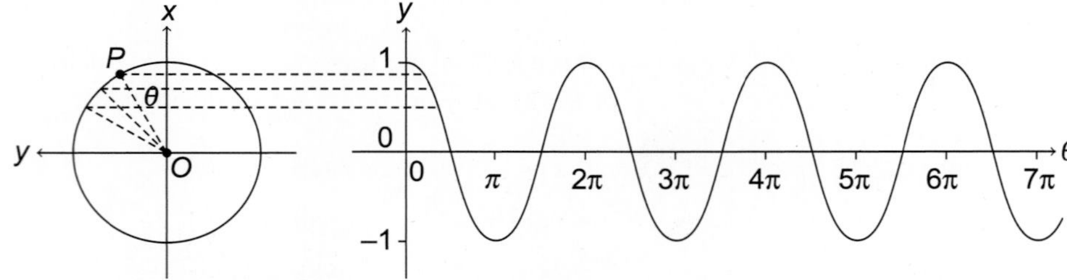

- $\cos 0° = 1$ so, the curve cuts the y-axis at (0,1).
- The maximum value of $\cos\theta$ is 1.
- The minimum value of $\cos\theta$ is −1.
- The graph repeats itself every 2π radians, so it is a **periodic function**.

Period = 2π

Range = $[-1,1]$

Graphing the Tangent Function ($y = \tan \theta$)

To graph $\tan \theta$, the tangent to the unit circle at (1,0) is drawn and OP is extended to meet the tangent at the point Q. The y co-ordinate at Q is equal to $\tan \theta$. Plotting the y co-ordinate for Q gives the tan curve.

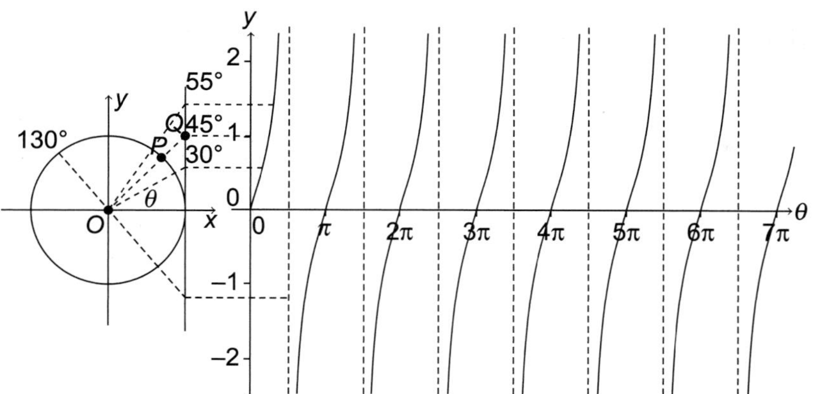

- $\tan 0° = 0$ so, the curve passes through the origin (0,0).
- There are no maximum and minimum values.
- The graph repeats itself every π radians, so it is a **periodic function**.
- There are asymptotes at $\theta = \pm\frac{\pi}{2}, \pm\frac{3\pi}{2}, \pm\frac{5\pi}{2}, \ldots$[$\theta$ given in radians] (at all odd multiples of $\frac{\pi}{2}$ radians).

Period = π

The period of the trigonometric function allows us to find the trigonometric ratio of angles that may not be on the given graph, e.g. if $f(x) = \sin x$, what is the value of $f(105\pi)$?

The sine function has a period of 2π. To find $\sin 105\pi$, simply subtract multiples of 2π to get an angle that can be found easily.

$105\pi - 2\pi - 2\pi - 2\pi - 2\pi - 2\pi \ldots -2\pi = \pi$ $\therefore f(105\pi) = \sin 105\pi = \sin \pi = 0$

Using Graphs to Find a Number of Angles with the Same Trigonometric Ratio

Worked Example 7.15

Find three angles with the same trigonometric ratio as:

(i) $\sin \frac{\pi}{4}$ (ii) $\cos \pi$ (iii) $\tan \left(\frac{\pi}{5}\right)$

Solution

(i)

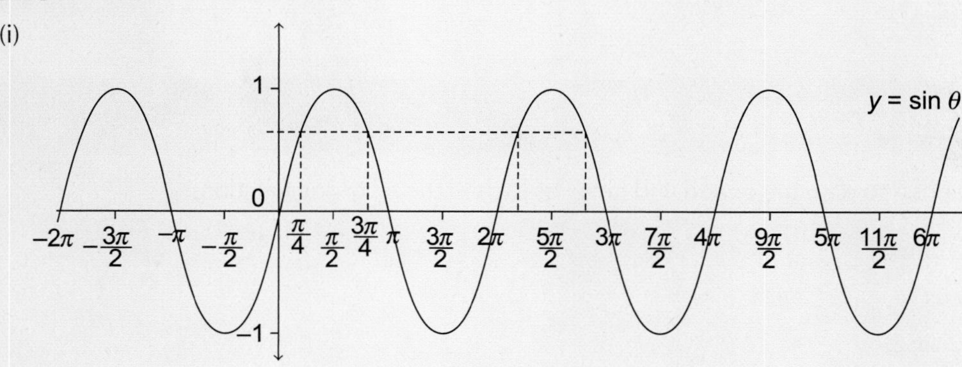

- By symmetry, $\sin\frac{3\pi}{4}$ has the same value as $\sin\frac{\pi}{4}$.
- The sin graph repeats every 2π radians.

$$\text{So } \sin\left(\frac{\pi}{4} + 2\pi\right) = \sin\frac{9\pi}{4}$$

$$\sin\left(\frac{3\pi}{4} + 2\pi\right) = \sin\frac{11\pi}{4}$$

So $\sin\frac{\pi}{4}$, $\sin\frac{3\pi}{4}$, $\sin\frac{9\pi}{4}$ and $\sin\frac{11\pi}{4}$ have the same value.

(ii)

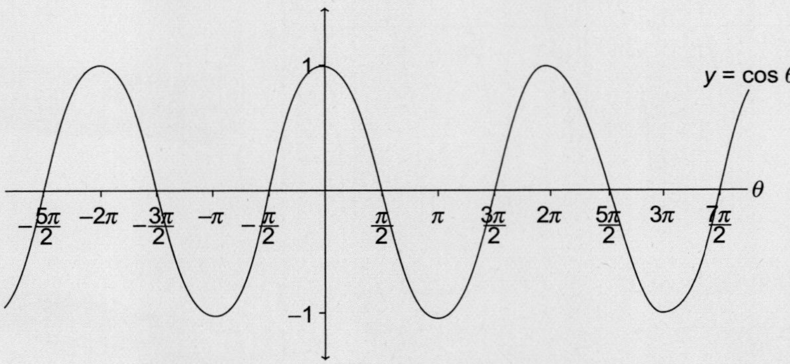

- The graph is symmetrical about the y-axis.

So $\cos\pi = \cos(-\pi)$

- The cos graph repeats every 2π radians.

$$\text{So } \cos(\pi + 2\pi) = \cos 3\pi$$

$$\cos(3\pi + 2\pi) = \cos 5\pi$$

So $\cos(-\pi)$, $\cos\pi$, $\cos 3\pi$ and $\cos 5\pi$ have the same values.

(iii) The tan graph repeats itself every π radians. So if one angle is known, others can be found by adding or subtracting π.

$$\tan\frac{\pi}{5} = \tan\left(\frac{\pi}{5} + \pi\right) = \tan\frac{6\pi}{5}$$

$$\tan\frac{\pi}{5} = \tan\left(\frac{\pi}{5} - \pi\right) = \tan\left(-\frac{4\pi}{5}\right)$$

$$\tan\frac{\pi}{5} = \tan\left(\frac{6\pi}{5} + \pi\right) = \tan\frac{11\pi}{5}$$

So $\tan\frac{\pi}{5}$, $\tan\frac{6\pi}{5}$, $\tan\left(-\frac{4\pi}{5}\right)$ and $\tan\frac{11\pi}{5}$ all have the same value.

Graphing Functions of the Form $a \sin n\theta$ and $a \cos n\theta$ for $a, n \in N$

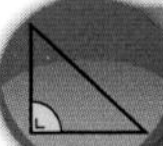

Worked Example 7.16

Sketch the graphs and state the period and range of each of the following functions:

(i) $y = 4 \sin\theta \qquad 0 \leqslant \theta \leqslant 2\pi$

(ii) $y = \cos 3\theta \qquad -\pi \leqslant \theta \leqslant \pi$

(iii) $y = 2 \sin 2\theta \qquad -\pi \leqslant \theta \leqslant \pi$

Solution

(i) Recall the important features of the graph:

- It passes through the origin.
- The shape of the graph.

θ	4	$\sin\theta$	y	Points to graph
0	4	0	0	$(0,0)$
$\frac{\pi}{2}$	4	1	4	$\left(\frac{\pi}{2},4\right)$
π	4	0	0	$(\pi,0)$
$\frac{3\pi}{2}$	4	–1	–4	$\left(\frac{3\pi}{2},-4\right)$
2π	4	0	0	$(2\pi,0)$

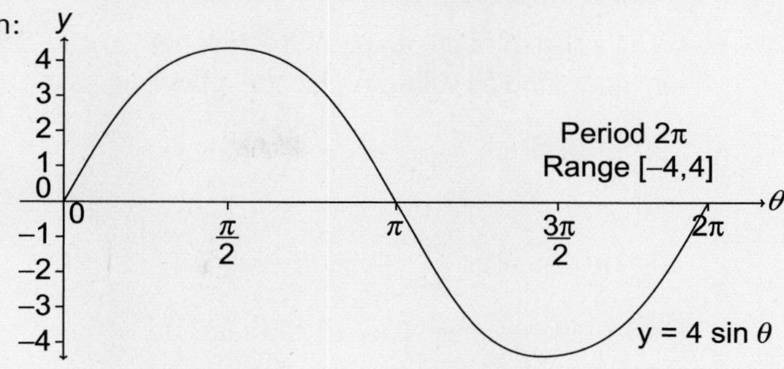

Note: The effect of the 4 is to stretch the graph of $y = \sin\theta$, by a factor of 4.

Connect the points with a smooth curve.

(ii)
- Recall the shape of graph $y = \cos\theta$.
- $\cos\theta = 1$.

θ	3	$\cos 3\theta$	y-value	Points to graph
$-\pi$	-3π	$\cos(-3\pi)$	–1	$(-\pi,-1)$
$-\frac{\pi}{2}$	$-\frac{3\pi}{2}$	$\cos\left(-\frac{3\pi}{2}\right)$	0	$(-\frac{\pi}{2},0)$
0	0	$\cos 0$	1	$(0,1)$
$\frac{\pi}{2}$	$\frac{3\pi}{2}$	$\cos\left(\frac{3\pi}{2}\right)$	0	$\left(\frac{\pi}{2},0\right)$
π	3π	$\cos 3\pi$	–1	$(\pi,-1)$

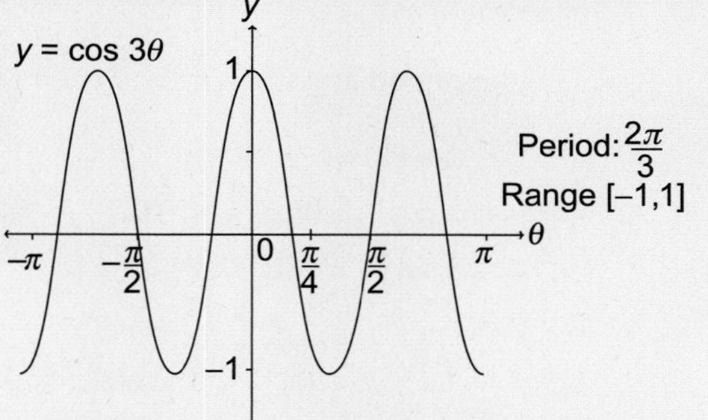

Note: The effect of the 3 is to reduce the period of the graph of $y = \cos\theta$. The period becomes $\frac{2\pi}{3}$.

(iii)

θ	2θ	$\sin 2\theta$	$2\sin 2\theta$	y-value	Point to graph
$-\pi$	-2π	0	2(0)	0	$(-\pi,0)$
$-\frac{3\pi}{4}$	$-\frac{3\pi}{2}$	1	2(1)	2	$\left(-\frac{3\pi}{4},2\right)$
$-\frac{\pi}{2}$	$-\pi$	0	2(0)	0	$\left(-\frac{\pi}{2},0\right)$
$-\frac{\pi}{4}$	$-\frac{\pi}{2}$	–1	2(–1)	–2	$\left(-\frac{\pi}{4},-2\right)$
0	0	0	2(0)	0	$(0,0)$
$\frac{\pi}{4}$	$\frac{\pi}{2}$	1	2(1)	2	$\left(\frac{\pi}{4},2\right)$
$\frac{\pi}{2}$	π	0	2(0)	0	$\left(\frac{\pi}{2},0\right)$
$\frac{3\pi}{4}$	$\frac{3\pi}{2}$	–1	2(–1)	–2	$\left(\frac{3\pi}{4},-2\right)$
π	2π	0	2(0)	0	$(\pi,0)$

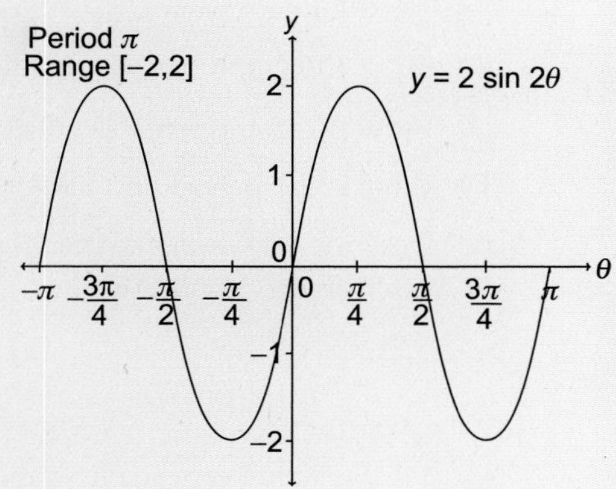

Note:

- $\sin n\theta$ and $\cos n\theta$ have a period of $\frac{2\pi}{n}$ radians.
- $\tan n\theta$ has a period of $\frac{\pi}{n}$ radians.
- Change the a value in the functions $a\sin\theta$, $a\cos\theta$, $a \in N$, does not affect the period of the function, but the range will be $[-a,a]$.

Exercise 7.4

1. Using a sketch of the graph of the trigonometric functions, find all values of θ in the following:

   (i) $\tan\theta = \tan\frac{\pi}{7}$ $\quad -2\pi \leqslant \theta \leqslant 2\pi$

   (ii) $\sin\theta = \sin 60^\circ$ $\quad 0^\circ \leqslant \theta \leqslant 720^\circ$

   (iii) $\sin\theta = \sin\left(-\frac{\pi}{3}\right)$ $\quad 0 \leqslant \theta \leqslant 4\pi$

2. Draw sketches of $\sin\theta$, $\cos\theta$ and $\tan\theta$ on separate axes for $-2\pi \leqslant \theta \leqslant 2\pi$.

   State the period and the range for each graph.

3. Sketch the graphs of the following functions on separate axes.

   State the period and the range for each graph.

   (i) $y = \sin 4x$ $\quad 0^\circ \leqslant x \leqslant 180^\circ$

   (ii) $y = 2\cos x$ $\quad 0^\circ \leqslant x \leqslant 360^\circ$

   (iii) $y = 3\sin x$ $\quad -2\pi \leqslant x \leqslant 2\pi$

   (iv) $y = \cos 2x$ $\quad -\pi \leqslant x \leqslant \pi$

   (v) $y = 3\cos 2x$ $\quad 0^\circ \leqslant x \leqslant 360^\circ$

   (vi) $y = 2\sin 4x$ $\quad 0^\circ \leqslant x \leqslant 90^\circ$

   (vii) $y = \tan 2x$ $\quad 0^\circ \leqslant x \leqslant 180^\circ$

4. State the period (in radians) and range for each of the following functions:

   (i) $\sin\theta$ $\qquad$ (v) $2\sin 3\theta$

   (ii) $\cos 4\theta$ $\qquad$ (vi) $4\cos 4\theta$

   (iii) $\tan 2\theta$ $\qquad$ (vii) $a\sin 3\theta$

   (iv) $\tan 3\theta$ $\qquad$ (viii) $3\cos k\theta$

5. Sketch the following three functions on the same axes for $-\pi \leqslant x \leqslant \pi$:

   $f(x) = \sin 3x$

   $g(x) = 3\sin 2x$

   $h(x) = 2\sin 3x$

   (i) Which function has the greatest range?

   (ii) Which function has the greatest period?

   (iii) Explain why these functions are periodic.

   (iv) Do all three functions intersect at any point? If so, explain why this is the case.

6. Sketch the graph of the function

   $$y = 4\cos\theta.$$

   If $\theta > 0$, give the range of values of θ for which the function has three distinct real roots.

7. Sketch the graphs of the following functions on the same axes:

   $f(x) = \cos 2x$

   $g(x) = \sin x$

   for $-\pi \leqslant x \leqslant \pi$.

   (i) From the graph, write down the points of intersection of the two functions.

   (ii) Explain how your answers could be verified.

8.

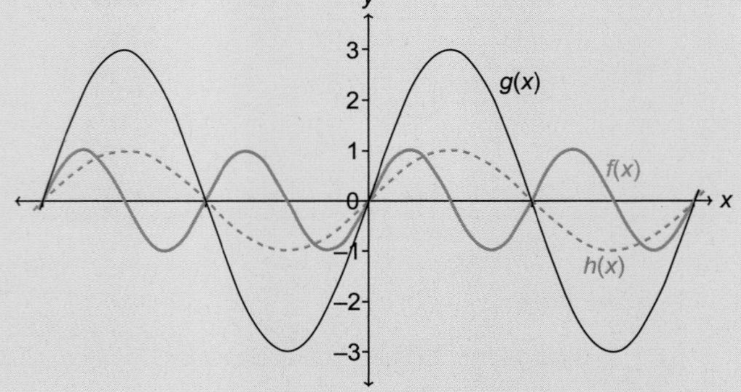

   (i) The green graph is $f(x) = \sin x$ (x in radians).

   (a) Identify the co-ordinates where it crosses the x-axis.

   (b) What are its maximum and minimum values?

   (ii) $h(x)$ is the graph of what function?

   (iii) Write down the equation of $g(x)$.

   (iv) What is the period and range of $g(x)$?

   (v) Describe how to make the graph of $f(x)$ from the graph of $h(x)$.

7.10 SPECIAL ANGLES 30°, 45° AND 60°

Special Angles 30° and 60°

A 60° angle can be constructed as follows, with just a ruler and a compass:

(a) Construct an equilateral triangle with sides of length 2 units.

(b) Bisect one of the angles in the triangle.

(c) Let x be the distance from the vertex of the bisected angle to the opposite side.

(d) Use the theorem of Pythagoras to find x.

$$x^2 + 1^2 = 2^2$$
$$x^2 = 4 - 1$$
$$x^2 = 3$$
$$x = \sqrt{3}$$

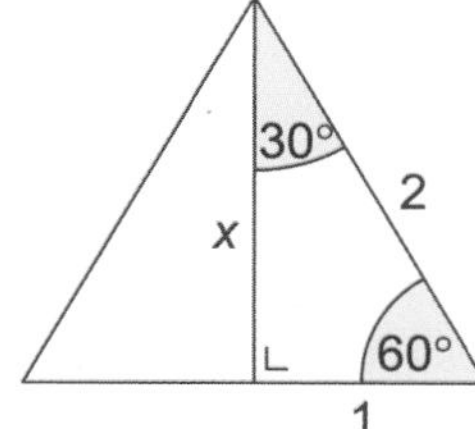

From the triangle, we have:

- $\sin 60° = \dfrac{\sqrt{3}}{2}$
- $\cos 60° = \dfrac{1}{2}$
- $\tan 60° = \sqrt{3}$

Also:

- $\sin 30° = \dfrac{1}{2}$
- $\cos 30° = \dfrac{\sqrt{3}}{2}$
- $\tan 30° = \dfrac{1}{\sqrt{3}}$

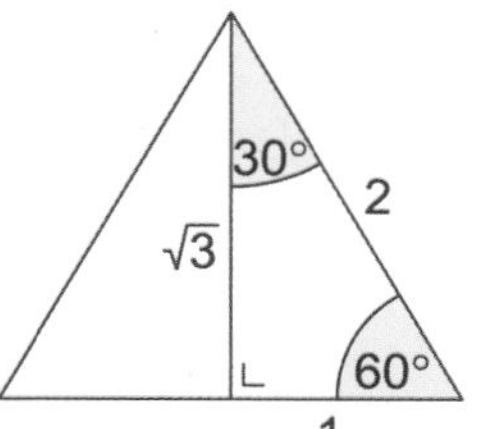

Special Angle 45°

A 45° angle can also be constructed with just a ruler and a compass.

(a) Construct a right-angled isosceles triangle with equal sides of 1 unit in length.

(b) Let x be the length of the hypotenuse.

(c) Use the theorem of Pythagoras to find x.

$$1^2 + 1^2 = x^2$$
$$2 = x^2$$
$$\sqrt{2} = x$$

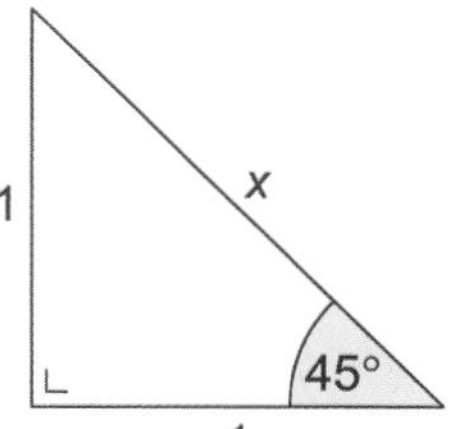

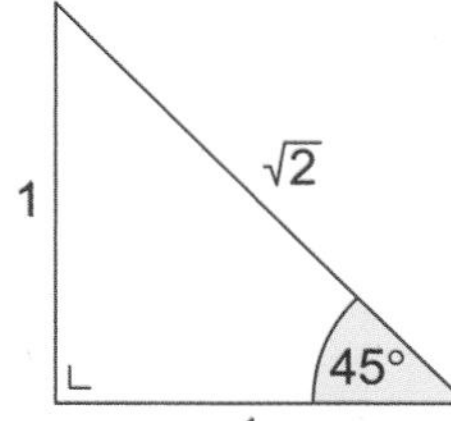

From the triangle, we have:

- $\sin 45° = \dfrac{1}{\sqrt{2}}$
- $\cos 45° = \dfrac{1}{\sqrt{2}}$
- $\tan 45° = 1$

These ratios appear on page 13 of *Formulae and Tables*.

Exercise 7.5

1. Copy and complete the following table. Give your answers in surd form.

A	30°	45°	60°
sin *A*			
cos *A*			
tan *A*			

2.

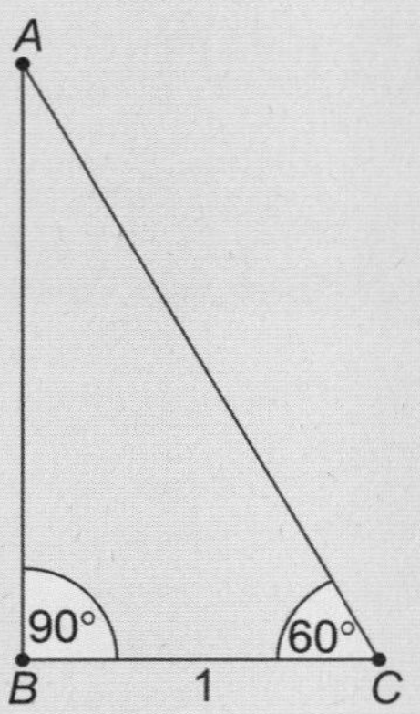

(i) What is the measure of $\angle BAC$?

(ii) Find $|AB|$ in surd form.

(iii) Use the theorem of Pythagoras to find $|AC|$.

3.

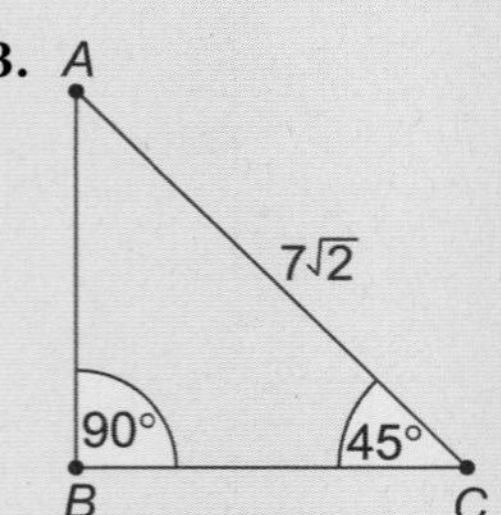

(i) Find the measure of $\angle BAC$.

(ii) Find $|BC|$.

4.

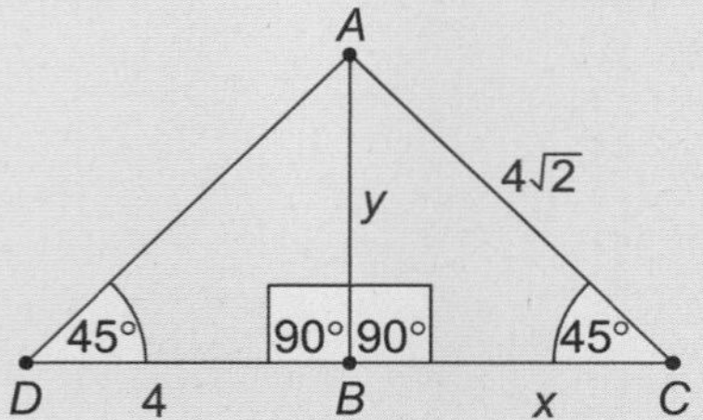

(i) Find the values of x and y.

(ii) What is the measure of $\angle DAB$?

5. Write down the values of:

(i) $\cos 135°$

(ii) $\sin 330°$

(iii) $\tan 120°$

(iv) $\cos 150°$

(v) $\sin 135°$

(vi) $\sin 225°$

(vii) $\cos \frac{3\pi}{4}$

(viii) $\sin\left(-\frac{7\pi}{4}\right)$

(ix) $\tan(-150°)$

(x) $\sin 405°$

(xi) $\sin 660°$

(xii) $\cos 540°$

(xiii) $\tan \frac{16\pi}{3}$

(xiv) $\sec \frac{7\pi}{6}$

(xv) $\text{cosec } 330°$

> Note: $\sec A = \frac{1}{\cos A}$
>
> $\text{cosec } A = \frac{1}{\sin A}$

6. Evaluate $\sin^2 45° + \cos^2 45°$.

> Note: $\sin^2 45° = (\sin 45°)^2$

7. Evaluate $\sin^2 60° + \cos^2 60° + \tan^2 60°$.

8. Evaluate $\tan^2 30° + \sin^2 30° + \cos^2 30°$.

9. Show that $\frac{\sin 30°}{\cos 30°} = \tan 30°$.

10. Using page 13 of the *Formulae and Tables*, evaluate the following:

(i) $\frac{\sin^2 270° + \cos^2 180°}{2\cos 0°}$

(ii) $\frac{\cos\frac{11\pi}{6} + \sin\frac{11\pi}{6}}{\sin 150°}$

(iii) $\frac{\text{cosec } 330°}{\tan 240°}$

7.11 SOLVING TRIGONOMETRIC EQUATIONS

The solutions to trigonometric equations are used in many professions. Engineers and carpenters make frequent use of these solutions in the design of roofs, bridges and many other structures.

One solution to a trigonometric equation can be found either by using a calculator or by using the special angles. From this one solution, other solutions can be found using the graph of the trigonometric function in question (as seen previously) or by considering the quadrant in which the angle lies.

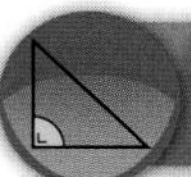

Worked Example 7.17

Solve for θ in each of the following:

(i) $\cos\theta = -\frac{\sqrt{3}}{2}$ for $0° \leqslant \theta \leqslant 360°$

(ii) $\sin\theta = \frac{1}{4}$ for $0° \leqslant \theta \leqslant 360°$

(iii) $\tan\theta = -\frac{1}{\sqrt{3}}$ for $0 \leqslant \theta \leqslant 2\pi$

(iv) $\tan 3\theta = 1$ for $0° \leqslant \theta \leqslant 360°$

(v) $\cos\theta = -\frac{1}{2}$ for $\theta \in R$, where θ is in radians

Solution

(i) $\cos\theta = -\frac{\sqrt{3}}{2}$ for $0° \leqslant \theta \leqslant 360°$

Step 1 Find the reference angle. Ignore the minus sign and find $\cos^{-1}\frac{\sqrt{3}}{2}$:

$\cos^{-1}\frac{\sqrt{3}}{2} = 30°$

Step 2 Establish where cos is negative, i.e. in the second and third quadrants.

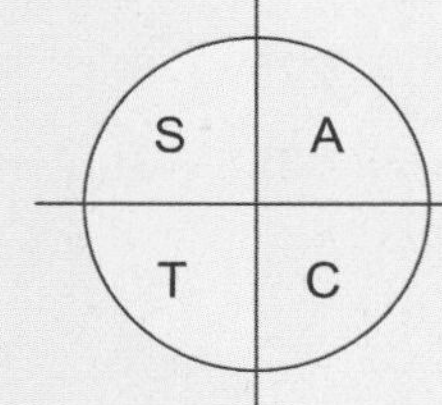

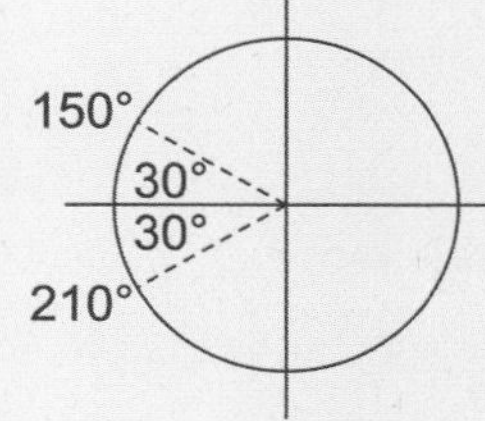

Thus, $\theta = 180° - 30° = 150°$
$\theta = 180° + 30° = 210°$

Answer: 150°, 210°

(ii) $\sin\theta = \frac{1}{4}$ for $0° \leqslant \theta \leqslant 360°$

Step 1 Find the reference angle: $\sin^{-1}\frac{1}{4} \approx 14.5°$

Step 2 Establish where sin is positive, i.e. in the first and second quadrants.

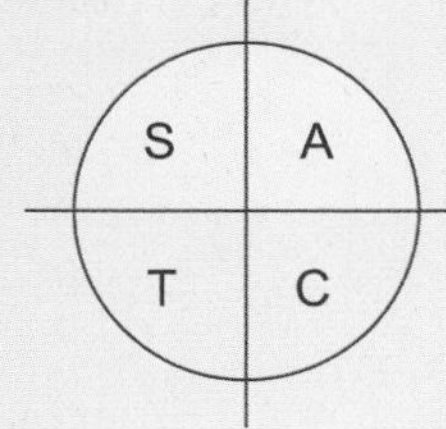

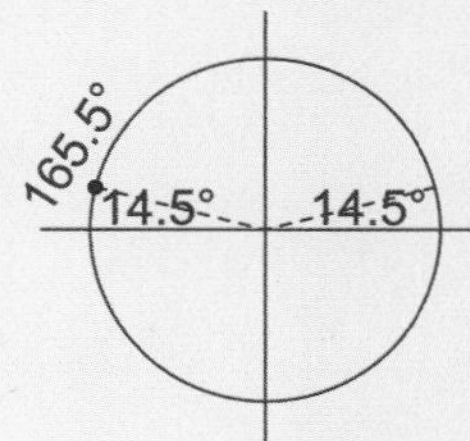

$\theta = 14.5°$
$\theta = 180° - 14.5° = 165.5°$

Answer: 14.5°, 165.5°

(iii) $\tan\theta = -\frac{1}{\sqrt{3}}$ for $0 \leqslant \theta \leqslant 2\pi$

Step 1 Find the reference angle: $\tan^{-1}\frac{1}{\sqrt{3}} = \frac{\pi}{6}$

Step 2 Establish where tan is negative, i.e. in the second and fourth quadrants.

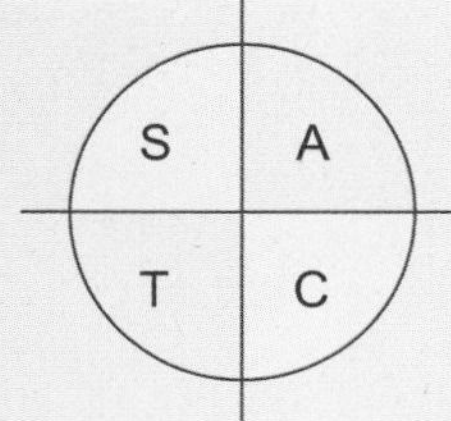

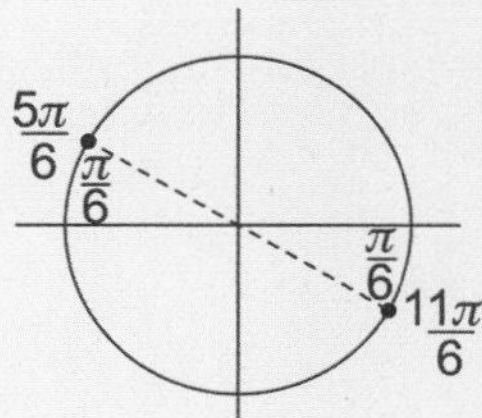

$\theta = \pi - \frac{\pi}{6} = \frac{5\pi}{6}$

$\theta = 2\pi - \frac{\pi}{6} = \frac{11\pi}{6}$

Answer: $\frac{5\pi}{6}, \frac{11\pi}{6}$

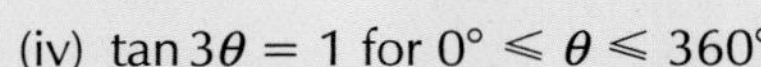

(iv) $\tan 3\theta = 1$ for $0° \leqslant \theta \leqslant 360°$

Step 1 Find the reference angle: $\tan^{-1} 1 = 45°$

Step 2 Establish where tan is positive, i.e. in the first and third quadrants.

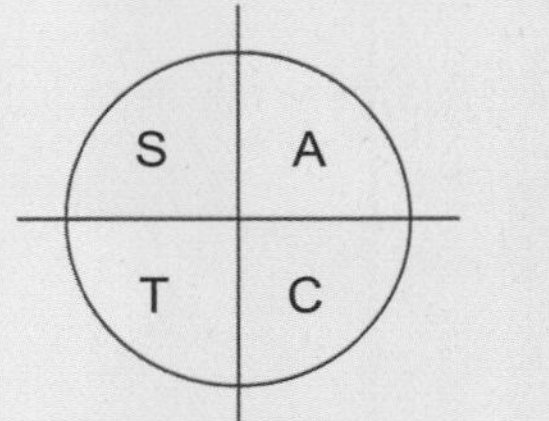

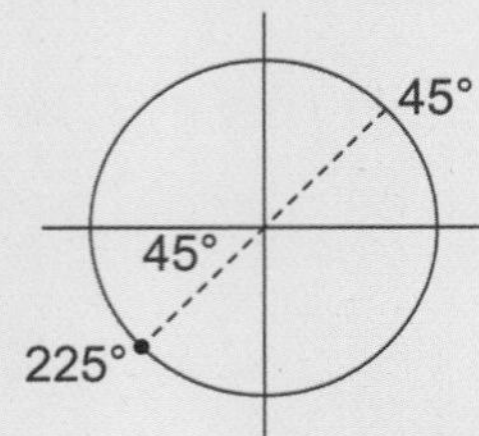

So, $3\theta = 45°$

$3\theta = 180° + 45° = 225°$

Step 3 If $0° \leqslant \theta \leqslant 360°$

$0° \times 3 \leqslant 3\theta \leqslant 360° \times 3$

$0° \leqslant 3\theta \leqslant 1080°$

Solutions for 3θ must be listed up to 1080°:

$3\theta = 45°$

$= 45° + 360° = 405°$

$= 405 + 360° = 765°$

$= 765° + 360° =$ outside range

$3\theta = 225°$

$= 225° + 360° = 585°$

$= 585° + 360° = 945°$

So, $3\theta = 45°, 225°, 405°, 585°, 765°, 945°$

$\therefore \theta = 15°, 75°, 135°, 195°, 255°, 315°$

(v) $\cos\theta = -\frac{1}{2}$ for $\theta \in R$, where θ is in radians

Step 1 Find the reference angle: $\cos^{-1}\frac{1}{2} = \frac{\pi}{3}$

Step 2 Establish where cos is negative, i.e. in the second and third quadrants.

Note: In this question, the range of values for θ is not specified, so it is necessary to give a general solution.

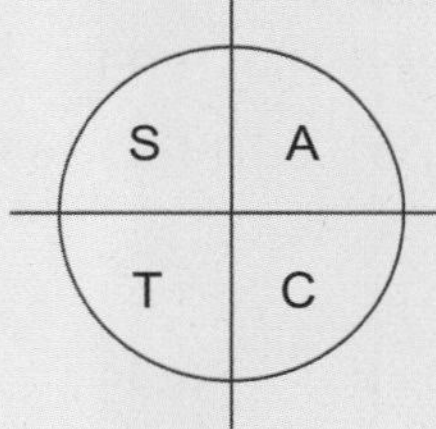

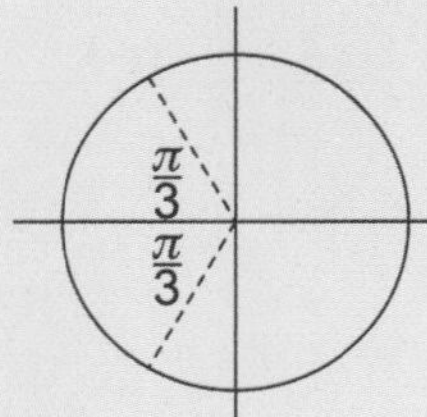

$\theta = \pi - \frac{\pi}{3} = \frac{2\pi}{3}$

So, $\theta = \pi + \frac{\pi}{3} = \frac{4\pi}{3}$

Step 3 With every full rotation, the same ratio is given: $\cos\frac{4\pi}{3} = \cos\left(\frac{4\pi}{3} + 2\pi\right) = \cos\left(\frac{4\pi}{3} + 4\pi\right)$, etc.

$\therefore \theta = \frac{2\pi}{3} + 2n\pi$ **or** $\theta = \frac{4\pi}{3} + 2n\pi$, where $n \in Z$

Z is used, as we have to allow for positive and negative angles.

Exercise 7.6

1. Solve each of the following equations for $0° \leqslant \theta. \leqslant 360°$:

(i) $\cos\theta = 0.5$

(ii) $\tan\theta = 1$

(iii) $\sin\theta = -\frac{\sqrt{3}}{2}$

(iv) $\cos\theta = -\frac{1}{\sqrt{2}}$

(v) $\sin\theta = \frac{\sqrt{3}}{2}$

(vi) $\sec\theta = -\sqrt{2}$ → Note: $\sec\theta = \frac{1}{\cos\theta}$

(vii) $2\sin^2\theta = 1$

(viii) $\cot\theta = -1$ → Note: $\cot\theta = \frac{\cos\theta}{\sin\theta}$

(ix) $4\cos^2\theta - 1 = 0$ → Note: $\cos^2\theta = (\cos\theta)^2$

2. Solve each of the following equations for $0 \leqslant x \leqslant 2\pi$ (give answers in radians):

(i) $\sin x = \frac{1}{2}$

(ii) $\tan x = \frac{1}{\sqrt{3}}$

(iii) $\cos x = \frac{1}{\sqrt{2}}$

(iv) $\sin x = -\frac{1}{\sqrt{2}}$

(v) $\sin x = 0$

(vi) $\cos x + 1 = 0$

3. Find, correct to one decimal place, the two values of A, where $0° \leqslant A \leqslant 360°$.

(i) $5\sin A = 2$

(ii) $7\cos A + 3 = 0$

(iii) $2\tan A = -7$

(iv) $3\sec A = 5$

(v) $2\operatorname{cosec} A - 11 = 0$

(vi) $17\cot A + 23 = 1$

4. Find, without using a calculator, the values of:

(i) $\sin\theta$, $\tan\theta$, if $\cos\theta = \frac{4}{5}$ and θ is acute

(ii) $\cos\theta$, $\tan\theta$, if $\sin\theta = \frac{5}{13}$ and θ is obtuse

5. For $0° \leqslant \theta \leqslant 360°$, find values of θ for the following (correct to one decimal place where necessary):

(i) $\sin 2\theta = \frac{1}{2}$

(ii) $\cos 2\theta = 0.5$

(iii) $\tan 3\theta = -0.1$

(iv) $\sin 3\theta = -1$

(v) $\cos\frac{\theta}{2} = -\frac{\sqrt{3}}{2}$

6. Solve for $\theta \in R$ (θ in radians).

(i) $\sin\theta = 1$

(ii) $\sin 3\theta = -1$

(iii) $\cos\theta = -\frac{1}{\sqrt{2}}$

(iv) $\cos\theta = 0$

(v) $2\sin\theta = \sqrt{2}$

7. Derek is an engineer, and part of his job is to design the ramps used in multi-storey car parks. Regulations state that there must 2.0 m clearance from the level below to the top of the ramp and the angle of elevation of the ramp must not exceed 15°.

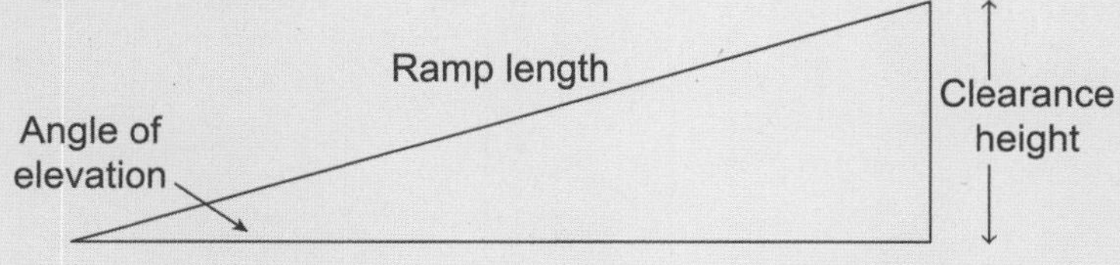

He designs two ramps. In his first design, the ratio of clearance height to ramp length is 2 : 8. In his second design, the ratio is 2 : 6.

Are his designs in line with the regulations specified? Explain why or why not.

8. When erecting a roof, it is more economical to have the pitch of the roof between 15° and 40°. However, trusses for support may be supplied at additional cost if a customer wishes to build outside this range.

The following plans were drawn up by an architect.
Is this an economical design for the roof?

(Note: Pitch = $\theta°$)

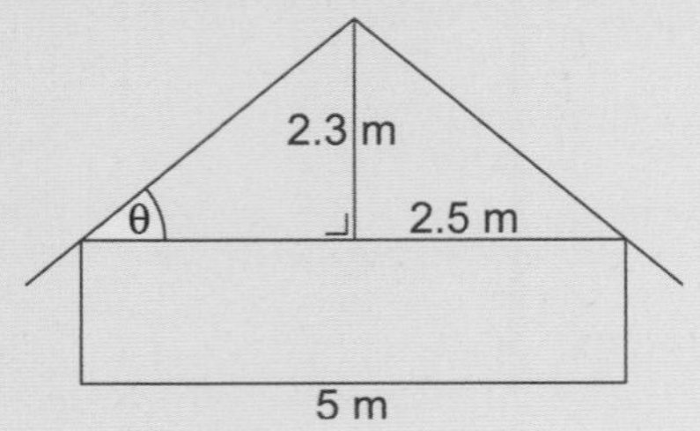

7.12 DERIVATION OF TRIGONOMETRIC FORMULAE 1, 2 AND 3

Students must be able to derive these formulae in examination.

Formula 1

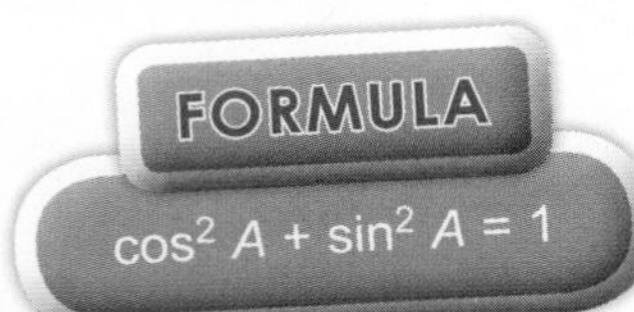

Proof

$(\cos A, \sin A)$ is a point on the unit circle.

Hence, the distance from $(\cos A, \sin A)$ to $(0,0)$ is one unit.

$$\therefore \sqrt{(\cos A - 0)^2 + (\sin A - 0)^2} = 1$$

$$(\cos A - 0)^2 + (\sin A - 0)^2 = 1 \quad \text{(square both sides)}$$

$$\cos^2 A + \sin^2 A = 1$$

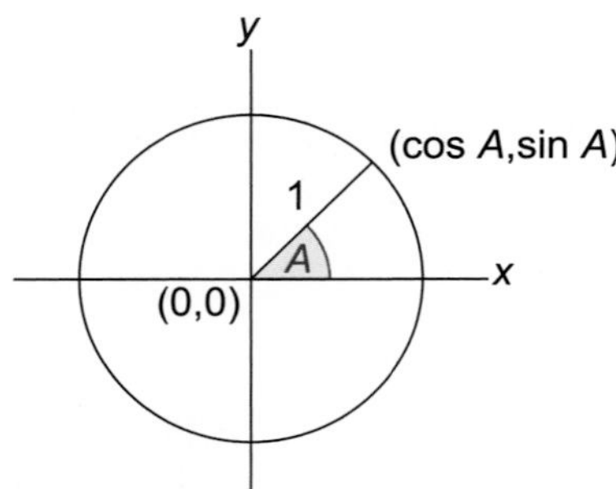

Formula 2

There are two cases:

1. **Acute-angled triangles**
2. **Obtuse-angled triangles**

FORMULA

Sine Formula: $\dfrac{a}{\sin A} = \dfrac{b}{\sin B} = \dfrac{c}{\sin C}$

Given:

ΔABC with sides a, b and c as shown below.

(i) $\angle C$ acute

(ii) $\angle C$ obtuse

To prove:

$$\frac{a}{\sin A} = \frac{b}{\sin B} = \frac{c}{\sin C}$$

(i)

B, c, a, A, D, b, C

(ii)

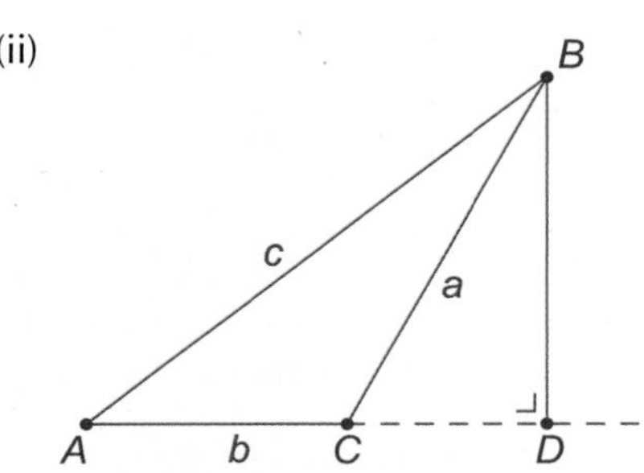

Construction:

In each triangle, draw BD perpendicular to AC.

Proof:

Acute case	Obtuse case
$\frac{\lvert BD \rvert}{c} = \sin A$ .... (1)	$\frac{\lvert BD \rvert}{c} = \sin A$ .... (1)
$\frac{\lvert BD \rvert}{a} = \sin C$ .... (2)	$\frac{\lvert BD \rvert}{a} = \sin (180° - C)$ $= \sin C$ .... (2)

$\therefore$ By dividing (1) by (2), we get:

$$\frac{a}{c} = \frac{\sin A}{\sin C}$$

Multiplying both sides by $\frac{c}{\sin A}$, we get $\frac{a}{\sin A} = \frac{c}{\sin C}$.

In like manner, by drawing a perpendicular from C to AB, we can prove that:

$$\frac{a}{b} = \frac{\sin A}{\sin B} \text{ or } \frac{a}{\sin A} = \frac{b}{\sin B}$$

Therefore, $\frac{a}{\sin A} = \frac{b}{\sin B} = \frac{c}{\sin C}$.

Formula 3

FORMULA
Cosine Formula:
a² = b² + c² – 2bc cos A

Proof:

Increase the unit circle by a factor of b.

$\therefore$ The radius is b, and any point on the circle can be described as $(b \cos A, b \sin A)$, where A is the angle between the x-axis and the radius to the point.

Based on the co-ordinate geometry distance formula, the distance between the vertices containing angles B and C is:

$$d = \sqrt{(x_2 - x_1)^2 + (y_2 - y_1)^2}$$

$$\therefore a = \sqrt{(b \cos A - c)^2 + (b \sin A - 0)^2}$$

$$a^2 = b^2 \cos^2 A - 2bc \cos A + c^2 + b^2 \sin^2 A$$

$$a^2 = b^2 (\cos^2 A + \sin^2 A) + c^2 - 2bc \cos A$$

$$a^2 = b^2 + c^2 - 2bc \cos A \qquad (1 = \cos^2 A + \sin^2 A)$$

7.13 USING THE SINE RULE

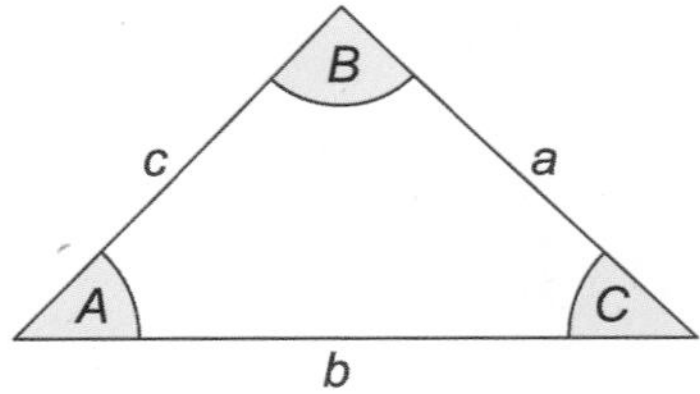

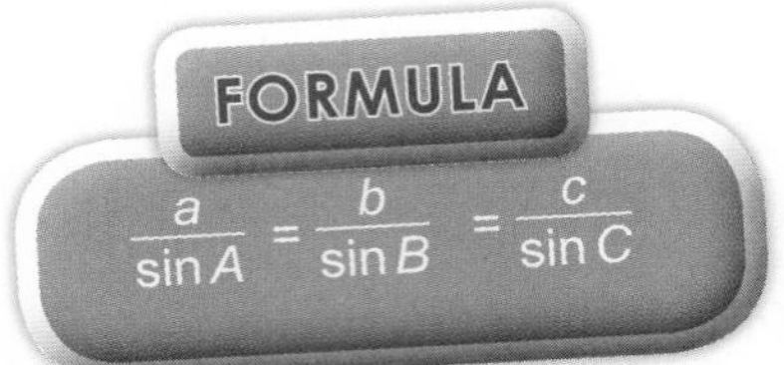

$$\frac{a}{\sin A} = \frac{b}{\sin B} = \frac{c}{\sin C}$$

OR

$$\frac{\sin A}{a} = \frac{\sin B}{b} = \frac{\sin C}{c}$$

You can find this formula on page 16 of the *Formulae and Tables*.

Note: If you are solving a triangle and you know an angle and the opposite side, use the Sine Rule formula.

Worked Example 7.18

Find the values of the unknown sides and angles correct to one decimal place.

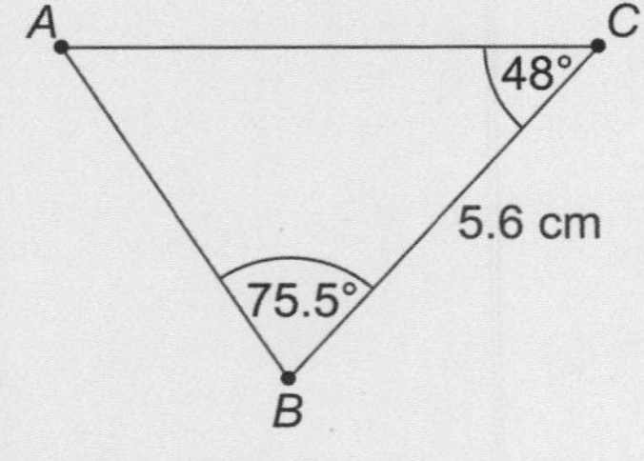

Solution

$|\angle BAC| = 180° - 48° - 75.5° = 56.5°$

$$|AC|: \frac{|AC|}{\sin 75.5°} = \frac{5.6}{\sin 56.5°}$$

$$|AC| = \frac{5.6 \sin 75.5°}{\sin 56.5°}$$

$$|AC| = 6.5016$$

$$|AC| \approx 6.5 \text{ cm}$$

$$|AB|: \frac{|AB|}{\sin 48°} = \frac{5.6}{\sin 56.5°}$$

$$|AB| = \frac{5.6 \sin 48°}{\sin 56.5°}$$

$$= 4.9906$$

$$\approx 5.0 \text{ cm}$$

Worked Example 7.19

Find the value of the remaining side and angles to two decimal places.

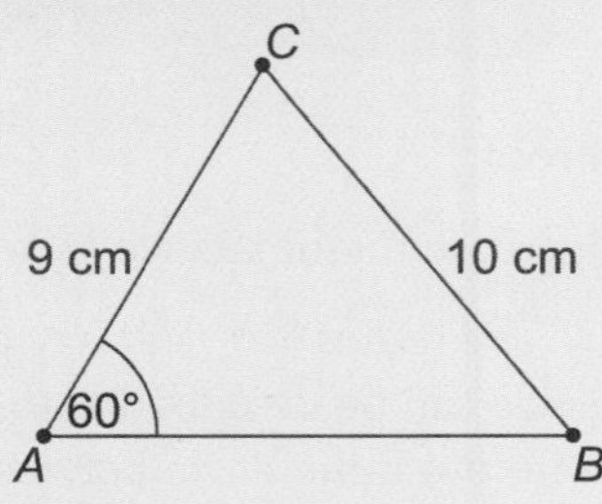

Solution

$$\frac{\sin B}{9} = \frac{\sin 60°}{10}$$

$$\sin B = \frac{9 \sin 60°}{10}$$

$$\sin B = 0.7794$$

$$B = \sin^{-1} 0.7794$$

$$B = 51.21°$$

So, $C = 180° - 51.21° - 60°$

$= 68.79°$

$$\frac{|AB|}{\sin 68.79°} = \frac{10}{\sin 60°}$$

$$|AB| = \frac{10 \sin 68.79°}{\sin 60°}$$

$$|AB| = 10.76 \text{ cm}$$

7.14 THE AMBIGUOUS CASE

If you are given two sides and an angle, more than one triangle may satisfy the data.

This is called the **ambiguous case**.

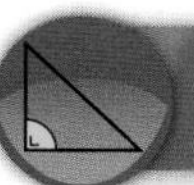

Worked Example 7.20

Find the values of the unknown sides and angles to the nearest metre and degree.

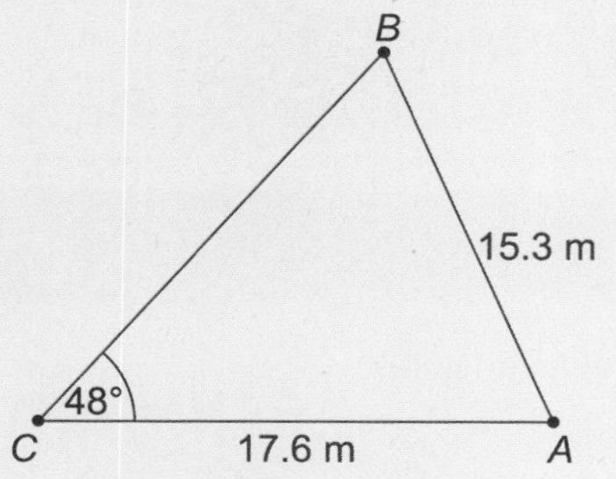

Solution

$$\frac{\sin|\angle CBA|}{17.6} = \frac{\sin 48}{15.3}$$

$$\sin|\angle CBA| = \frac{17.6 \sin 48}{15.3}$$

$$= 0.8549$$

$$|\angle CBA| = \sin^{-1} 0.8549$$

$$= 58.7442$$

$$\approx 59°$$

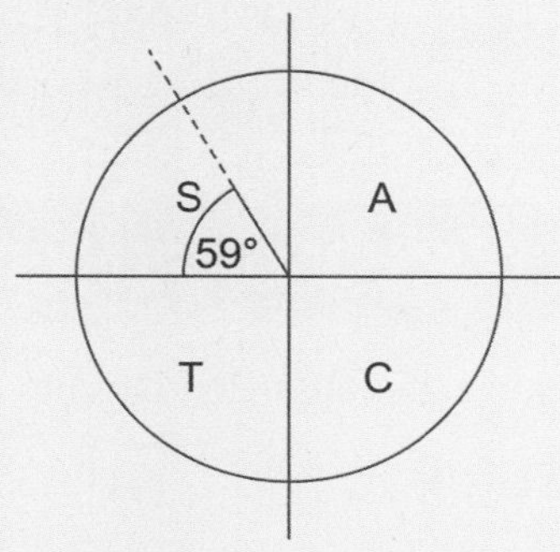

But $\sin|\angle CBA| = 0.8549$ could also give an angle in the second quadrant.

So, $|\angle CBA| = 180° - 59° = 121°$

This could also be the value, as $48° + 121° = 169°$, and $169° < 180°$ (angles of a triangle).

So we need to allow for both possible triangles:

$\Delta 1 \quad |\angle CBA| = 59° \qquad \Delta 2 \quad |\angle CBA| = 121°$

Here are two possible triangles:

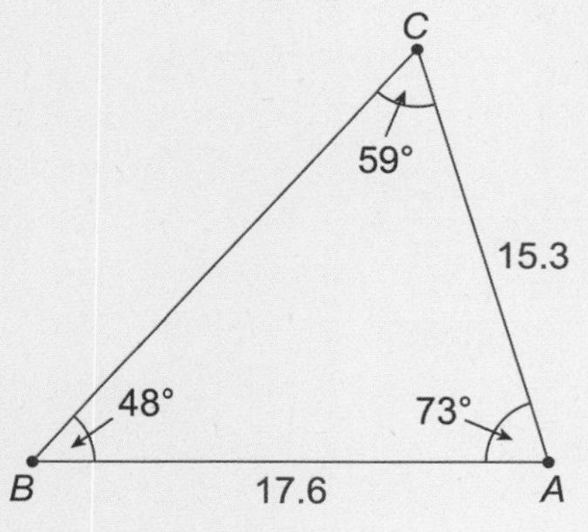

Note: There is no ambiguity with the Cosine Rule, as the cosine is positive in the first quadrant and negative in the second quadrant, giving acute and obtuse angles respectively. Therefore, where possible, use the Cosine Rule, as it is more dependable.

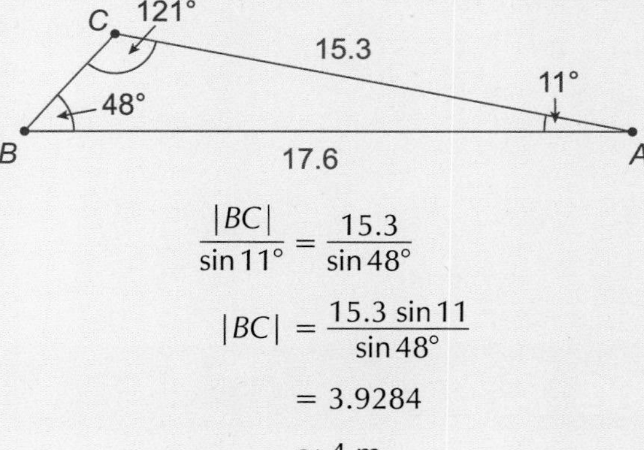

$$\frac{|BC|}{\sin 73°} = \frac{15.3}{\sin 48°}$$

$$|BC| = \frac{15.3 \sin 73°}{\sin 48°}$$

$$= 19.6886$$

$$\approx 20 \text{ m}$$

$$\frac{|BC|}{\sin 11°} = \frac{15.3}{\sin 48°}$$

$$|BC| = \frac{15.3 \sin 11}{\sin 48°}$$

$$= 3.9284$$

$$\approx 4 \text{ m}$$

7.15 USING THE COSINE RULE

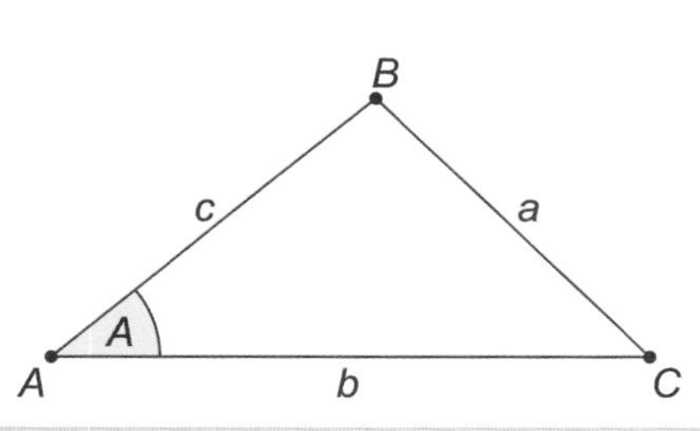

FORMULA

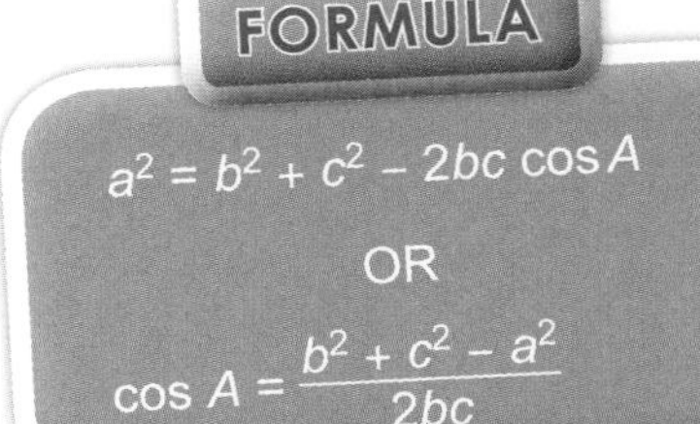

$$a^2 = b^2 + c^2 - 2bc \cos A$$

OR

$$\cos A = \frac{b^2 + c^2 - a^2}{2bc}$$

ACTIVITY 7.14

You can find this formula on page 16 of the *Formulae and Tables*.

Note: If the lengths of two sides of a triangle and the angle between these sides are known, then we can use the Cosine Rule to find the length of the third side in the triangle.

Note: If we know the lengths of all three sides in a triangle, then we can use the Cosine Rule to find the measure of any angle in the triangle.

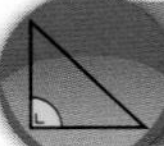

Worked Example 7.21

Find x, the distance from A to B. Give your answer correct to three significant figures.

Solution

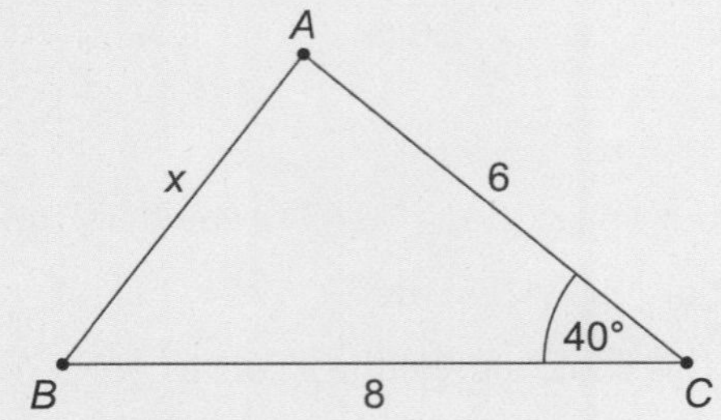

$$a^2 = b^2 + c^2 - 2bc\cos A$$

$$\therefore x^2 = 6^2 + 8^2 - 2(6)(8)\cos 40^\circ$$

$$\therefore x^2 = 26.4597$$

$$\therefore x = 5.1439$$

$$x \approx 5.14$$

Worked Example 7.22

Calculate the measure of the angle A.

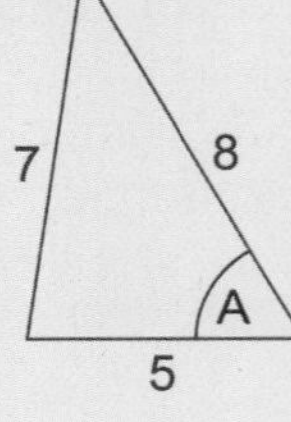

Solution

Method 1

$$a^2 = b^2 + c^2 - 2bc\cos A$$

$$7^2 = 5^2 + 8^2 - 2(5)(8)\cos A$$

$$49 = 25 + 64 - 80\cos A$$

$$80\cos A = 89 - 49$$

$$80\cos A = 40$$

$$\cos A = \frac{40}{80} = \frac{1}{2}$$

$$\Rightarrow A = \cos^{-1}\frac{1}{2} \qquad \Rightarrow A = 60^\circ$$

Method 2

$$\cos A = \frac{b^2 + c^2 - a^2}{2bc}$$

$$\therefore \cos A = \frac{(5)^2 + (8)^2 - (7)^2}{2(5)(8)}$$

$$\cos A = \frac{40}{80} = \frac{1}{2}$$

$$\Rightarrow A = \cos^{-1}\frac{1}{2} \qquad \Rightarrow A = 60^\circ$$

Exercise 7.7

1. Use the Sine Rule to find the values of the unknown sides and angles to one decimal place where necessary. In any ambiguous case, give both solutions.

(i)

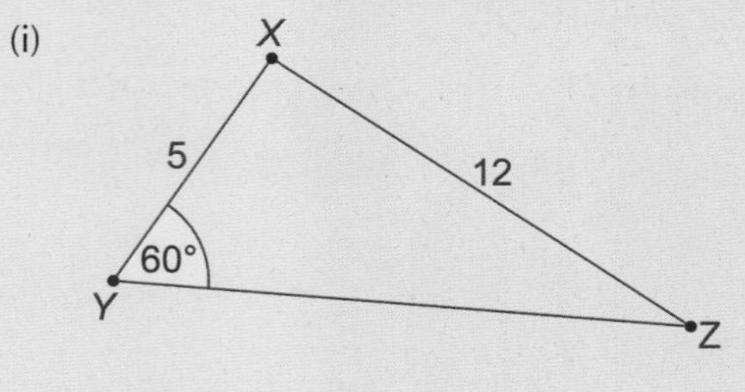

(ii)

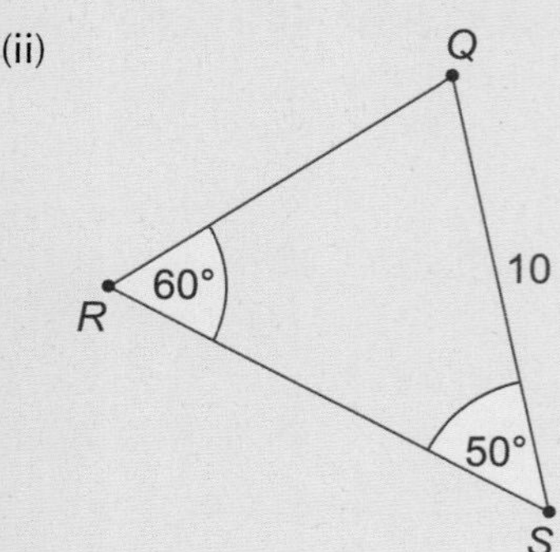

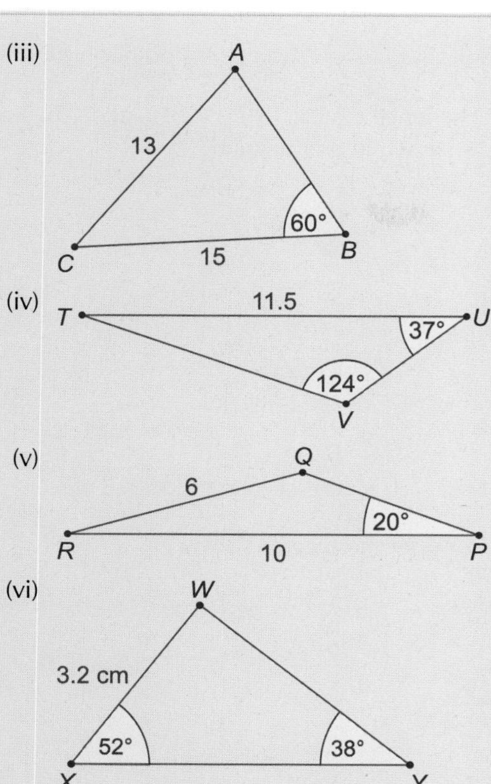

2. Find the values of the unknowns in these triangles without using a calculator:

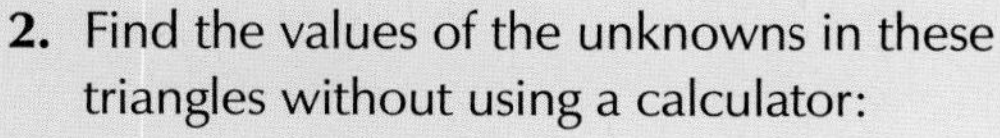

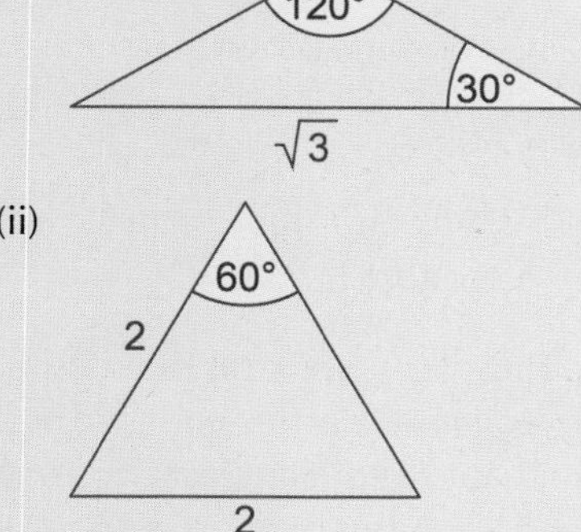

3. In parts (i) to (v), use the Cosine Rule to find the value of a. Write each answer correct to two decimal places.

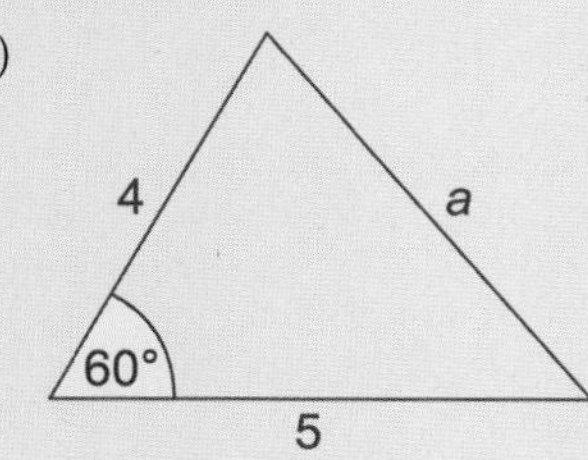

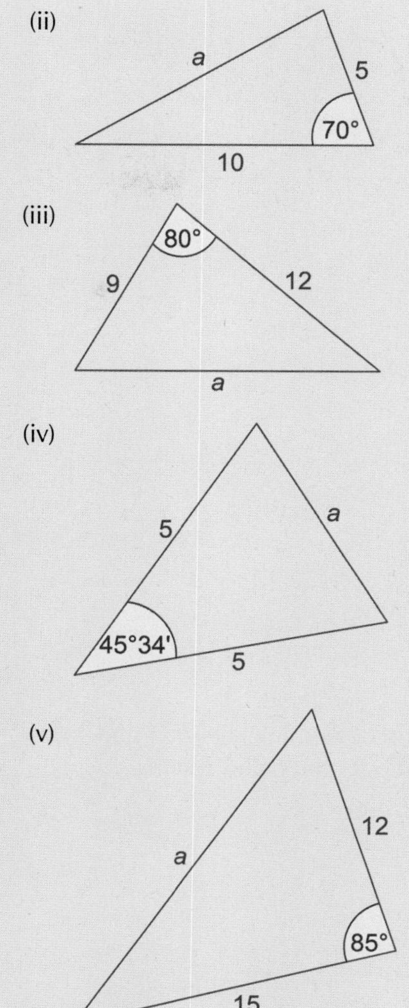

4. In parts (i) to (v), use the Cosine Rule to find the value of A. Give your answers to the nearest degree.

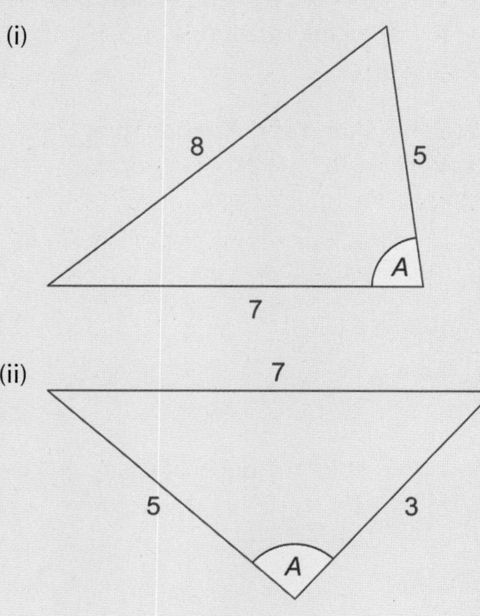

(iii)

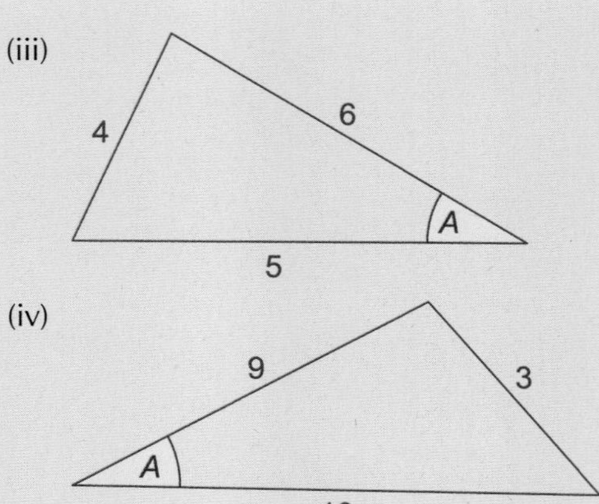

(iv)

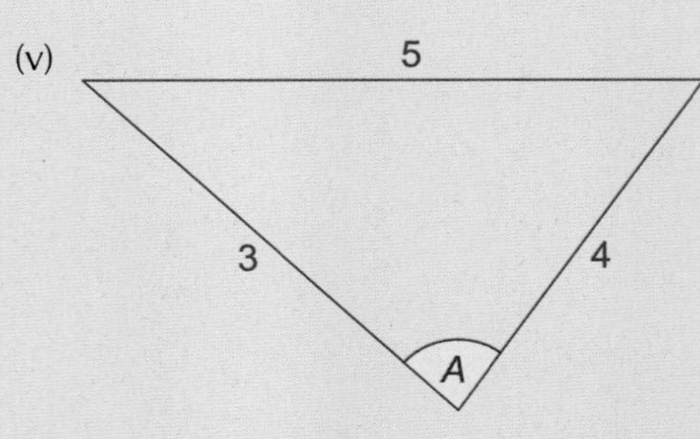

(v)

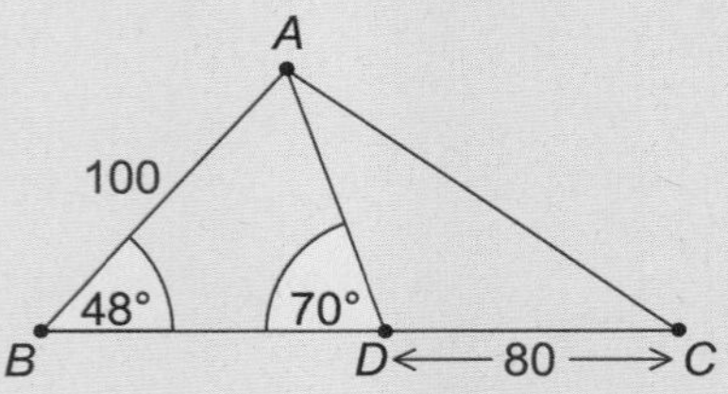

5. Find to the nearest integer $|AC|$ and $|AD|$, given that B, C and D are collinear.

6. The sides of a triangle have lengths 10 cm, 8 cm and 4 cm. Find the measure of the largest angle to the nearest degree.

7. Construct the two possible triangles, given the following information: $a = 8$, $b = 9$ and $A = 60°$.

8. In the diagram, Y is the midpoint of $[XZ]$. $|\angle WXY| = 48°$, $|WX| = 10$ and $|WY| = 11$.

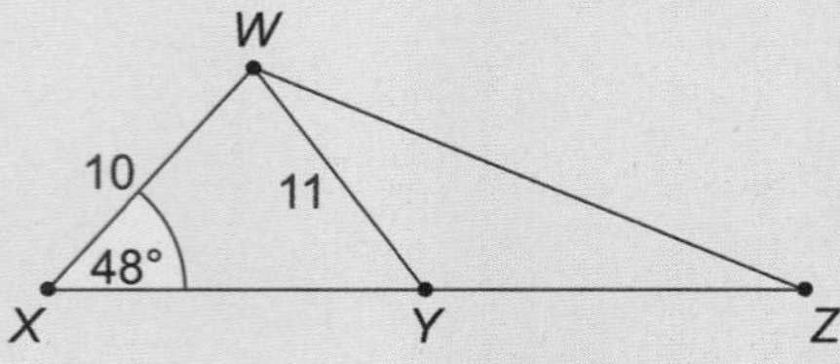

Find, correct to one decimal place:

(i) $|\angle WYX|$

(ii) $|XY|$

(iii) $|WZ|$

9. ABC is a triangle, and D is a point on $[BC]$.

The lengths $|AB|$, $|AD|$, $|AC|$ and $|BD|$ are as shown in the diagram.

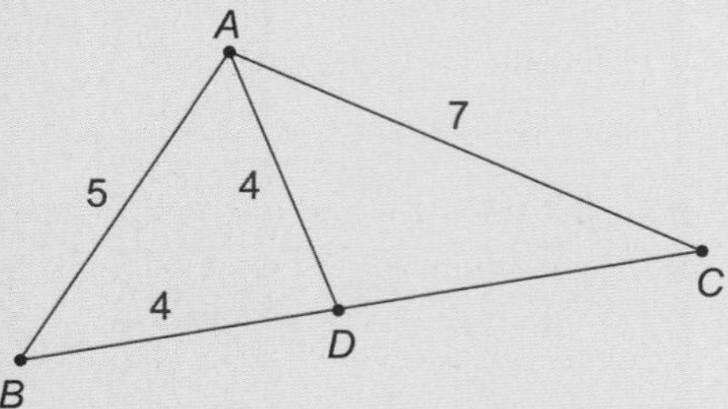

Find $|DC|$, correct to one decimal place.

10. Consider the diagram below.

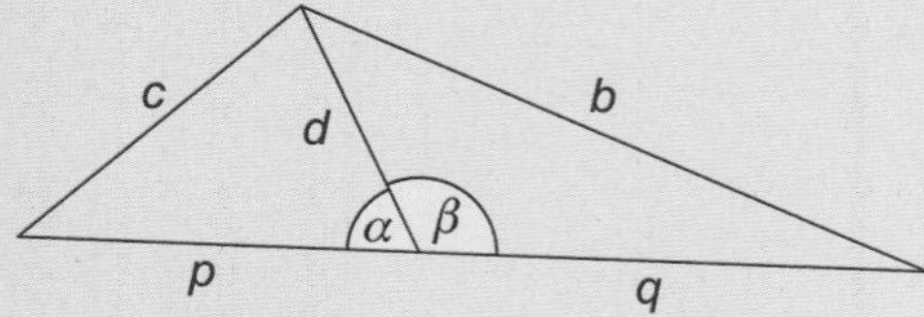

(i) Express $\cos\alpha$ and $\cos\beta$ in terms of the labelled lengths.

(ii) Show that:
$pb^2 + qc^2 = (p + q)(pq + d^2)$

11. Using the Sine Formula, prove that:

(i) $a \sin B = b \sin A$

(ii) $a(\sin B - \sin C) + b(\sin C - \sin A) + c(\sin A - \sin B) = 0$

12. John is standing at a point P on the southern bank of a river. He wants to swim across to the northern bank. There are just two landing points, Q and R, on the northern bank. R is 80 m downstream from Q. The path $[PQ]$ makes an angle of 50° with the bank, and the path $[PR]$ makes an angle of 60° with the bank. The situation is shown in the diagram below.

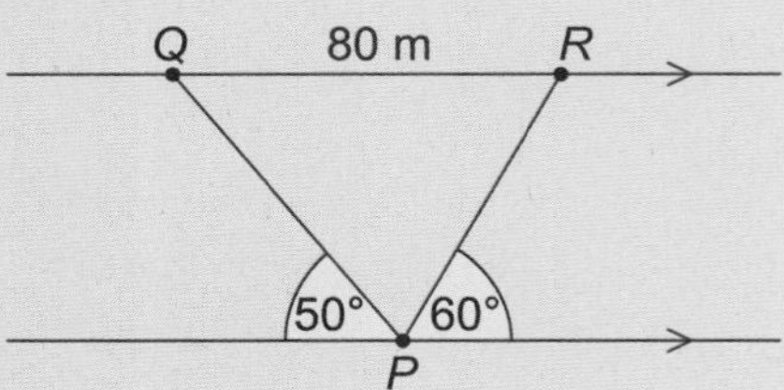

Using the Sine Rule, calculate $|PQ|$ and $|PR|$.

13. A boat is anchored at sea. Alice wants to find out the distance from the boat to the shore. She measures the distance between two points, A and B, on the shore. She then measures the angles CAB and CBA.

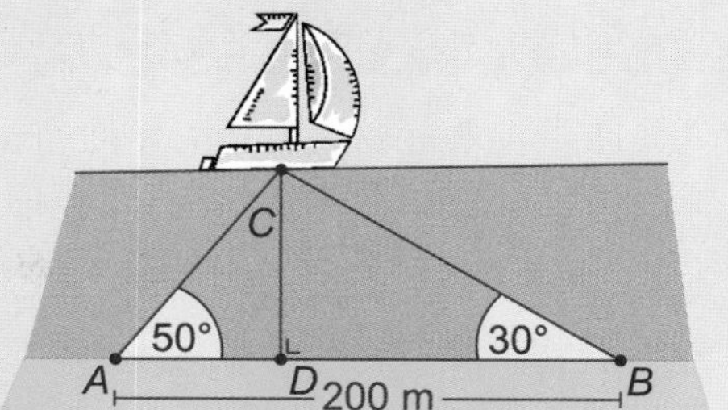

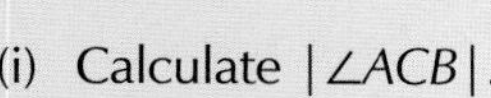

(i) Calculate $|\angle ACB|$.

(ii) Using the Sine Rule, calculate $|AC|$.

(iii) Now, find $|CD|$, the distance from the boat to the shore. Give your answer to one decimal place.

14. Windows are sometimes in the shape of a pointed arch, like the one shown in the picture.

A person is designing such an arched window. The outline is shown in the diagram below the picture.

The centre for the arc AB is C, and the centre for the arc AC is B.
$|BD| = 2.4$ metres and $|DE| = 1.8$ metres.

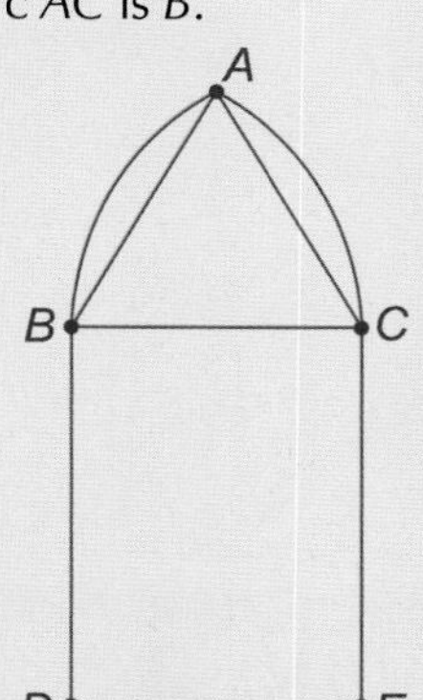

(a) Show that $|\angle ABC| = 60°$.

(b) Find the length of the arc AB. Give your answer in metres, correct to three decimal places.

(c) Find the length of the perimeter of the window.

Give your answer in metres, correct to two decimal places.

SEC Project Maths Paper 2, Leaving Certificate Higher Level, 2010

15. Roofs of buildings are often supported by frameworks of timber called roof trusses.

A quantity surveyor must find the total length of timber needed in order to make the triangular truss shown below.

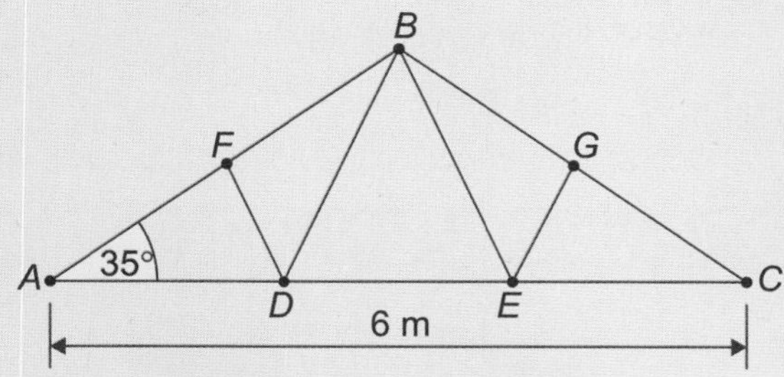

The length of $[AC]$ is 6 metres, and the pitch of the roof is 35°, as shown.

$|AD| = |DE| = |EC|$ and
$|AF| = |FB| = |BG| = |GC|$

(i) Calculate the length of $[AB]$ in metres, correct to two decimal places.

(ii) Calculate the total length of timber required to make the truss.

SEC Project Maths Paper 2, Leaving Certificate Higher Level, 2010

7.16 AREA OF A TRIANGLE

We derived a formula for the area of a triangle in the previous activity.

Area of a triangle = $\frac{1}{2}ab \sin C$

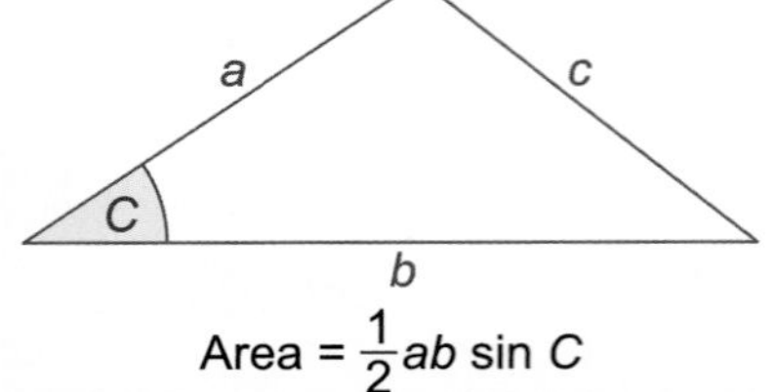

Area = $\frac{1}{2}ab \sin C$

This formula is also given on page 16 of the *Formulae and Tables*.

To use this formula, we need to know the lengths of two sides of the triangle and the angle **between** these two sides.

Worked Example 7.23

Find the area of ΔABC.

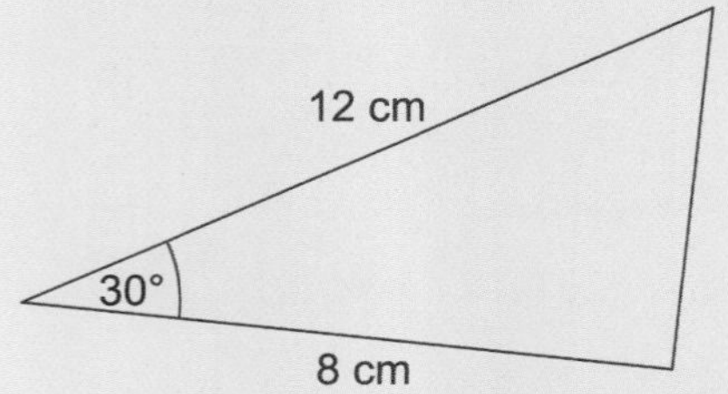

Solution

$$\text{Area} = \frac{1}{2}ab \sin C$$
$$= \frac{1}{2}(12)(8)(\sin 30°)$$
$$= \frac{1}{2} \times 12 \times 8 \times \frac{1}{2}$$
$$\text{Area} = 24 \text{ cm}^2$$

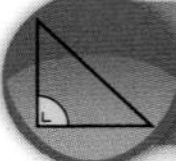

Worked Example 7.24

In the given triangle the area is 13.6 cm^2.

Find the measure of the angle A to the nearest degree.

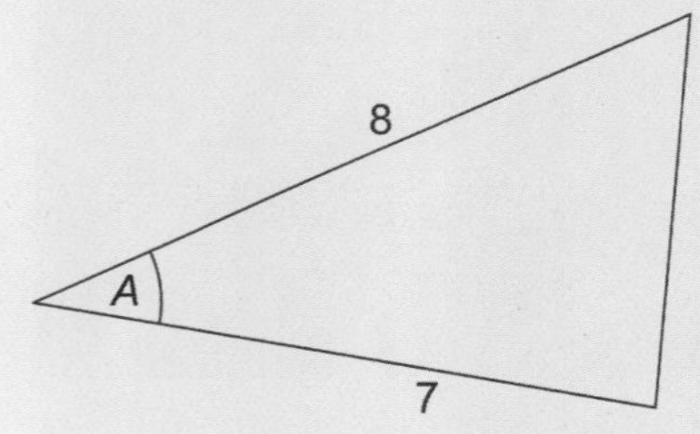

Solution

$$\frac{1}{2}(8)(7) \sin A = 13.6 \text{ cm}^2$$
$$28 \sin A = 13.6$$
$$\sin A = \frac{13.6}{28}$$
$$A = \sin^{-1} \frac{13.6}{28}$$
$$A \approx 29° \quad \text{or} \quad A \approx 151°$$

From the diagram, A is clearly acute.

$$\therefore A \approx 29°$$

7.17 AREA OF A SECTOR AND LENGTH OF AN ARC

ACTIVITY 7.16

Area of a sector of a circle = $(\pi r^2)\left(\frac{\theta}{360}\right)$, where θ is measured in degrees.

Length of an arc of a circle = $(2\pi r)\left(\frac{\theta}{360}\right)$, where θ is measured in degrees.

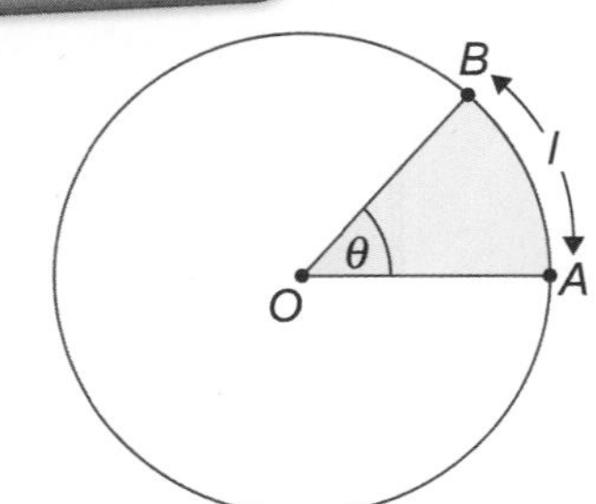

The same is also true for radian measure.

Length of arc $l = 2\pi r \dfrac{\theta}{2\pi}$

$l = r\theta$ where θ is in radians.

Area of sector $A = \pi r^2 \left(\dfrac{\theta}{2\pi}\right)$

$A = \dfrac{r^2\theta}{2}$

$A = \dfrac{1}{2}r^2\theta$ where θ is in radians.

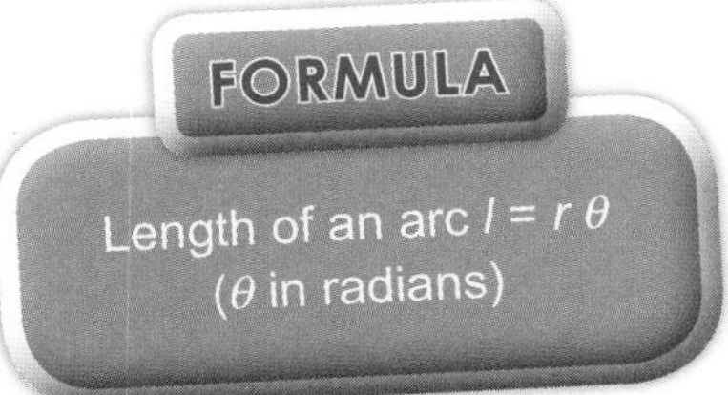

FORMULA

Area of a sector $A = \dfrac{1}{2}r^2\,\theta$
(θ in radians)

These formulae appear on page 9 of the *Formulae and Tables*.

Worked Example 7.25

The arc AB subtends an angle $\frac{\pi}{4}$ at the centre, O, of a circle radius 8 cm.

(i) Find the length of the arc AB

(ii) Find the area of the sector OAB.

Solution

(i) Length of the arc AB

$l = r\theta$

$= 8\left(\dfrac{\pi}{4}\right)$

Length of arc $= 2\pi$ cm

(ii) Area of the sector OAB

Area $= \dfrac{1}{2}r^2\theta$

$= \dfrac{1}{2}(8^2)\left(\dfrac{\pi}{4}\right)$

$= 32\left(\dfrac{\pi}{4}\right)$

$= 8\pi$ cm^2

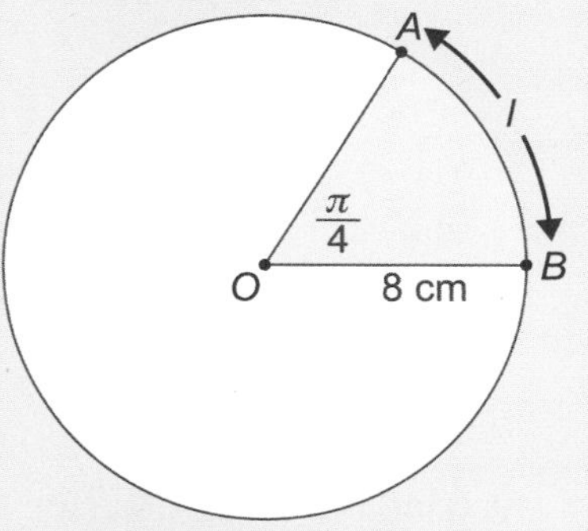

Exercise 7.8

Find the area of each of the triangles in Questions 1 to 6 (answers correct to two decimal places).

1.

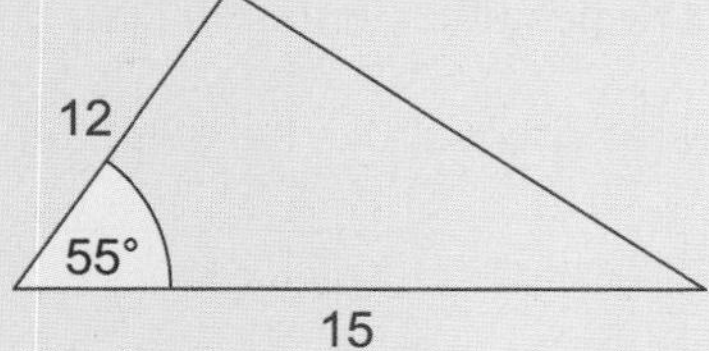

2.

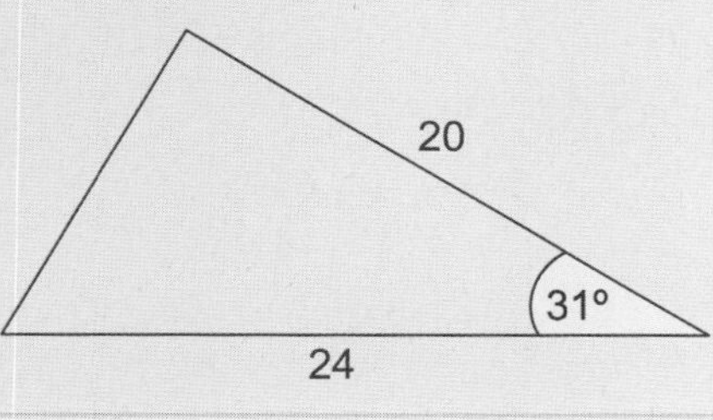

3.

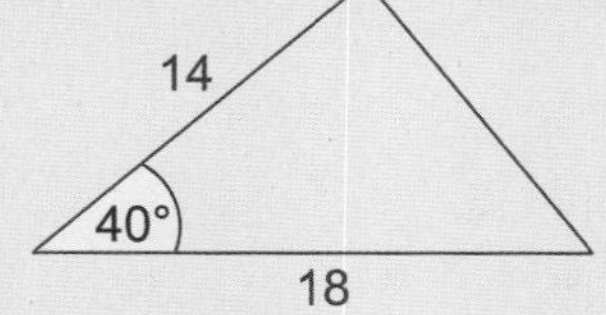

4.

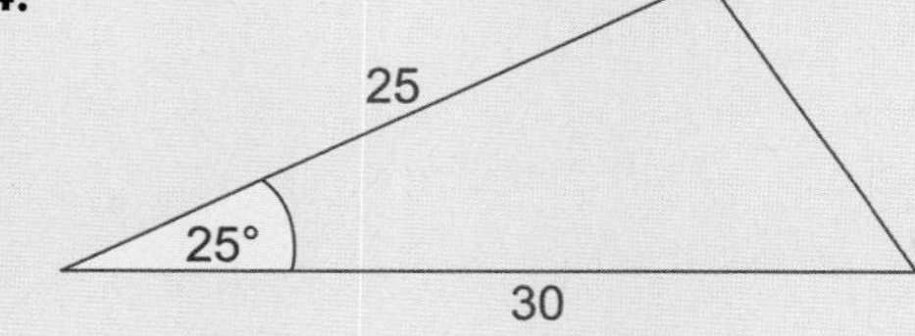

5.

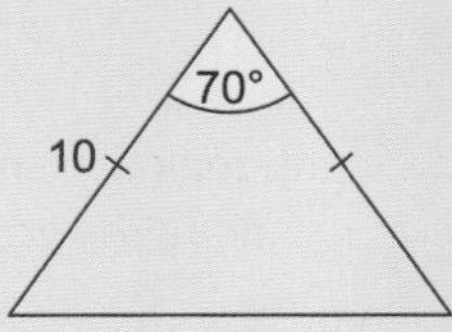

6.

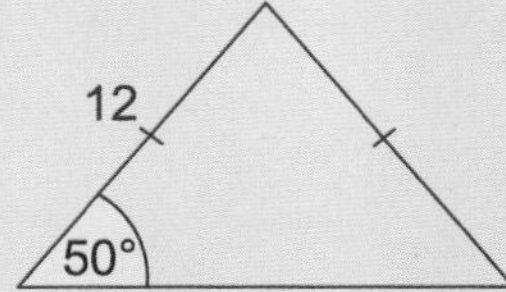

7. Find the area of the triangle ABC in which:

(i) $A = 90°$ $B = 27°$ $a = 15$ cm

(ii) $a = b = 12$ cm $c = 4$ cm

(iii) $a = b = 12$ cm $A = 80°$

8. Solve for x in each of the following triangles (to the nearest centimetre or degree where necessary):

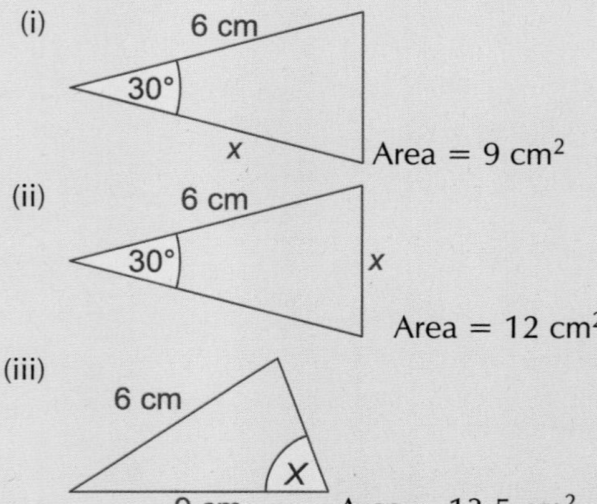

9. Find the length of an arc that subtends an angle of 0.8 radians at the centre of a circle of radius 10 cm.

10. Find the area and the length of the arc of each of the following sectors. (Angles given in radians.)

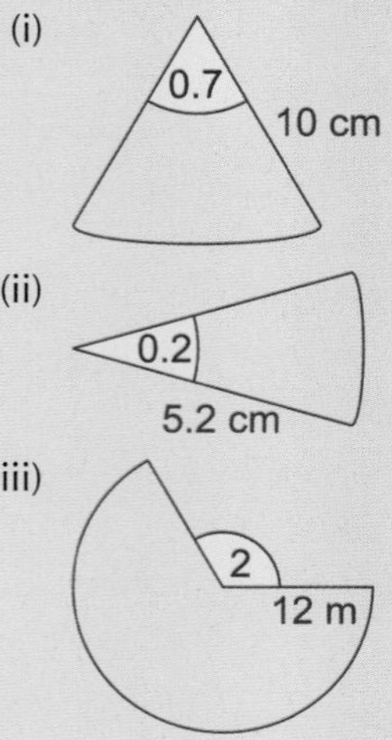

11. The diameter of a circle is 16 cm long. Find the angle in radians at the centre that is subtended by an arc of length 12 cm.

12. A pizza with a 30 cm diameter is shared equally between six people. Find the perimeter and the area of each slice.

13. The arc AB of a sector of a circle, centre O, radius 3 cm, is 6 cm long. Find:

(i) The area of the sector AOB

(ii) The area of the triangle AOB

(iii) The area of the minor segment cut off by the line AB

14. The diagram shows the cross-section of a table-tennis ball, radius r cm, floating in water. The surface of the ball touches the water at A and B. AB subtends an angle of $\frac{2\pi}{3}$ at the centre of the ball.

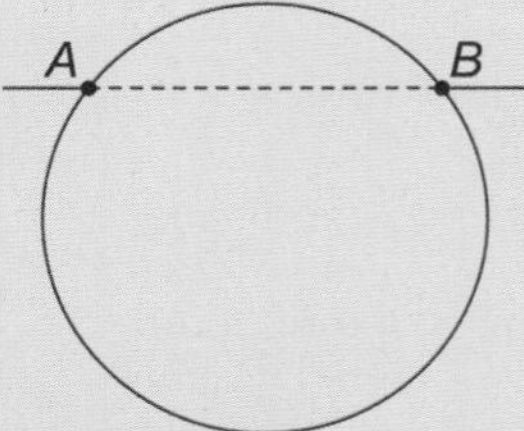

(i) Find the length of the chord AB in terms of r.

(ii) Hence, find, in terms of r, the circumference of the circle where the ball crosses the surface of the water.

15. Three bottles of perfume come in a special gift set. Each bottle is in its own individual canister. Then the three canisters are placed in a gift box as shown.

Each canister has a radius of 5 cm, and all three canisters touch each other in the gift box.

What is the area of the space between the canisters?

7.18 THREE-DIMENSIONAL (3D) PROBLEMS

To solve a three-dimensional (3D) problem, it is important to be able to identify the right-angled triangles in the question. Then redraw these right-angled triangles and use appropriate trigonometric ratios or Pythagoras' theorem to solve them.

Worked Example 7.26

A vertical tower stands 91 metres tall on a horizontal plane. A tourist is standing at point C. From C, the angle of elevation to the top of the tower, A, is 32°. The tourist's husband is standing at a point which is 235 metres from the base of the tower. Given $|\angle CBD| = 49°$, calculate (to two decimal places):

(i) $|BC|$ (ii) $|CD|$

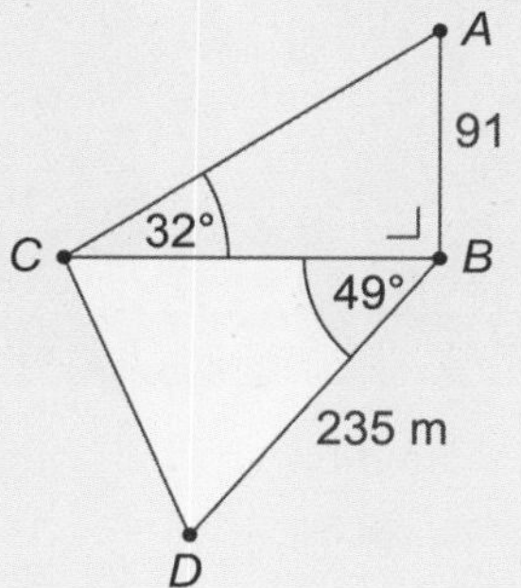

Solution

(i) $\tan 32° = \dfrac{91}{|BC|}$

$|BC| = \dfrac{91}{\tan 32°}$

$= 145.60344$

≈ 145.63 m

(ii)

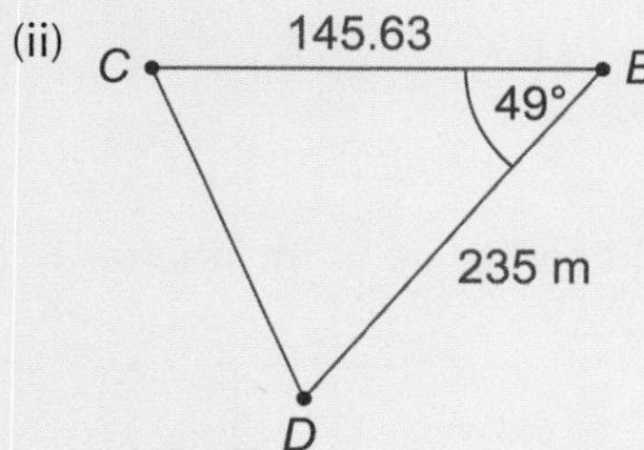

Using the Cosine Rule: $a^2 = b^2 + c^2 - 2bc \cos A$

$|CD|^2 = (145.63)^2 + (235)^2 - 2(145.63)(235)\cos 49°$

$= 76{,}433.0969 - 44{,}904.6819$

$|CD|^2 = 31{,}528.415$

$|CD| = 177.5624$

$|CD| \approx 177.56$ m

Exercise 7.9

1. [SP], [TQ] are vertical poles each of height 10 m. P, Q, R are points on level ground. Two wires of equal length join S and T to R, i.e. $|SR| = |TR|$.

If $|PR| = 8$ m and $|\angle PRQ| = 120°$, calculate:

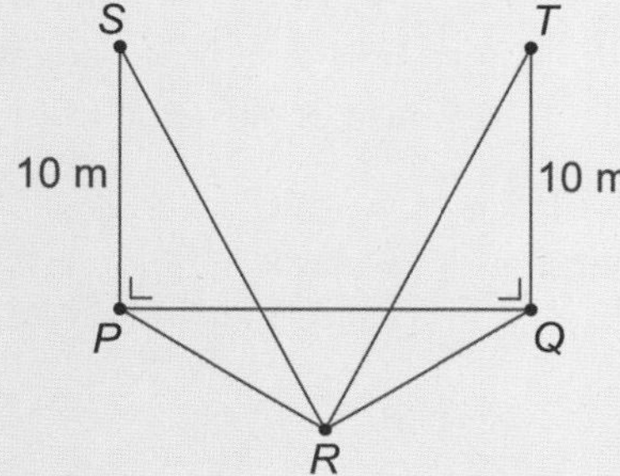

(i) $|PQ|$ to the nearest metre

(ii) $|SR|$ in surd form

(iii) $|\angle SRT|$ to the nearest degree

Leaving Certificate Maths Paper 2, 1996

2. A vertical radio mast [PQ] stands on flat horizontal ground. It is supported by three cables that join the top of the mast Q to the points A, B and C on the ground. The foot of the mast P lies inside the triangle ABC.

Each cable is 52 m long and the mast is 48 m high.

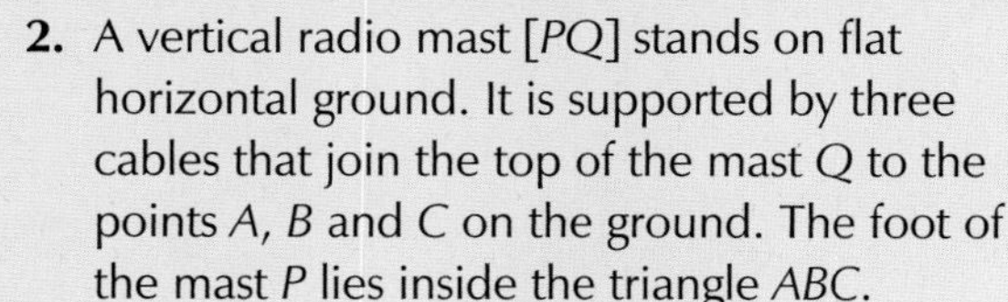

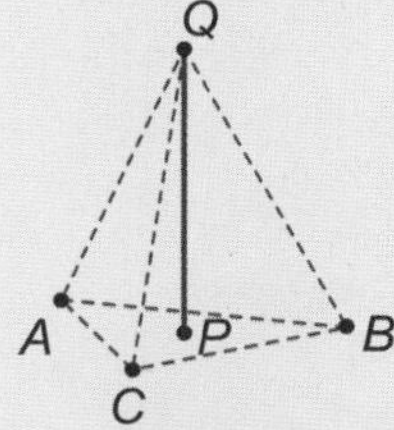

(i) Find the (common) distance from P to each of the points A, B and C.

(ii) Given that $|AC| = 38$ m and $|AB| = 34$ m, find $|BC|$ correct to one decimal place.

Leaving Certificate Maths Paper 2, 2002

3. The diagram shows a rectangular box. Rectangle *ABCD* is the top of the box and rectangle *EFGH* is the base of the box.

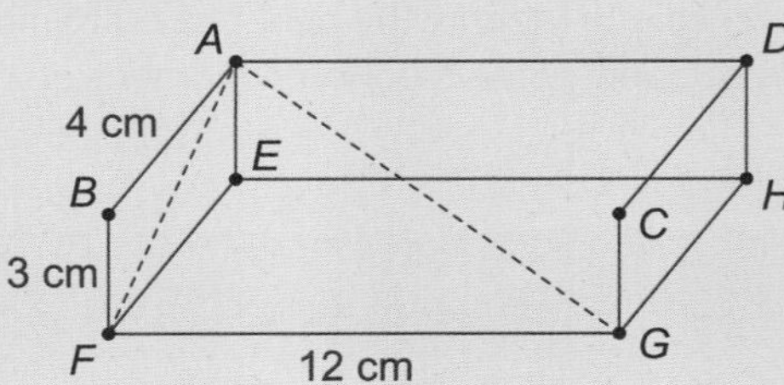

$|AB| = 4$ cm, $|BF| = 3$ cm and $|FG| = 12$ cm.

Find:

(i) $|AF|$

(ii) $|AG|$

(iii) $|\angle AGE|$

(iv) $|\angle BGF|$

Give angles correct to two decimal places.

4.

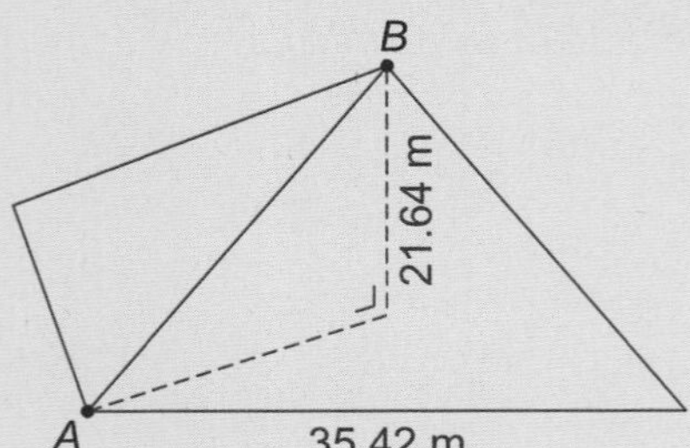

The Louvre Pyramid has the following dimensions:

Width 35.42 m   Height 21.64 m

(i) What is the slant height *AB* of the pyramid?

(ii) What is the angle of elevation from the point *A* to the top, *B*?

5. The diagram shows an international squash singles court. All measurements are in millimetres.

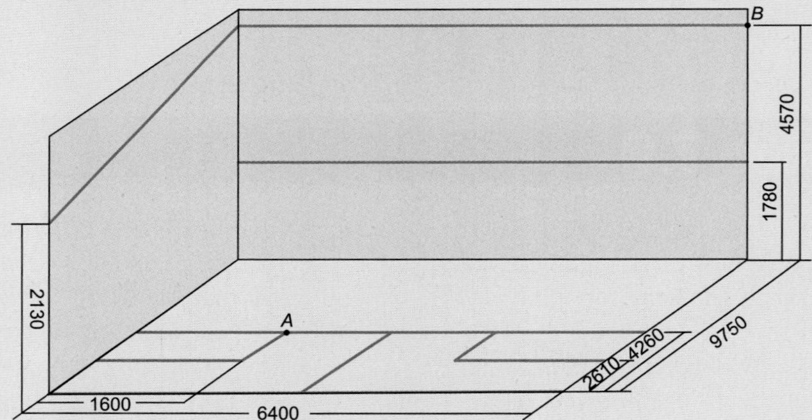

If Carol is standing at the point *A* when she hits the ball, what is the angle of elevation from this point to the point *B*?

6.

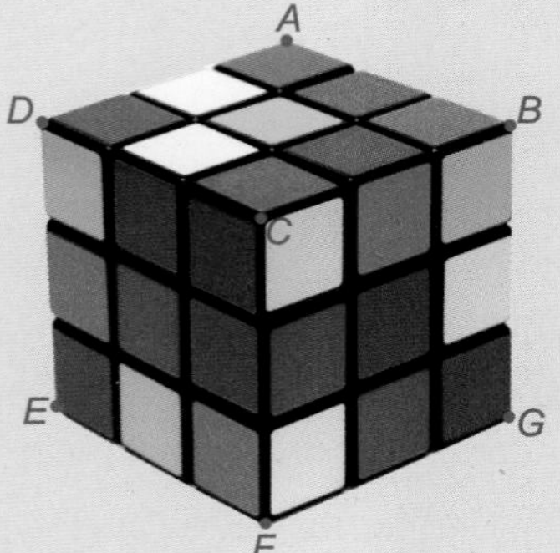

A Rubik cube has the dimensions 5.75 cm × 5.75 cm × 5.75 cm.

Find: (i) $|AC|$

(ii) $|AF|$

(iii) $|\angle AFE|$ to the nearest degree

7.19 DERIVATION OF TRIGONOMETRIC FORMULAE 4, 5, 6, 7 AND 9

Formula 4

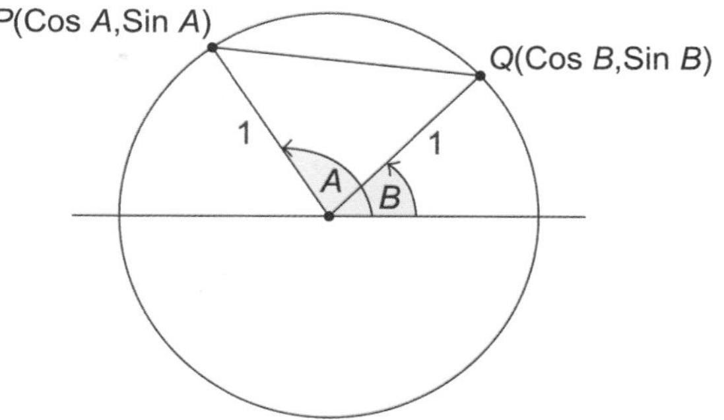

Let $P(\cos A, \sin A)$ and $Q(\cos B, \sin B)$ be two points on the unit circle.

> With any proof, always consider the tools available:
> - The Sine Rule
> - The Cosine Rule
> - The Distance formula
> - Any previous proof may also be used.

Using the Cosine Rule:

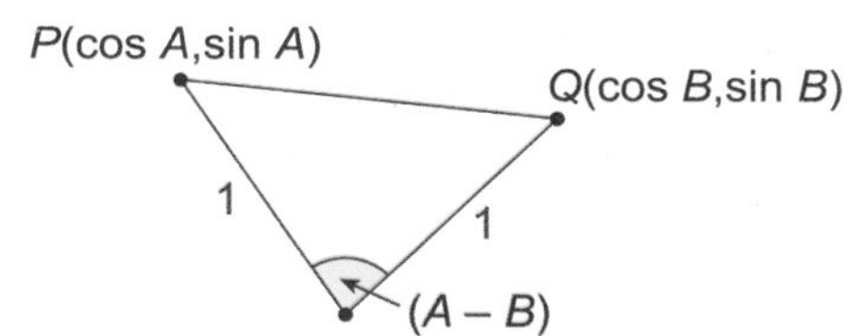

$|PQ|^2 = 1^2 + 1^2 - 2(1)(1)\cos(A - B)$

$= 1 + 1 - 2\cos(A - B)$

$|PQ|^2 = 2 - 2\cos(A - B)$ .....①

Using the distance formula:

$|PQ| = \sqrt{(\cos A - \cos B)^2 + (\sin A - \sin B)^2}$

$|PQ|^2 = (\cos A - \cos B)^2 + (\sin A - \sin B)^2$

$|PQ|^2 = \cos^2 A - 2\cos A\cos B + \cos^2 B + \sin^2 A - 2\sin A\sin B + \sin^2 B$

$= \cos^2 A + \sin^2 A + \cos^2 B + \sin^2 B - 2\cos A\cos B - 2\sin A\sin B$

$= 1 + 1 - 2\cos A\cos B - 2\sin A\sin B$ (by Formula 1)

$|PQ|^2 = 2 - 2\cos A\cos B - 2\sin A\sin B$ ....②

① = ②

$\cancel{2} - 2\cos(A - B) = \cancel{2} - 2\cos A\cos B - 2\sin A\sin B$ Divide by -2

$\cos(A - B) = \cos A\cos B + \sin A\sin B$

Formula 5

Use the same proof as for Formula 4 above. Then replace B with $-B$ on both sides:

$\cos(A - (-B)) = \cos A\cos(-B) + \sin A\sin(-B)$

$\cos(A + B) = \cos A\cos B - \sin A\sin B$

[as $\cos(-B) = \cos B$ and $\sin(-B) = -\sin B$]

Recall the graph of the cos function.

Formula 6

Given: $\cos(A + B) = \cos A \cos B - \sin A \sin B$

Proof: $\cos(A + A) = \cos A \cos A - \sin A \sin A$

$$\cos 2A = \cos^2 A - \sin^2 A$$

Formula 7

Given: $\cos(A - B) = \cos A \cos B + \sin A \sin B$

Proof:

$\therefore$ Replace A with $\left(\frac{\pi}{2} - A\right)$ on both sides:

$$\cos\left[\left(\frac{\pi}{2} - A\right) - B\right] = \cos\left(\frac{\pi}{2} - A\right)\cos B + \sin\left(\frac{\pi}{2} - A\right)\sin B$$

$\cos\left(\frac{\pi}{2} - A\right) = \sin A$ … (proof not needed for this course)

Also, $\sin\left(\frac{\pi}{2} - A\right) = \cos A$

$$\therefore \cos\left(\frac{\pi}{2} - A - B\right) = \sin A \cos B + \cos A \sin B$$

$$\cos\left(\frac{\pi}{2} - (A + B)\right) = \sin A \cos B + \cos A \sin B$$

$$\Rightarrow \sin(A + B) = \sin A \cos B + \cos A \sin B$$

Formula 9

Given: $\tan A = \dfrac{\sin A}{\cos A}$

Proof: $\tan A = \dfrac{\sin A}{\cos A}$

$$\tan(A + B) = \frac{\sin(A + B)}{\cos(A + B)}$$

$$= \frac{\sin A \cos B + \cos A \sin B}{\cos A \cos B - \sin A \sin B}$$

Divide above and below by $\cos A \cos B$:

$$= \frac{\dfrac{\sin A \cos B + \cos A \sin B}{\cos A \cos B}}{\dfrac{\cos A \cos B - \sin A \sin B}{\cos A \cos B}}$$

$$= \frac{\dfrac{\sin A \cos B}{\cos A \cos B} + \dfrac{\cos A \sin B}{\cos A \cos B}}{\dfrac{\cos A \cos B}{\cos A \cos B} - \dfrac{\sin A \sin B}{\cos A \cos B}}$$

$$= \frac{\tan A + \tan B}{1 - \tan A \tan B}$$

7.20 APPLICATION OF FORMULAE 1–24

1. $\cos^2 A + \sin^2 A = 1$	**7.** $\sin(A + B) = \sin A \cos B + \cos A \sin B$
2. Sine Formula: $\dfrac{a}{\sin A} = \dfrac{b}{\sin B} = \dfrac{c}{\sin C}$	**8.** $\sin(A - B) = \sin A \cos B - \cos A \sin B$
3. Cosine Formula: $a^2 = b^2 + c^2 - 2\,bc\cos A$	**9.** $\tan(A + B) = \dfrac{\tan A + \tan B}{1 - \tan A \tan B}$
4. $\cos(A - B) = \cos A \cos B + \sin A \sin B$	**10.** $\tan(A - B) = \dfrac{\tan A - \tan B}{1 + \tan A \tan B}$
5. $\cos(A + B) = \cos A \cos B - \sin A \sin B$	**11.** $\sin 2A = 2 \sin A \cos A$
6. $\cos 2A = \cos^2 A - \sin^2 A$	**12.** $\sin 2A = \dfrac{2\tan A}{1 + \tan^2 A}$

13. $\cos 2A = \frac{1 - \tan^2 A}{1 + \tan^2 A}$	**19.** $2 \sin A \sin B = \cos(A - B) - \cos(A + B)$
14. $\tan 2A = \frac{2 \tan A}{1 - \tan^2 A}$	**20.** $2 \cos A \sin B = \sin(A + B) - \sin(A - B)$
15. $\cos^2 A = \frac{1}{2}(1 + \cos 2A)$	**21.** $\cos A + \cos B = 2 \cos\frac{A+B}{2} \cos\frac{A-B}{2}$
16. $\sin^2 A = \frac{1}{2}(1 - \cos 2A)$	**22.** $\cos A - \cos B = -2 \sin\frac{A+B}{2} \sin\frac{A-B}{2}$
17. $2 \cos A \cos B = \cos(A + B) + \cos(A - B)$	**23.** $\sin A + \sin B = 2 \sin\frac{A+B}{2} \cos\frac{A-B}{2}$
18. $2 \sin A \cos B = \sin(A + B) + \sin(A - B)$	**24.** $\sin A - \sin B = 2 \cos\frac{A+B}{2} \sin\frac{A-B}{2}$

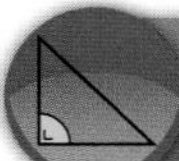

Worked Example 7.27

Express, in surd form: (i) $\cos 15°$

(ii) $\tan 105°$

Solution

(i) $\cos 15° = \cos(45° - 30°)$

$$\cos(A - B) = \cos A \cos B + \sin A \sin B$$

$$= \cos 45 \cos 30 + \sin 45 \sin 30$$

$$= \left(\frac{1}{\sqrt{2}}\right)\left(\frac{\sqrt{3}}{2}\right) + \left(\frac{1}{\sqrt{2}}\right)\left(\frac{1}{2}\right)$$

$$= \frac{\sqrt{3}}{2\sqrt{2}} + \frac{1}{2\sqrt{2}}$$

$$= \frac{\sqrt{3} + 1}{2\sqrt{2}}$$

(ii) $\tan 105° = \tan(60° + 45°)$

$$\tan(A + B) = \frac{\tan A + \tan B}{1 - \tan A \tan B}$$

$$= \frac{\tan 60 + \tan 45}{1 - \tan 60 \tan 45}$$

$$= \frac{\sqrt{3} + 1}{1 - (\sqrt{3})(1)}$$

$$= \frac{\sqrt{3} + 1}{1 - \sqrt{3}}$$

Worked Example 7.28

If $\tan(A + B) = 4$, and $\tan B = 3$, find the value of $\tan A$.

Solution

$$\tan(A + B) = \frac{\tan A + \tan B}{1 - \tan A \tan B}$$

Let $\tan A = t$.

Substitute what you know:

$$4 = \frac{t + 3}{1 - 3t}$$

Multiply both sides by $(1-3t)$:

$$4(1-3t) = t + 3$$

$$4 - 12t = t + 3$$

$$1 = 13t$$

$$t = \frac{1}{13}$$

$$\therefore \tan A = \frac{1}{13}$$

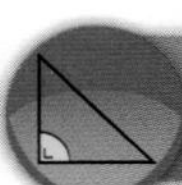

Worked Example 7.29

If $\cos 2A = \frac{1}{49}$, find two values of $\cos A$ without using a calculator.

Solution

$$\cos 2A = \frac{1 - \tan^2 A}{1 + \tan^2 A}$$

Let $\tan A = t$.

$$\frac{1}{49} = \frac{1 - t^2}{1 + t^2}$$

$$1 + t^2 = 49 - 49t^2$$

$$50t^2 = 48$$

$$t^2 = \frac{48}{50}$$

$$t = \pm\sqrt{\frac{48}{50}} = \pm\sqrt{\frac{24}{25}} = \pm\frac{\sqrt{24}}{5}$$

$$\tan A = \pm\frac{\sqrt{24}}{5}$$

$$\therefore \cos A = \frac{5}{7} \text{ or } -\frac{5}{7}$$

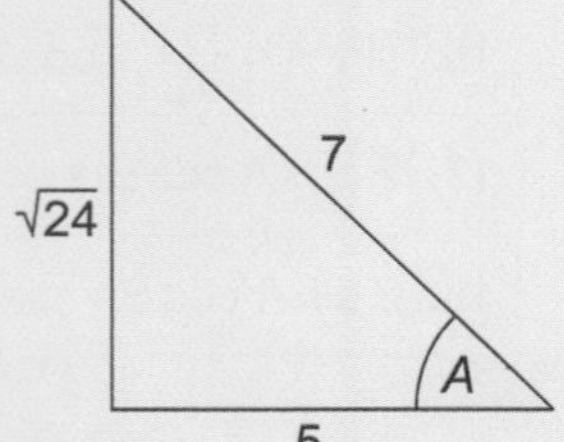

Changing Products to Sums to Products (Formulae 17–24)

Worked Example 7.30

Write: (i) $\cos 5x \cos x$ as a sum

(ii) $\sin 6x + \sin 4x$ as a product

Solution

(i) $2 \cos A \cos B = \cos(A + B) + \cos(A - B)$

$$\cos A \cos B = \frac{1}{2}[\cos(A + B) + \cos(A - B)]$$

$$\therefore \cos 5x \cos x = \frac{1}{2}[\cos(5x + x) + \cos(5x - x)]$$

$$= \frac{1}{2}[\cos 6x + \cos 4x]$$

(ii) $\sin A + \sin B = 2 \sin\frac{A + B}{2} \cos\frac{A - B}{2}$

$$\therefore \sin 6x + \sin 4x = 2 \sin\frac{6x + 4x}{2} \cos\frac{6x - 4x}{2}$$

$$= 2 \sin 5x \cos x$$

Exercise 7.10

1. A and B are acute angles such that $\cos A = \frac{3}{5}$ and $\cos B = \frac{12}{13}$.

   Find the value of:

   (i) $\sin A$
   (ii) $\tan A$
   (iii) $\sin B$
   (iv) $\tan B$
   (v) $\cos(A + B)$
   (vi) $\tan(A + B)$

2. Write the following in surd form:

(i) $\sin 15°$ (v) $\sin 165°$

(ii) $\sin 105°$ (vi) $\cos 240°$

(iii) $\cos 75°$ (vii) $\sin 75°$

(iv) $\tan 75°$ (viii) $\sec 120°$

(ix) $\cos 25° \cos 20° - \sin 25° \sin 20°$

(x) $\sin 12° \cos 18° + \cos 12° \sin 18°$

3. A and B are acute angles such that $\tan A = \frac{3}{4}$ and $\tan B = \frac{1}{4}$. Find $\tan(A + B)$.

4. If $\tan A = \frac{1}{5}$, find the value of $\tan 2A$.

5. Verify that $\sin\left(\frac{\pi}{2} - A\right) = \cos A$.

6. Verify that $\sin(180° - A) = \sin A$.

7. (i) If $\tan\alpha = \frac{1}{2}$ and $\tan\beta = \frac{3}{8}$, find $\tan(\alpha + \beta)$.

(ii) If $\tan(\alpha + \beta + \lambda) = -27$, find λ, given that λ is acute.

8. If $\tan 2A = \frac{4}{3}$, find two possible values for $\tan A$.

9. If $\cos 2A = \frac{12}{13}$, find two possible values of $\tan A$.

10. Prove that $\tan(A + B) = \frac{\tan A + \tan B}{1 - \tan A \tan B}$.

11. If $\tan A = \frac{1}{4}$ and $\tan(A + B) = 1$, find $\tan B$.

12. If $\tan A = \frac{1}{3}$, $\tan B = \frac{1}{5}$, $\tan C = \frac{1}{7}$ and $\tan D = \frac{1}{8}$, find:

(i) $\tan(A + B)$

(ii) $\tan(C + D)$

(iii) $\tan(A + B + C + D)$

Deduce that $A + B + C + D = \frac{\pi}{4}$.

13. Prove that $\tan 3\theta = \dfrac{3\tan\theta - \tan^3\theta}{1 - 3\tan^2\theta}$.

14. Write the following as sums:

(i) $2\sin 6\theta \cos 2\theta$

(ii) $\cos 3\theta \cos\theta$

(iii) $\cos 3A \sin A$

(iv) $\sin 5x \sin 3x$

(v) $2\cos 4\theta \cos\theta$

(vi) $\sin 6x \cos 2x$

(vii) $-2\sin 4\theta \sin\theta$

(viii) $2\cos\frac{1}{2}\theta \sin\frac{1}{2}\theta$

(ix) $\cos x \sin 5x$

(x) $2\cos\left(x + \frac{\pi}{2}\right)\cos\left(x - \frac{\pi}{2}\right)$

15. Find the exact value of:

(i) $\cos 75° \cos 15°$

(ii) $2\sin 75° \sin 105°$

16. Write the following as products:

(i) $\sin 4x + \sin 2x$

(ii) $\sin 3x - \sin x$

(iii) $\cos 9x + \cos 3x$

(iv) $\sin x + \sin 3x$

(v) $\sin 2x - \sin x$

(vi) $\sin 10x + \sin 2x$

(vii) $\cos 8\theta - \cos 2\theta$

(viii) $\cos x - \cos 5x$

(ix) $\cos(30° + x) - \cos(30° - x)$

(x) $\sin(x + 60°) + \sin(x - 60°)$

17. Find the exact value of:

(i) $\sin 75° - \sin 15°$

(ii) $\cos 75° - \cos 15°$

18. Show that $\dfrac{\cos 80° - \cos 40°}{\sin 80° - \sin 40°} = -\sqrt{3}$.

19. Prove that $\dfrac{\sin 3A + \sin A}{\cos 3A + \cos A} = \tan 2A$.

20. Prove that $\sin 3\theta + \sin\theta = 4\sin\theta\cos^2\theta$.

Revision Exercises

1. Find the value of x and complete the tables below.

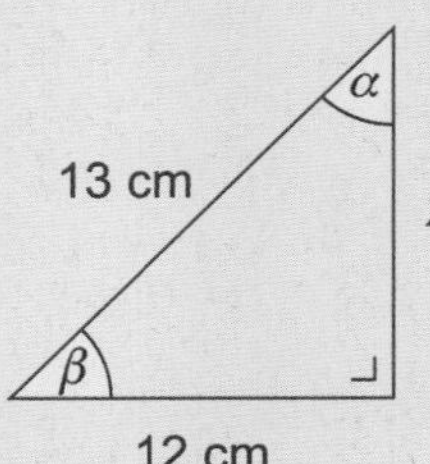

$\sin\alpha$	$\cos\alpha$	$\tan\alpha$

$\sin\beta$	$\cos\beta$	$\tan\beta$

2. Copy and complete the table.

Degrees	90°	180°		360°	120°	45°	
Radians			$\frac{3\pi}{2}$				$\frac{\pi}{3}$

3. Convert to degrees:

(i) $\frac{6\pi}{5}$ rads (ii) $\frac{2\pi}{10}$ rads (iii) $\frac{5\pi}{3}$ rads

4. Convert to radians:

(i) 150° (ii) 288° (iii) 108°

5. A department store has the space $PQRS$ available for two new departments. The store manager provides the following measurements to two potential clients.

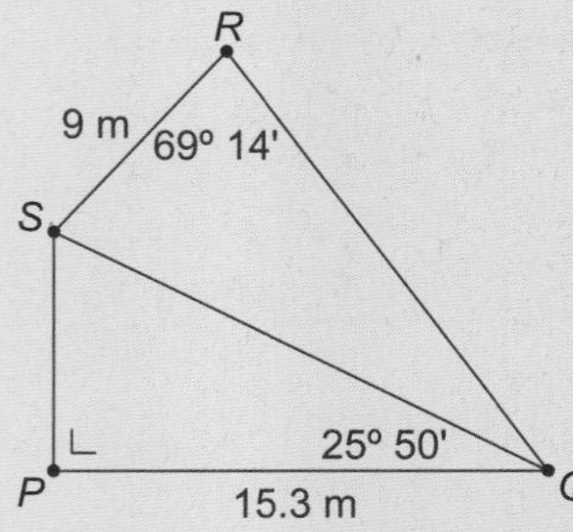

More details are required before a decision can be reached by the clients. You have been asked to provide the following:

(i) Find $|SQ|$ correct to the nearest metre.

(ii) Find $|\angle SQR|$ to the nearest degree.

6. A triangle has sides of lengths a, b and c. The angle opposite the side of length a is A. Prove the following:

(i) $a^2 = b^2 + c^2 - 2bc \cos A$

(ii) $\dfrac{a}{\sin A} = \dfrac{b}{\sin B} = \dfrac{c}{\sin C}$

7. (a) Study the unit circle below. Then complete the table in terms of P and Q.

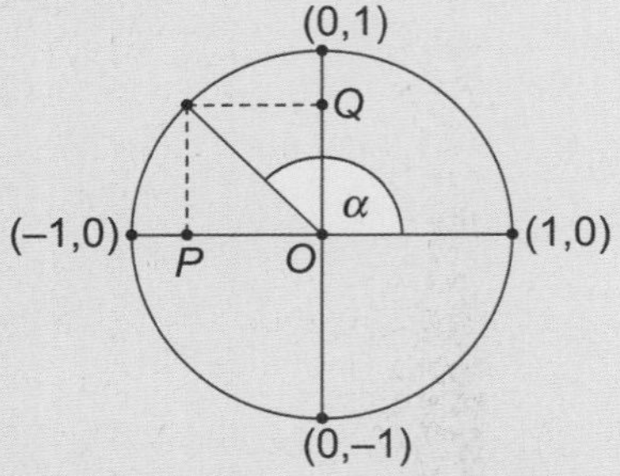

$\sin\alpha$	$\cos\alpha$	$\tan\alpha$

(b)

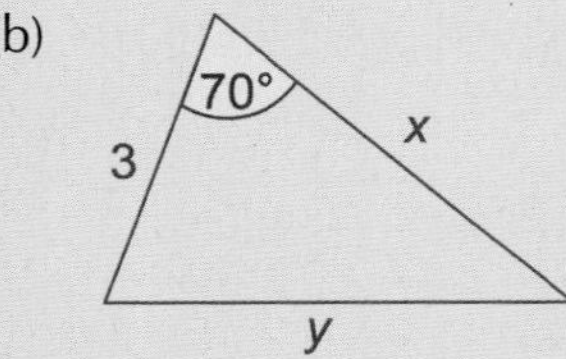

The area of the triangle shown above is 15 square units.

(i) Find the value of x, correct to two decimal places.

(ii) Using the Cosine Rule, find the value of y.

8. Write down the values of each of the following. Give your answer in surd form where appropriate.

(i) $\sin 45°$ (iv) $\sin 102°$

(ii) $\cos \frac{11\pi}{6}$ (v) $\cos \frac{6\pi}{7}$

(iii) $\tan 94°$

9. Sketch the graphs of the following functions for $-2\pi \leqslant x \leqslant 2\pi$:

(i) $\cos x$ (iii) $2 \cos x$ (v) $3 \sin 2x$

(ii) $\sin x$ (iv) $\tan 2x$ (vi) $2 \cos 3x$

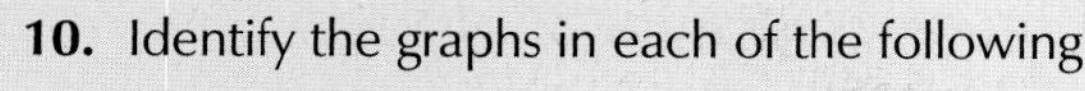

10. Identify the graphs in each of the following.

(i)

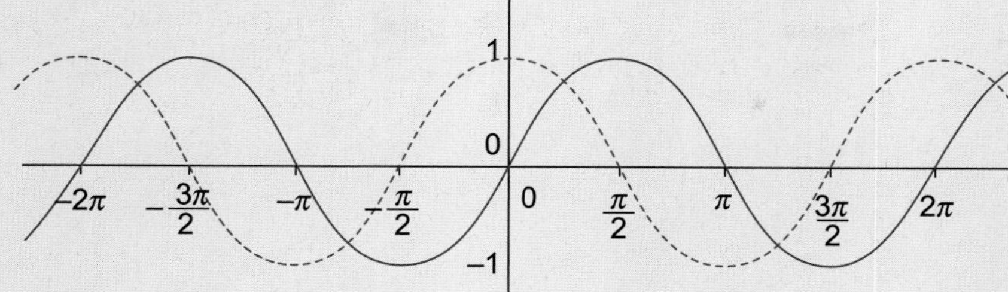

(ii)

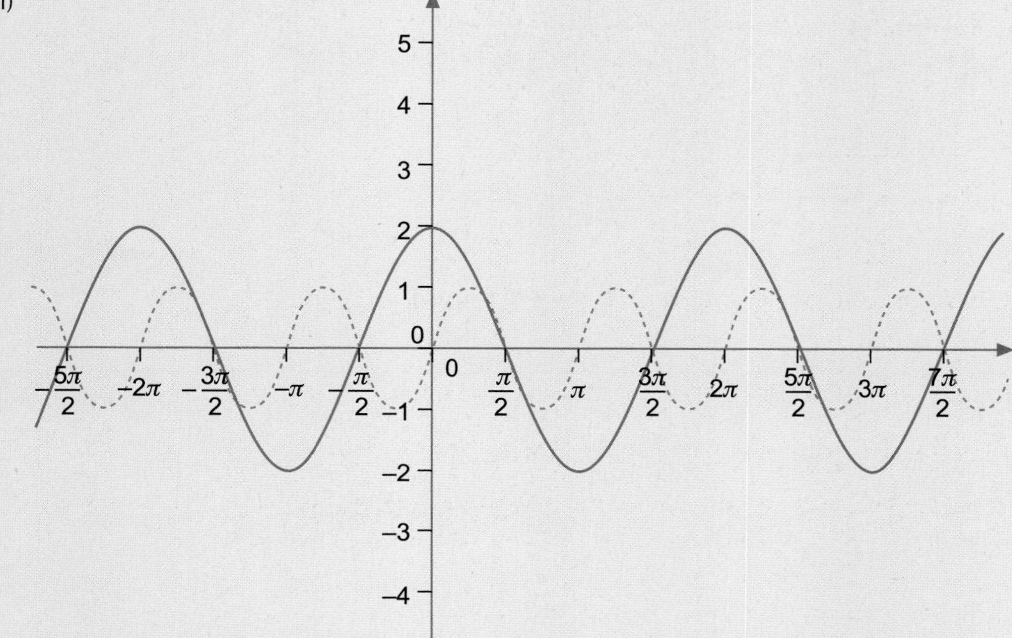

(iii)

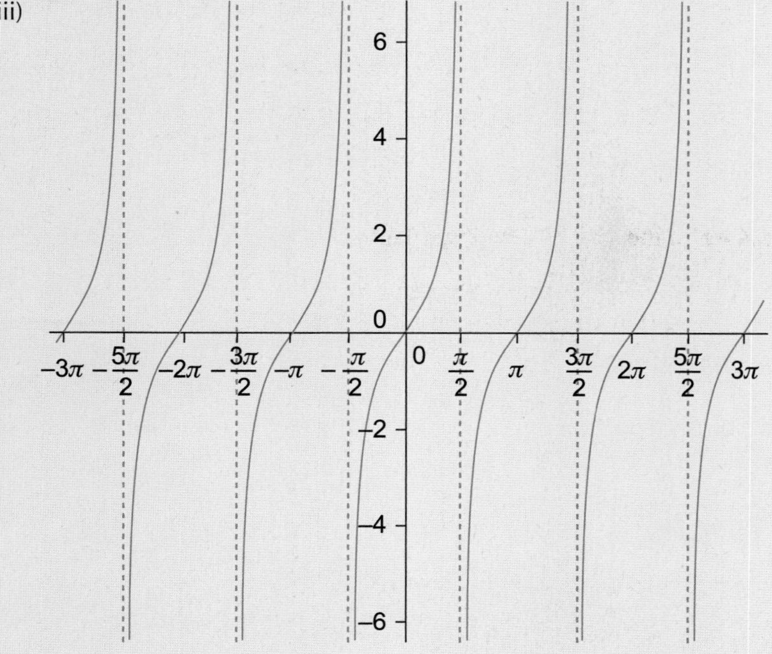

(iv)

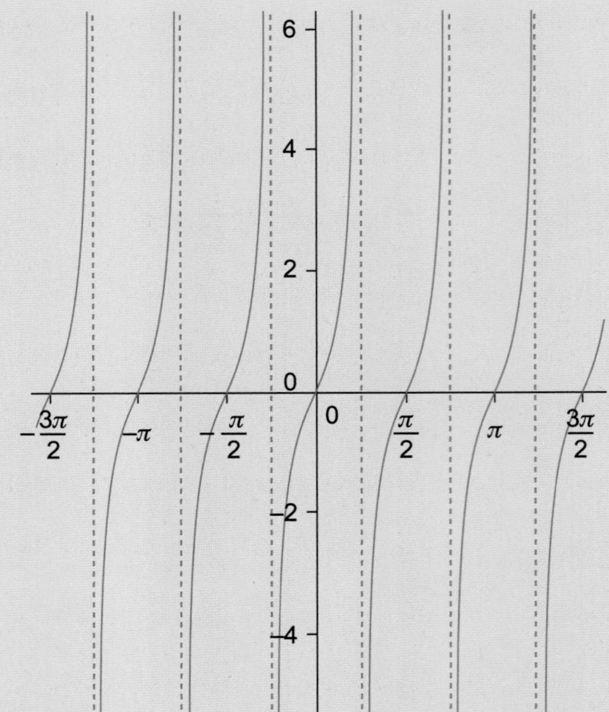

11. Prove that $\cos 2A = \cos^2 A - \sin^2 A$.

12. Prove that $\tan (A + B) = \dfrac{\tan A + \tan B}{1 - \tan A \tan B}$.

13. Show that $\dfrac{\sin 2A}{1 + \cos 2A} = \tan A$.

14. Show that $(\cos A + \sin A)^2 = 1 + \sin 2A$.

15. Using $\cos 2A = \cos^2 A - \sin^2 A$, or otherwise, prove that $\cos^2 A = \frac{1}{2}(1 + \cos 2A)$.

16. (i) Prove that $\cos 2A = \cos^2 A - \sin^2 A$.

(ii) Deduce that $\cos 2A = 2\cos^2 A - 1$.

17. Express each of the following as a product of two trigonometric functions:

(i) $\sin 5X - \sin 3X$

(ii) $\cos X + \cos 7X$

18. Find the exact value of $\cos 37.5° \sin 7.5°$.

19. Copy and complete the table below (entries in surd form, where necessary).

A	30°	45°	60°
$\sin A$			
$\cos A$			
$\tan A$			

Using the given table, solve the following equations for A, B, C and D:

(i) $\sin A = \cos 60°$

(ii) $\tan B = 1$

(iii) $\sin C = \cos C$

(iv) $\sin D \cos 30° = \frac{3}{4}$

20. (a) Find, correct to one decimal place, the two values of A where $0° \leqslant A \leqslant 360°$.

(i) $5 \sin A = 2$

(ii) $7 \cos A + 3 = 0$

(iii) $2 \tan A + 7 = 0$

(iv) $\cos A = -\frac{1}{2}$

(v) $2 \sin A - \sqrt{3} = 0$

(b) Solve the equations:

(i) $\cos 3\theta = \frac{1}{2}, \theta \in R$ (where θ is in radians)

(ii) $\sin 2\theta = \frac{\sqrt{3}}{2}, \theta \in R$

21. Nicola and Carol took part in a bootcamp. There were two different ramps, A and B, side by side on the obstacle course.

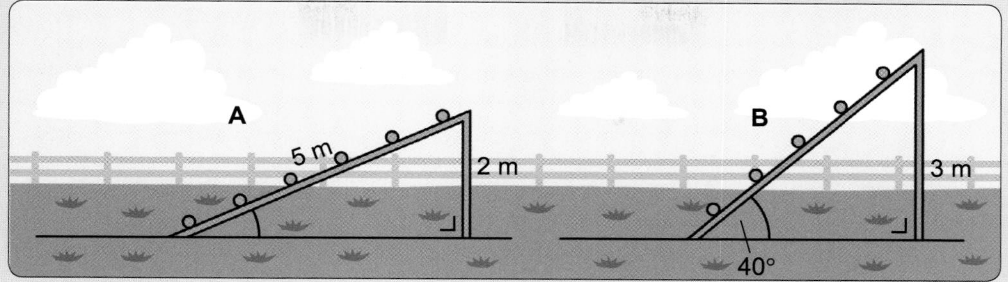

Carol ran up ramp A and Nicola ran up ramp B.

(i) What is the angle of elevation of ramp A (to the nearest degree)?

(ii) Who ran the furthest?

22. 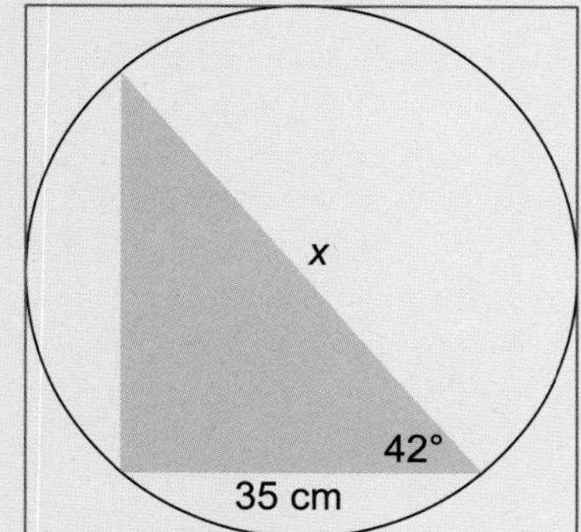

Given that x is the diameter, find:

(i) The area of the circle that is not covered by the triangle

(ii) The area of the square that is not covered by the circle and triangle

23. The diagram shows a blueprint for a house. All measurements are in metres.

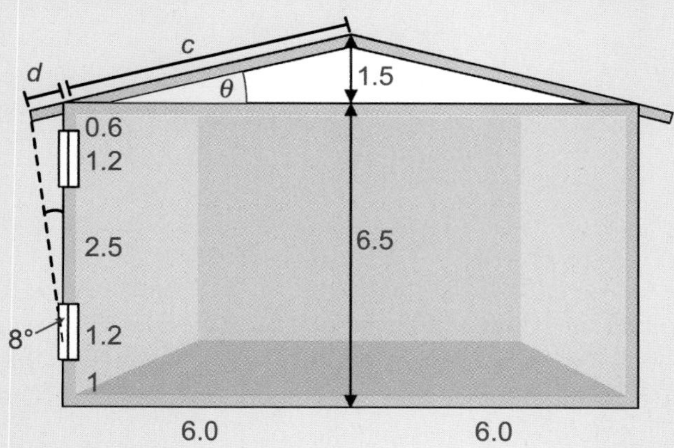

(i) Find the pitch of the roof (θ).

(ii) Find the sloping distance c, from the top of the roof to the top of the walls.

(iii) The overhang of the roof is a distance d. The angle between the base of the bottom window and the overhang is 8°.

Find the length of the overhang, d.

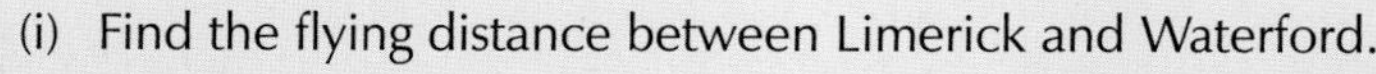

24. A helicopter pilot has plotted her route on a map. She plans to fly from Dublin to Limerick, from Limerick on to Waterford and, finally, from Waterford back to Dublin. She knows that the flying distance between Dublin and Limerick is 176 km and that the distance between Waterford and Dublin is 135 km. She also has the measure of one angle on the triangular route.

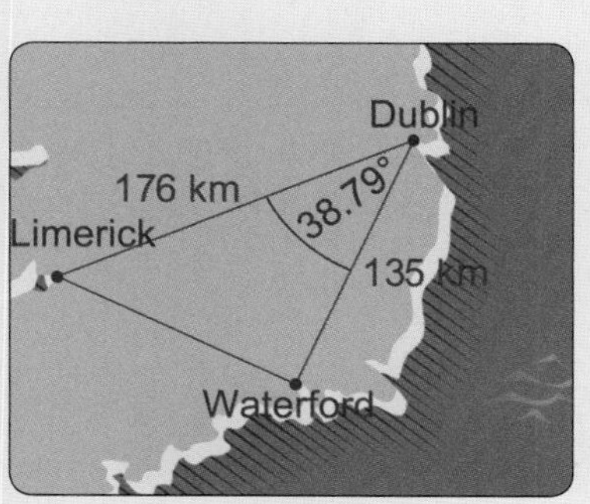

(i) Find the flying distance between Limerick and Waterford.

(ii) If the helicopter has an average flying speed of 280 km/h and the pilot stops over in Limerick for 1 hour and in Waterford for 2 hours, find to the nearest minute the time taken for the pilot to complete the trip.

(iii) An Internet route planner gives the road distance between Limerick and Waterford as 127 km. As the helicopter takes off from Dublin, a driver begins his journey from Limerick to Waterford travelling at an average speed of 50 km/h. He has scheduled a meeting with the pilot. What is the maximum time the meeting can last if the pilot has to stick with the 2-hour stopover?

(iv) Suggest another method for finding the flying distance between Limerick and Waterford.

25. 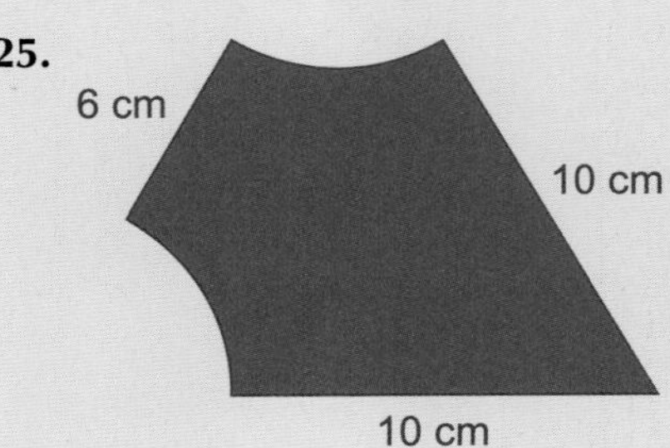

This is the new company logo for ABC Ltd. The logo is made by removing two equal sectors from an equilateral triangle. The sectors have their centres, respectively, on two vertices of the equilateral triangle. On the logo there are three straight edges, two measuring 10 cm and one measuring 6 cm.

(i) Find the radius length of one of the sectors that have been removed.

(ii) Find the area of the sectors that were removed.

(iii) Find the area of the equilateral triangle from which the logo has been taken.

(iv) Find the area of the logo.

26. *QRST* is a vertical rectangular wall of height h on level ground. P is a point on the ground in front of the wall.

The angle of elevation of R from P is θ, and the angle of elevation of S from P is 2θ. $|PQ| = 3|PT|$.

Find the measure of θ.

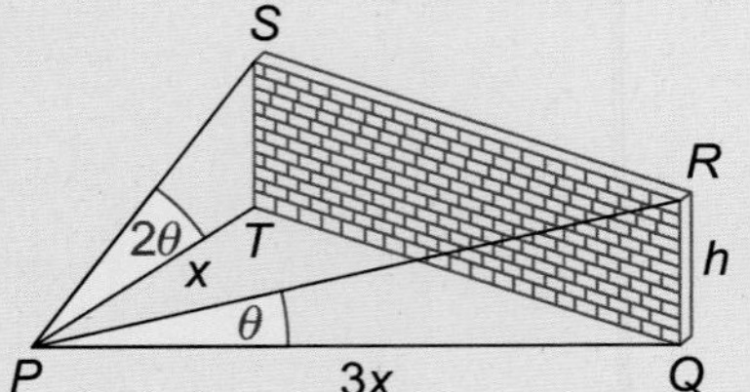

27. A rectangular swimming-pool has the dimensions 18 m × 6 m × 1.8 m as shown.

(i) Find the length of the diagonal [*EB*].

(ii) What is the angle formed between the bottom of the pool and the line [*EB*]?

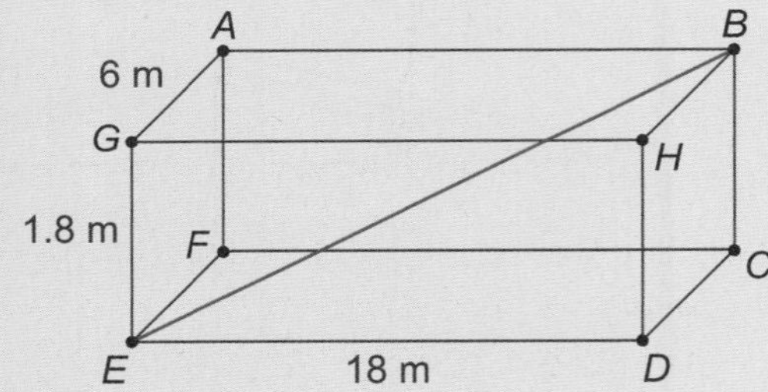

28. A Fifth Year maths class has been asked to find the width and height of a soccer goal. The students are equipped with just a clinometer. Any measurements have to be taken from the point P. The teacher has already given the class the distance from P to the foot of both uprights and also the measure of the angle at P, formed by the two uprights and the point P.

The students decide to measure the angle of elevation from P to the top of one of the uprights. They find the angle of elevation to be 22°.

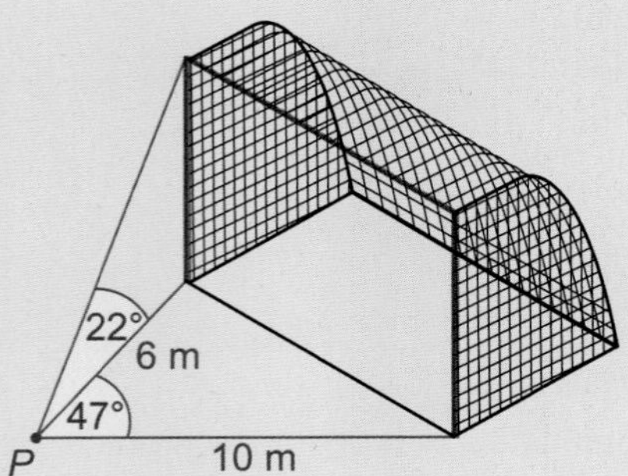

(i) Find the width of the goal. Give your answer to two decimal places.

(ii) Find the height of the goal. Give your answer to the nearest centimetre.

(iii) If the class had chosen to measure the angle of elevation of the other upright from P, then what measurement should they have found? Give your answer to the nearest degree.

29. Paul is waterskiing on a calm, flat river. His body forms a 55° angle with the surface of the water. The angle formed between his legs and the ski is 105°. From the foot-hold to the top of the ski measures 0.7 m. Paul is 1.6 m tall.

(i) Estimate the distance from the top of Paul's head to the surface of the water.

(ii) Estimate the distance from the top of Paul's head to the top of the ski.

30. P, Q and R are three points on horizontal ground. $[SR]$ is a vertical pole of height h metres.

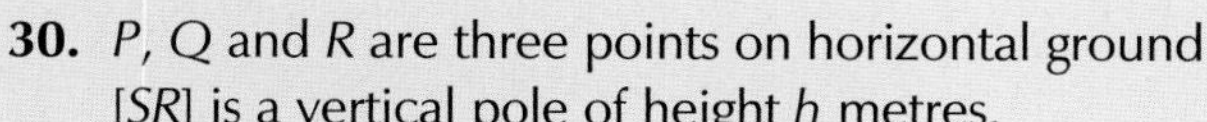

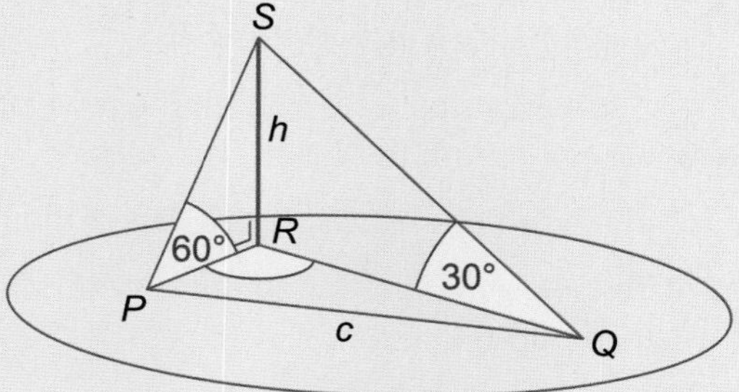

The angle of elevation of S from P is 60°, and the angle of elevation of S from Q is 30°. $|PQ| = C$ metres.

Given that $3c^2 = 13h^2$, find $|\angle PRQ|$.

31. Niall and Barry buy a half cylinder pop-up tent for the Oxegen music festival. The dimensions of the tent are as shown.

(i) What is the height of the tent?

(ii) What is the length of the diagonal $[AB]$?

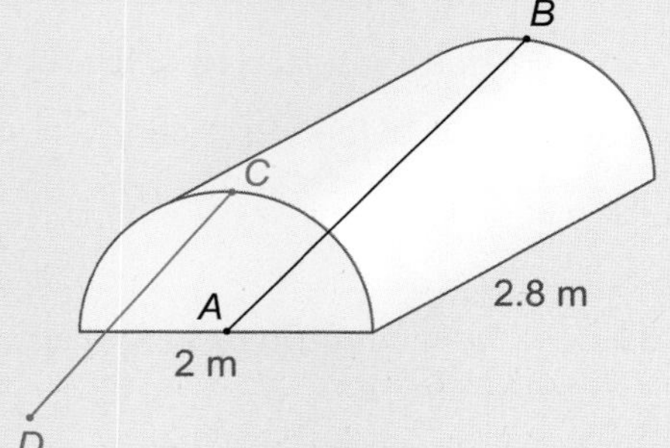

During the weekend the tent is damaged. Niall uses the laces from his runners to form a support. He connects the end of his laces to point C and pegs it to point D as shown. Points B and C are exactly in the middle of the tent.

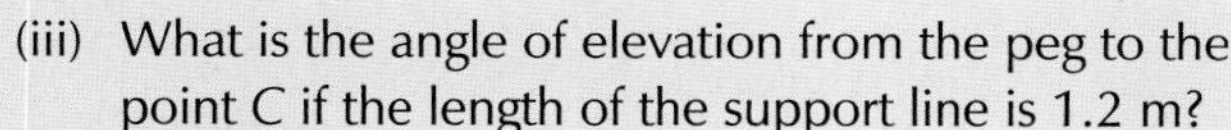

(iii) What is the angle of elevation from the peg to the point C if the length of the support line is 1.2 m?

32. Two surveyers want to find the height of an electricity pylon. There is a fence around the pylon that they cannot cross for safety reasons. The ground is inclined at an angle. They have a clinometer and a 100 metre tape measure. They have already used the clinometer to determine that the ground is inclined at 10° to the horizontal.

(a) Explain how they could find the height of the pylon.

Your answer should be illustrated on the diagram. Show the points where you think they should take measurements, and write down clearly what measurements they should take.

(b) Write down possible values for the measurements taken, and use them to show how to find the height of the pylon. (That is, find the height of the pylon using your measurements, and showing your work.)

SEC Project Maths Sample Paper 2, Leaving Certificate Higher Level, 2010

33. Ahmad is sitting beside the classroom window and sees a bird in a tree. The angle of elevation to the bird is 36°. Ahmad is 1.5 m tall when sitting at his desk. He is on the second floor, which is 10 m above the ground. The base of the tree is 16 m from the wall of the building. At what height from the ground is the bird in the tree?

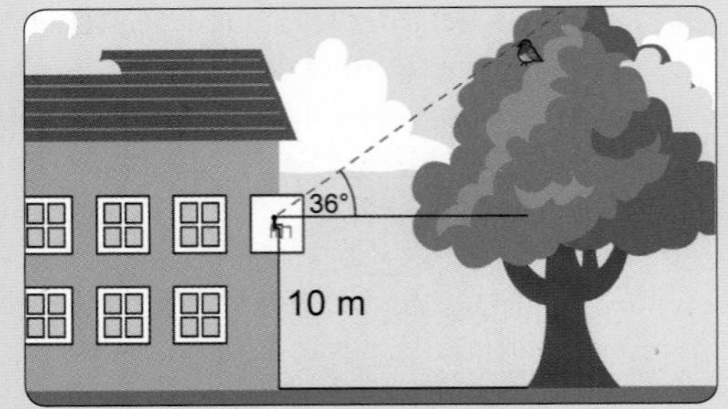

34. A tower that is part of a hotel has a square base of side 4 m and a roof in the form of a pyramid. The owners plan to cover the roof with copper. To find the amount of copper needed, they need to know the total area of the roof.

A surveyor stands 10 m from the tower, measured horizontally, and makes observations of angles of elevation from the point *O* as follows:

The angle of elevation of the top of the roof is 46°.

The angle of elevation of the closest point at the bottom of the roof is 42°.

The angle of depression of the closest point at the bottom of the tower is 9°.

O

10 m

(i) Find the vertical height of the roof.

(ii) Find the total area of the roof.

(iii) If all of the angles observed are subject to a possible error of ±1°, find the range of possible areas for the roof.

SEC Project Maths Paper 2, Leaving Certificate Higher Level, 2011

35. The Titanium Building in Santiago, Chile, was completed in 2009 and is the third tallest building in South America.

Two engineering students from the Universidad de Chile, Fernando and Alejandra, were asked to use a clinometer, tape measure and calculator to estimate the height of the tower to the nearest centimetre, as the first part of their final exam in trigonometry.

They decided to take three measurements at different times on the same day and to use the average of these as their estimate of the buildings's height.

The method they decided to use was to measure the length of the shadow of the building on the ground in the afternoon sun, along with the corresponding angle of inclination from the end of the shadow to the top of the building. The building is situated in a very flat part of the city, so the two students were able to neglect changes in elevation as they took their measurements.

Fernando measured the shadow lengths while Alejandra measured the angles of inclination. These measurements are presented here.

Time	Shadow length	Angle of inclination
12:07	56.38 m	73.68°
13:25	72.07 m	69.47°
15:56	164.29 m	49.52°

Fernando determined that Alejandra held the clinometer 1.62 m above the ground when taking each clinometer reading.

(a) Draw a suitable diagram representing the taking of the first reading. (The diagram should include the unknown building height, the measured shadow length, the measured angle of inclination and the measured height above the ground of the clinometer.)

(b) With the aid of this diagram, calculate the first estimate of the building's height of the two students. Give your answer in metres, correct to four decimal places.

(c) Calculate the second estimate and the third estimate of the building's height. Give your answers in metres, correct to four decimal places.

(d) What was the final estimate of the building's height that the students arrived at? Give your answer correct to the nearest centimetre.

The second part of the two students' trigonometry exam involved investigating the oscillation of the range of the tide at the nearby port of Valparaiso on the Pacific coast.

The range of a tide is defined as the difference between high and low tides. For example, if on a particular day, the high tide is measured as 4.2 m and the low tide as 1.7 m, then the tidal range for that day is 4.2 – 1.7 = 2.5 m.

The students were presented with the following table showing the recorded tidal ranges for a three-week period (tidal range is given in metres):

Day	Tidal range	Day	Tidal range	Day	Tidal range
1	4.3	8	5.7	15	3.7
2	3.8	9	6.3	16	3.0
3	3.3	10	6.6	17	2.8
4	3.0	11	6.5	18	3.1
5	3.2	12	6.0	19	3.7
6	4.0	13	5.5	20	4.3
7	4.9	14	4.6	21	4.7

(e) The students were then asked to draw a graph of Tidal Range (on the vertical axis) against Day (on the horizontal axis). Draw the graph that the students would have drawn.

(f) Fernando estimates the period of the above graphed function to be 13 days. Explain how you think he came to this conclusion.

(g) What estimate do you think the students got for the range of the above graphed function? Explain how you arrived at your answer.

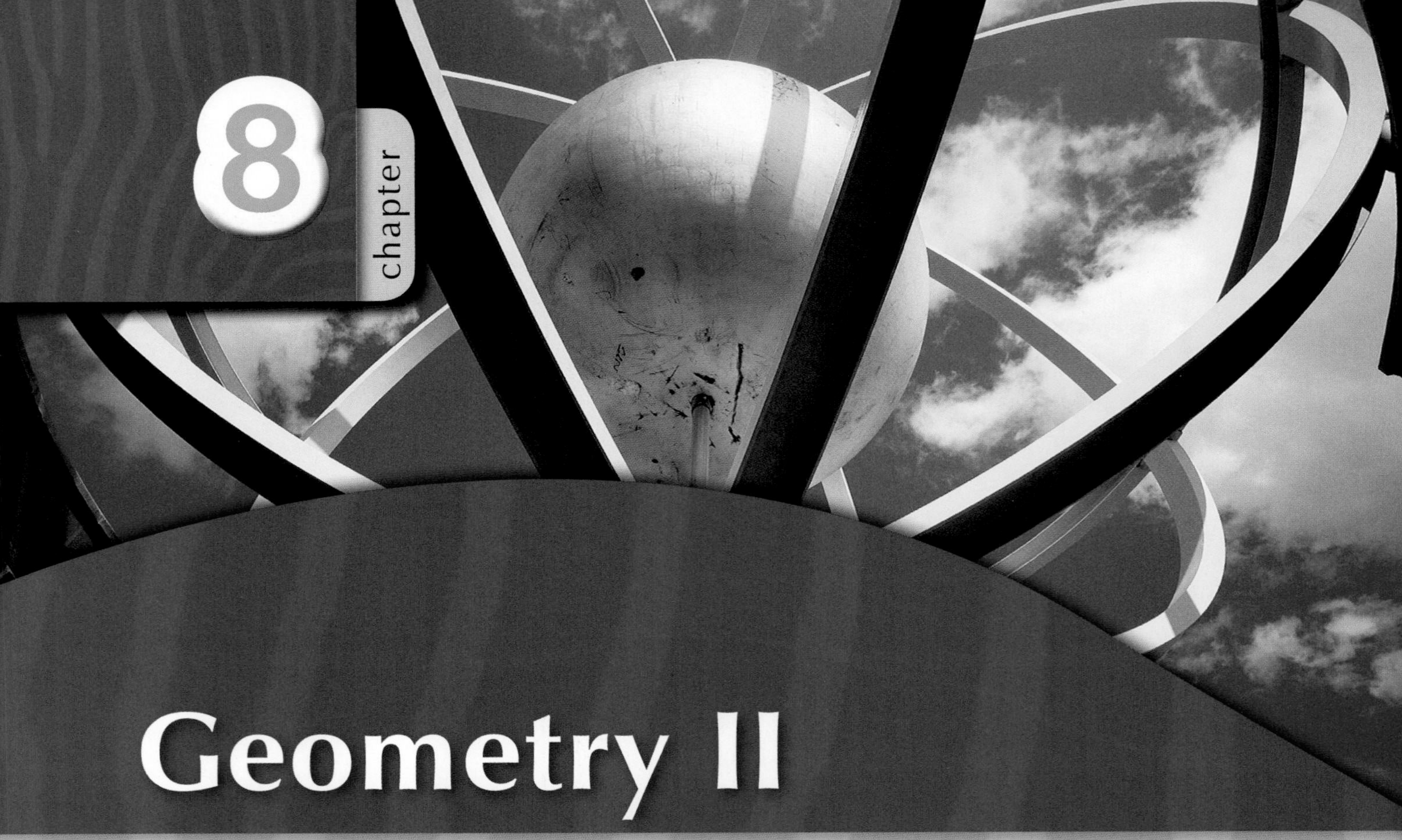

Geometry II

Learning Outcomes

In this chapter you will learn:

- Theorem 13. If two triangles are similar, then their sides are proportional, in order.
- Theorem 14. The theorem of Pythagoras: In a right-angled triangle the square of the hypotenuse is the sum of the squares of the other two sides.
- Theorem 15. If the square of one side of a triangle is the sum of the squares of the other two sides, then the angle opposite the first side is a right angle.
- Theorem 16. For a triangle, base times height does not depend on the choice of base.
- Theorem 17. A diagonal of a parallelogram bisects the area.
- Theorem 18. The area of a parallelogram is the base times the height.
- Theorem 19. The angle at the centre of a circle standing on a given arc is twice the angle at any point of the circle standing on the same arc.
- Corollary 2. All angles at points of a circle, standing on the same arc, are equal.
- Corollary 5. If $ABCD$ is a cyclic quadrilateral, then opposite angles sum to 180°.
- Corollary 3. Each angle in a semicircle is a right angle.
- Corollary 4. If the angle standing on a chord $[BC]$ at some point of the circle is a right angle, then $[BC]$ is a diameter.
- Theorem 20. Each tangent is perpendicular to the radius that goes to the point of contact. If P lies on s, and a line l is perpendicular to the radius to P, then l is a tangent to s.
- Corollary 6. If two circles intersect at one point only, then the two centres and the point of contact are collinear.
- Theorem 21. (i) The perpendicular from the centre to a chord bisects the chord. (ii) The perpendicular bisector of a chord passes through the centre.
- The following terms related to logic and deductive reasoning: *is equivalent to; if and only if; proof by contradiction*

8.1 SIMILAR TRIANGLES

An important relationship that two triangles can have is that of similarity.

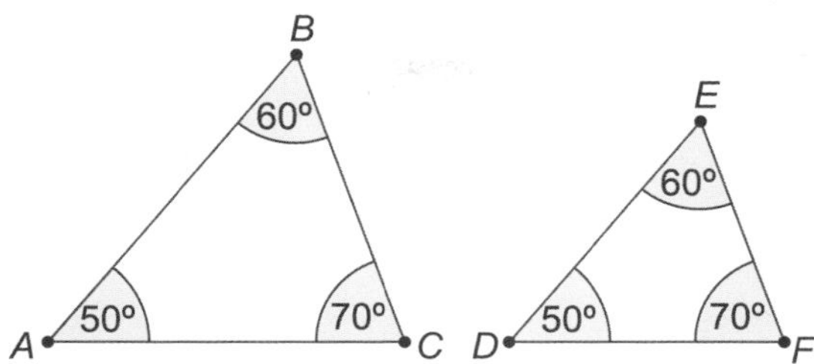

In **similar** or **equiangular** triangles, all three angles in one triangle have the same measurement as the corresponding three angles in the other triangle.

As our investigations have shown, the sides of two similar triangles have a special property.

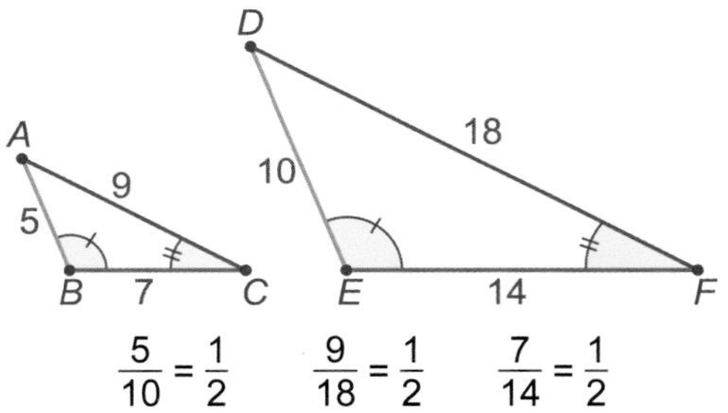

$$\frac{5}{10} = \frac{1}{2} \qquad \frac{9}{18} = \frac{1}{2} \qquad \frac{7}{14} = \frac{1}{2}$$

It is clear that when we have two similar triangles:

The corresponding sides of similar triangles are in the same ratio.

This now allows us to state the following theorem:

Theorem 13 (Formal proof in Appendix)

If two triangles are similar, then their sides are proportional, in order.

In the following similar triangles, the corresponding sides are proportional:

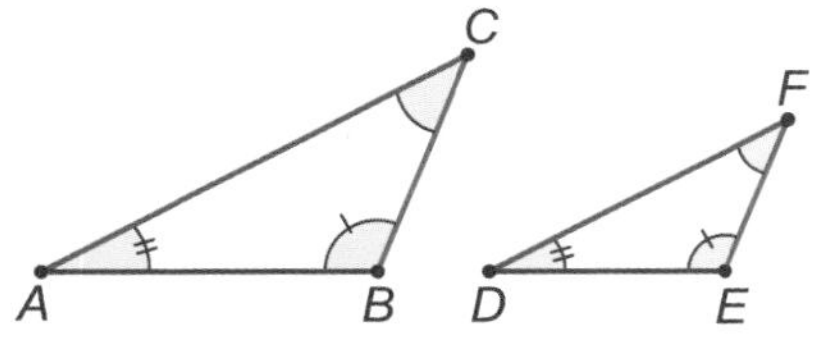

FORMULA

$$\frac{|AB|}{|DE|} = \frac{|AC|}{|DF|} = \frac{|BC|}{|EF|} \quad \text{or} \quad \frac{|DE|}{|AB|} = \frac{|DF|}{|AC|} = \frac{|EF|}{|BC|}$$

YOU SHOULD REMEMBER...

- Notation, theorems and axioms from Chapter 5
- How to deal with fractions
- How to prove certain theorems

KEY WORDS

- **Similar triangle**
- **Ratio**
- **Pythagoras**
- **Area**
- **Circle**
- **Diameter**
- **Chord**
- **Perpendicular**
- **Tangent**
- **Proof**

Usually, we only need to use two of the ratios to determine the missing side.

The converse of Theorem 13 also applies:

> If, in any two triangles, the sides (in order) are proportional,
> i.e. if $\frac{|AB|}{|DE|} = \frac{|AC|}{|DF|} = \frac{|BC|}{|EF|}$,
> then the two triangles are similar to each other.

It is also apparent that:

> If a triangle is cut by a line parallel to one of its sides, this line divides the triangle into two similar triangles.

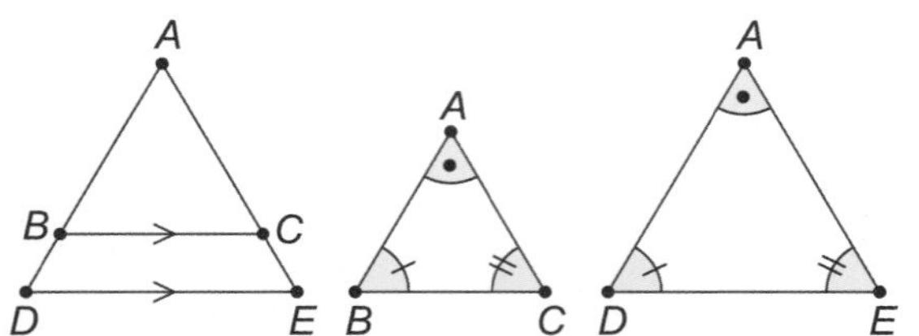

Worked Example 8.1

In the similar triangles shown, find the value of:

(i) $|AC|$ (ii) $|DE|$

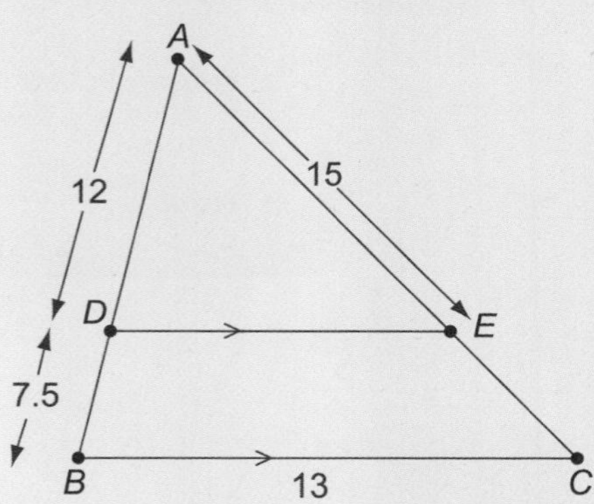

Solution

(i) To find $|AC|$

We can use Theorem 12 to find $|AC|$.

$$\frac{|AC|}{15} = \frac{19.5}{12}$$

$$\therefore 12|AC| = 19.5 \times 15$$

$$\therefore 12|AC| = 292.5$$

$$\therefore |AC| = \frac{292.5}{12}$$

$$\therefore |AC| = 24.375$$

(ii) To find $|DE|$:

It is a good idea to redraw the triangles, but this time into two separate similar triangles.

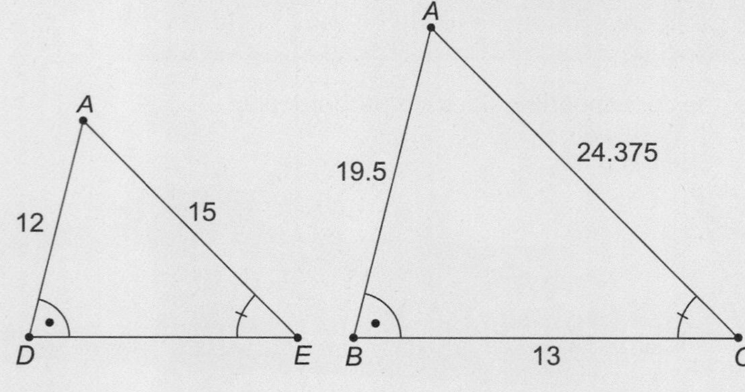

$$\frac{|DE|}{13} = \frac{12}{19.5}$$

$$\therefore 19.5|DE| = 12 \times 13$$

$$\therefore 19.5|DE| = 156$$

$$\therefore |DE| = \frac{156}{19.5}$$

$$\therefore |DE| = 8$$

Exercise 8.1

1. Find the value of x and y in each case.

(i)

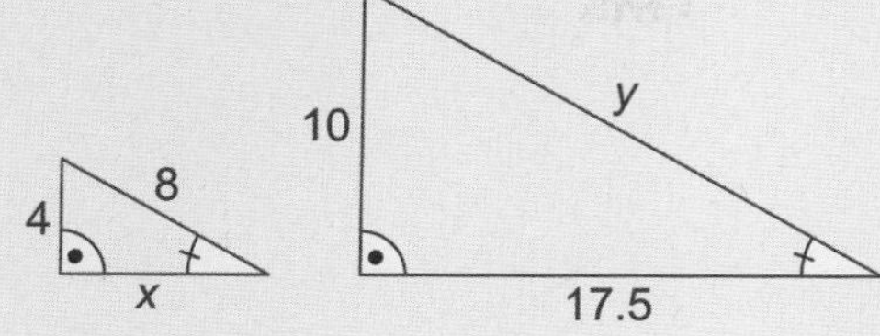

(ii)

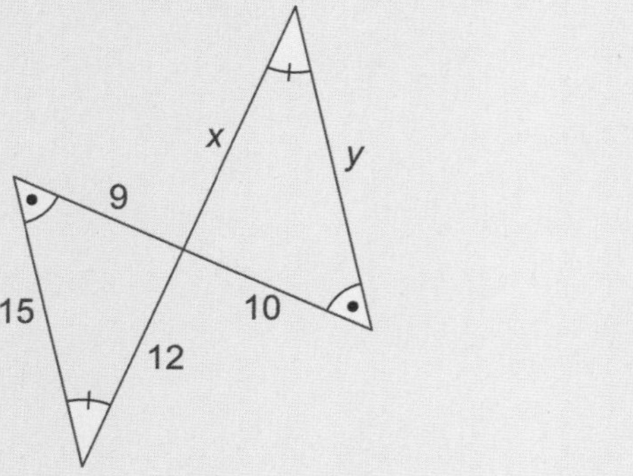

(iii)

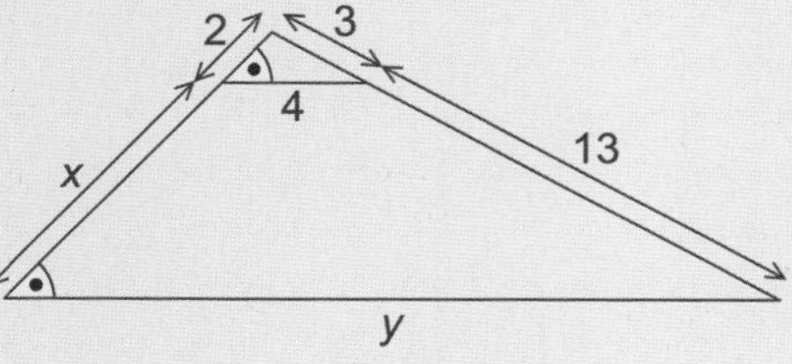

(iv)

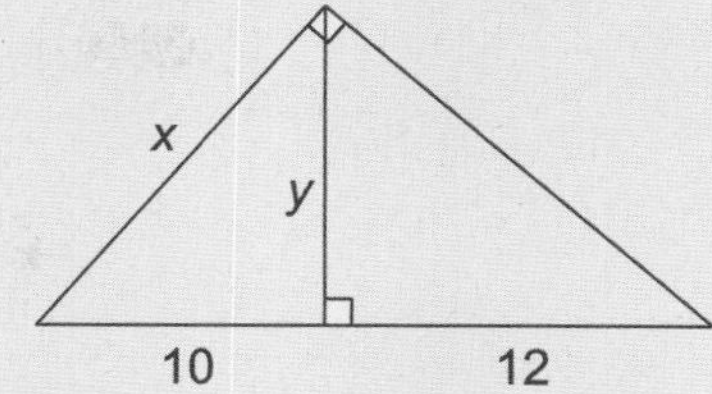

(v)

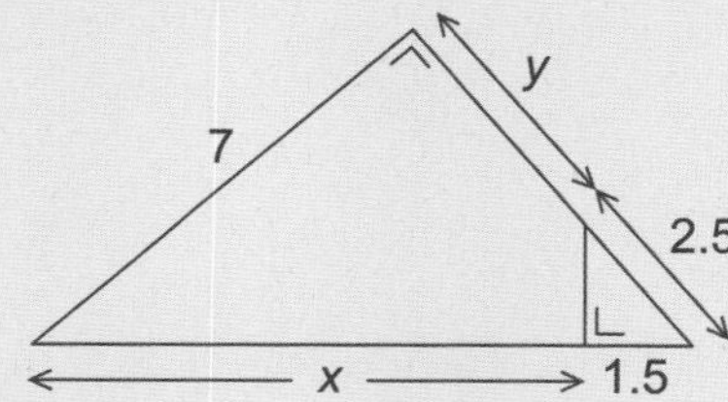

(vi)

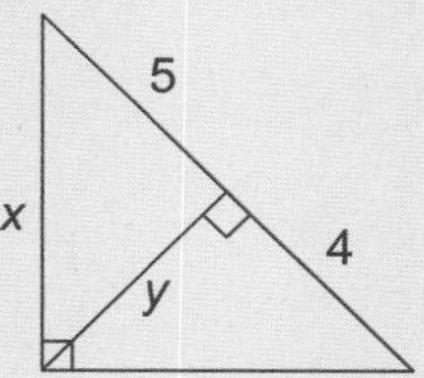

(vii)

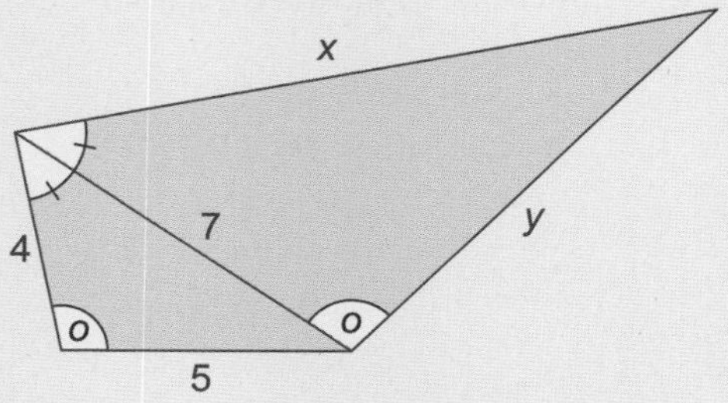

2. Investigate if the following pairs of triangles are similar to each other. Explain your answer.

(i) Is ΔABC similar to ΔXYZ?

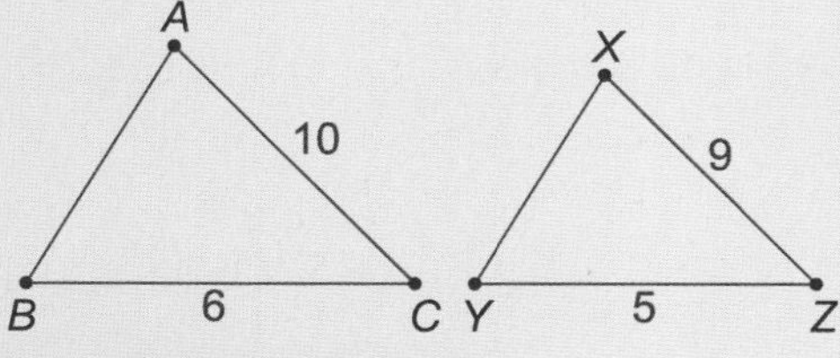

(ii) Is ΔCDE similar to ΔABC?

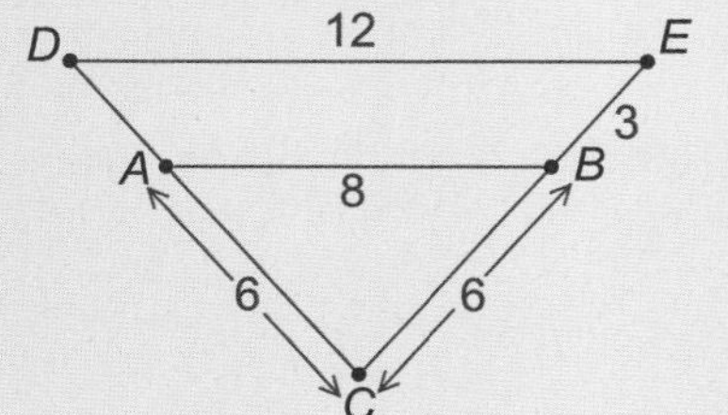

3. In the given diagram, $AB \perp BC$ and $EC \perp ED$.

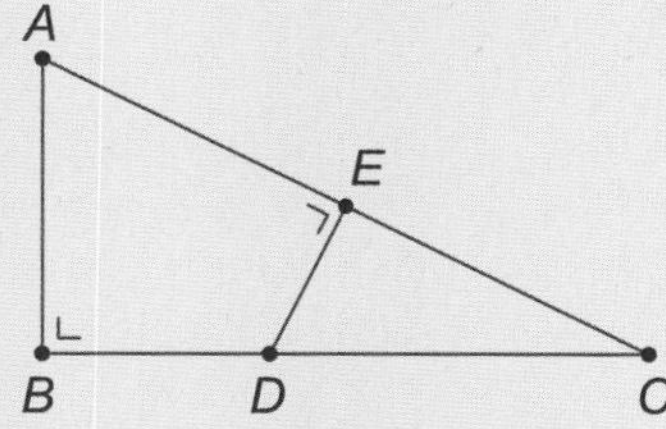

(i) Show that the two triangles ABC and EDC are similar.

Given that $|ED| = 6$, $|AB| = 12$ and $|DC| = 10$, find:

(ii) $|AC|$

(iii) $|BC|$

(iv) $|EC|$

4. The two triangles *ABC* and *DEF* are similar.

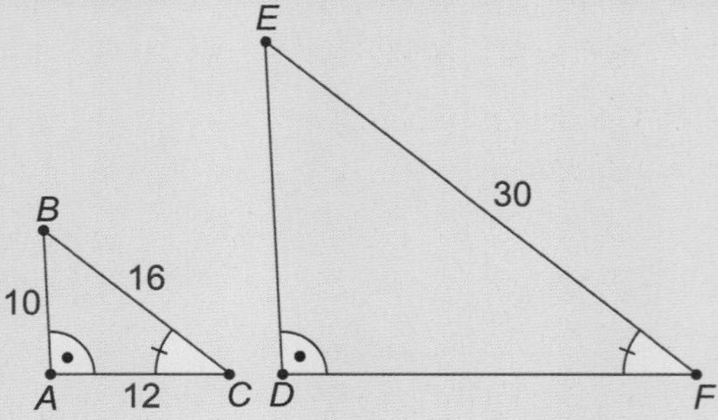

Find:

(i) $|ED|$

(ii) $|DF|$

(iii) The area of ΔABC

(iv) The area of ΔDEF

(v) The perimeter of ΔDEF

What do you notice about the relationship between the perimeters of the two triangles?

5. Consider the following diagram.

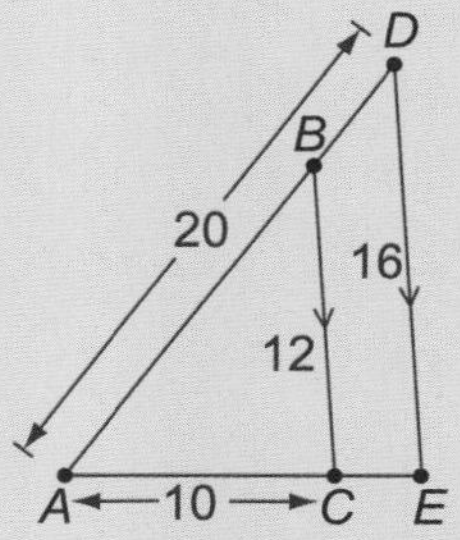

(i) Show that ΔABC and ΔADE are similar.

Find:

(ii) $|AE|$ (iii) $|CE|$ (iv) $|BD|$

6. *ABCD* is a parallelogram.

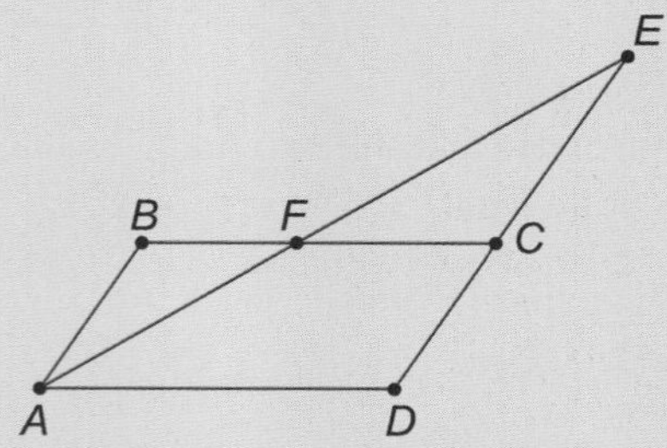

(i) Prove that ΔABF and ΔEFC are similar.

(ii) If $|BF| : |FC| = 3 : 5$, $|DC| = 16$ and $|FE| = 32$, find $|ED|$.

7. In the triangle *PQR*, $ST \parallel PR$, $|QS| = |ST|$, $|TR| = |PS|$ and $|PR| = 26$.

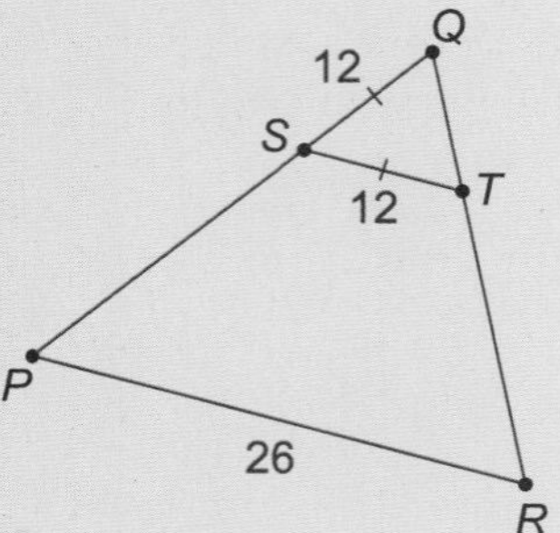

Find:

(i) $|PS|$

(ii) $|QT|$

(iii) $|QR|$

8. In the triangle *DGH*, $EF \parallel GH$.

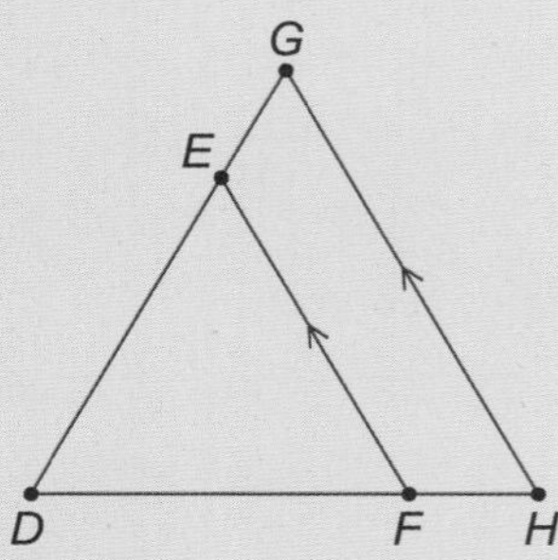

If $|DH| : |FH| = 7 : 3$, find the following ratios:

(i) $|DG| : |EG|$

(ii) $|FH| : |DH|$

(iii) $|EF| : |GH|$

9. In the given diagram, $AB \perp BE$ and $DE \perp BE$.

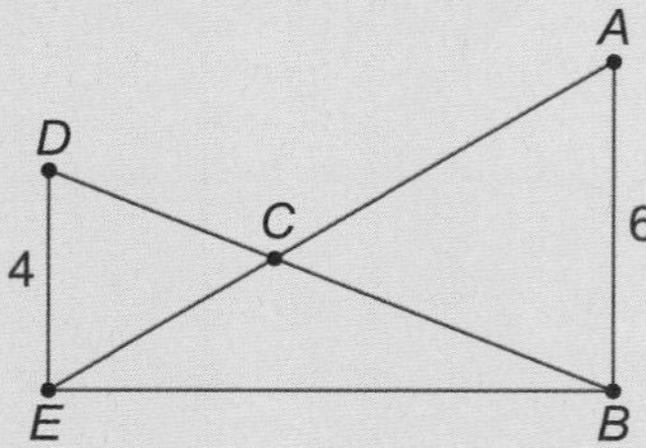

Find the perpendicular distance from *C* to [*EB*].

GEOMETRY II

8.2 THE THEOREM OF PYTHAGORAS

One of the best-known theorems concerns the properties of right-angled triangles.

While this theorem is named after the Greek mathematician Pythagoras of Samos, who lived in the sixth century BCE, it was widely known before then.

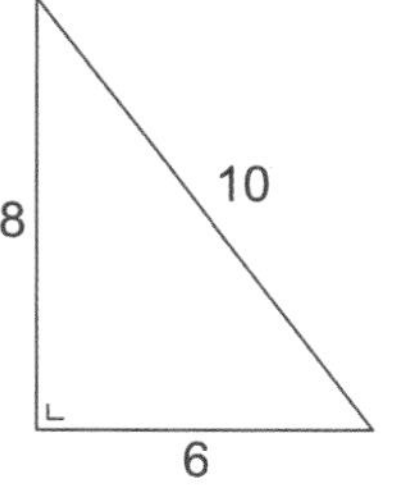

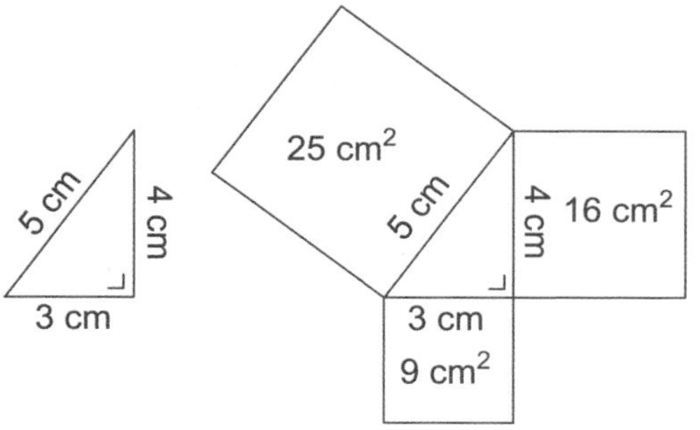

In the given right-angled triangle, it was noticed that $5^2 = 25$ and also that $3^2 + 4^2 = 25$.

We can show that:

Theorem 14: The theorem of Pythagoras (Formal proof in Appendix)
In a right-angled triangle the square of the hypotenuse is the sum of the squares of the other two sides.

This leads to the equation:

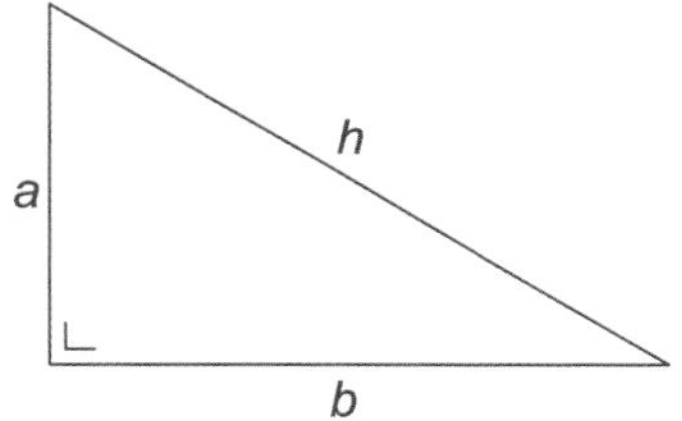

h is the hypotenuse: this is the longest side and also the side opposite the right angle.

We can also show that the angle opposite the longest side is a right angle.

This then leads us to the next theorem based on Pythagoras' theorem:

Theorem 15
If the square of one side of a triangle is the sum of the squares of the other two sides, then the angle opposite the first side is a right angle.

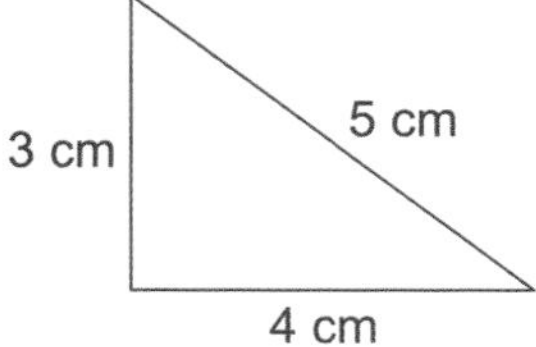

$5^2 = 3^2 + 4^2 \Rightarrow$ The angle opposite the side of 5 cm is a right angle.

GEOMETRY II

Worked Example 8.2

Calculate the value of x and the value of y in the given diagram.

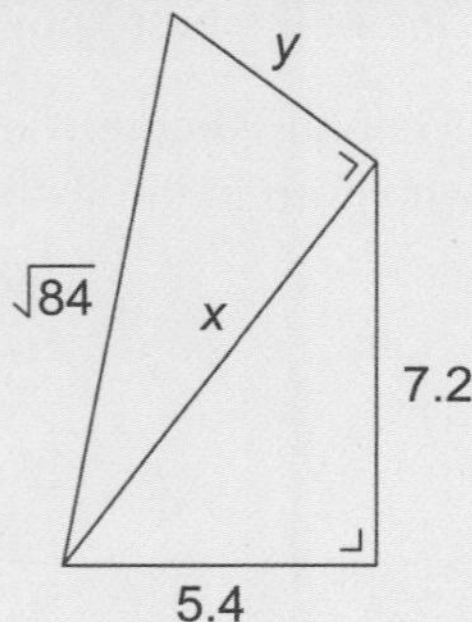

Solution

(i) To calculate x:

Write Pythagoras' theorem.	$h^2 = a^2 + b^2$
Write down the given values.	$a = 5.4$, $b = 7.2$
Put these values into the equation and solve.	$h^2 = (5.4)^2 + (7.2)^2$ $h^2 = 29.16 + 51.84$ $h^2 = 81$
Find the square root.	$h = \sqrt{81}$ $h = 9$
$\therefore x = 9$	

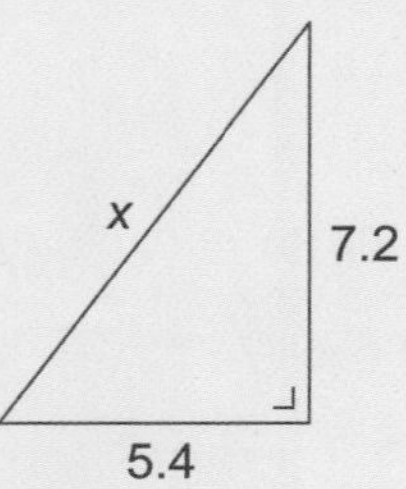

(ii) To calculate y:

Write Pythagoras' theorem.	$h^2 = a^2 + b^2$
Write down the given values.	$h = \sqrt{84}$, $a = 9$
Put these values into the equation and simplify.	$(\sqrt{84})^2 = (9)^2 + b^2$ $84 = 81 + b^2$
Put the unknown value on one side and solve.	$84 - 81 = b^2$ $b^2 = 3$
Find the square root. Leave b in surd form (unless told otherwise).	$b = \sqrt{3}$
$\therefore y = \sqrt{3}$	

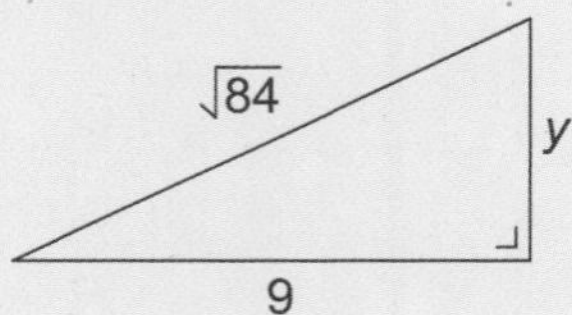

Exercise 8.2

1. Find the value of x in each of the following triangles. Leave your answers in surd form where appropriate.

(i) 12, 16, x

(ii)

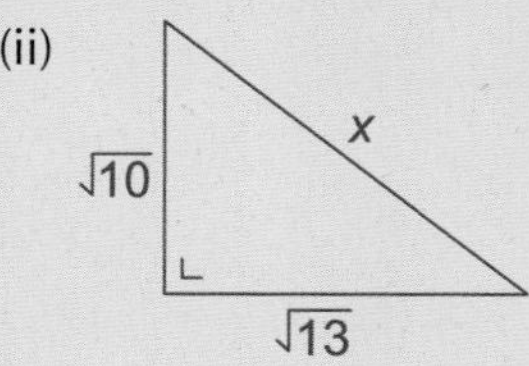

(iii)

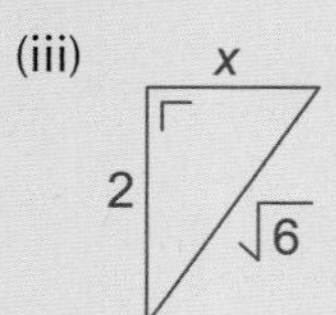

(iv)

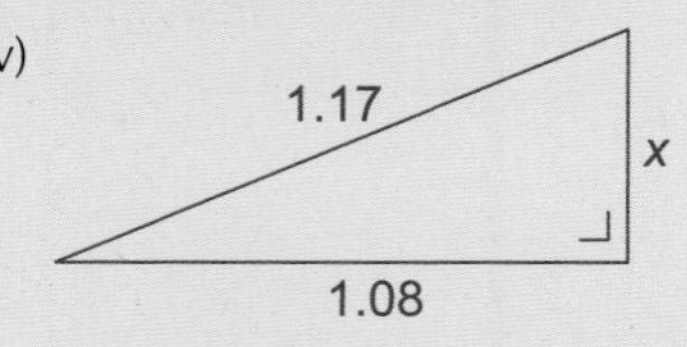

2. Find the length of x and y in each of the following triangles:

(i)

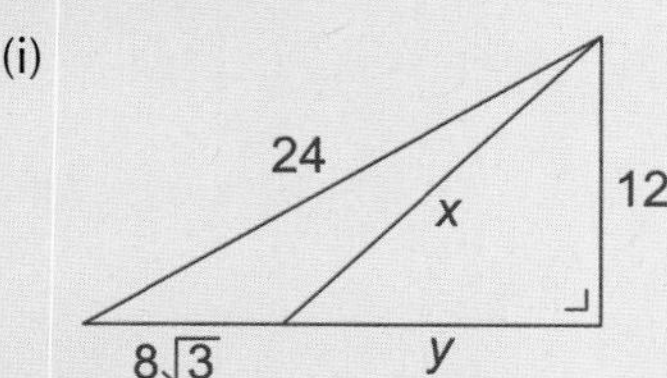

(ii)

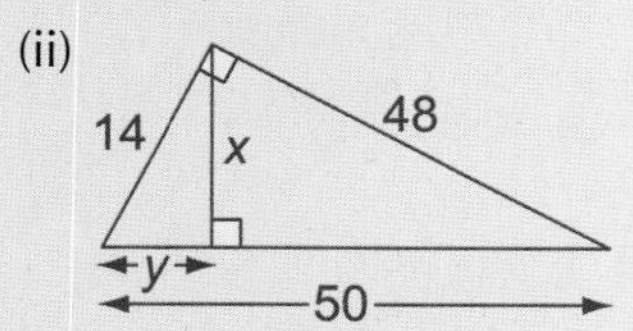

(iii)

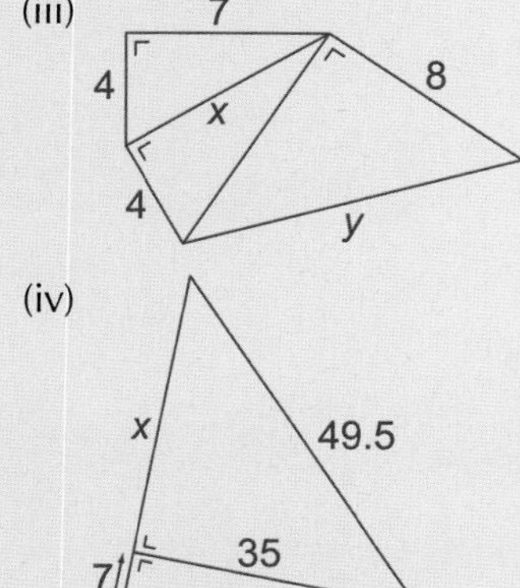

(iv)

3. The sides of a triangle are $(x^2 + y^2)$, $(x^2 - y^2)$ and $2xy$ as shown in the diagram.

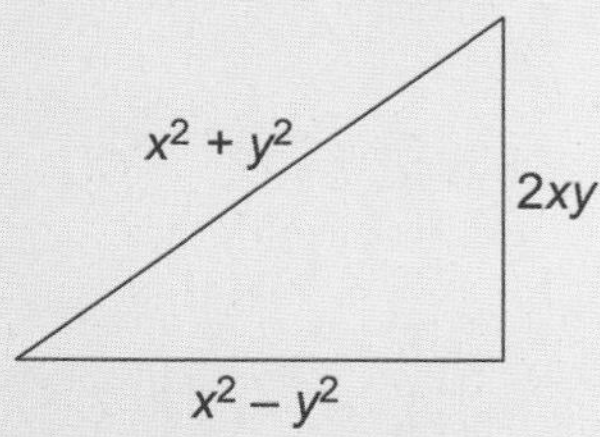

(i) Prove that the triangle as shown is right-angled.

(ii) Find the lengths of the three sides of the triangle if $x = 10$ and $y = 1$.

4. The perimeter of this right-angled triangle is 182 cm.

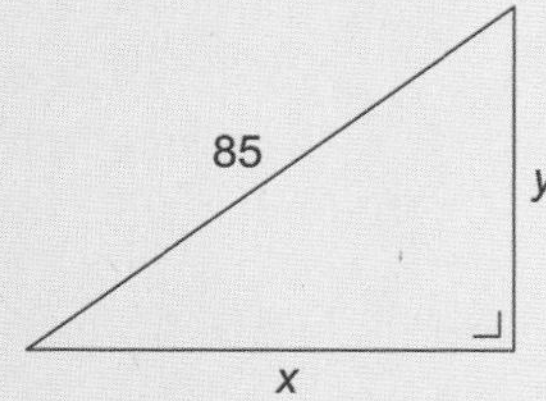

(i) Write down two equations in x and y.

(ii) Find the values of x and y, given that $x > y$.

5. A right-angled triangle has side lengths of $x - 2$, $x + 3$ and hypotenuse length $2x$. Find the value of x to two decimal places.

6. Consider the following diagram:

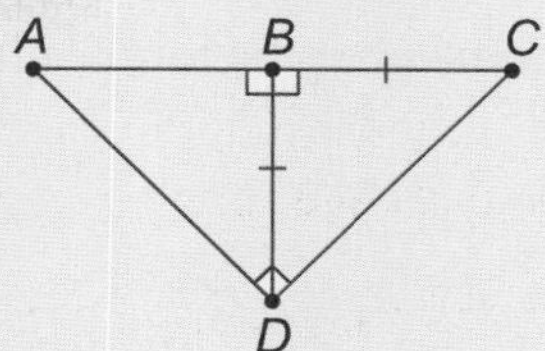

(i) Show that $|AD|^2 = |AB|^2 + |BC|^2$.

(ii) Show that $|DC|^2 = |AC| \, . \, |AB|$.

7. A rectangular box is shown.

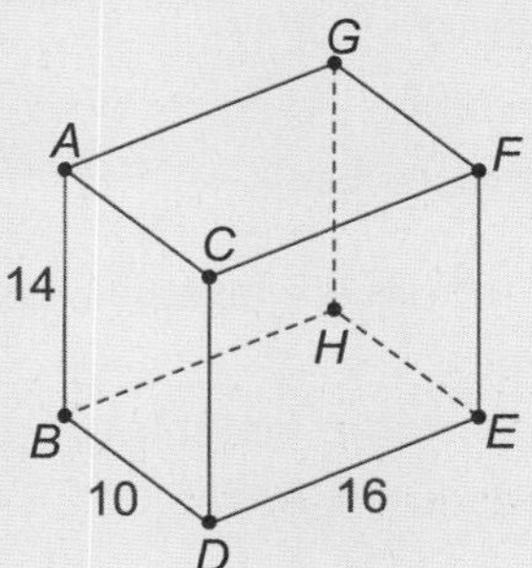

Find:

(i) $|AD|$ (ii) $|DF|$ (iii) $|AE|$

8. A square-based pyramid is shown. Its sides are four identical triangles.

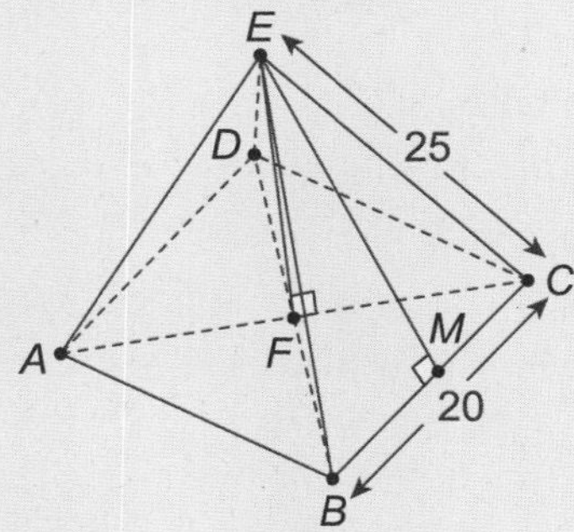

(i) Find $|AC|$.

(ii) Find $|FE|$.

(iii) If M is the midpoint of $[BC]$, calculate $|EM|$.

9. The sides of a triangle are $\sqrt{x^2 + 2x + 10}$, $\sqrt{x^2 + 2x + 10}$ and $2x + 2$.

(i) Sketch this triangle.

(ii) Find the perpendicular height of the triangle, using $(2x + 2)$ as the base.

8.3 AREA OF A TRIANGLE AND AREA OF A PARALLELOGRAM

Area of a Triangle

We should remember the formula for the area of a triangle:

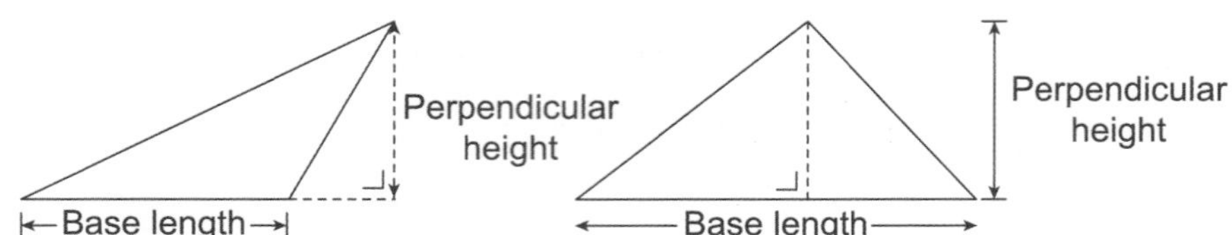

FORMULA

Area of a triangle = $\frac{1}{2}$ (base length) × perpendicular height

It is also clear from our investigations that in calculating the area of a triangle:

It does not matter which base of the triangle we choose, as long as we know the perpendicular height from the corresponding base.

Area $\Delta\, ABC$

$= \frac{1}{2}(9)(3)$

$= 13.5$ units^2

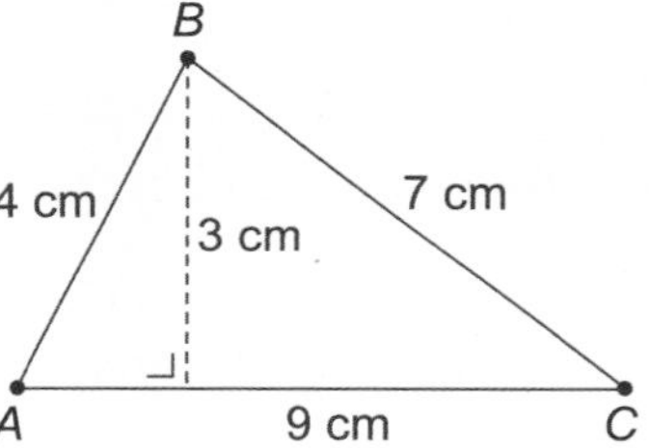

Area ΔABC

$= \frac{1}{2}(4)(6.75)$

$= 13.5$ units^2

This is stated as:

Theorem 16

For a triangle, base times height does not depend on the choice of base.

Worked Example 8.3

Find the value of x in the following triangle.

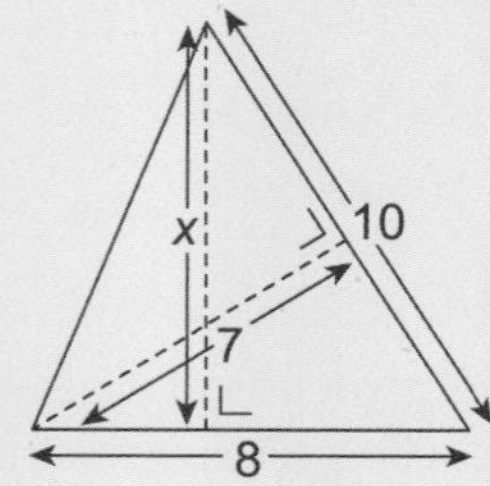

Solution

Area of triangle $= \frac{1}{2}$ (base length) by perpendicular height.

$$\therefore \frac{1}{2} \times 7 \times 10 = \frac{1}{2} \times x \times 8$$

$$\therefore 35 = 4x$$

$$\therefore 8.75 = x$$

Area of a Parallelogram

We can now consider how to find the area of a parallelogram.

Theorem 17

A diagonal of a parallelogram bisects the area.

From Theorem 17, a parallelogram can be cut into two triangles of equal area.

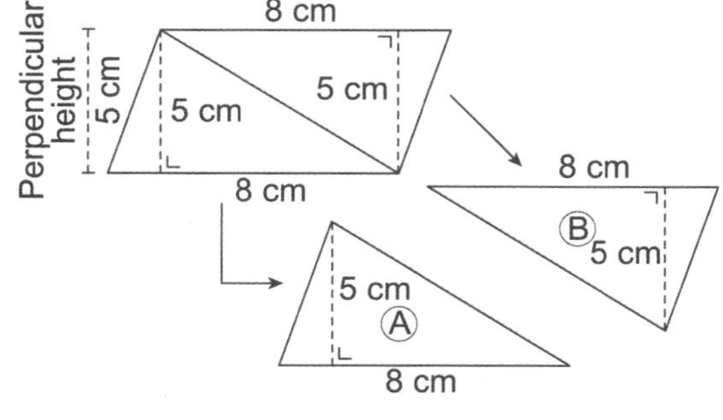

Area triangle Ⓐ $= \frac{1}{2}$ base × height

$= \frac{1}{2} \times 8 \times 5 = 20 \text{ cm}^2$

Area triangle Ⓑ $= \frac{1}{2}$ base × height

$= \frac{1}{2} \times 8 \times 5 = 20 \text{ cm}^2$

Area of parallelogram = Area of triangles Ⓐ + Ⓑ

Area of parallelogram $= 20 \text{ cm}^2 + 20 \text{ cm}^2 = 40 \text{ cm}^2$

This is known as:

Theorem 18

The area of a parallelogram is the base times the height.

Exercise 8.3

1. Find the area of each of the following triangles and parallelograms:

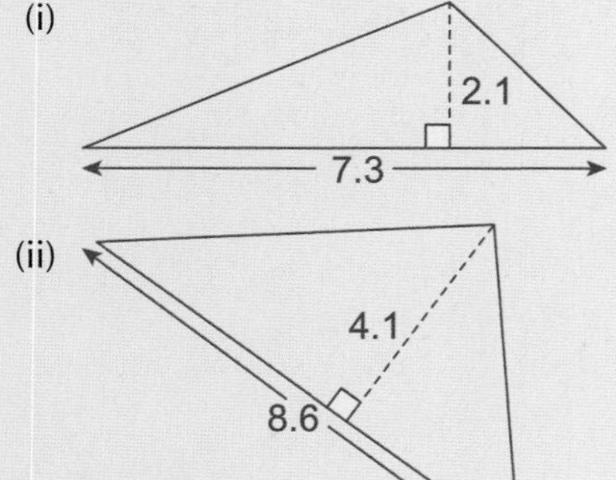

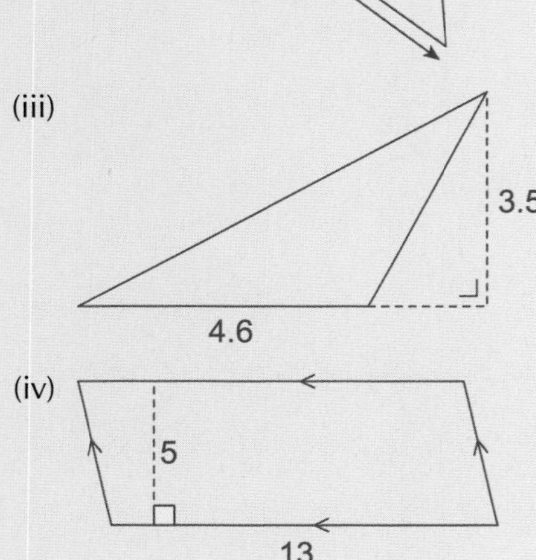

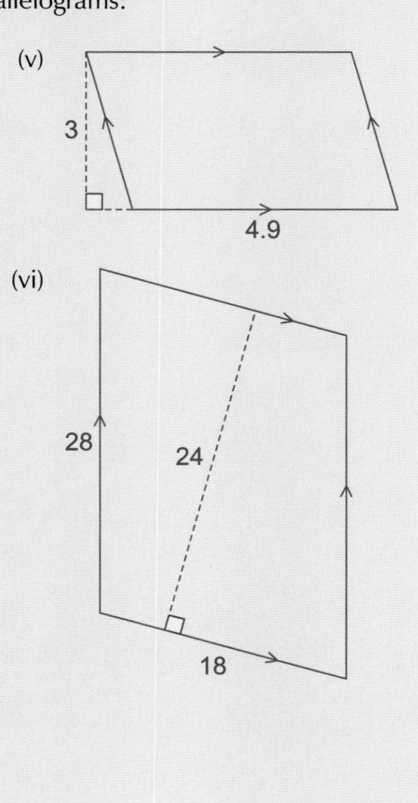

2. Find the area of the shaded region in each of the following diagrams (to the nearest whole number):

(i)

(ii)

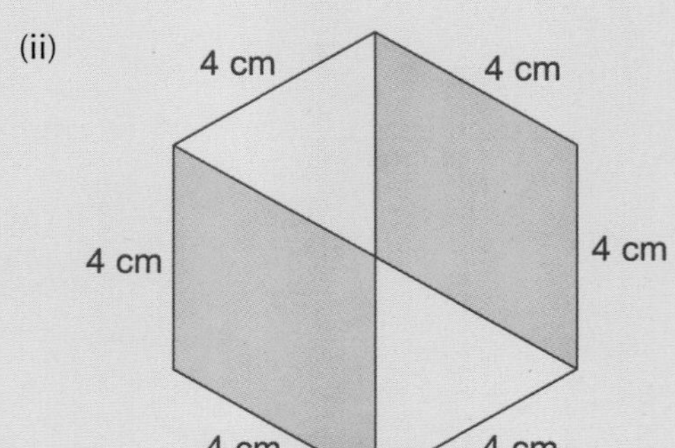

(iii)

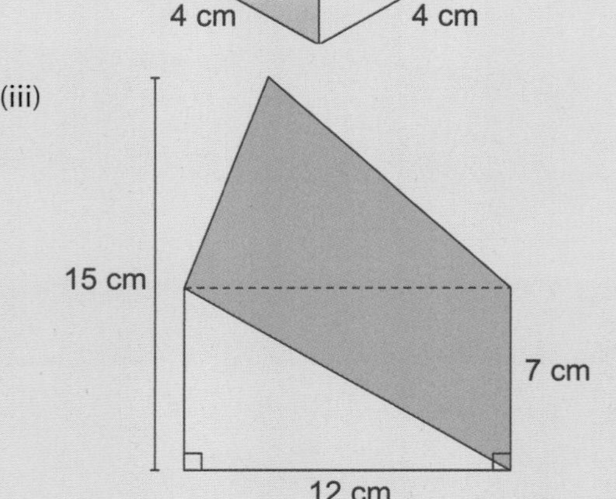

(iv)

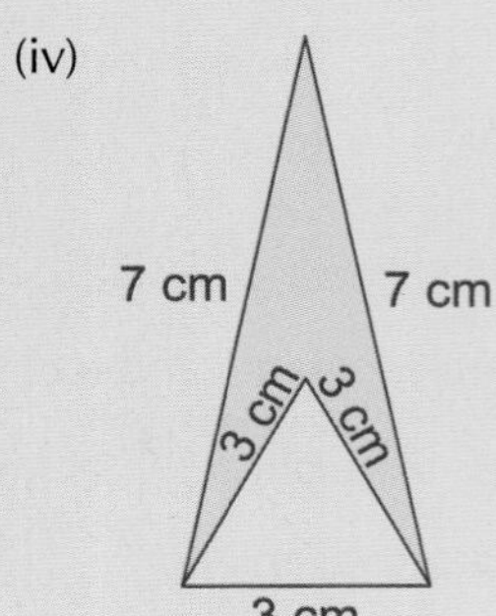

(v)

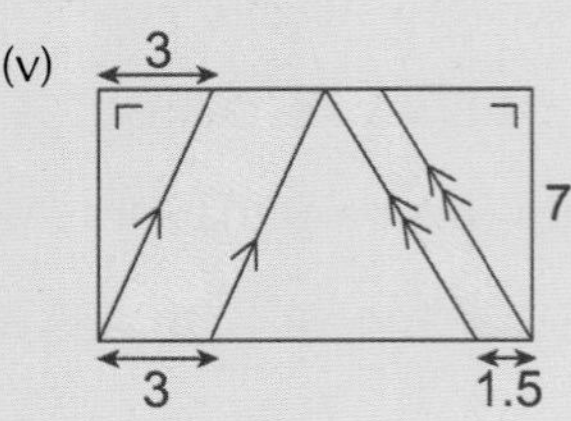

(vi)

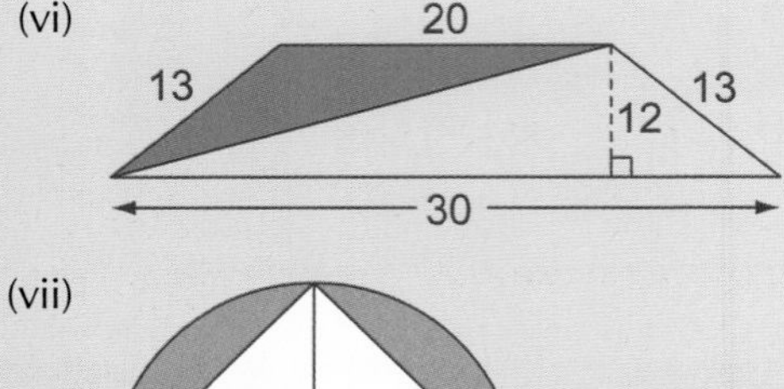

(vii)

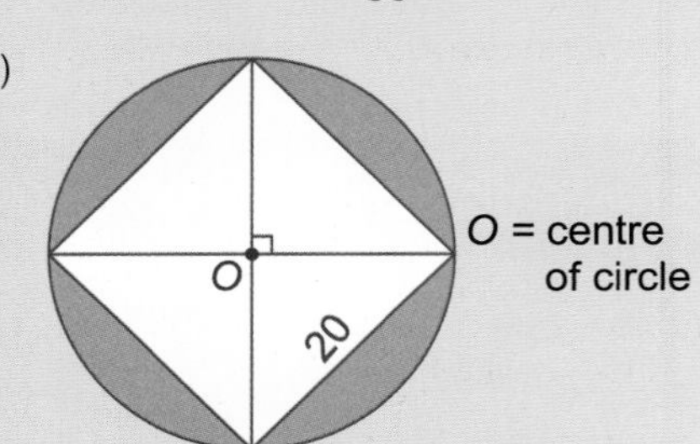

3. Find the value of x in each of the following shapes:

(i)

(ii)

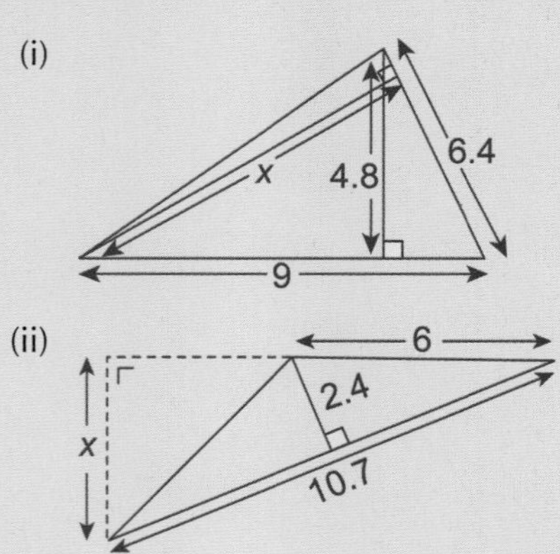

(iii)

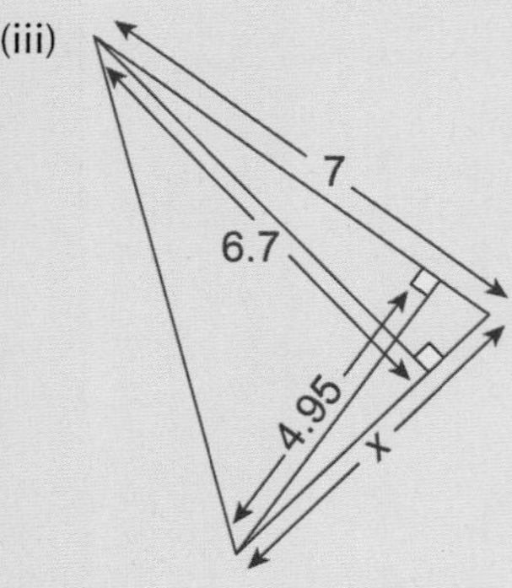

4. A parallelogram $ABCD$ is such that $|AB| = 5$ cm and $|BC| = 3$ cm.

(i) What is the maximum height of this parallelogram?

(ii) What is the maximum area of this parallelogram?

5. A square *ABCD* is shown. *Y* is the midpoint of [*DC*] and *X* is the midpoint of [*BC*].

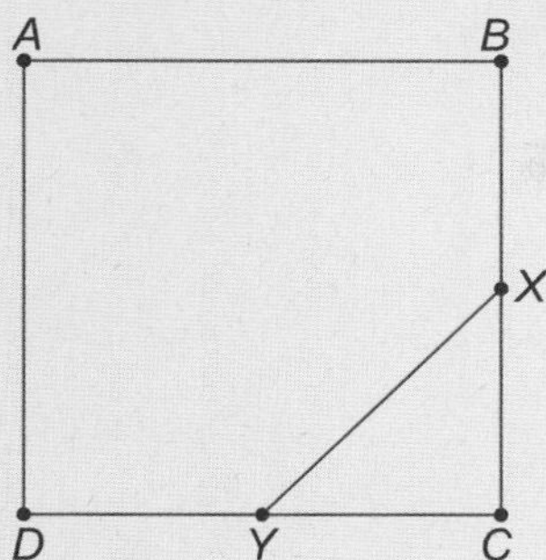

What is the ratio of the area of the square to the triangle *XYC*?

6. The circumcircle of an equilateral triangle with an area of $4\sqrt{3}$ is drawn as shown.

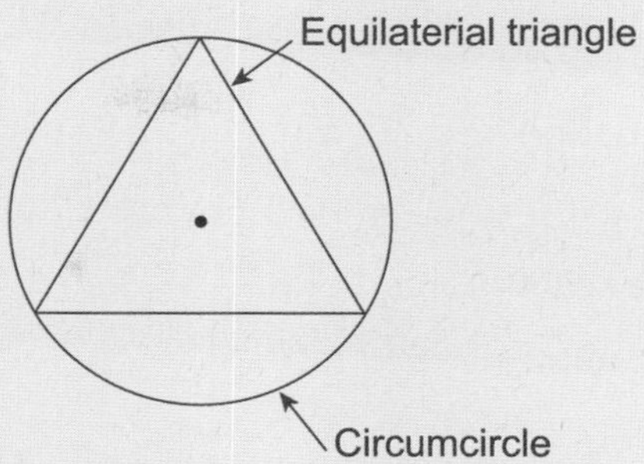

Calculate the radius length of the circumcircle.

8.4 CIRCLES

A circle is a very common shape found in all aspects of everyday life.

Some common terms associated with circles:

A **circle** is a set of points in a plane that are all equidistant from a fixed point, its centre.

Radius – the line segment from the centre of the circle to any point on the circle.

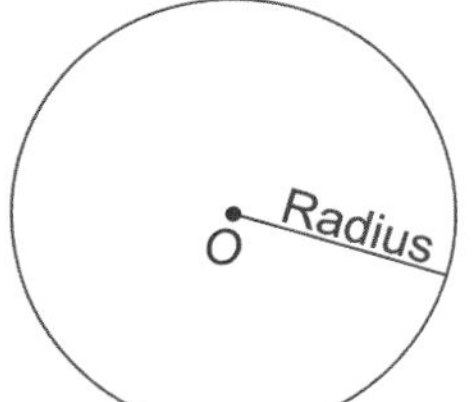

The centre of a circle is usually marked with a dot and sometimes the letter *O*.

The plural of radius is **radii**.

Chord – any segment that joins two points on a circle.

Diameter – a chord that passes through the centre of a circle. The diameter is twice the radius in length.

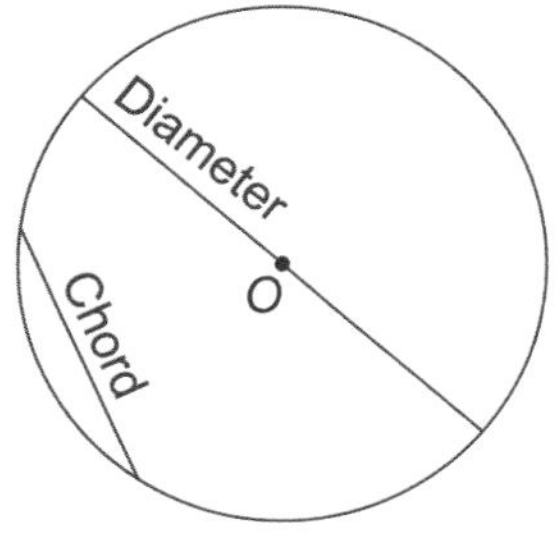

Circumference – the perimeter or length of the circle.

Arc – any part of the circumference or curve of the circle.

Tangent – a line which touches the circle at only one point. Where the tangent touches the circle is called the point of contact, or point of tangency.

Sector – the region of the circle enclosed by two radii and the arc between these radii.

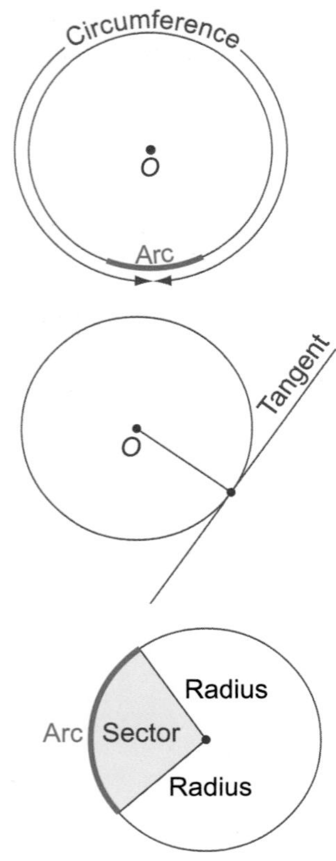

Circle Properties

We can now investigate some properties of circles.

From our explorations of circles we can draw a number of conclusions, which we will now investigate in greater detail.

(a) Angle at the Centre of a Circle Compared with the Angle at the Circumference

The circle in the diagram below contains the angles *BOC* (angle at the centre) and *BAC* (angle at the circumference).

The angle at the centre of the circle is twice the measure of the angle at the circumference.

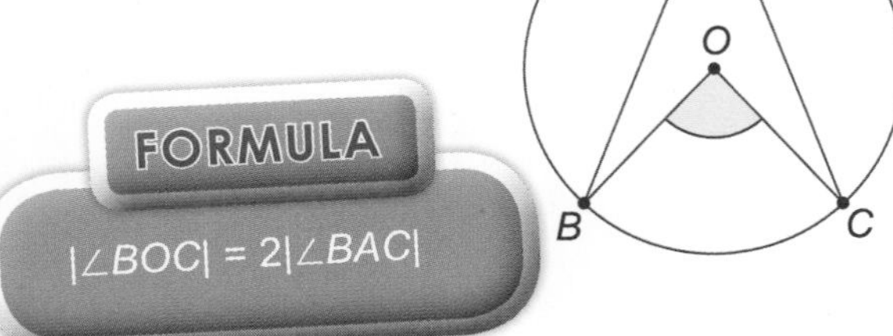

This leads us to state the following theorem:

Theorem 19 (Formal proof in Appendix)

The angle at the centre of a circle standing on a given arc is twice the angle at any point of the circle standing on the same arc.

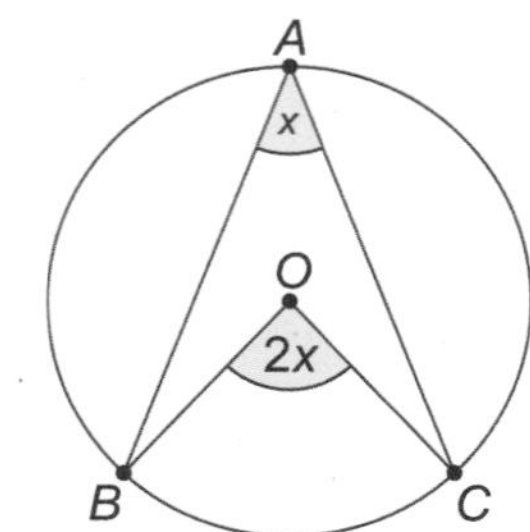

(b) Two Angles in a Circle Standing on the Same Arc

In the diagram, both angles at B and D are on the same arc, AC.

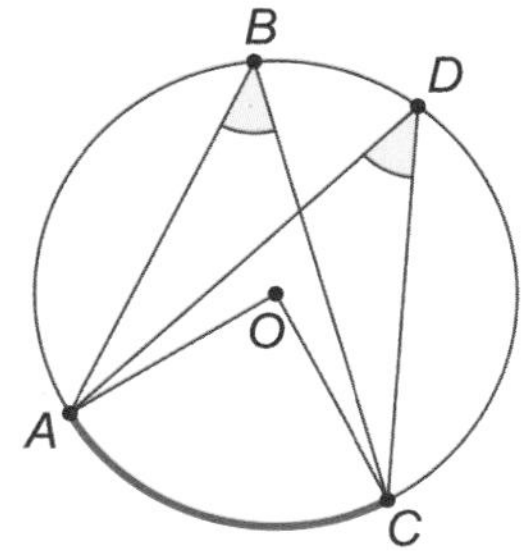

Corollary 2

All angles at a point of a circle, standing on the same arc, are equal.

The converse of this corollary also applies:

If the angles at points of the circle are equal, then they must be standing on the same arc.

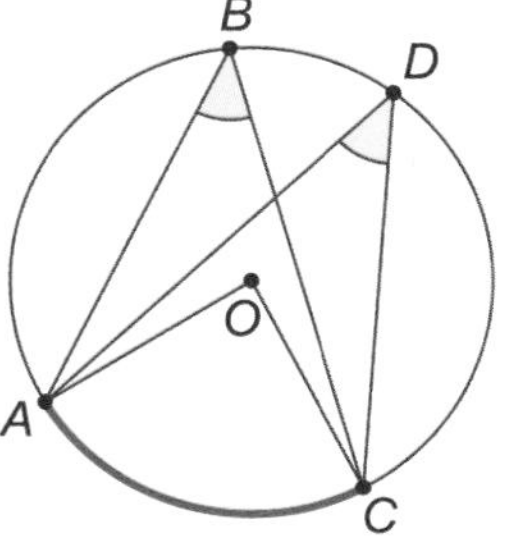

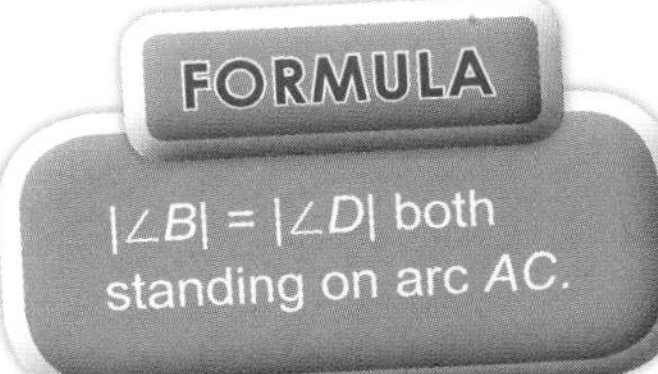

Worked Example 8.4

Consider the following diagram of a circle with centre O and diameter $[AB]$:

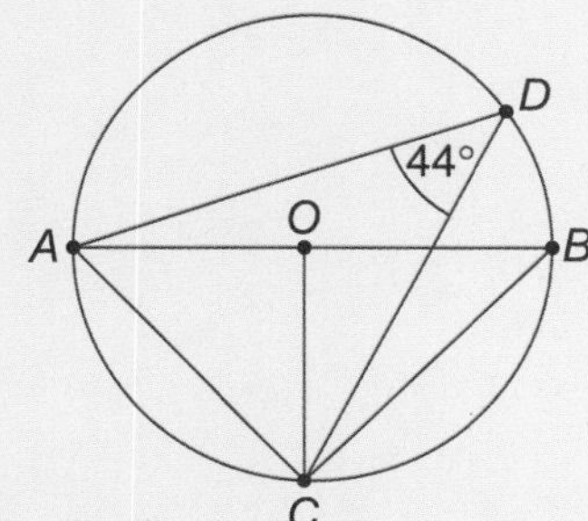

Find:

(i) $|\angle ABC|$

(ii) $|\angle AOC|$

(iii) $|\angle OCA|$

Solution

(i) $|\angle ABC| = 44°$ (angle on same arc)

(ii) $|\angle AOC| = 88°$ (angle at centre of circle is twice the measure of angle at arc)

(iii) $|\angle OCA|$

ΔAOC is an isosceles triangle.

$\therefore |\angle OCA| = (180° - 88°) \div 2$

$\therefore |\angle OCA| = 46°$

(c) Cyclic Quadrilaterals

A quadrilateral in which all four vertices (corners) are points of a circle is referred to as a **cyclic quadrilateral**.

Opposite angles in a cyclic quadrilateral add up to 180°.

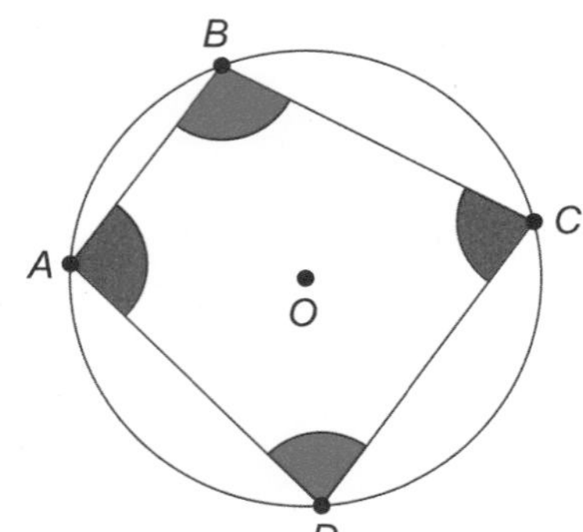

From this, we can state the following corollary:

Corollary 5
If *ABCD* is a cyclic quadrilateral, then opposite angles sum to 180°.

The converse of this corollary states:

If the opposite angles of a quadrilateral sum to 180°, then it is cyclic, i.e. the vertices of the quadrilateral will lie on the circle.

(d) Angles in a Semicircle

The angle opposite the diameter in a circle is a right angle or 90°.

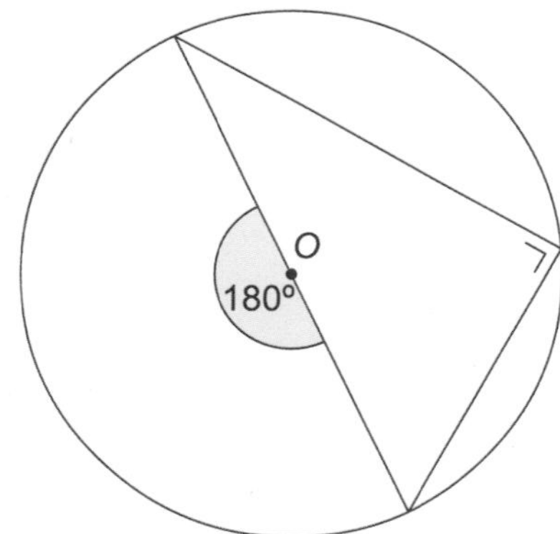

This can be stated as:

Corollary 3
Each angle in a semicircle is a right angle.

From this corollary, we can also show another property of a circle:

Corollary 4
If the angle standing on a chord [*BC*] at some point of the circle is a right angle, then [*BC*] is a diameter.

This corollary could be considered the converse of Corollary 3.

(e) Tangents

Another important theorem based on a circle concerns the properties of a **tangent** to the circle.

A tangent to a circle is at a right angle to the radius at the point of contact.

This is more formally stated as:

Theorem 20

Each tangent is perpendicular to the radius that goes to the point of contact.

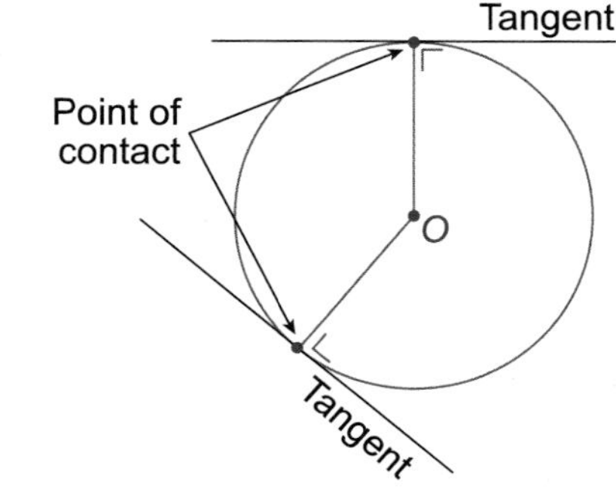

This theorem also includes the converse of this statement:

If a point P lies on a circle s and a line l which passes though the point P is perpendicular to the radius, then this line is a tangent to the circle at the point P.

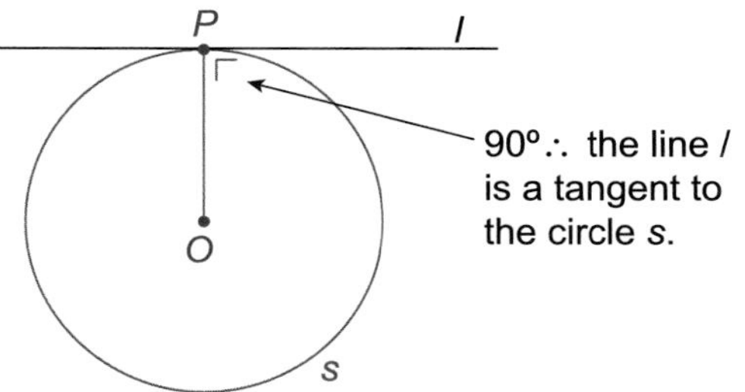

This can be more formally stated as:

If P lies on s, and a line l is perpendicular to the radius to P, then l is tangent to s.

External:

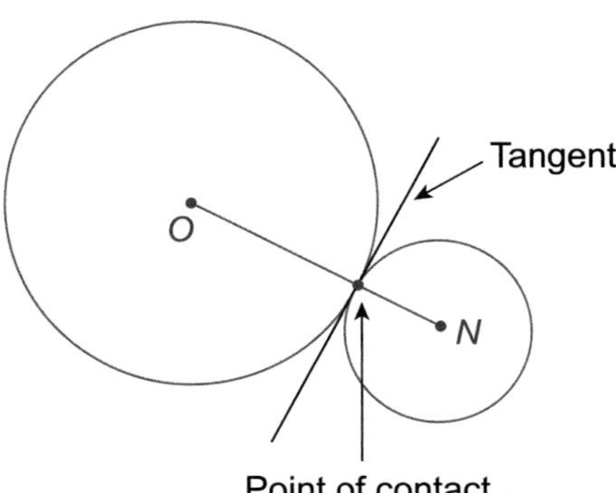

Internal:

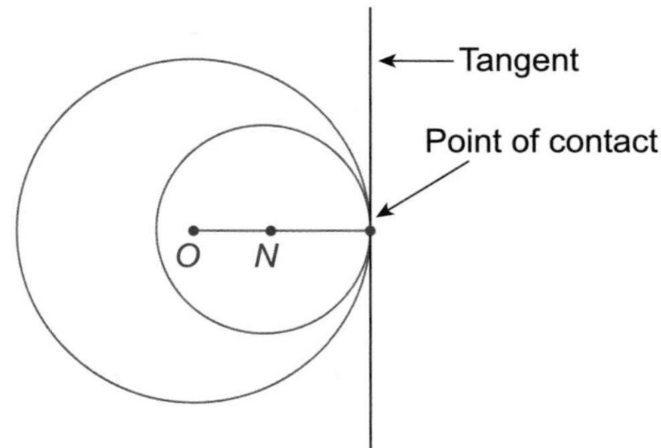

Tangents can also be found when two circles meet at one point only.

Circles can meet internally or externally.

From our investigations, it is evident that:

Corollary 6

If two circles intersect at one point only, then the two centres and the point of contact are collinear.

Worked Example 8.5

A circle, with centre O and radius $[OP]$ is shown. t is a tangent to the circle with a point of contact P.

$|OP| = 7$ cm and $|PS| = \sqrt{15}$ cm.

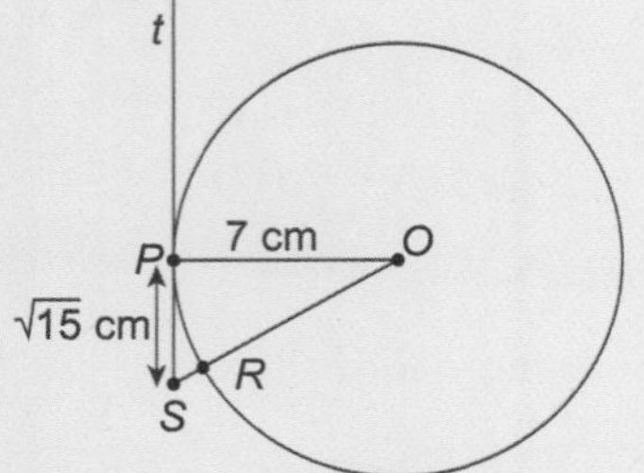

Find:

(i) $|OS|$ (ii) $|RS|$

Solution

(i) To find $|OS|$:

ΔOPS is a right-angled triangle, and $[OS]$ is the hypotenuse.

$h^2 = a^2 + b^2$

$a = 7, b = \sqrt{15}$

$h^2 = 7^2 + (\sqrt{15})^2$

$\therefore h^2 = 49 + 15$

$\therefore h^2 = 64$

$\therefore h = 8 \quad \therefore |OS| = 8$ cm

(ii) To find $|RS|$:

Remember that the radius length $|OP| = 7 = |OR|$.

$\therefore |RS| = 8 - 7$

$|RS| = 1$ cm

(f) Perpendicular to a Chord

We can also consider the relationship between any chord of a circle and the centre of the circle.

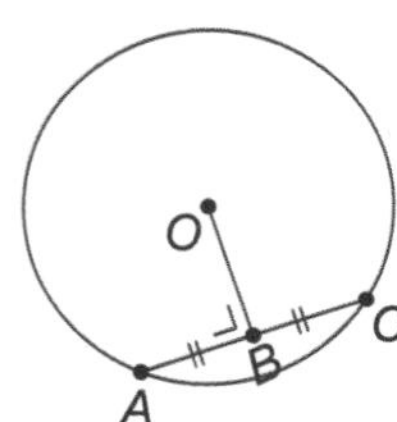

From Activity 8.5 we know that:

If a line is drawn at right angles to a chord and this line goes through the centre of the circle, it will cut the chord into two equal segments.

This can more formally be written as:

Theorem 21 part (i)

The perpendicular from the centre to a chord bisects the chord.

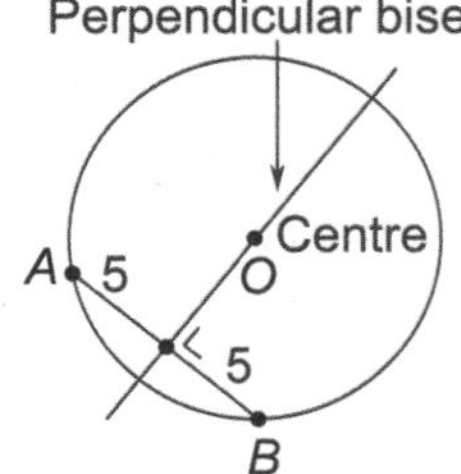

Theorem 21 Part (ii)

The perpendicular bisector of a chord passes through the centre.

By constructing the perpendicular bisectors of two chords, we can use this theorem to find the centre of a given circle.

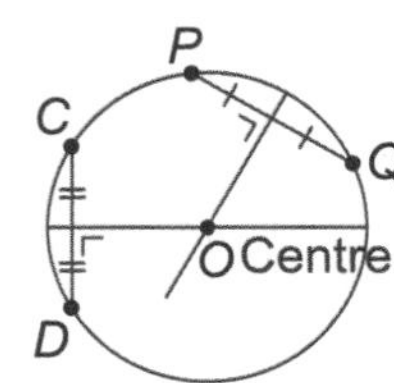

GEOMETRY II

Worked Example 8.6

[AB] is the diameter of a circle with centre O. [CD] is a chord with a midpoint M.

$AB \perp CD$

$|CD| = 64$ cm and $|OM| = 24$ cm

Find:

(i) $|OC|$

(ii) $|BC|$ in simplest surd form

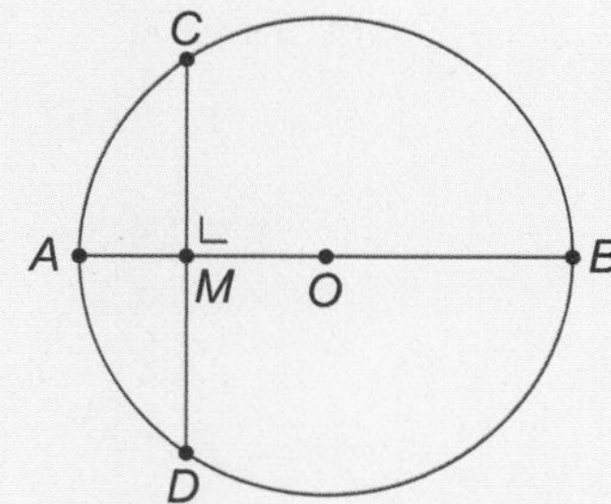

Solution

(i) To find $|OC|$:

$|CM| = 32$ cm (the perpendicular from the centre to a chord bisects the chord)

ΔCMO is a right-angled triangle.

Using the theorem of Pythagoras:

$$|OC|^2 = |CM|^2 + |OM|^2$$

$$= (32)^2 + (24)^2$$

$$|OC|^2 = 1{,}600$$

$$\therefore\ |OC| = 40 \text{ cm}$$

(ii) To find $|BC|$:

ΔCMB is a right-angled triangle.

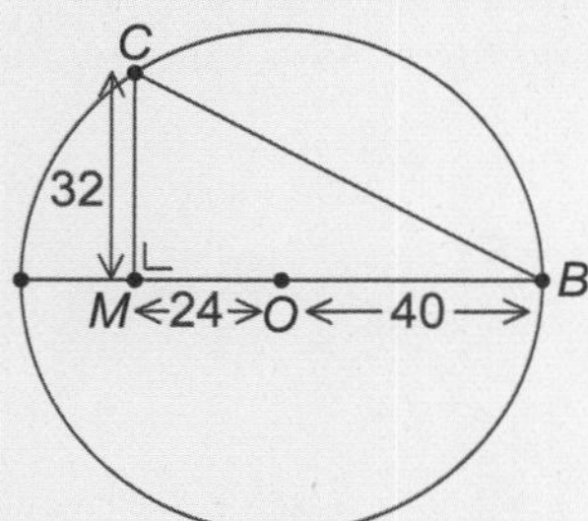

$|OB| = |OC| = 40$ cm (radius)

$|CM| = 32$ cm and $|MB| = 64$ cm $(24 + 40)$

Using the theorem of Pythagoras, $|BC| = 32\sqrt{5}$ cm.

Exercise 8.4

1. Find $|\angle A|$ and $|\angle B|$ in each of the following diagrams.
Remember to show as much work as possible. O is the centre in each case.

(i)

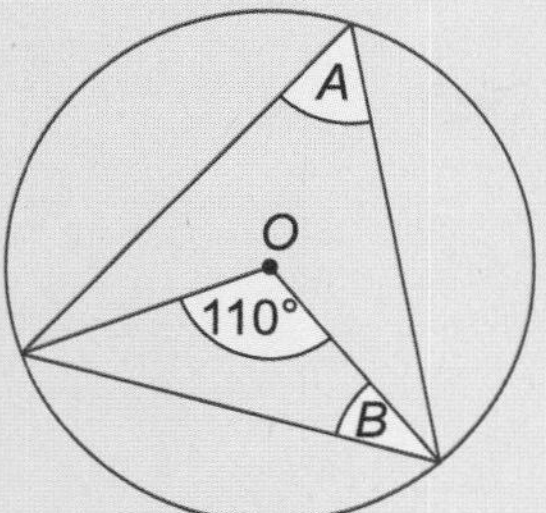

(ii)

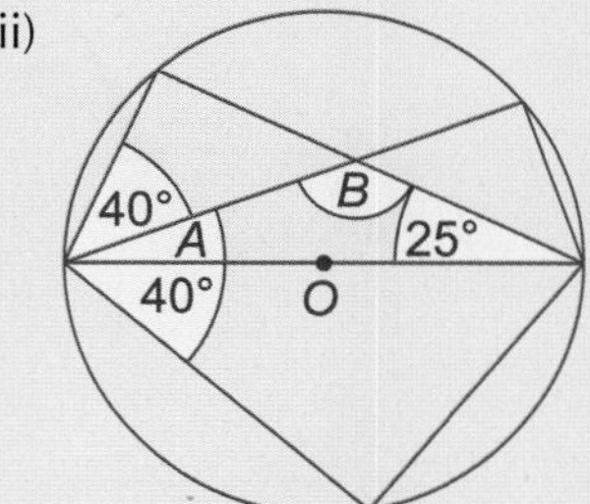

(iii)

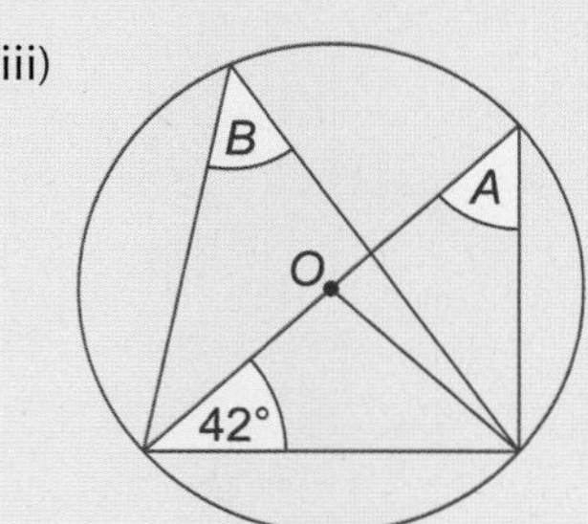

GEOMETRY II

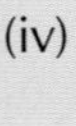

(iv)

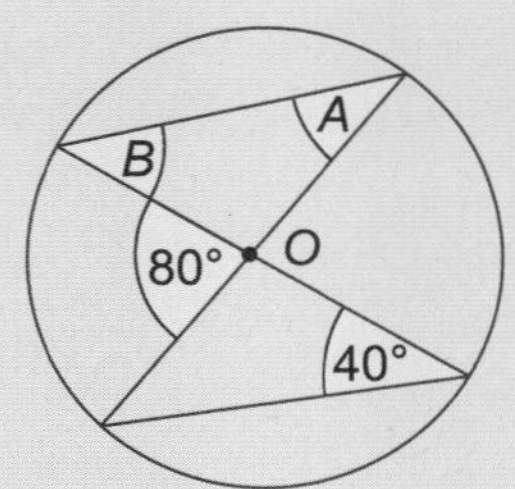

(v)

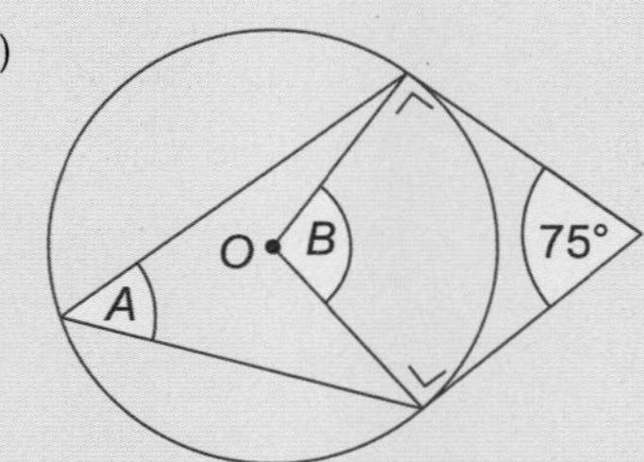

(vi)

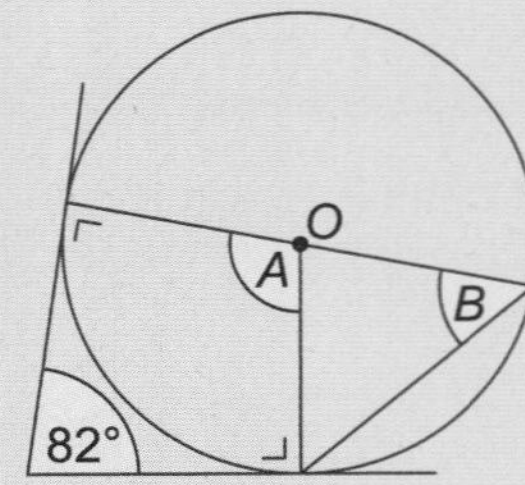

(vii)

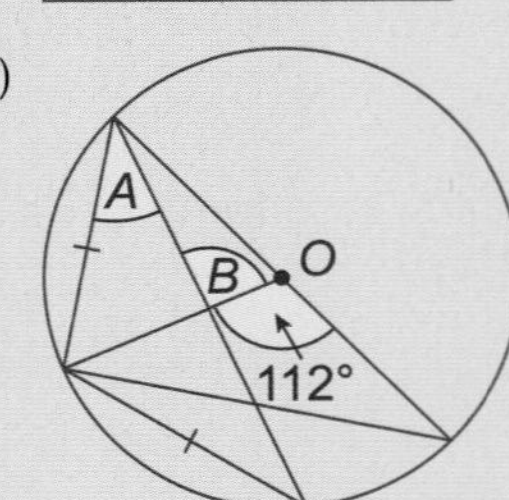

2. Consider the following circle with centre O:

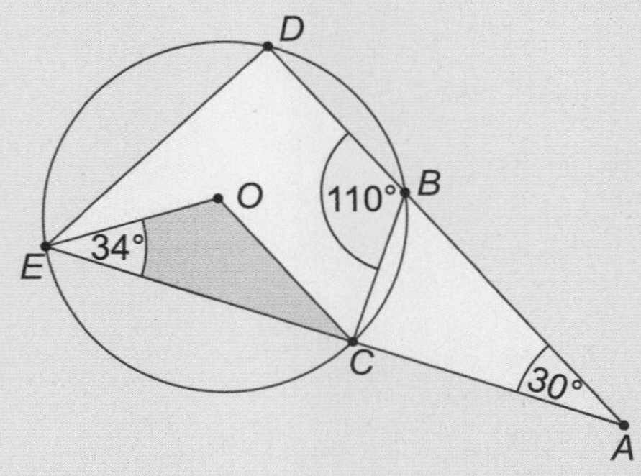

Find:

(i) $|\angle EOC|$

(ii) $|\angle BCA|$

(iii) $|\angle ECB|$

(iv) $|\angle EDA|$

3. In each diagram, O is the centre of the circle. P is the point of contact between a tangent and the circle. Find the value of x in each case.

(i)

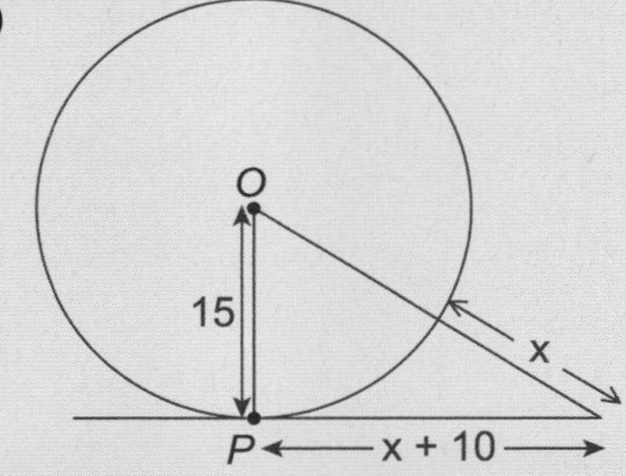

(ii)

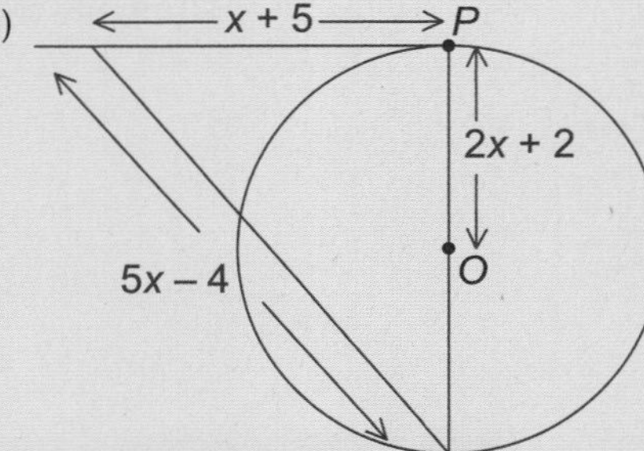

4. In the diagram below, C is the the centre of the circle and XT is a tangent. $|\angle XTQ| = 50°$ and $|\angle PCT| = 140°$.

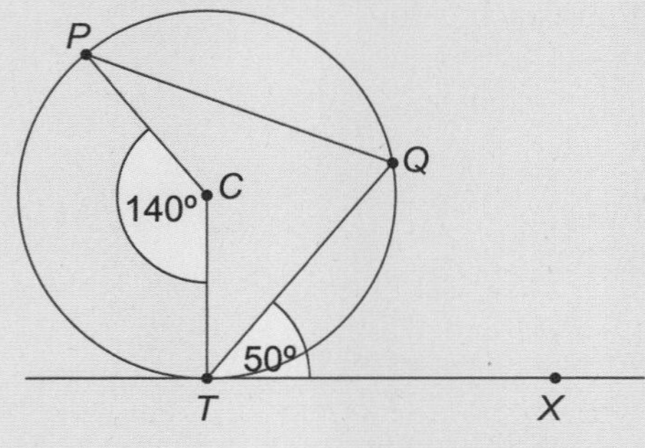

Write down the value of the following angles:

(i) $|\angle CTX|$

(ii) $|\angle CTQ|$

(iii) $|\angle PQT|$

(iv) $|\angle CQT|$

(v) $|\angle CQP|$

(vi) $|\angle QPC|$

5. *PQRS* are points of circle a with centre *C*.

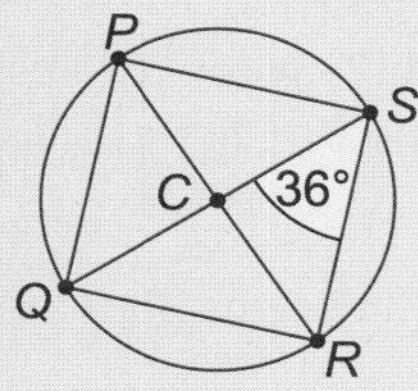

Name an angle equal in measure to:

(i) $2|\angle RPS|$

(ii) $|\angle QSP|$

(iii) A right angle

6. Two tangents *PT* and *PS* are drawn to a circle with centre *O* from the point *P*.

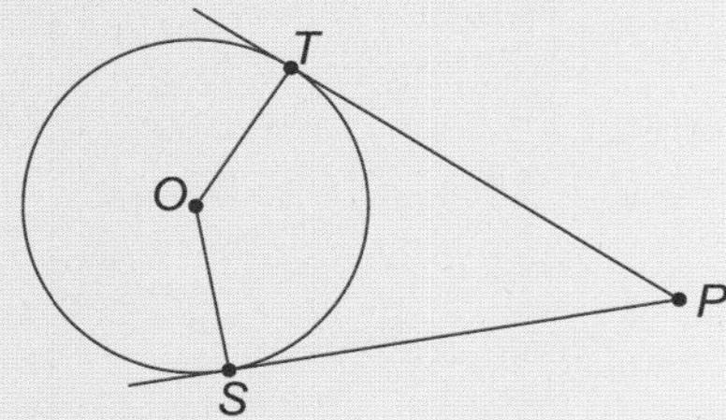

Prove that $|PT| = |PS|$.

7. A circle with centre *O* has a radius of 25 cm. The chord $|RS| = 14$ and $RS \perp PQ$.

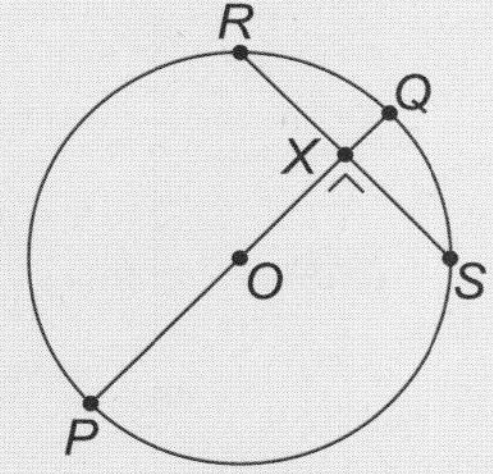

Find:

(i) $|RX|$

(ii) $|QX|$

(iii) $|PX|$

(iv) $|PS|$

8. A circle with centre *O* of radius 25 cm has two chords [*AB*] and [*CD*]. $OM \perp AB$ and $ON \perp CD$.

$|OM| = 24$ cm
$|ON| = 20$ cm

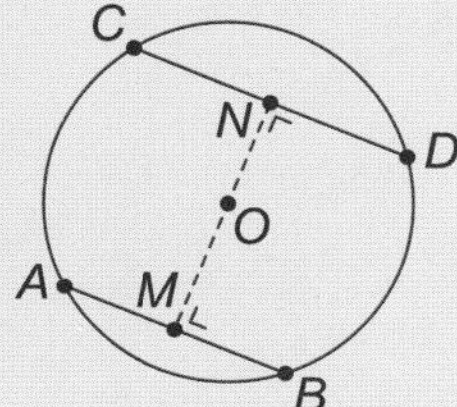

Find:

(i) $|CD|$

(ii) $|AB|$

9. The circle *s* with centre *O* and the circle *p* with centre *C* are shown. *AB* is a tangent to both circles.
$|OA| = 12$ cm and $|BC| = 3$ cm.

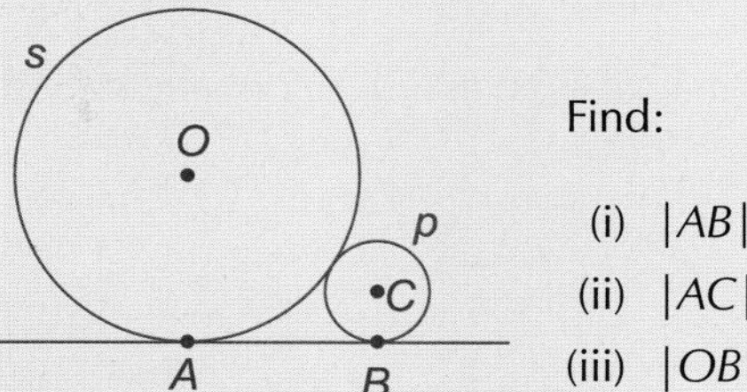

Find:

(i) $|AB|$

(ii) $|AC|$

(iii) $|OB|$

10. The circles *x*, *y* and *z* are shown, with centres *O*, *P* and *R* respectively.

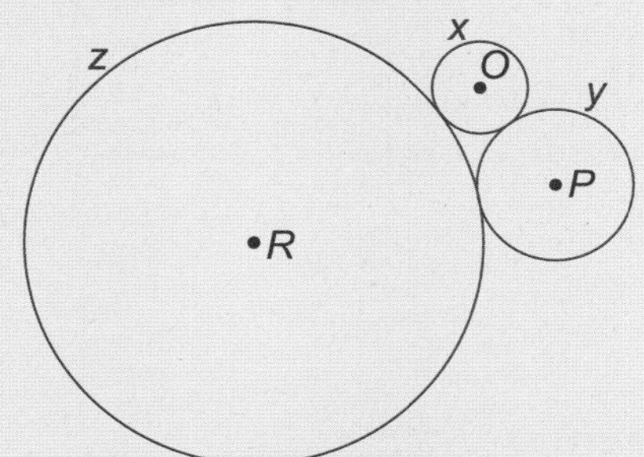

The radius length of circle *x* is 12 cm, and the radius length of circle *y* is 20 cm.

If $|\angle ROP| = 90°$ find the radius length of circle z.

We sometimes encounter geometry questions that require the use of trigonometry as well.

11. A circle with centre *O* is inscribed in triangle *ABC* as shown.

$|AB| = |BC| = 92$ mm and
$|AC| = 120$ mm.

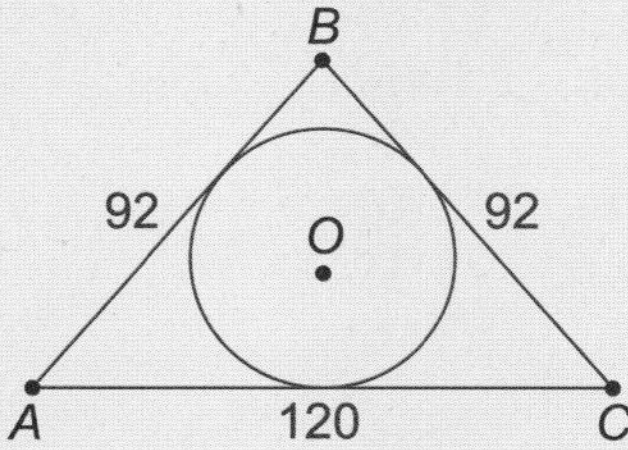

Find:

(i) $|\angle BAC|$

(ii) The radius of the circle

(iii) The perpendicular height of the triangle

8.5 PROOFS: THEOREMS AND TERMS

We must be able to prove certain theorems and to answer proofs based on all the axioms, theorems and corollaries from our course. The formal proofs of all geometry theorems stated in the syllabus are given in the Appendix.

Students may also be asked to formally state the **proof** of the following theorems from the Junior Certificate Course:

A **proof** is a series of logical steps that we use to prove a theorem.

Theorem 4

The angles in any triangle add to 180

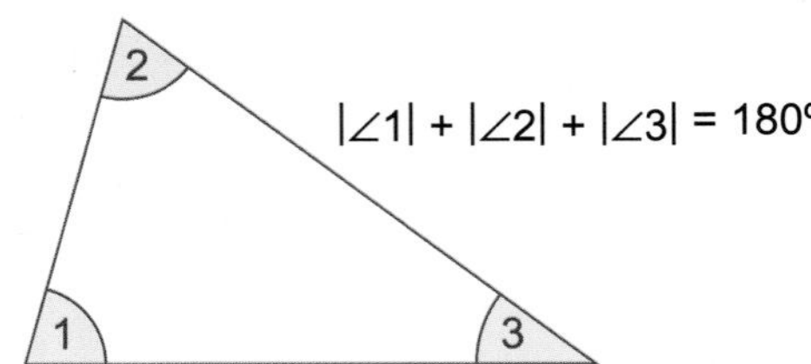

Theorem 6

Each exterior angle of a triangle is equal to the sum of the interior opposite angles.

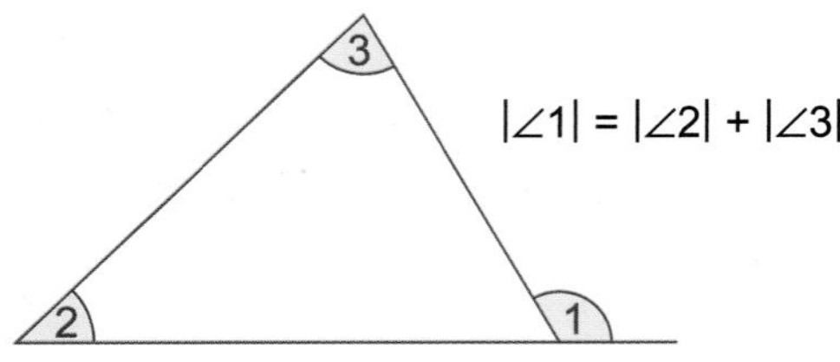

Theorem 9

In a parallelogram, opposite sides are equal and opposite angles are equal.

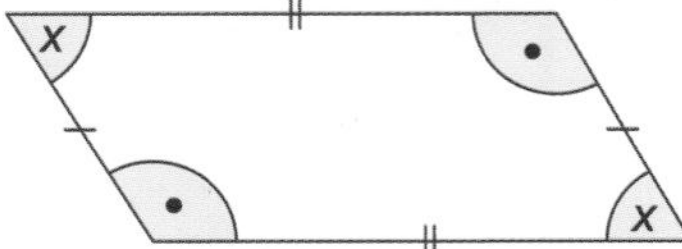

Theorem 14: The Theorem of Pythagoras

In a right-angled triangle, the square of the hypotenuse is the sum of the squares of the other two sides.

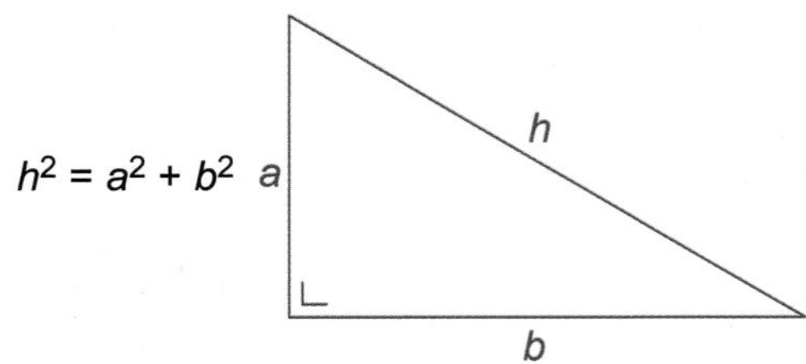

Theorem 19

The angle at the centre of a circle standing on a given arc is twice the angle at any point of the circle standing on the same arc.

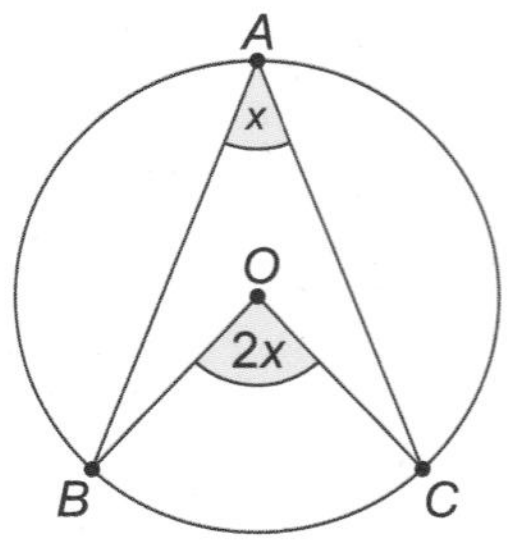

How to Write a Formal Proof

We must remember the steps involved when we are asked to 'prove', 'show' or 'find as certain'. Here is an example of a formal proof, with a description of each step involved:

Theorem 19

The angle at the centre of a circle standing on a given arc is twice the angle at any point of the circle standing on the same arc.

Theorem: Usually used only when you are asked to formally prove a certain theorem.

Given: A circle with centre O and an arc AC. A point B on the circle.

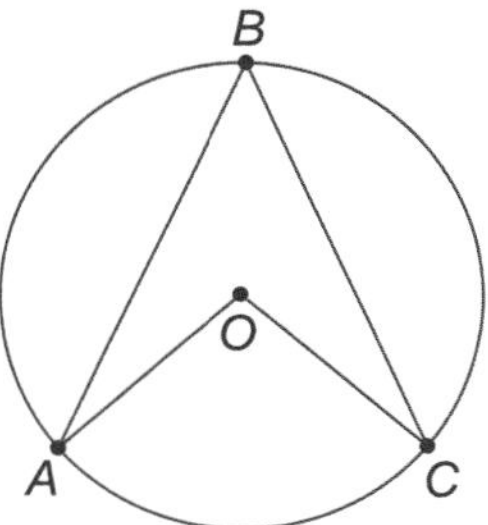

Given: Write down the given information and draw any diagrams.

To prove: $|\angle AOC| = 2|\angle ABC|$.

To prove: Write down what you need to prove.

Construction: Join B to O and continue to a point D. Label angles 1, 2, 3, 4, 5 and 6.

Construction: Any label, line, angle etc. that you added to the diagram to help solve the question.

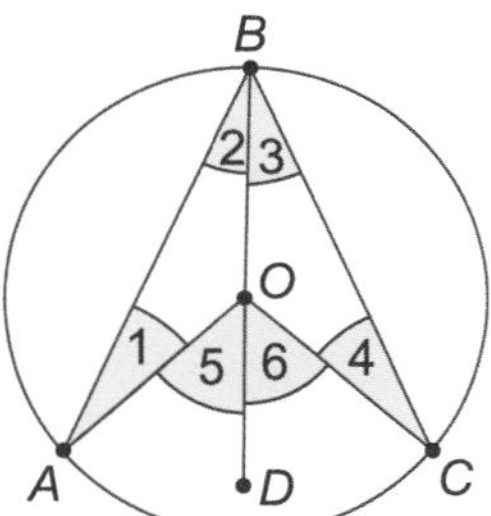

$|\angle AOC| = |\angle 5| + |\angle 6|$

$|\angle ABC| = |\angle 2| + |\angle 3|$

Proof:

Statement	Reason
$\lvert OA\rvert = \lvert OB\rvert$	Radii
$\lvert\angle 1\rvert = \lvert\angle 2\rvert$	Isosceles triangle
$\lvert\angle 5\rvert = \lvert\angle 1\rvert + \lvert\angle 2\rvert$	Exterior angle
$\Rightarrow \lvert\angle 5\rvert = 2\lvert\angle 2\rvert$	Since $\lvert\angle 1\rvert = \lvert\angle 2\rvert$
Similarly, $\lvert\angle 6\rvert = 2\lvert\angle 3\rvert$	
$\lvert\angle 5\rvert + \lvert\angle 6\rvert = 2\lvert\angle 2\rvert + 2\lvert\angle 3\rvert$	
$\Rightarrow \lvert\angle 5\rvert + \lvert\angle 6\rvert = 2(\lvert\angle 2\rvert + \lvert\angle 3\rvert)$	
$\lvert\angle AOC\rvert = 2\lvert\angle ABC\rvert$	
Q.E.D.	

Proof: A proof is made up of a series of statements that follow a logical progression, which leads to the answer. When writing down statements, we must always try to give a reason for each statement, whether we have been given this information or whether we have used a previous theorem.

Useful Terms

Geometrical cuts: In our course, we may encounter 'geometrical cuts'. These are questions which can usually be answered with a series of statements and the reasons behind each statement. These 'cuts' could be considered as mini-proofs.

Remember that other mathematical skills may be needed to solve questions. For example, you may need to use trigonometry to solve a geometry question.

Occasionally, we may also encounter the following terms in a proof:

Is equivalent to: This means that something has the same value or measure as, or corresponds to, something else. For example, \$2 is equivalent to €1.50.

If and only if: Ben will go to the cinema if, and only if, his favourite film is on. This means that if his favourite film is on, Ben will go to the cinema **and** if he is going to the cinema then his favourite film is on.

In geometry, we meet the phrase 'if and only if' in statements such as the following:

Two lines are parallel if, and only if, for any transversal, corresponding angles are equal.

A parallelogram is a rhombus if, and only if, all four of its sides have the same lengths.

Proof by contradiction (indirect proof): Occasionally, there are times when we cannot directly prove a statement. However, we can show that the statement cannot be false. This is known as proof by contradiction – we prove that a statement or assumption is true by showing that the statement or assumption being false would imply a contradiction (impossibility). For example the statement 'If $x > 10$ then $x > 15$' is not true. We can disprove the statement by letting $x = 11$.

The term *reductio ad absurdum* is a form of proof by contradiction where we use an **absurd** contradiction to prove our statement.

Worked Example 8.7

XYZ is a triangle. Prove that $|\angle 1| + |\angle 2| + |\angle 3| = 360°$.

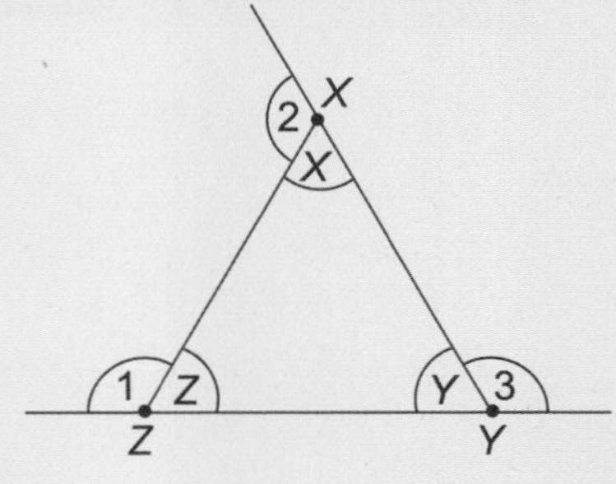

Solution

Given: ΔXYZ as shown.

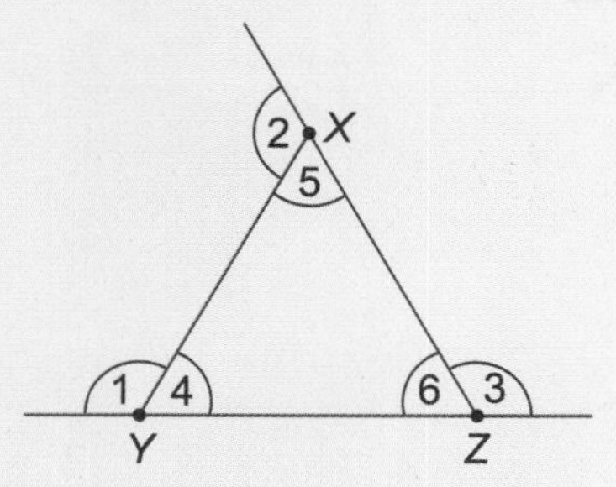

To prove: $|\angle 1| + |\angle 2| + |\angle 3| = 360°$.

Construction: Label angles 4, 5 and 6.

Proof:

$\lvert\angle 1\rvert = \lvert\angle 5\rvert + \lvert\angle 6\rvert$	Exterior angle
$\lvert\angle 2\rvert = \lvert\angle 4\rvert + \lvert\angle 6\rvert$	Exterior angle
$\lvert\angle 3\rvert = \lvert\angle 4\rvert + \lvert\angle 5\rvert$	Exterior angle
$\Rightarrow \lvert\angle 1\rvert + \lvert\angle 2\rvert + \lvert\angle 3\rvert = 2(\lvert\angle 4\rvert + \lvert\angle 5\rvert + \lvert\angle 6\rvert)$	Adding the 3 lines above
But $\lvert\angle 4\rvert + \lvert\angle 5\rvert + \lvert\angle 6\rvert = 180°$	Angles in a triangle
$\Rightarrow \lvert\angle 1\rvert + \lvert\angle 2\rvert + \lvert\angle 3\rvert = 2(180°) = 360°$	
Q.E.D.	

Worked Example 8.8

ABCD is a square. *BDEF* is another square.

Prove that the area of *BDEF* is twice the area of *ABCD*.

Solution

Given: Squares *ABCD* and *DBFE*.

To prove: Area *BDEF* = 2 × (Area *ABCD*):

Construction: Mark the sides of *ABCD* as x and the sides of *BDEF* as y.

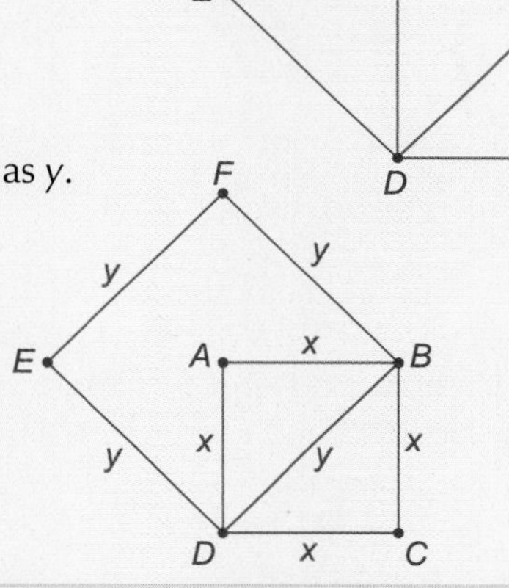

Proof: Using Pythagoras' theorem:

$x^2 + x^2 = y^2$

$\Rightarrow 2x^2 = y^2$

$\Rightarrow$ 2(Area *ABCD*) = Area *BDEF*

Q.E.D.

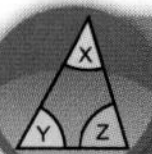

Worked Example 8.9

Prove that is $\sqrt{2}$ irrational.

Solution

This is an example of proof by contradiction.

We begin by assuming that it is not irrational (i.e. that it is rational) and then try to arrive at a contradiction.

Suppose $\sqrt{2}$ is rational. Then it can be written in the form of $\frac{p}{q}$, where p and q have no common factors other than 1 (a fraction in its simplest form).

Thus if $\sqrt{2} = \frac{p}{q}$, then squaring both sides gives $2 = \frac{p^2}{q^2}$.

Multiplying both sides by q^2 gives $2q^2 = p^2$ and so p^2 is clearly even.

If p^2 is even then we know that p must be even.

Therefore it can be written as $p = 2m$ where m is an integer.

Squaring both sides gives $p^2 = 4m^2$.

$p^2 = 2q^2$ and $p^2 = 4m^2$.

Therefore, $2q^2 = 4m^2$.

Dividing both sides by 2, gives $q^2 = 2m^2$.
Therefore q^2 is clearly even which means q is even.

If p and q are both even then they have 2 as a common factor, which contradicts the assumption that they have no common factor other than 1.

Thus our assumption is incorrect and $\sqrt{2}$ is therefore irrational.

Exercise 8.5

1. ΔABC is an isosceles triangle such that $|AB| = |BC|$. M is the midpoint of $[AC]$.

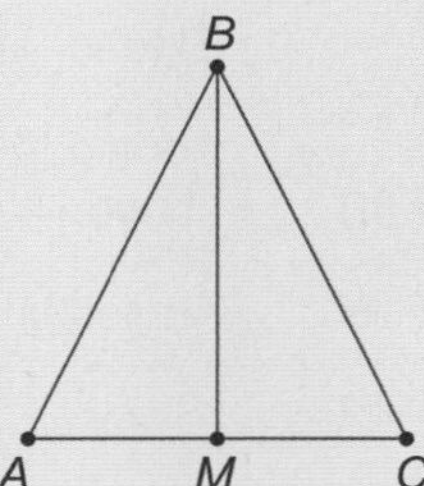

Show that $[MB]$ bisects the angle ABC.

2. Consider the following diagram.

$|AE| = |AD|$ and $|AB| = |AC|$.

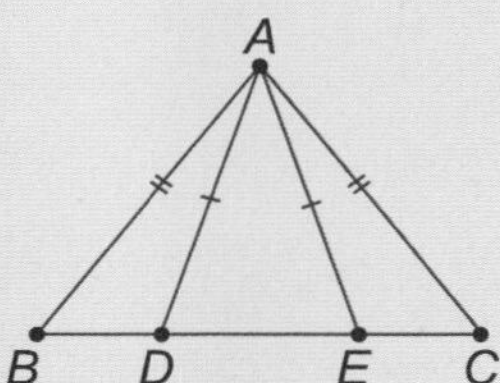

(i) Prove that $\Delta ABD \equiv \Delta AEC$.

(ii) Prove that $\Delta ABE \equiv \Delta ACD$.

3. $ABCD$ is a quadrilateral.

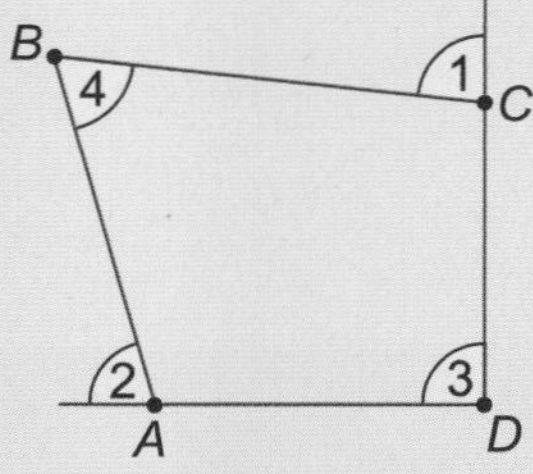

Show that $|\angle 1| + |\angle 2| = |\angle 3| + |\angle 4|$.

4. A part for a metal support of a bridge is being manufactured.

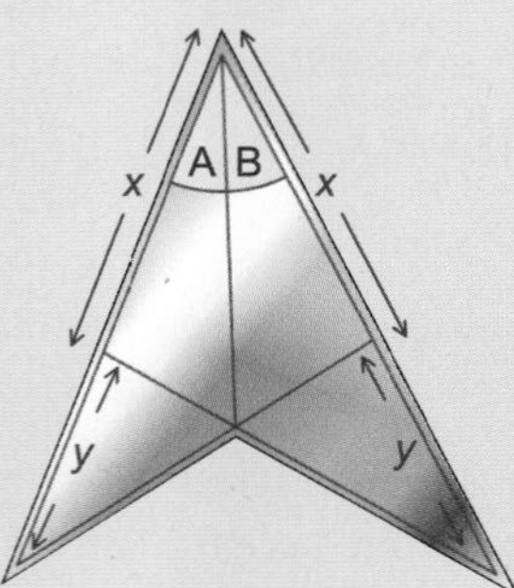

For the design to be stable, $|\angle A| = |\angle B|$. Show that this is the case.

5. Consider the rectangle $ABCD$.

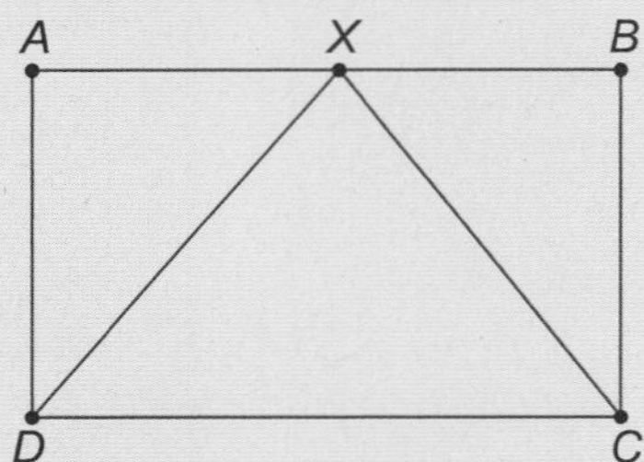

If X is the midpoint of $[AB]$, show that ΔDAX and ΔCBX have equal areas.

6. O is the centre of a circle with the chord $[AB]$ as shown.

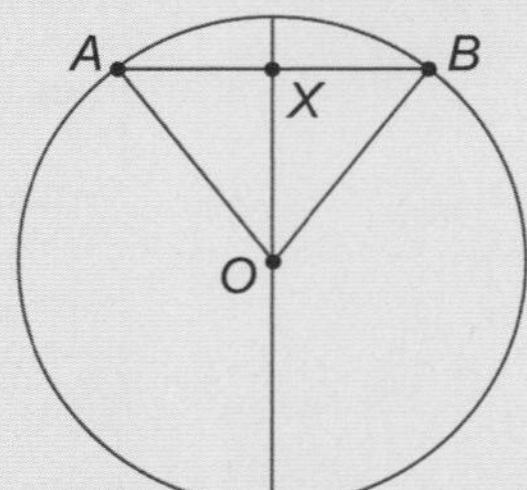

If $[OX]$ bisects $[AB]$, explain fully why $AB \perp OX$.

7. l and k are parallel lines.

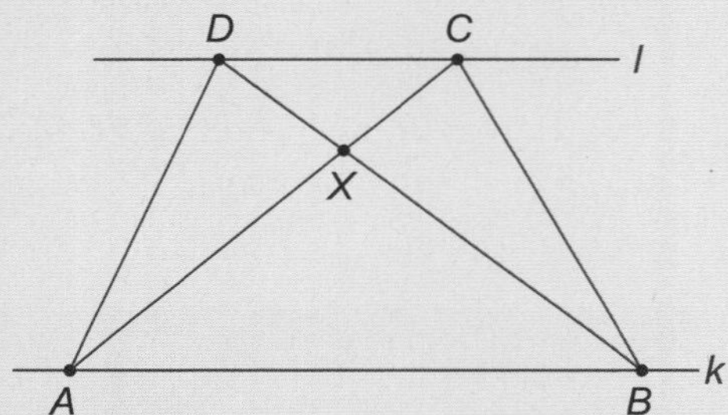

(i) Show that area of ΔABD = area of ΔABC.

(ii) Show that area of ΔADX = area of ΔBCX.

8. AB and CD are parallel lines. $|CA| = |CD|$.

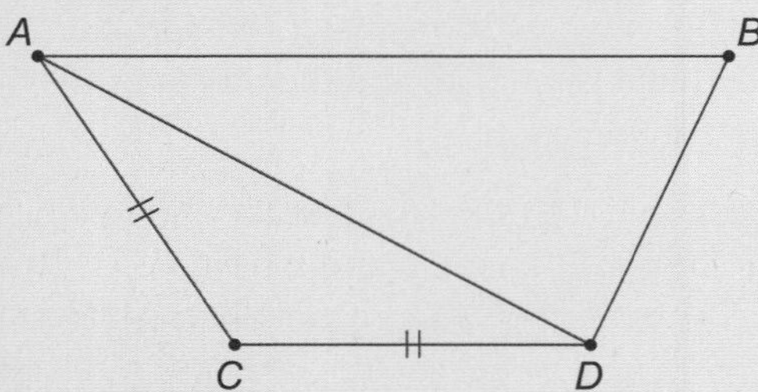

Show that AD bisects $\angle BAC$.

9. *DEFG* is a parallelogram.

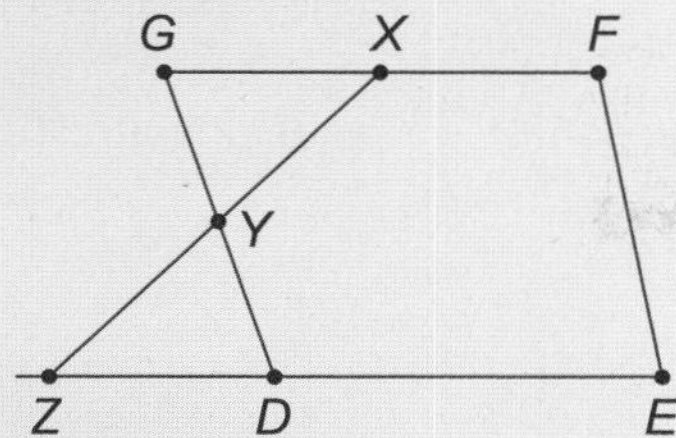

If *Y* is the midpoint of [*GD*], show that the area of *DEFG* = the area of *ZEFX*.

10. *ABCD* is a parallelogram. [*AX*] and [*BX*] are bisectors of the angles at *A* and *B*.

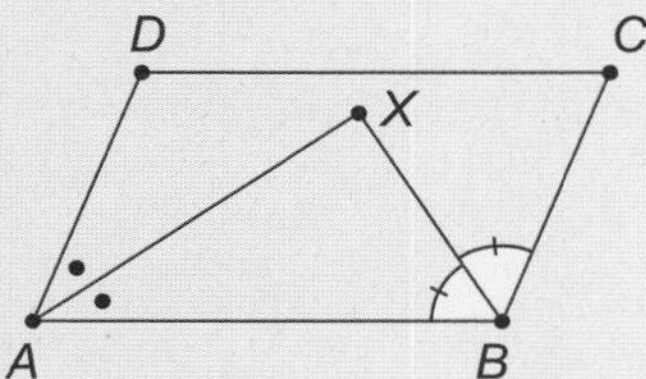

Prove that $|\angle AXB| = 90°$.

11. Consider the following diagram:

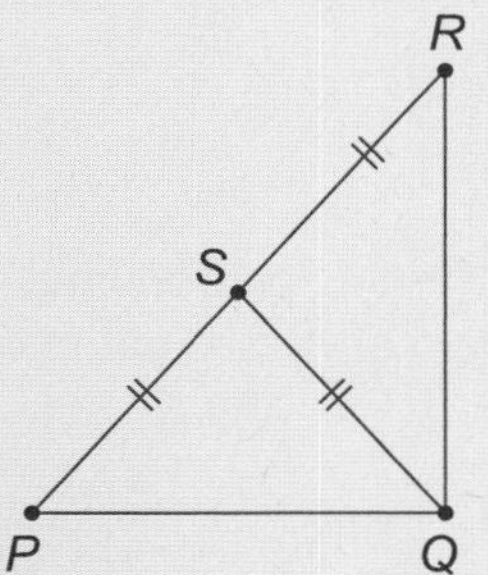

Prove that $|\angle PQR| = 90°$.

12. ΔABC is an isosceles triangle as shown. $|AB| = |AC|$.

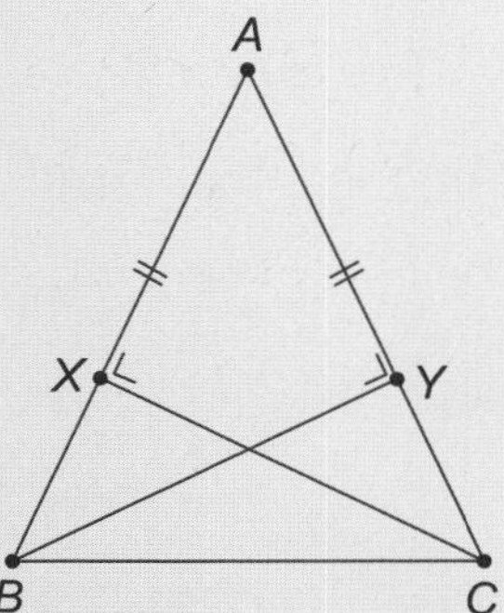

Prove that $\Delta AXC \equiv \Delta AYB$.

13. *ABC* is a triangle as shown.

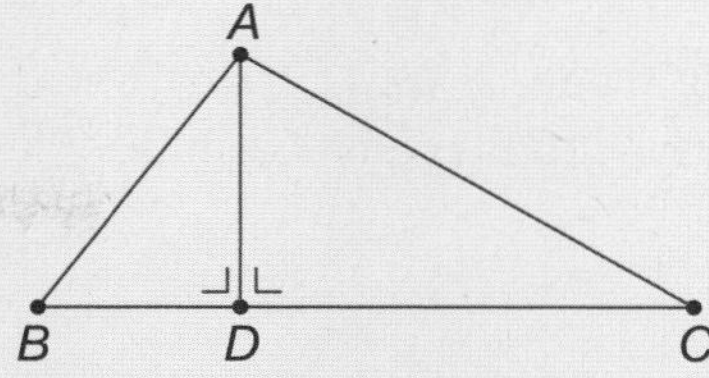

Prove that $|AB|^2 + |DC|^2 = |BD|^2 + |AC|^2$.

14. *ABC* is a triangle as shown. *E* is the midpoint of [*AB*] and *D* is the midpoint of [*AC*].

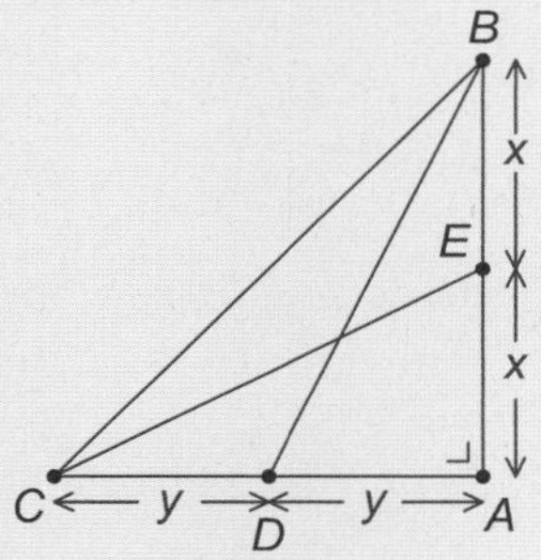

(i) Write $|BD|^2$ and $|CE|^2$ in terms of x and y.

(ii) Prove that $4|BD|^2 + 4|CE|^2 = 5|BC|^2$.

15. [*AB*] and [*QP*] are two diameters of a circle.

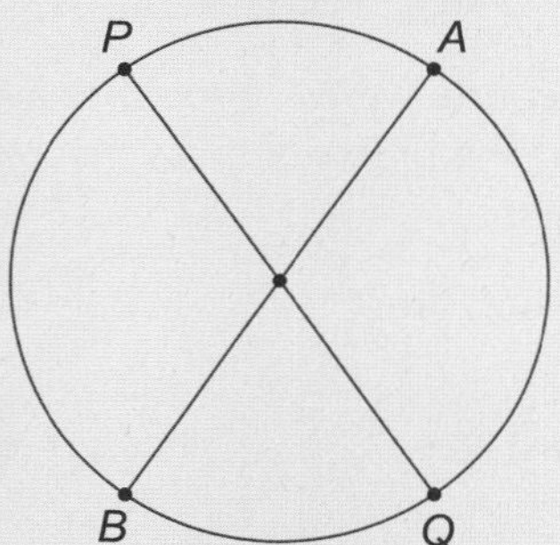

(i) Prove that $|\angle QAB| = |\angle QPB|$.

(ii) Prove that $AQ \parallel PB$.

16. *O* is the centre of a circle which has *TB* as a tangent.

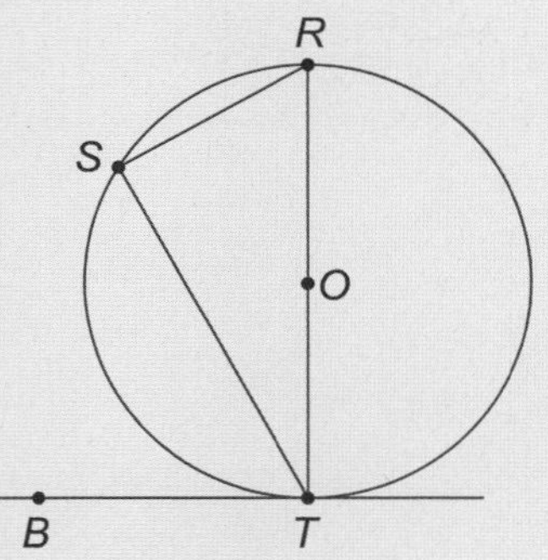

Show that $|\angle SRT| = |\angle STB|$.

17. [AB] is the diameter of a circle with centre O and tangent BT. $|\angle ADC| = 120°$.

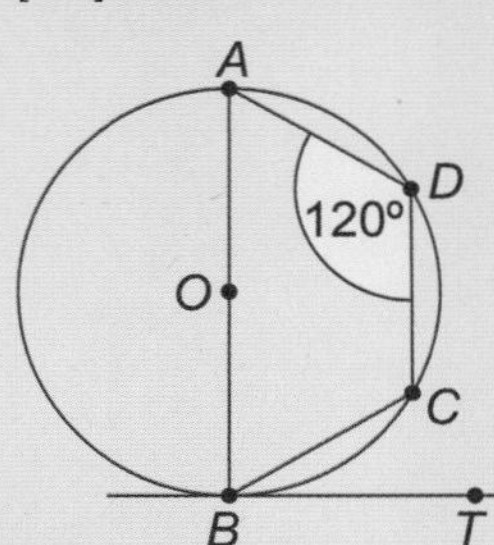

(i) Show that ΔBOC is equilateral.

(ii) If $|AD| = |DC|$, prove that $ADCO$ is a parallelogram.

18. PQR is a triangle with an incircle as shown.

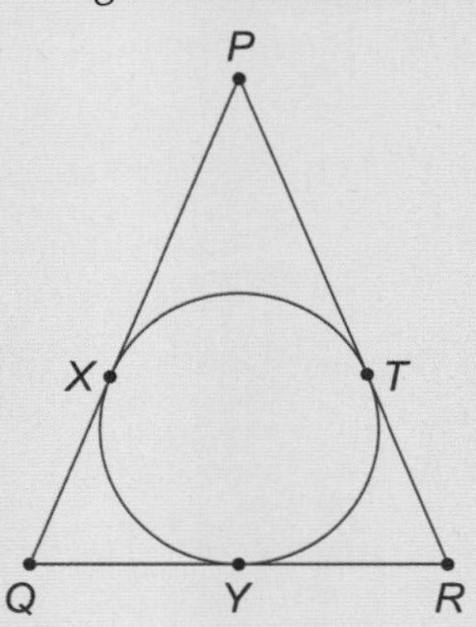

Prove that $|PR| + |RQ| > |PQ|$.

19. In the diagram, [AC] is the bisector of $|\angle TAB|$.

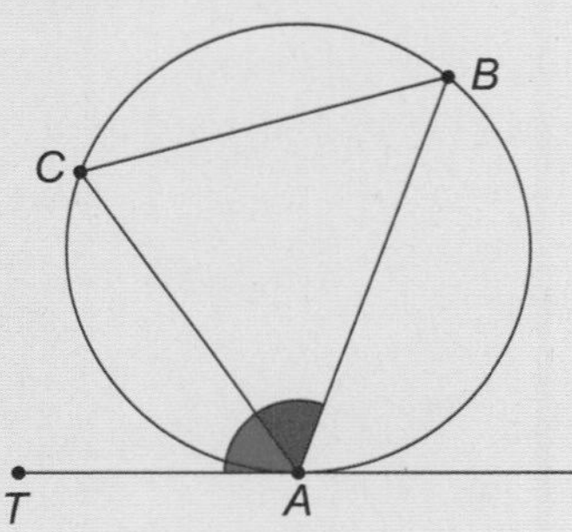

Prove that $|AC| = |CB|$.

8.6 THEOREMS 11, 12, 13

On our course we will also cover a set of very important theorems concerning parallel lines and similar triangles. The proofs of these theorems can be used to prove the theorem of Pythagoras, a cornerstone of geometry.

These proofs are:

Theorem 11 (Formal proof in Appendix)

If three parallel lines cut off equal segments on some transversal line, then they will cut off equal segments on any other transversal.

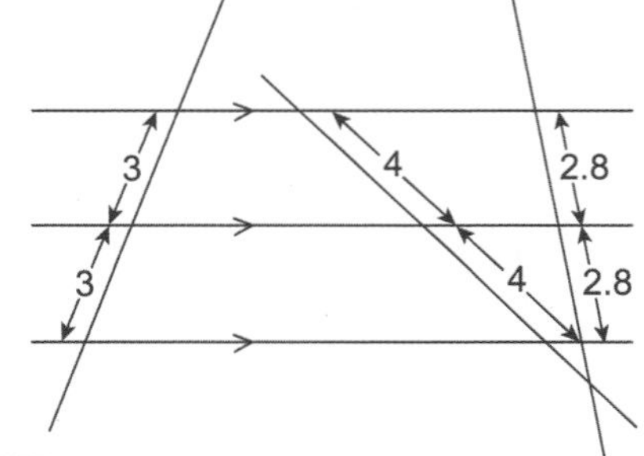

Theorem 12 (Formal proof in Appendix)

Let ABC be a triangle. If a line l is parallel to BC and cuts [AB] in the ratio $m : n$, then it also cuts [AC] in the same ratio.

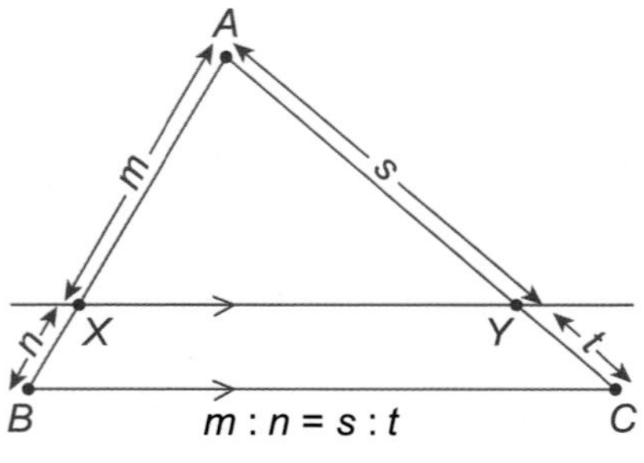

FORMULA

$$\frac{|AX|}{|XB|} = \frac{|AY|}{|YC|} \quad \text{or} \quad \frac{|AB|}{|XB|} = \frac{|AC|}{|YC|} \quad \text{or} \quad \frac{|AX|}{|XB|} = \frac{|AY|}{|YC|}$$

Theorem 13 (Formal proof in Appendix)

If two triangles are similar, then their sides are proportional, in order.

In the following similar triangles, the corresponding sides are proportional:

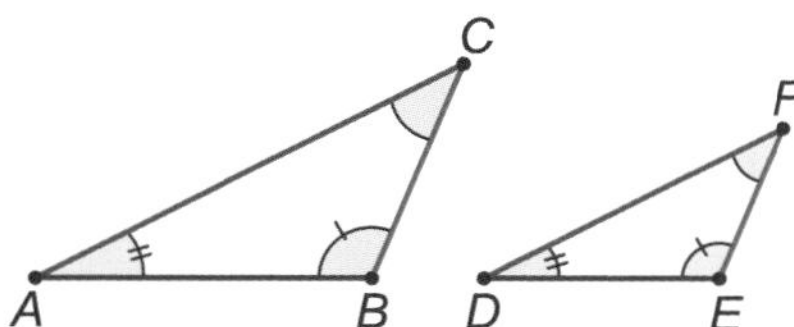

FORMULA

$$\frac{|AB|}{|DE|} = \frac{|AC|}{|DF|} = \frac{|BC|}{|EF|}$$

Remember that we can also use these theorems to prove that lines are parallel.

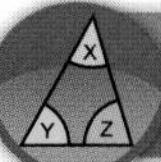

Worked Example 8.10

In the diagram, $XY \parallel BC$ and $YZ \parallel CD$.

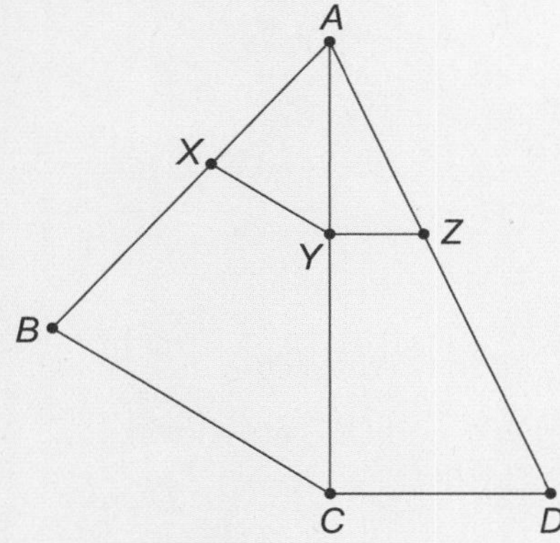

Prove that $XZ \parallel BD$.

Solution

We must identify which sides and which ratios we will use.

$XY \parallel BC$ $\quad\quad$ $YZ \parallel CD$

$$\Rightarrow \frac{|AX|}{|XB|} = \frac{|AY|}{|YC|} \quad\quad \Rightarrow \frac{|AY|}{|YC|} = \frac{|AZ|}{|ZD|}$$

We can see that these two sides are linked by the ratio $\frac{|AY|}{|YC|}$.

$$\Rightarrow \frac{|AX|}{|XB|} = \frac{|AZ|}{|ZD|}$$

$\therefore XZ \parallel BD$

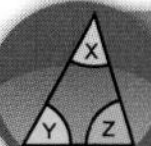

Worked Example 8.11

In the diagram, $BD \parallel CE$ and $DF \parallel EG$.

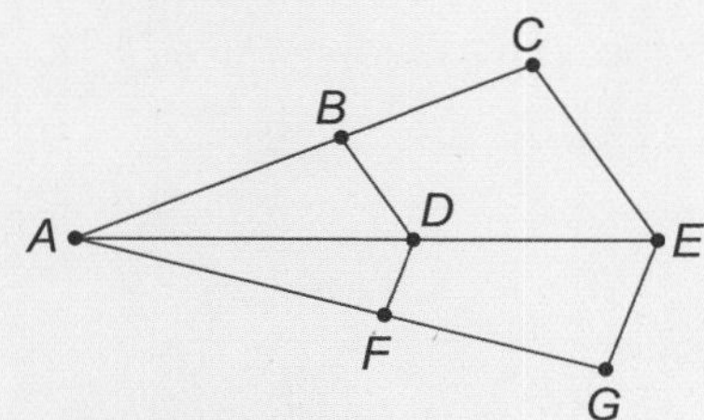

Prove that $|AC| . |FG| = |AG| . |BC|$.

Solution

We note that $|AC| . |FG| = |AG| . |BC|$ could also be written as $\frac{|AC|}{|BC|} = \frac{|AG|}{|FG|}$.

$BD \parallel CE$

$$\Rightarrow \frac{|AC|}{|BC|} = \frac{|AE|}{|DE|}$$

$DF \parallel EG$

$$\Rightarrow \frac{|AE|}{|DE|} = \frac{|AG|}{|FG|}$$

$$\Rightarrow \frac{|AC|}{|BC|} = \frac{|AG|}{|FG|}$$

$\therefore |AC| . |FG| = |AG| . |BC|$ (cross-multiply)

Exercise 8.6

1. Consider the following diagram:

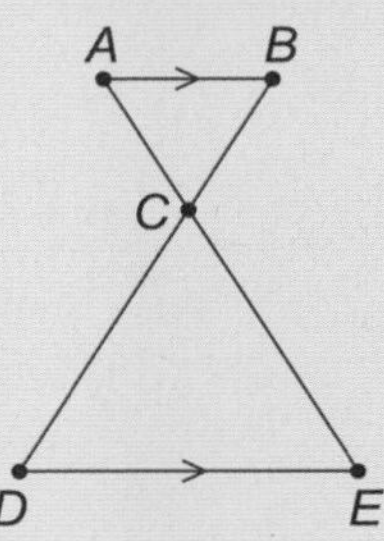

(i) Prove that ΔABC is similar to ΔCDE.

(ii) Prove that $\frac{|AC|}{|CE|} = \frac{|BC|}{|CD|}$.

2. Consider the following diagram:

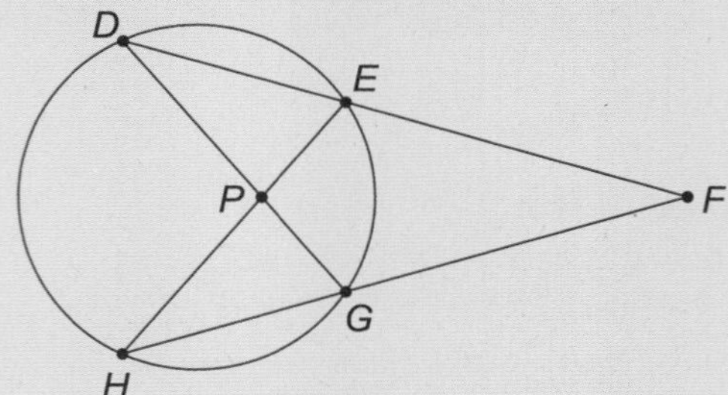

Show that ΔDGF and ΔHEF are similar.

3. *PQRS* is a trapezium (where one side of a quadrilateral is parallel to one other side) as shown.

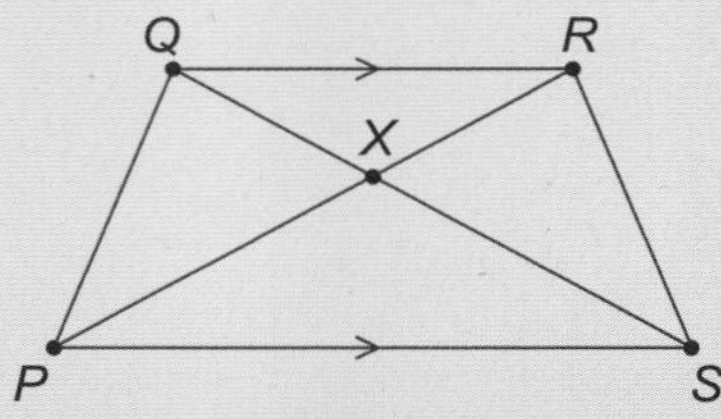

(i) Prove that ΔPXS is similar to ΔQXR.

(ii) Show that $|PX| \,.\, |QX| = |XR| \,.\, |XS|$.

4. In the triangle *XYZ*, $|XR| = |ZS|$ and $|YR| = |YS|$.

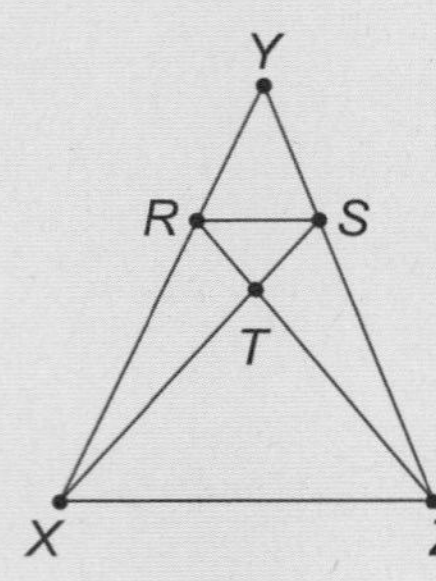

(i) Prove that $RS \parallel XZ$.

(ii) Prove that ΔRTX and ΔSTZ are similar.

(iii) Prove that ΔXTZ is an isosceles triangle.

5. *ABC* is a triangle as shown. $EF \parallel BC$ and $DF \parallel EC$.

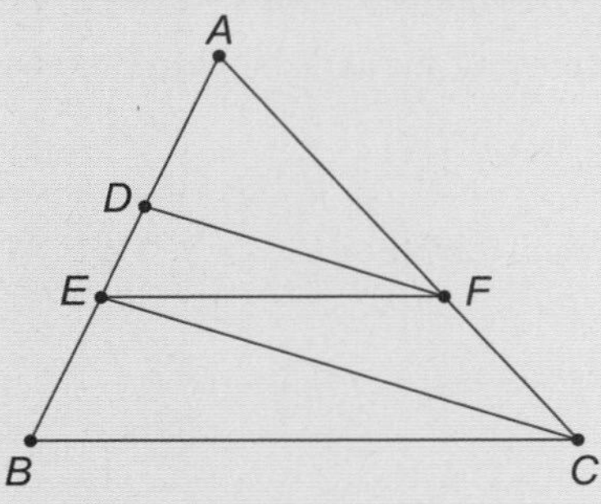

Prove that $\frac{|AD|}{|DE|} = \frac{|AE|}{|EB|}$.

6. In the diagram shown, $SU \parallel QR$ and $ST \parallel QU$.

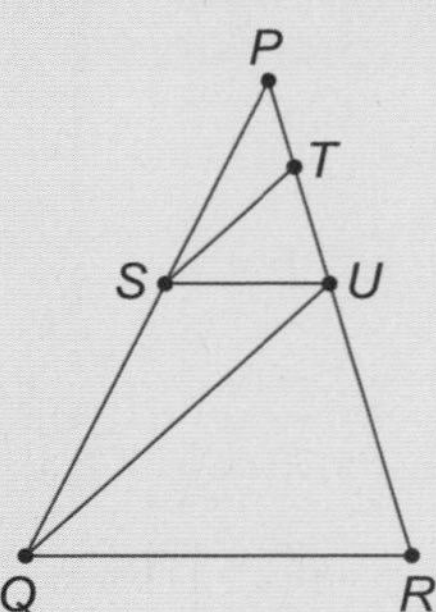

Prove that $|PT| : |TU| = |PU| : |UR|$.

7. Two triangles *ABC* and *DBC* are shown. $EF \parallel AB$ and $EG \parallel BD$.

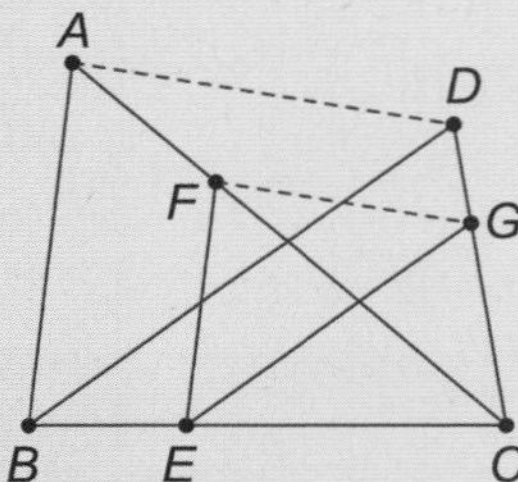

Prove that $FG \parallel AD$.

8. *ABCD* is a trapezium as shown. $AB \parallel EF \parallel DC$.

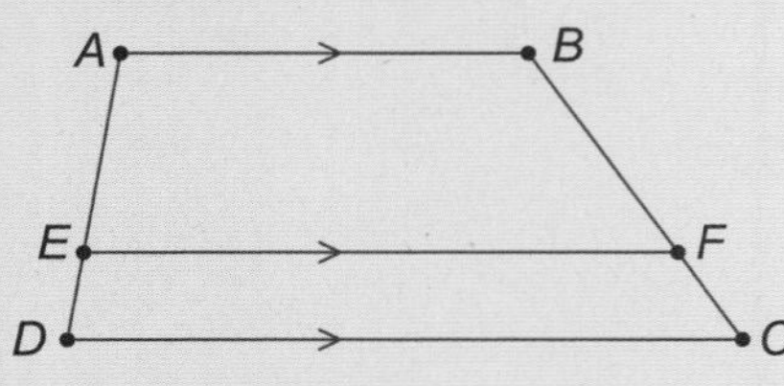

Prove that $\frac{|AE|}{|ED|} = \frac{|BF|}{|FC|}$.

GEOMETRY II

9. ΔABC is right-angled at C. $CD \perp AB$.

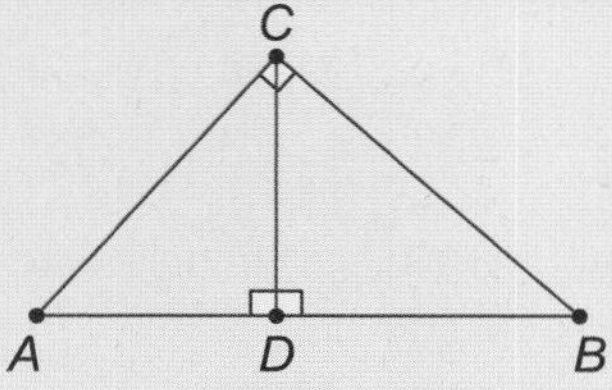

(i) Establish that ΔABC and ΔBDC are similar (equiangular).

(ii) Prove that $|BC|^2 = |AB| \,.\, |BD|$.

10. ΔABC is right-angled at C. $CD \perp AB$.

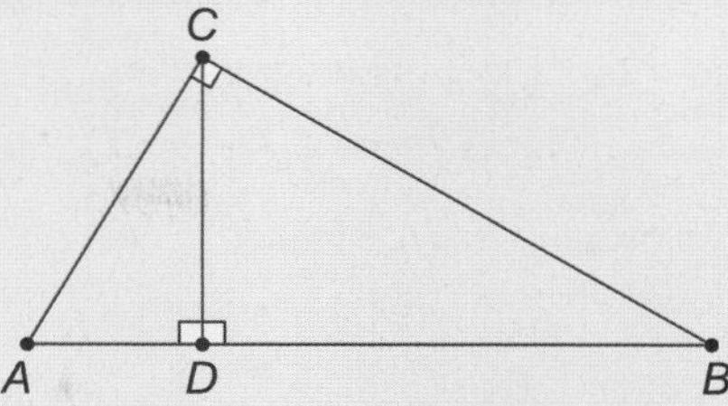

(i) Establish that ΔABC and ΔADC are similar (equiangular).

(ii) Prove that $|AC|^2 = |AB| \,.\, |AD|$.

11. ABC is a triangle inscribed in a circle of centre O. Prove that $|AC|^2 = |AD| \,.\, |AB|$.

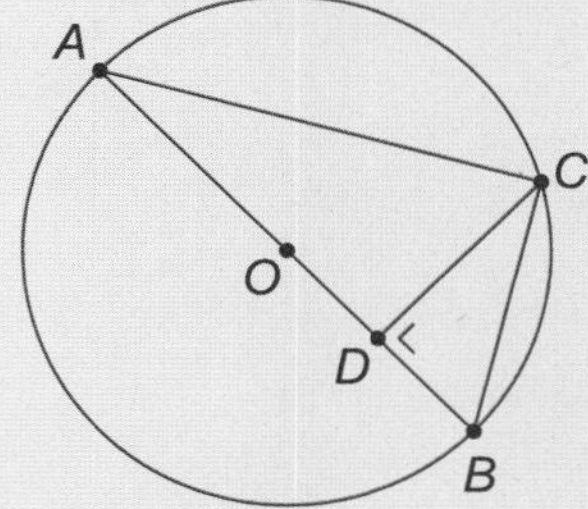

12. XD and BY are straight lines such that:

- In ΔABC, $|AX| : |XB| = |AP| : |PC|$.
- In ΔACD, $|AP| : |PC| = |AY| : |YD|$.

(i) Prove that $BPDC$ is a parallelogram.

(ii) Prove that $XY \parallel BD$.

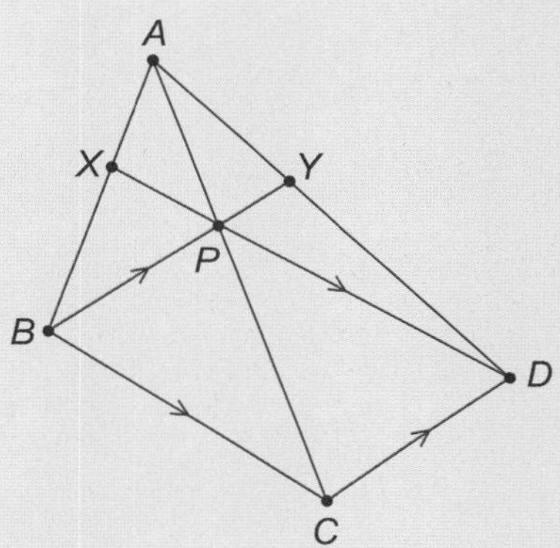

13. A triangle ABC with altitudes $[AD]$, $[BE]$ and $[CF]$ is shown.

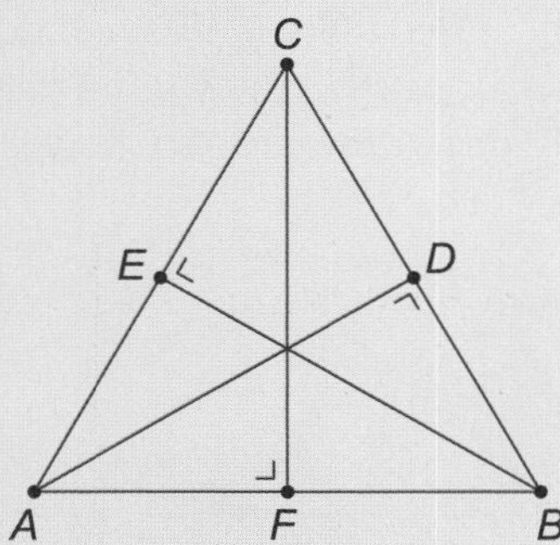

(i) Prove that ΔABD and ΔBCF are equiangular.

(ii) Prove that
$|AB| \,.\, |CF| = |BC| \,.\, |AD| = |AC| \,.\, |BE|$.

The formal proofs of theorems 4, 6, 9, 11, 12, 13, 14 and 19 can be found in the Appendix at the back of this book.

Revision Exercises

Note: Some questions will require the use of trigonometry.

1. (a) Two equilateral triangles ABC and DEF are shown.

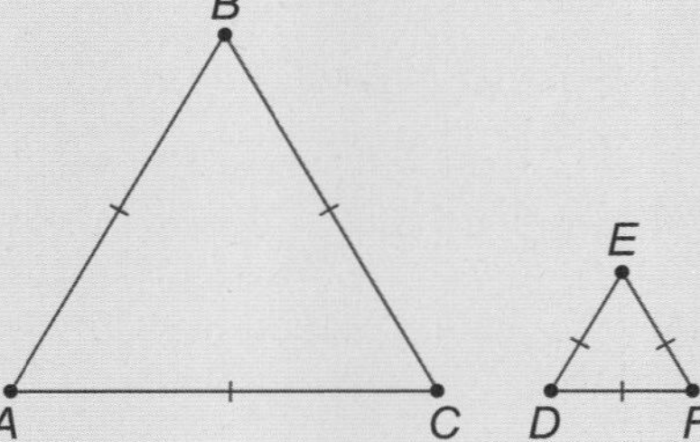

If $|AB|$ is three times the length of $|DE|$, how many triangles congruent to triangle DEF would fit inside triangle ABC?

(b) A regular hexagon of side 4 cm is inscribed in a circle with centre O as shown.

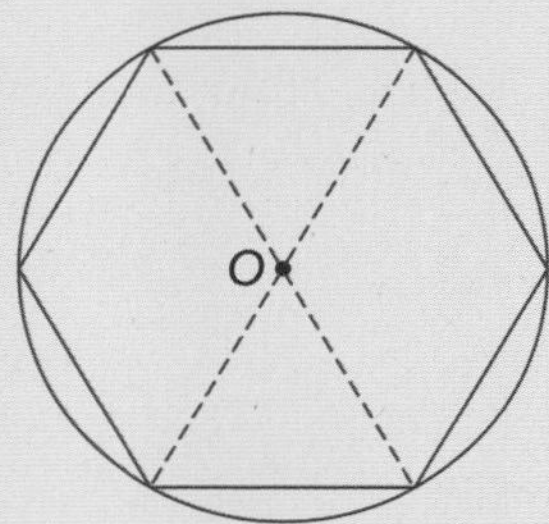

(i) Find the area of the circle.

(ii) Find the area of the hexagon.

(c) A design for a construction company's new logo is shown. It consists of a square of side length y inscribed in a circle s and a circle p inscribed in the square.

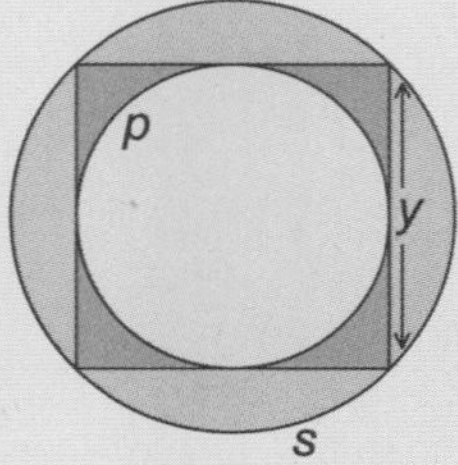

(i) Find the radius of the circle s in terms of y.

(ii) Find the radius of the circle p in terms of y.

(iii) Find the ratio of the area of the circle s to the area of the circle p.

2. (a) A circle circumscribes a triangle with side lengths of 7, 24 and 25.

(i) Find the area of the triangle.

(ii) Find the radius of the circle.

(b) A diagram for a plot of agricultural land $ABCD$ is shown.

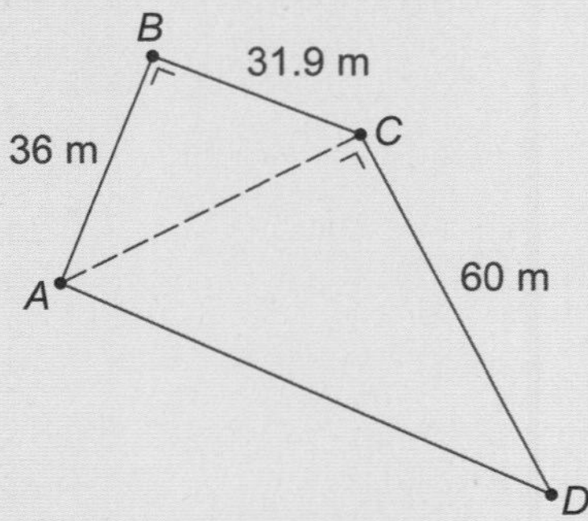

(i) Find the area of the plot of land.

It is decided to fertilise the plot at a cost of €5 per square metre.

(ii) Find the cost of fertilising the land to the nearest euro.

A fence is erected from B to D to divide the plot of land in two.

(iii) Find the area of each of the smaller plots and the length of the fence $[BD]$.

(c) The right-angled triangle ABC with side lengths of a, b and c is shown. The altitude d and the side length y are also shown.

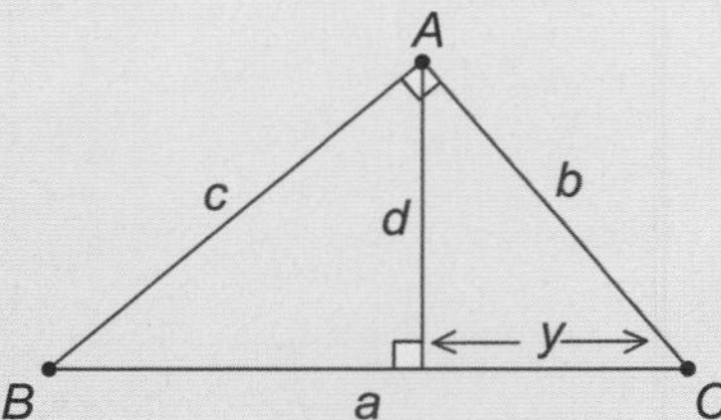

(i) Find the value of d^2 in terms of a and y.

(ii) Find the value of c^2 in terms of a and y.

(iii) Find the value of b^2 in terms of a and y.

(iv) Hence, show that $b^2 d^2 = c^2 y^2$.

3. (a) A sail boat has two similar sails as shown.

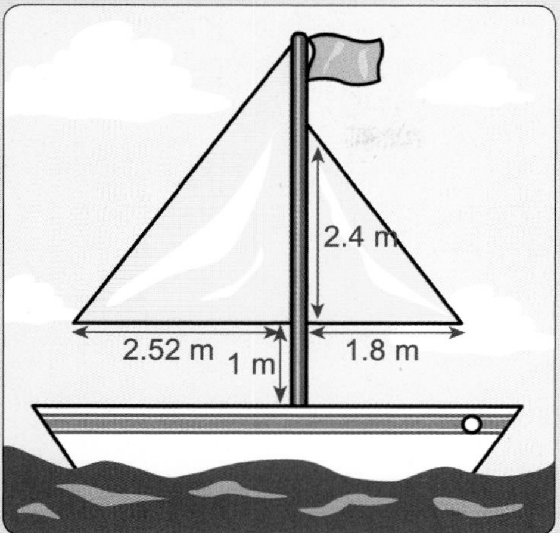

(i) Find the height of the mast.

(ii) Find the total area of sail.

(b) A square $ABCD$ is shown.

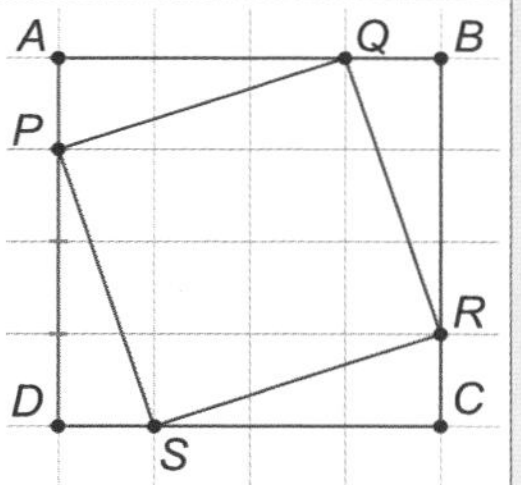

Find the area of the quadrilateral $PQRS$.

(c) The circumcircle of an equilateral triangle ABC has a radius length of 12 cm.

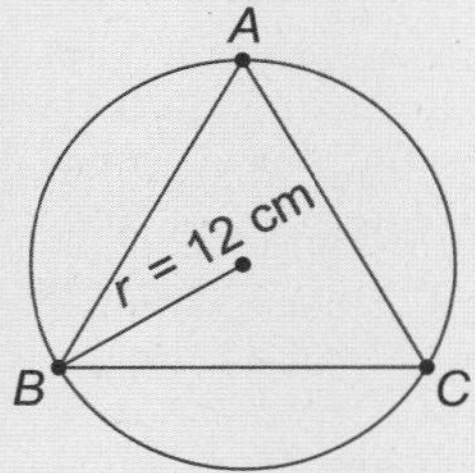

(i) Find $|AB|$.

(ii) Find the area of the triangle ABC.

4. (a) O is the centre of a circle with tangents RP and QT.

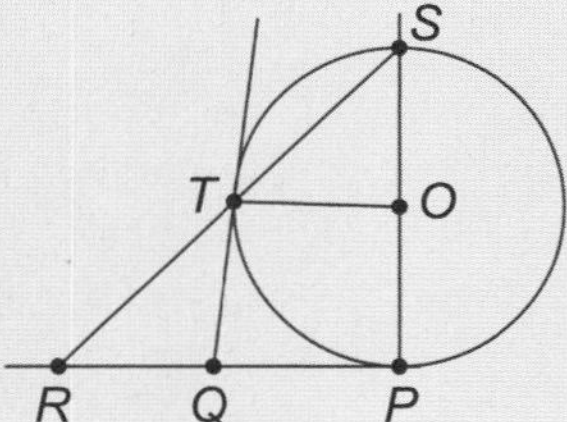

Show that the triangle QRT is an isosceles triangle.

(b) A building is 6 m from the point B as shown in the diagram.

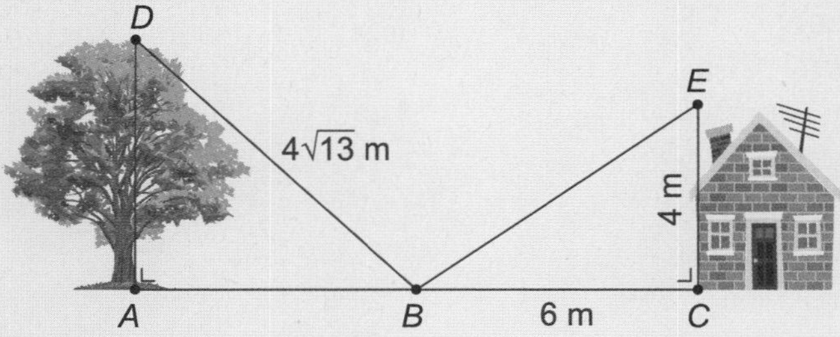

If $|\angle DBA| = |\angle EBC|$, find:

(i) The height of the tree

(ii) The distance between the tree and the house

(c) Two pylons A and B are 100 m apart and connected by supporting cables.

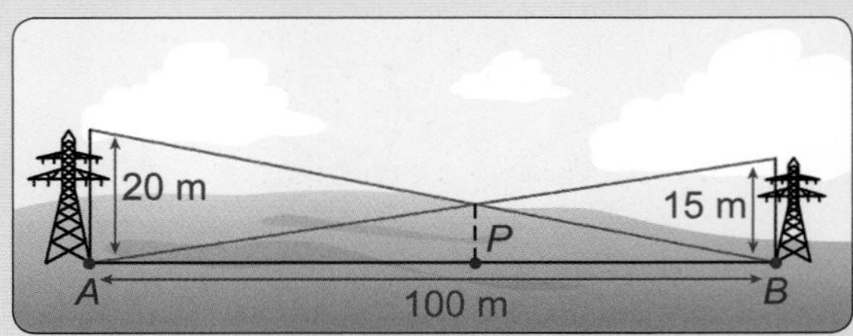

To increase stability, it is decided to put another smaller pylon between the two at the point P, the point of intersection of the two cables.

Find, to the nearest metre:

(i) The height of this smaller pylon

(ii) The distance from the smaller pylon to pylons A and B

The two pylons A and B are now x metres apart.

(iii) Show that the height of the smaller pylon is independent of x.

5. (a) Consider the circle with centre O and tangents RP and RT.

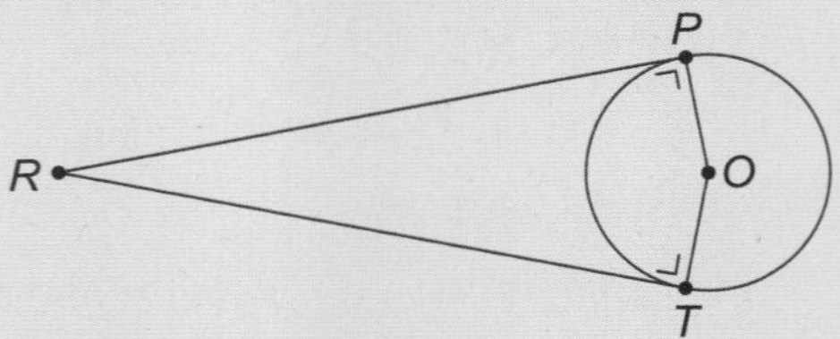

Prove that RPT is an isosceles triangle.

(b) A regular rectangular solid is shown.

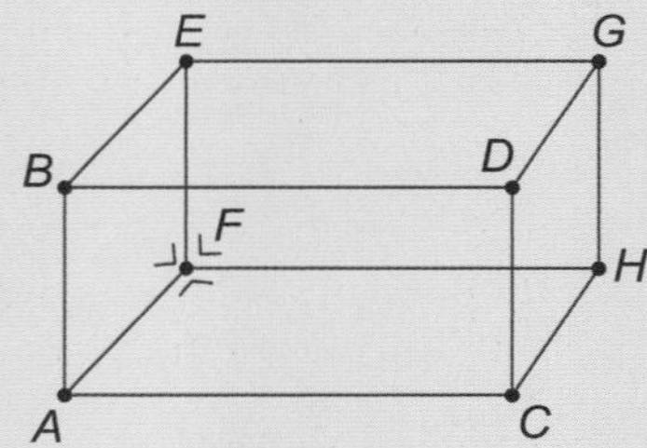

Prove that $|EC|^2 = |AF|^2 + |AC|^2 + |AB|^2$.

(c) A rectangular sheet of metal $ABCD$ is shown. A triangular piece of metal AEF is to be cut from this sheet. The line AF bisects the angle BAE.

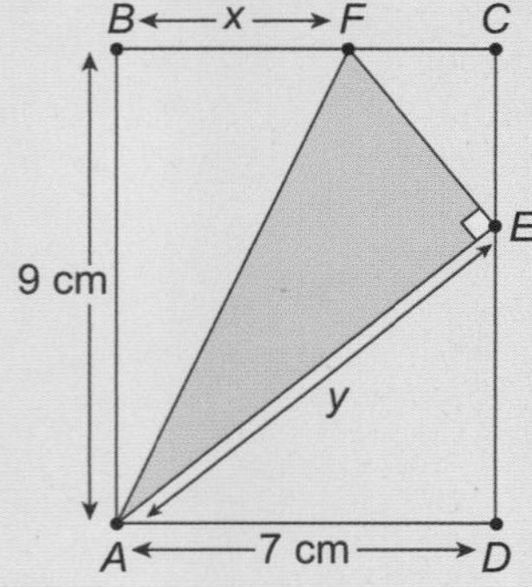

(i) Show that $|CE|^2 = 7(2x - 7)$.

(ii) Find the value of y.

(iii) Find the area of the triangle AFE in terms of x.

6. (a) The isosceles triangle PQR is inscribed in a circle with centre O. RS is a tangent to the circle.

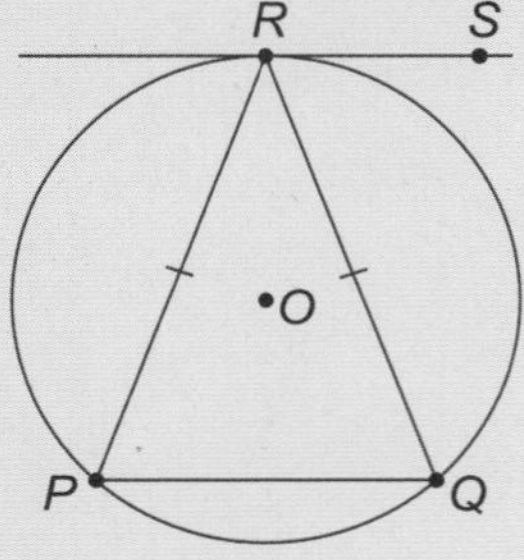

Prove that $PQ \parallel SR$.

(b) A person 1.4 m high measures the length of her shadow and the length of a tree shadow on a sunny day. She records the results as shown on the diagram.

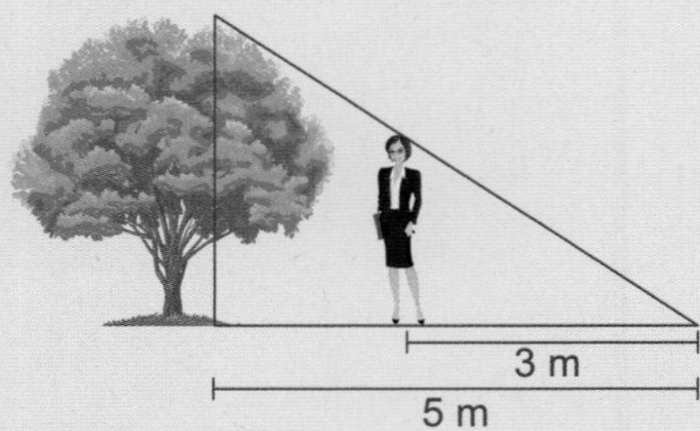

Calculate the height of the tree (to the nearest centimetre).

(c) A right-angled triangle ABC is shown.

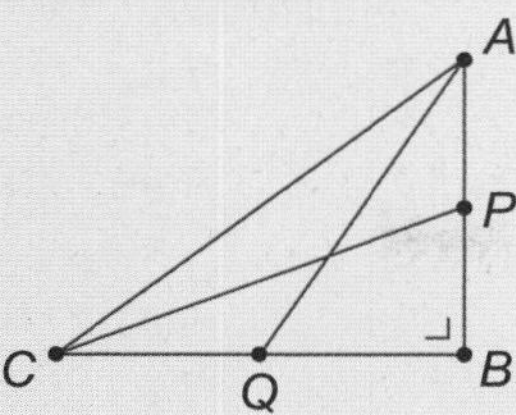

(i) Prove that $|AC|^2 - |PC|^2 = |AB|^2 - |PB|^2$.

(ii) Show that $|AC|^2 - |PC|^2 = |AQ|^2 - |PQ|^2$.

7. (a) Two circles intersect at the points X and Y as shown. O is the centre of the smaller circle.

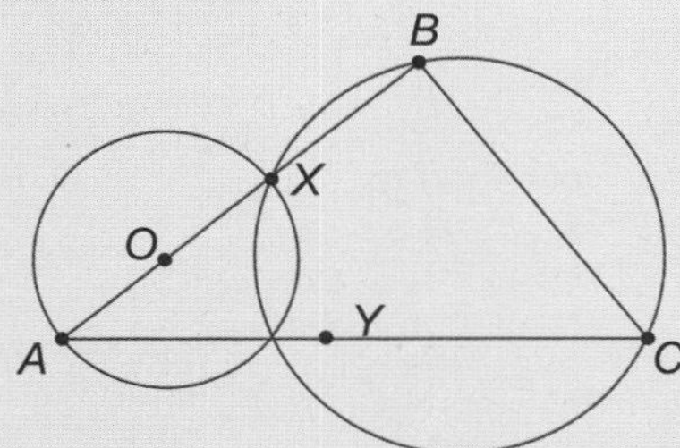

Show that $|\angle ABC| = 90°$.

(b) Two circles with centres O and M are shown. AC and EC are tangents to both circles. (Diagram is not to scale.)

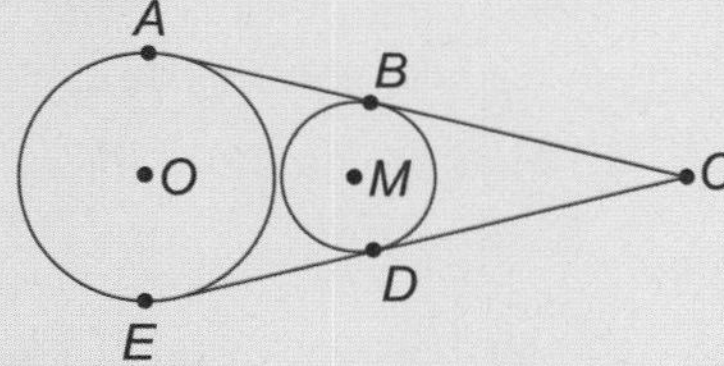

If $|AB| : |BC|$ is 1 : 4 and $|EC| = 25$ cm, find $|ED|$.

(c) A river 5 m wide with two parallel sides AB and CD is shown. A boat can moor at points A, B, C or D.

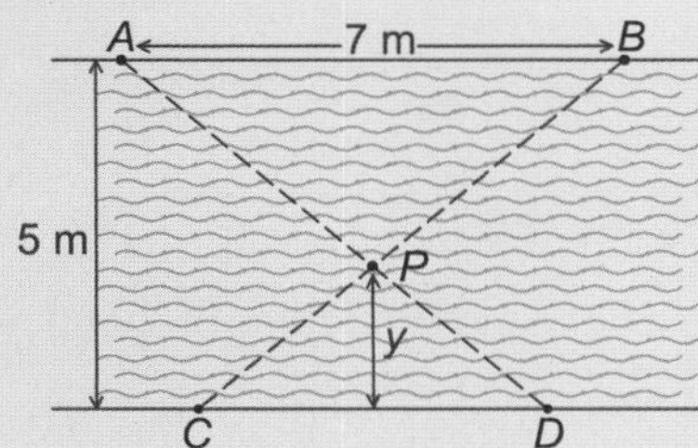

It is decided to place a buoy at a point P, the intersection of $[AB]$ and $[CD]$. The perpendicular distance between P and $[CD]$ is y.

(i) Find $|CD|$ in terms of y.

(ii) Find the sum of the area of ΔABP and ΔCDP in terms of y.

8. (a) $PQRS$ is a quadrilateral with diagonals $[PR]$ and $[QS]$ such that $|PR| = |QS|$. Also, $|PS| = |QR|$.

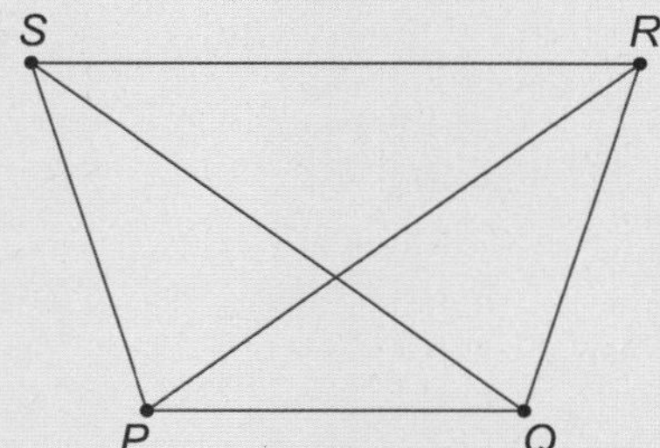

(i) Identify two congruent triangles. Give reasons for your answer.

(ii) Identify two isosceles triangles. Give reasons for your answer.

(iii) Show that PQ must be parallel to RS.

(b) k is a circle of radius r and centre O. M is the midpoint of $[OP]$.

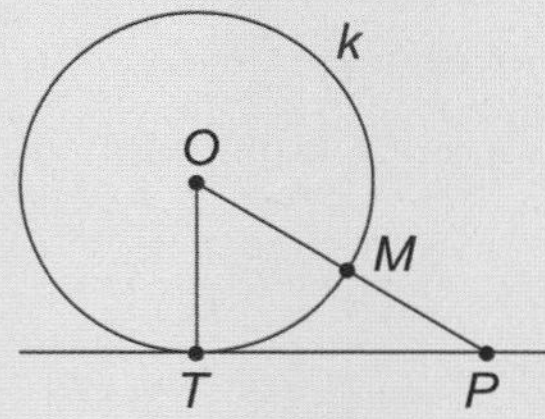

A tangent is drawn to the circle from P. It touches the circle at T.

Find $|PT|$ in terms of r.

(c) In the triangle ABC, O is the centre of the incircle with a radius length of r cm.

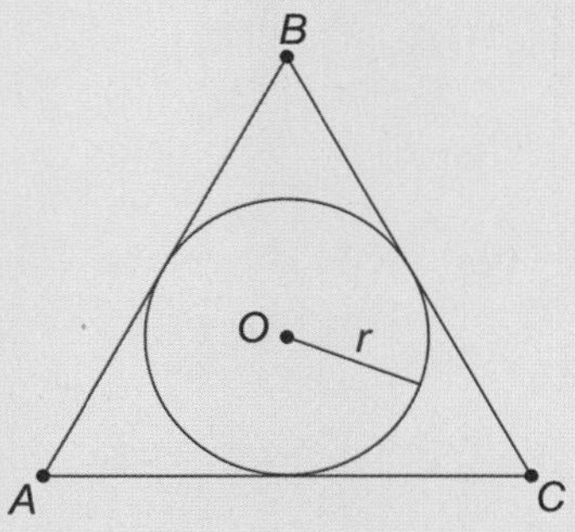

(i) Show that:

Area $\Delta ABC = \frac{1}{2}$(Perimeter ΔABC) $\times r$.

(ii) Find the perimeter of a triangle with an incircle radius length of 8 cm and an area of 500 cm^2.

9. (a) A council wishes to build a new swimming pool that will service three towns A, B and C. The distance between each town is 24 km.

The swimming pool will be located at an equal distance from all three towns. Find the distance between the swimming pool and each town.

(b) Consider the triangle PQR. $ST \parallel QR$ and $|\angle PTS| = |\angle STQ|$.

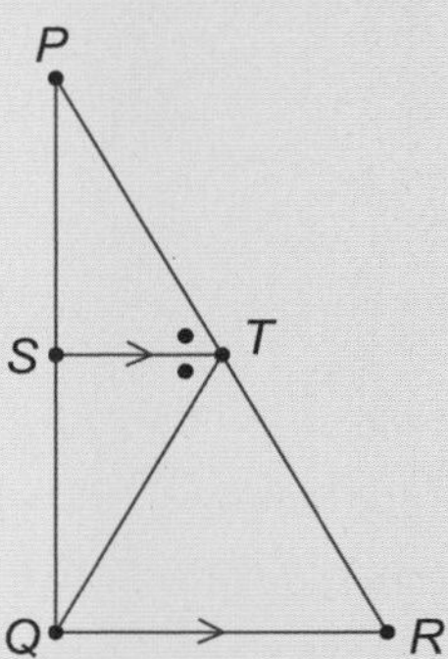

(i) Prove that TQR is an isosceles triangle

(ii) Show that $|PS| \cdot |TQ| = |PT| \cdot |SQ|$.

(c) In a rectangle $ABCD$, $|AB| = 2|BC|$.

The point E is the midpoint of $[AD]$.

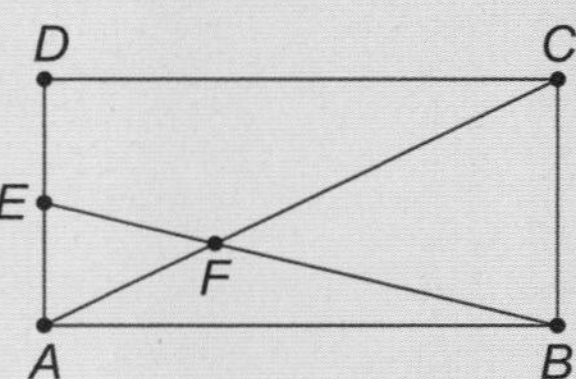

(i) Show that ΔAEF and ΔBFC are similar.

(ii) If $BC = x$ units, find $|AC|$ in terms of x.

(iii) If the point E is moved such that $|AE| = \frac{1}{5}|AD|$, find $|EB|$ in terms of x.

10. (a) A truncated right-circular cone is shown.

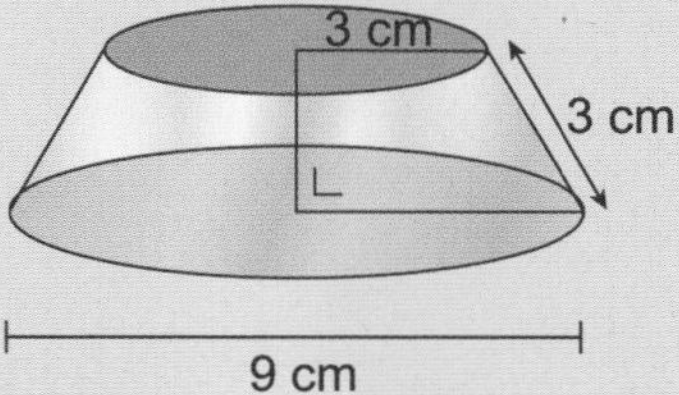

Find the height of the original cone.

(b) (i) Construct the circumcentre of an equilateral triangle. Label as in diagram shown.

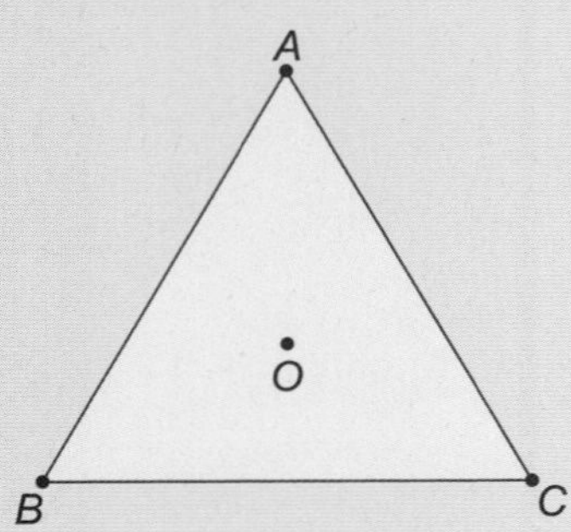

(ii) Let the length of $[AB] = y$. Find the shortest distance between O and $[AB]$ in terms of y and r, where r is the radius of the circumcircle.

(c) An equilateral triangle of side length x is inscribed in a circle as shown.

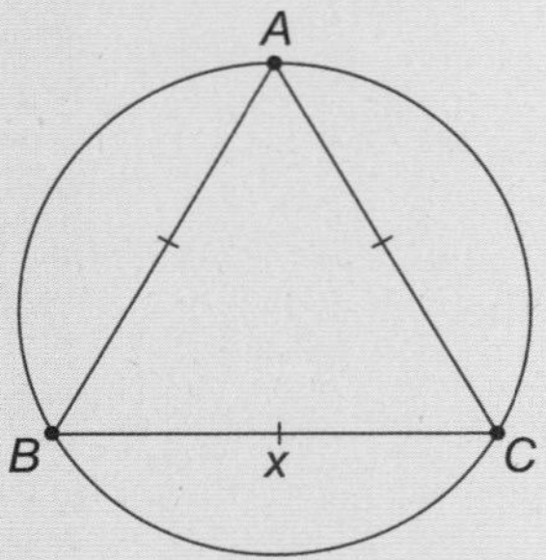

(i) Find the perpendicular height of the triangle in terms of x.

(ii) Find the radius of the circumcircle in terms of x.

The incircle of the triangle is then drawn as shown.

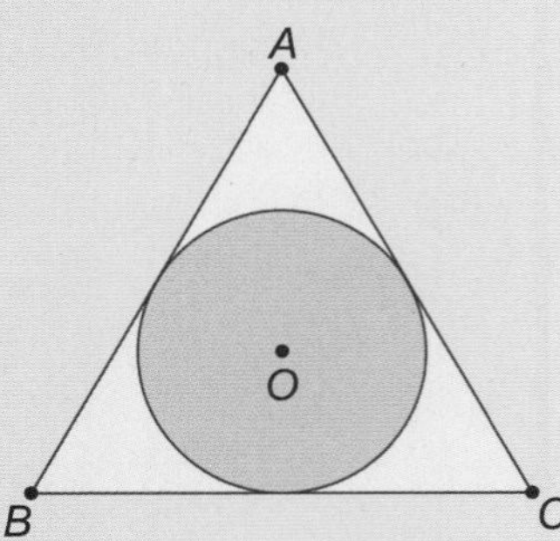

(iii) Find the radius of the incircle in terms of x.

(iv) Find the ratio of the area of the incircle to the area of the circumcircle.

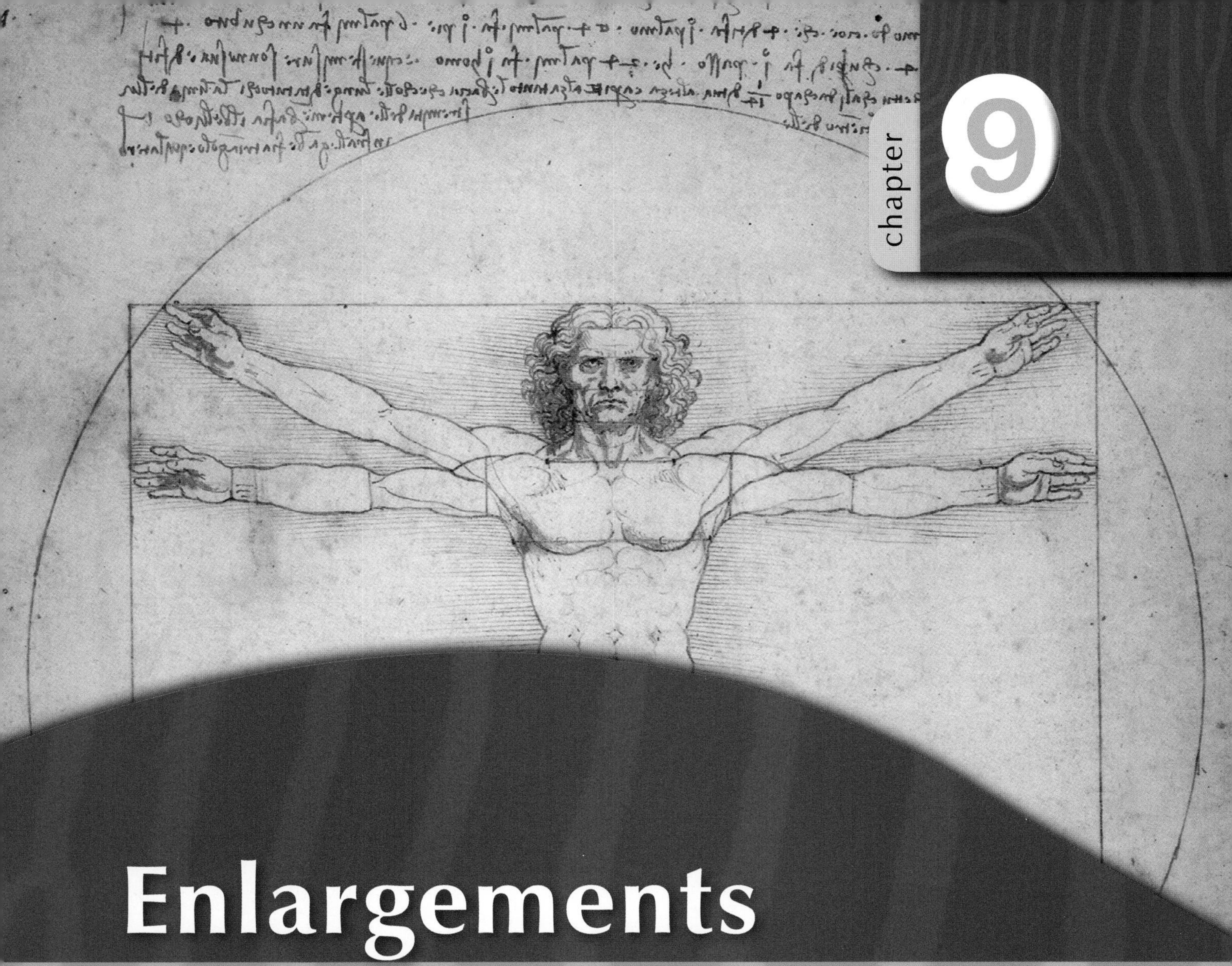

chapter 9

Enlargements

Learning Outcomes

In this chapter you will:

- Investigate enlargements, paying attention to:
  - Centre of enlargement
  - Scale factor k, where $0 < k < 1$, $k > 1$, $k \in Q$
  - Area
- Solve problems involving enlargements

9.1 TRANSFORMATIONS

In geometry, a **transformation** occurs when a shape's size or position is changed or transformed. The point or shape we start with is called the **object**. The transformed shape is called the **image**.

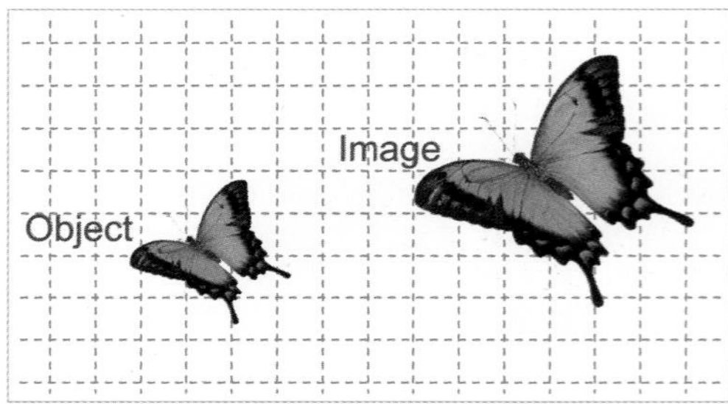

YOU SHOULD REMEMBER...

- Transformations
- Area of a triangle is $\frac{1}{2}ab \sin C$

KEY WORDS

- **Object**
- **Image**
- **Enlargement**
- **Centre of enlargement**
- **Scale factor**

There are many different types of transformations.

Translation

We can move the triangle ABC under the **translation** $\overrightarrow{PQ}$.

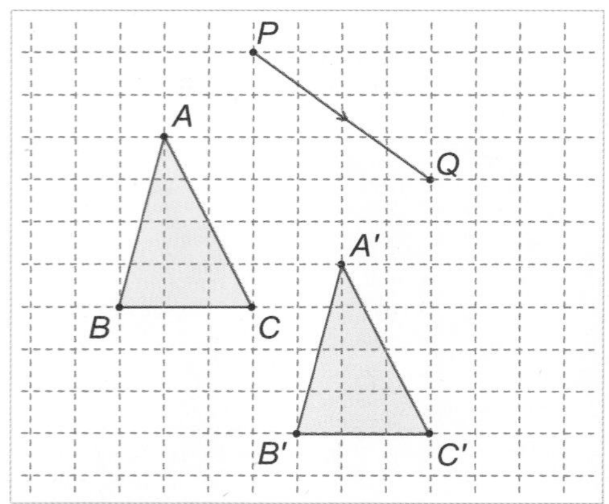

A **translation** is when a point or shape is moved in a straight line. A translation moves every point the same distance and in the same direction without changing orientation of the shape or rotating it.

In a translation the image and the object are identical and face the same way.

Each point in the object shape has been moved the same distance as $|PQ|$, parallel to PQ and in the direction of P to Q.

If ΔABC is the object then the image can be labelled as $\Delta A'B'C'$.

Central Symmetry (Through a Point)

In a **central symmetry**, each point is mapped through the point O and reflected out the other side. $|DO| = |OD'|$, $|EO| = |OE'|$ and $|FO| = |OF'|$.

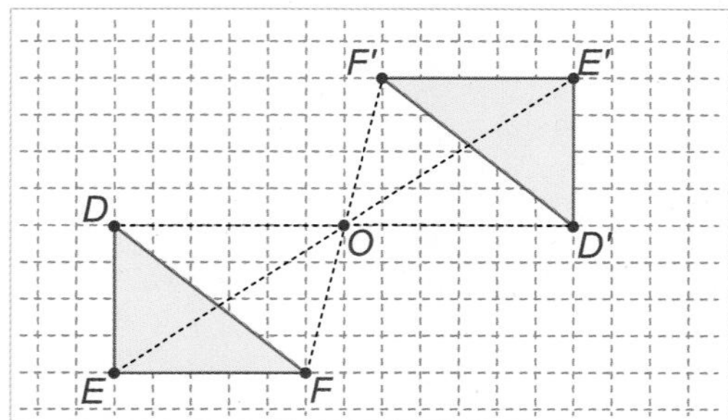

A **central symmetry** is a reflection through a point.

In a central symmetry, the image will be upside down and facing the object.

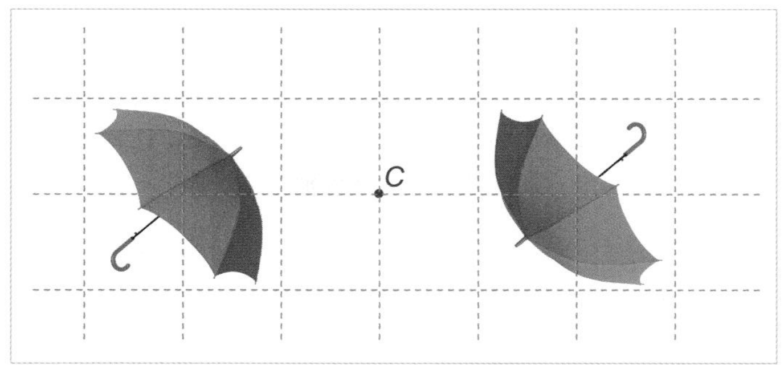

Axial Symmetry (Through a Line)

In an axial symmetry, each point is mapped through a line (axis) at right angles and reflected the same distance out the other side.

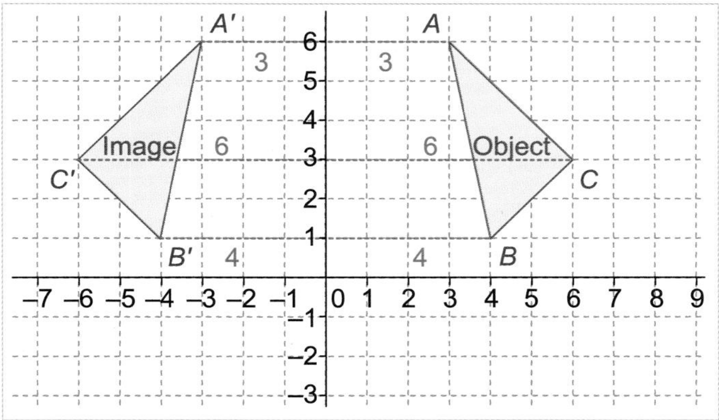

In an **axial symmetry** in the y-axis, each point is mapped through the y-axis at right angles and reflected the same distance out the other side.

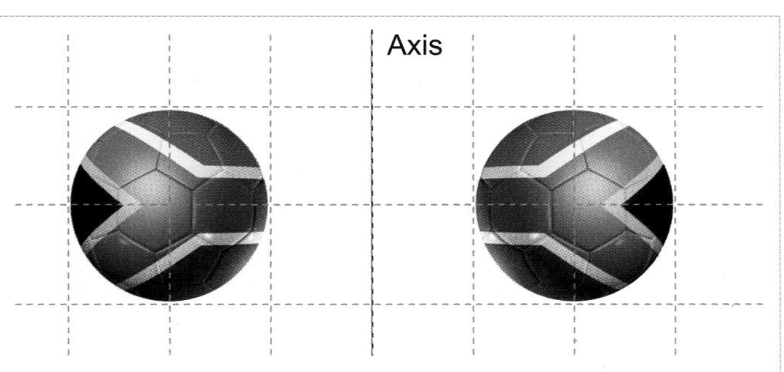

An **axial symmetry** is a reflection in a line or axis. The line acts as a mirror.

In an axial symmetry, the image and object are the same distance from the axis used, and one is a mirror image of the other.

Enlargement

A transformation that we will encounter on our course is that of an **enlargement**.

An **enlargement** is a transformation in which both the size and the position of a shape changes.

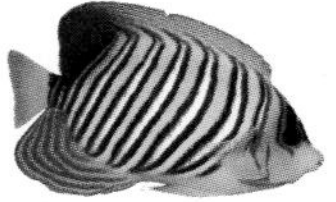
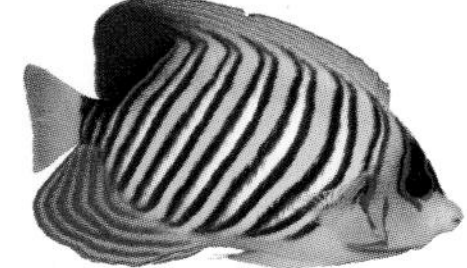

To enlarge a shape, we need to know two things:

- The **centre of enlargement**
- The **scale factor**, k

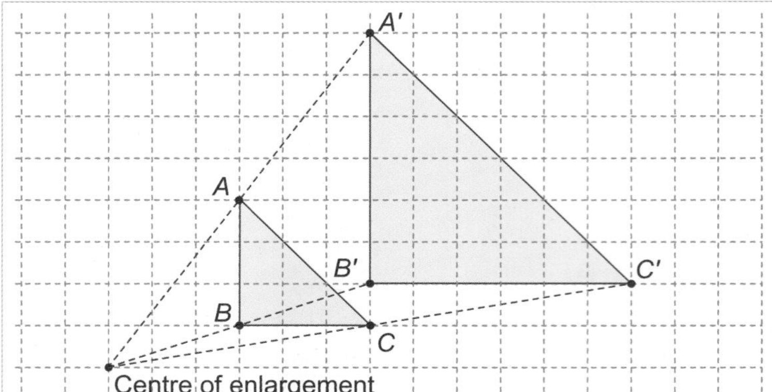

The **centre of enlargement** is the point from which the enlargement is constructed.

The **scale factor**, k, is the number by which the object is enlarged.

If a shape is enlarged by a scale factor of k, then each side of the image will be k times the length of the corresponding side of the object.

A scale factor of 3 means that the length of each image side will be three times the length of the corresponding object side.

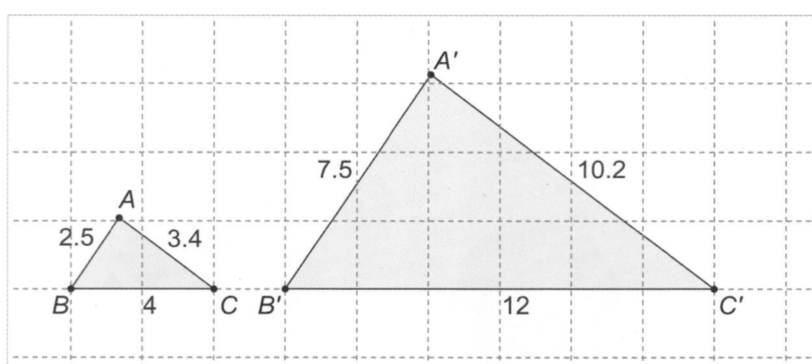

Any scale factor k which is greater than 1 will result in the image being bigger than the object.

A scale factor of $\frac{1}{3}$ would mean that the length of each image side will be $\frac{1}{3}$ the length of the corresponding object side.

Any scale factor that is greater than 0 and less than 1 will result in the image being smaller than the object. This can still be described as an enlargement but is more commonly called a reduction.

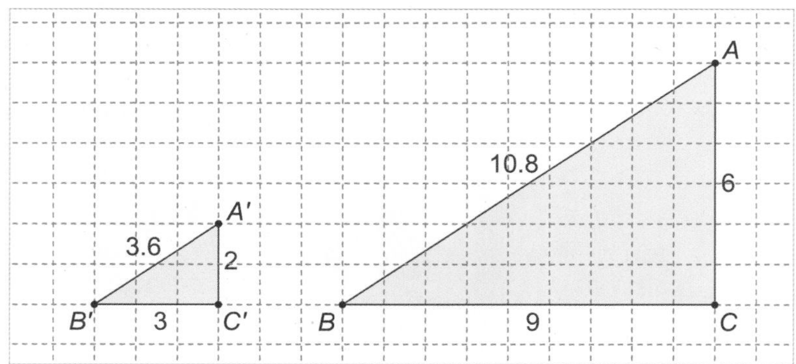

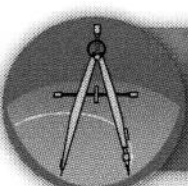

Worked Example 9.1

Enlarge the triangle *ABC* by a scale factor of 2.5, with a centre of enlargement *O*.

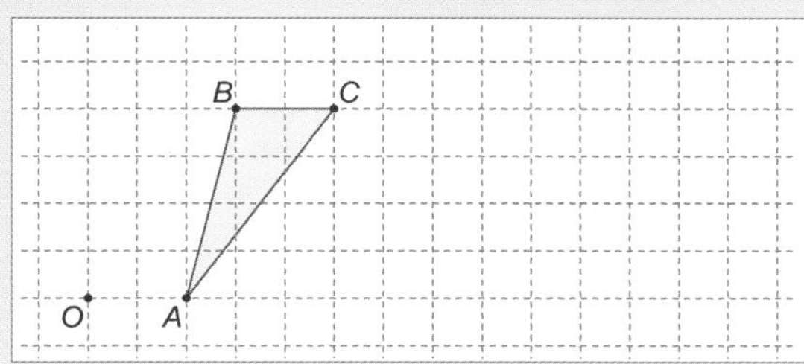

Solution

1 Draw rays from *O*, the centre of enlargement, though each of the vertices of the object shape.

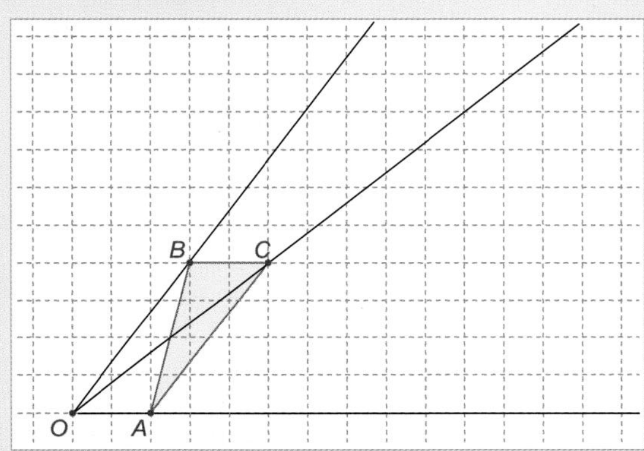

3 Mark off a new point *A′* such that |*OA′*| is 2.5 times the distance |*OA*|.

|*OA′*| = 2.5 |*OA*|

= 2.5 × 3

|*OA′*| = 7.5 cm

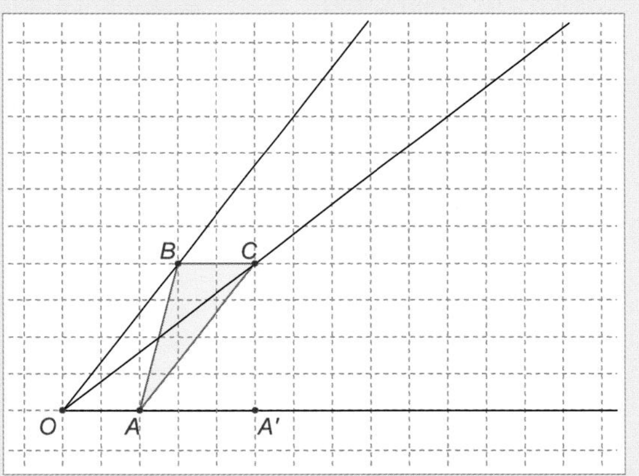

2 Using a compass or ruler, measure the distance |*OA*|.

|*OA*| = 3 cm

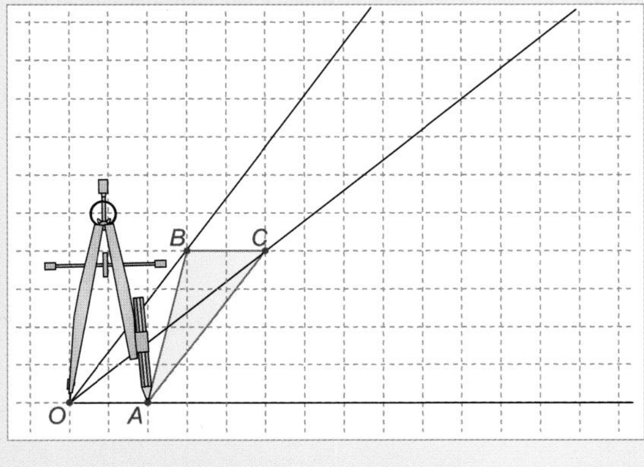

4 Measure |*OB*|.

Mark off a new point *B′* such that |*OB′*| is 2.5 times the distance |*OB*|.

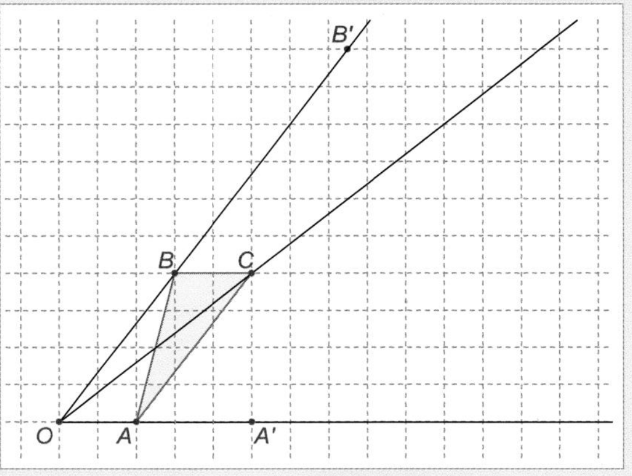

5 Measure $|OC|$.

Mark off a new point C' such that $|OC'|$ is 2.5 times the distance $|OC|$.

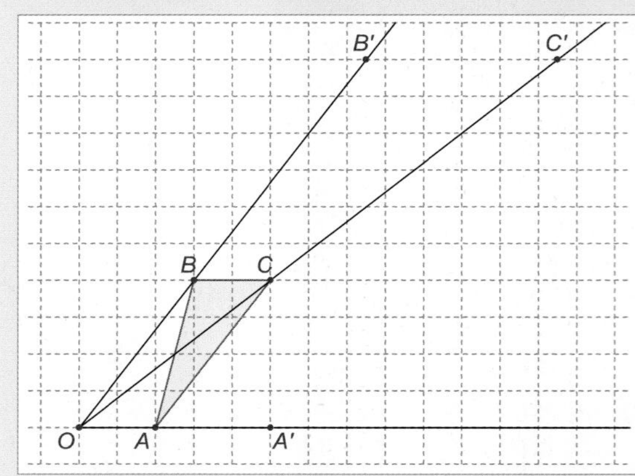

6 Draw the triangle $A'B'C'$.

The triangle $A'B'C'$ is the image of the triangle ABC under the required enlargement.

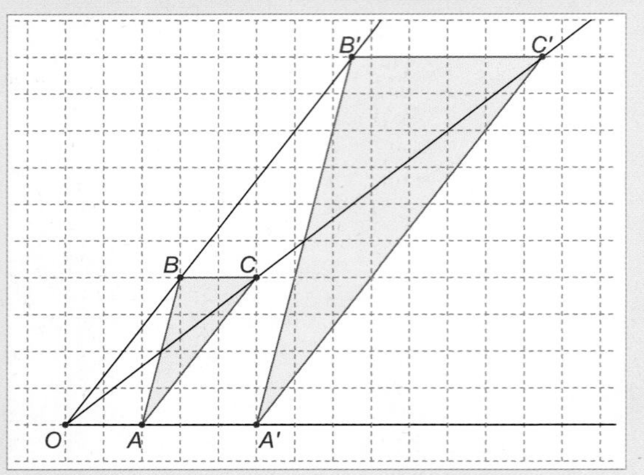

We sometimes encounter enlargements where the centre of enlargement is a point either on or inside the object.

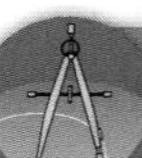

Worked Example 9.2

Enlarge the triangle ABC by a scale factor of 1.8 with a centre of enlargement A.

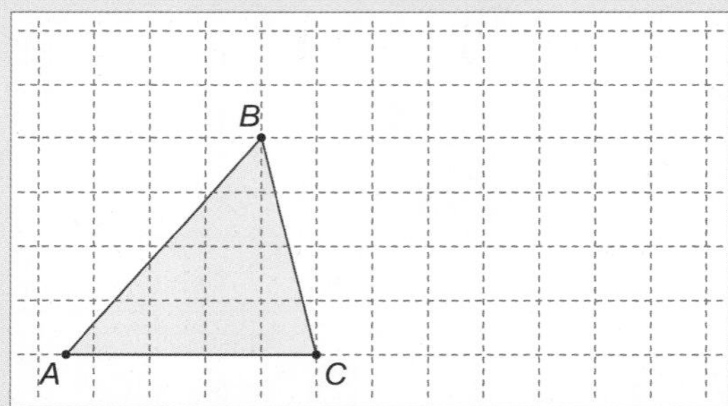

Solution

1 Draw rays from A through each of the remaining vertices.

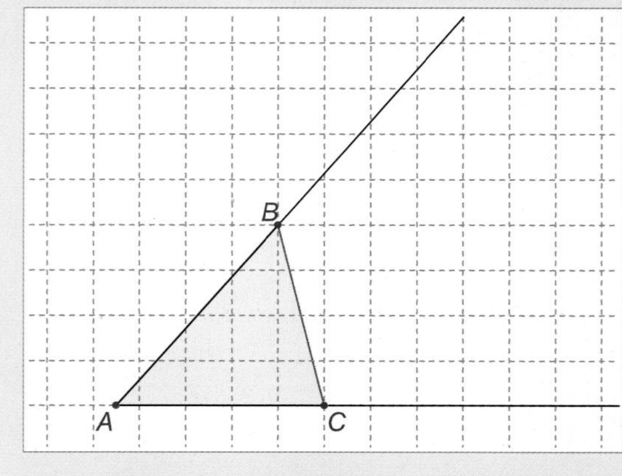

2 Using a compass or ruler, find $|AB|$.

Mark off a new point B' such that $|AB'| = 1.8 \times |AB|$.

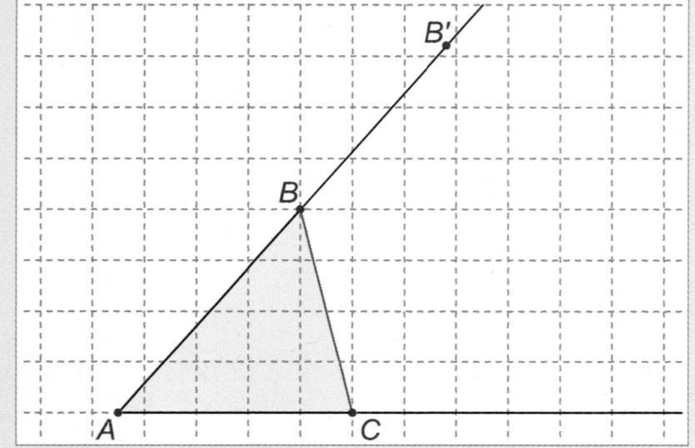

3 Find $|AC|$.

Mark off a new point C' such that $|AC'| = 1.8 \times |AC|$.

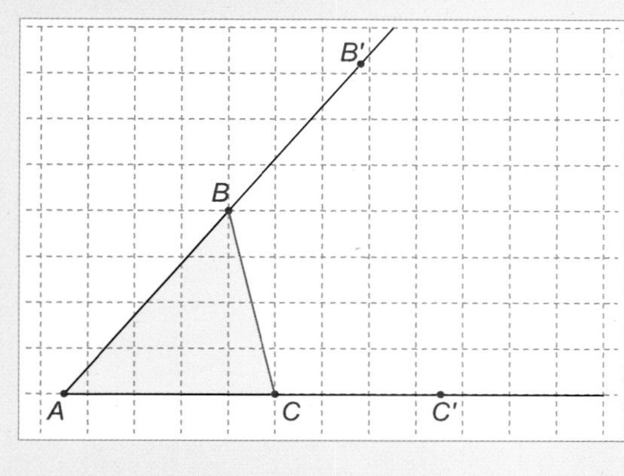

4 Draw the triangle $AB'C'$.

The triangle $AB'C'$ is the image of the triangle ABC under the required enlargement.

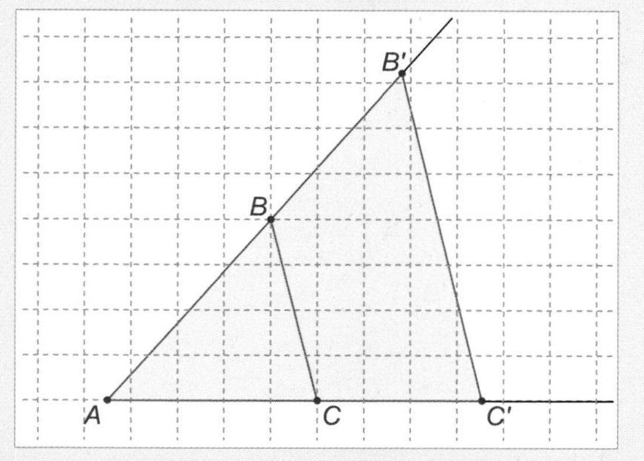

Exercise 9.1

1. Copy the following diagrams onto graph paper, and show the image of each of the shapes under an enlargement with a scale factor of 1.5 and centre O.

(i)

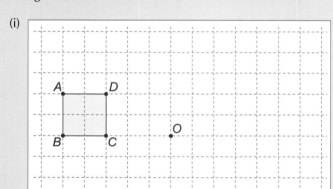

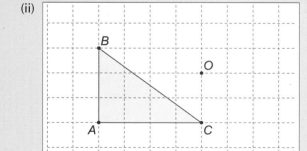

A D
O
B C

(ii)

B
O
A C

(iii)

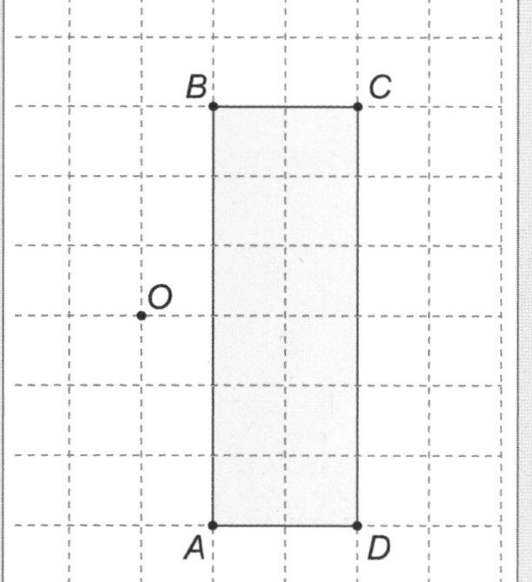

(iv)

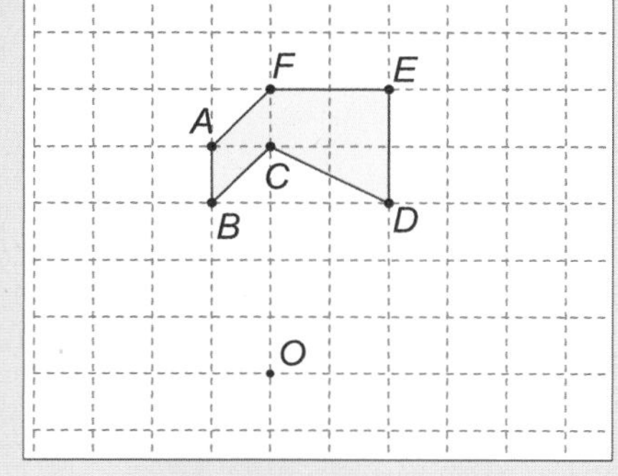

2. Copy the following diagrams onto graph paper, and show the image of each of the shapes under an enlargement with a scale factor of $\frac{1}{2}$ and centre O.

(i)

(iii)

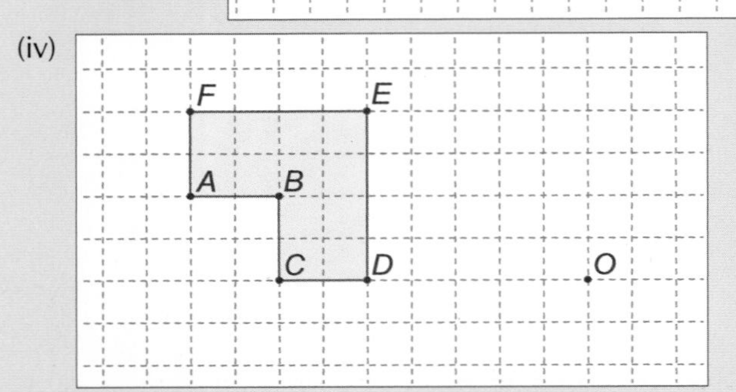

(ii)

(iv)

3. Copy the following diagrams onto graph paper, and show the image of each of the shapes under an enlargement with a scale factor of 1.6 and centre A.

(i)

(iii)

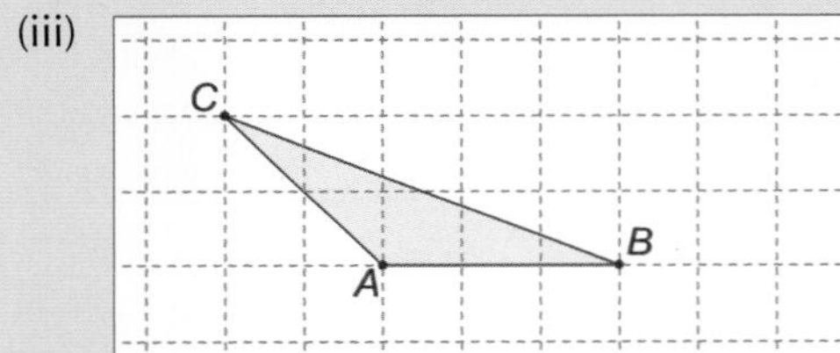

(ii)

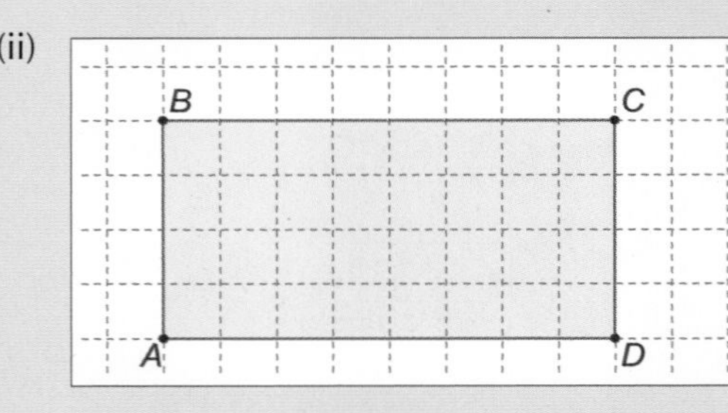

(iv)

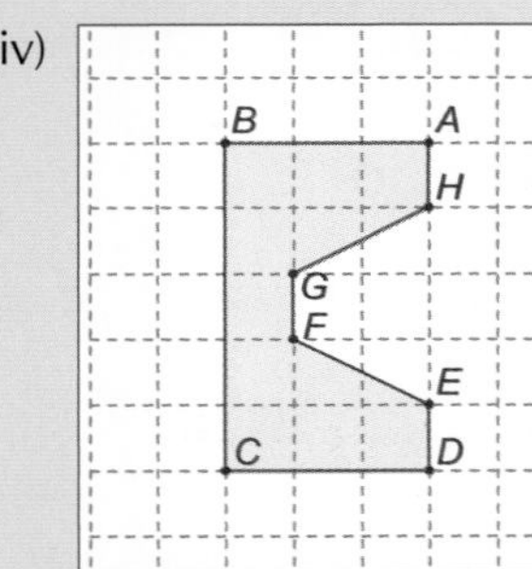

4. Copy the following diagrams onto graph paper, and show the image of each of the shapes under an enlargement with a scale factor of $\frac{2}{3}$ and centre A.

(i)

(ii)

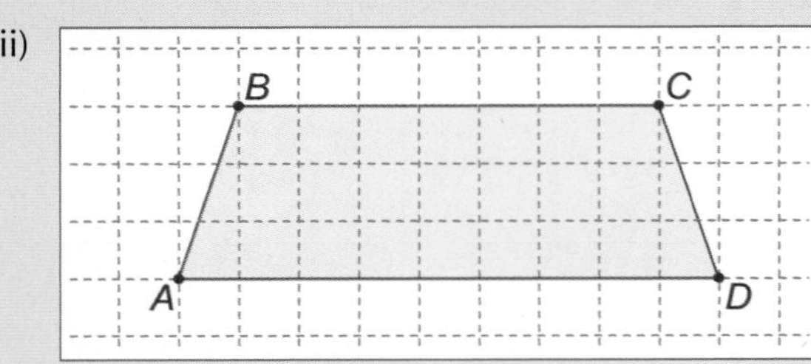

9.2 PROPERTIES OF ENLARGEMENTS

Now that we have explored how enlargements are constructed, we can investigate the various properties of enlargements.

From our investigations, we can determine the following characteristics of enlargements.

Similarity

Under an enlargement, **the object and image are similar to each other**.

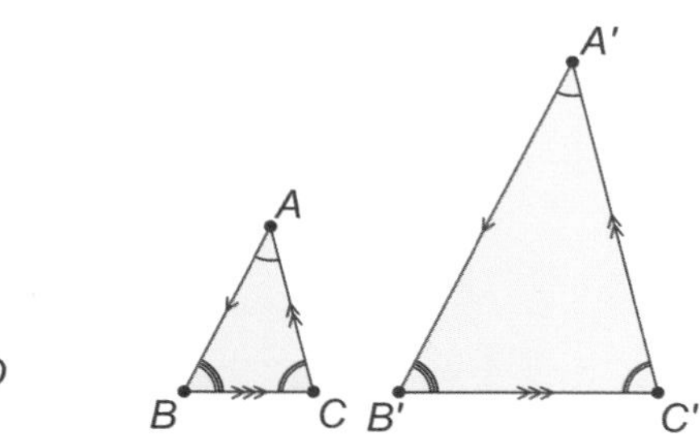

$|\angle ABC| = |\angle A'B'C'|$

$|\angle ACB| = |\angle A'C'B'|$

$|\angle BAC| = |\angle B'A'C'|$

$AB \parallel A'B'$

$AC \parallel A'C'$

$BC \parallel B'C'$

The corresponding sides of the object and image are in the same ratio:

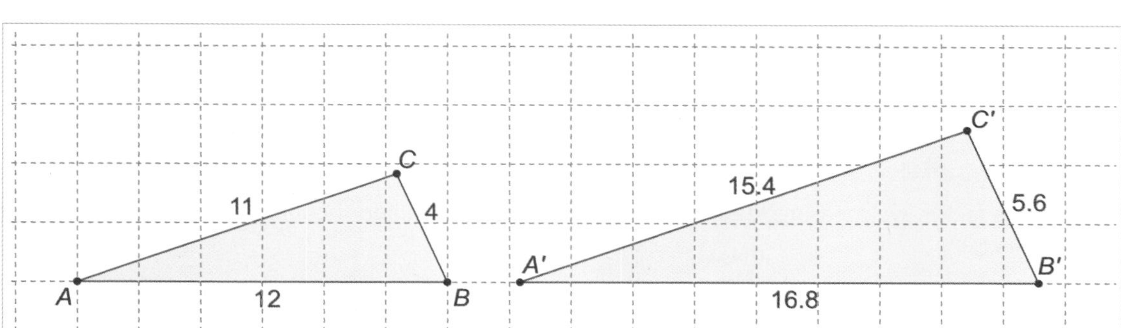

or

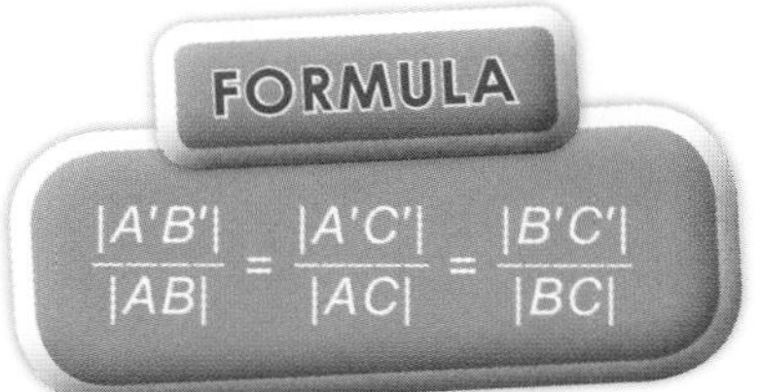

In this case:

$$\frac{|AB|}{|A'B'|} = \frac{12}{16.8} = \frac{5}{7} \qquad \frac{|AC|}{|A'C'|} = \frac{11}{15.4} = \frac{5}{7} \qquad \frac{|BC|}{|B'C'|} = \frac{4}{5.6} = \frac{5}{7}$$

Find the Centre of Enlargement

To find the centre of enlargement, usually labelled as the point O, we draw lines through the corresponding vertices of the object and image.

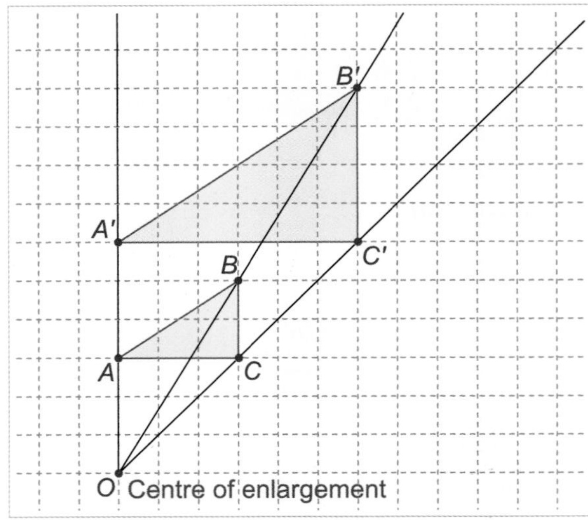

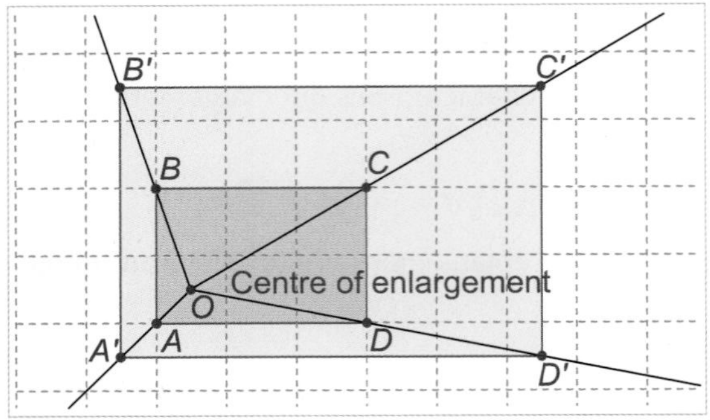

The point where these lines intersect is called the **centre of enlargement**.

We usually only need to connect two corresponding vertices to find the centre of enlargement.

Find the Scale Factor

To find the scale factor, we measure the length of a side of the image and the length of the corresponding side of the object.

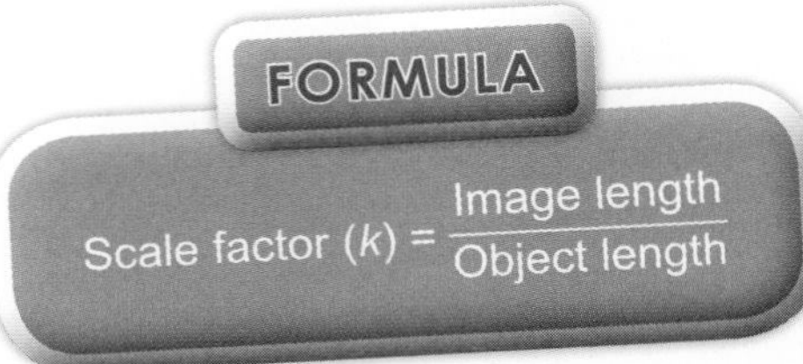

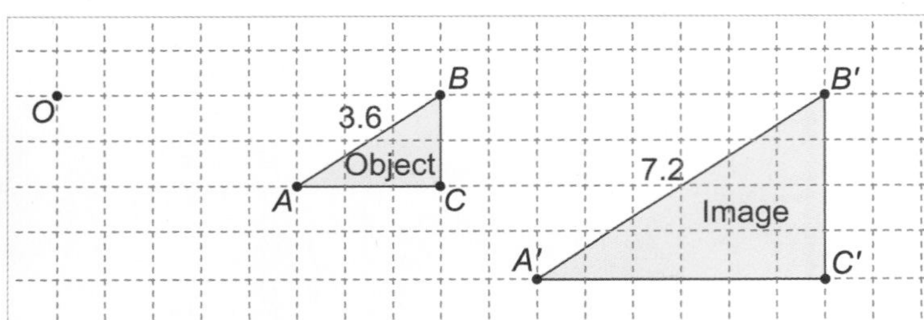

In this example:

Scale factor $= \frac{7.2}{3.6} = 2 = k$

It is important to remember that it is **Image length ÷ Object length** that will give us the scale factor.

Scale Factor and Area

If an object is enlarged by a scale factor of k, then the area of the image will be increased by a factor of k^2. This is written as the following formula:

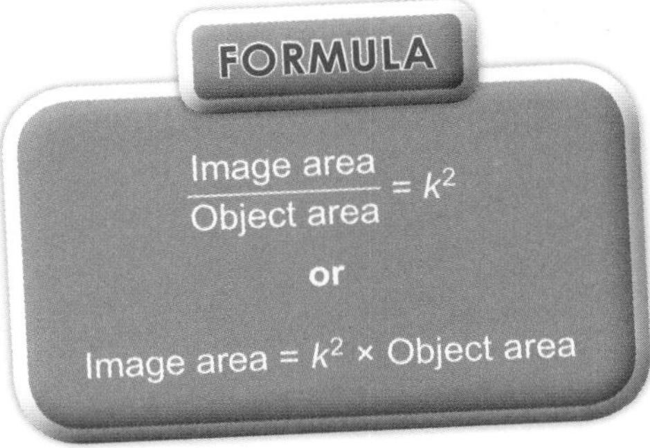

For the example shown:

Image area $= (2)^2 \times$ Object area

$= 4 \times 24$

$= 96$ units^2

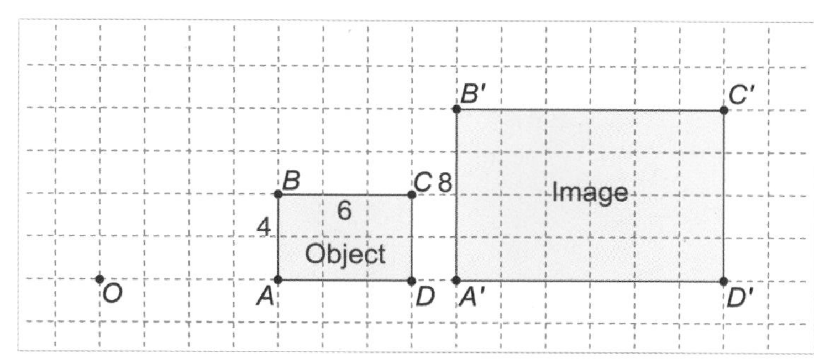

Worked Example 9.3

$\Delta A'B'C'$ is the image of ΔABC under an enlargement of scale factor k and centre O.

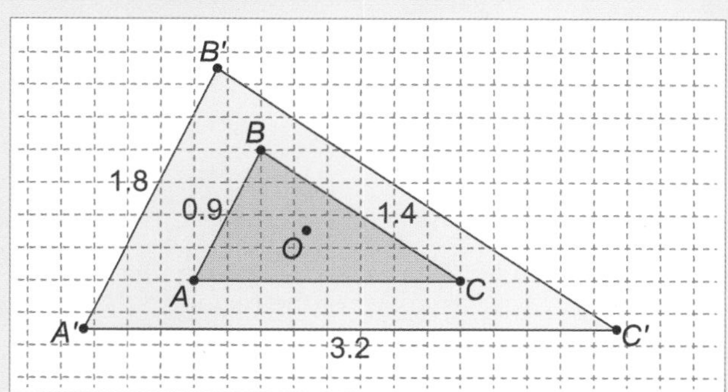

(i) Find the value of k.

(ii) Find $|B'C'|$.

(iii) Find $|AC|$.

(iv) The area of ΔABC is 0.65 square units; find the area of $\Delta A'B'C'$.

Solution

(i) Find the value of k

$$k = \frac{\text{Image length}}{\text{Object length}} = \frac{1.8}{0.9} = 2$$

(ii) Find $|B'C'|$.

$$k = 2$$

$$\therefore |B'C'| = 2 \times |BC|$$

$$|B'C'| = 2 \times 1.4$$

$$|B'C'| = 2.8$$

We could also have used the properties of similar triangles to find $|B'C'|$:

$$\frac{|B'C'|}{|BC|} = \frac{|A'B'|}{|AB|}$$

$$\frac{|B'C'|}{1.4} = \frac{1.8}{0.9} \Rightarrow \frac{|B'C'|}{1.4} = \frac{2}{1}$$

$$|B'C'| = 2 \times 1.4$$

$$|B'C'| = 2.8$$

(iii) Find $|AC|$.

$$k = 2$$

$$\therefore |A'C'| = 2 \times |AC|$$

$$\Rightarrow |AC| = \frac{1}{2} \times |A'C'|$$

$$|AC| = \frac{1}{2} \times 3.2$$

$$|AC| = 1.6$$

Again, we could have used the properties of similar triangles to find $|AC|$:

$$\frac{|AC|}{3.2} = \frac{0.9}{1.8}$$

$$\frac{|AC|}{3.2} = \frac{1}{2}$$

$$2|AC| = 3.2$$

$$|AC| = 1.6$$

(iv) The area of ΔABC is 0.65 square units; find the area of $\Delta A'B'C'$.

We remember that $\frac{\text{Image area}}{\text{Object area}} = k^2$,

and let the area of $\Delta A'B'C' = x$.

$$\Rightarrow \frac{x}{0.65} = (2)^2$$

$$\frac{x}{0.65} = 4$$

$$x = 4 \times 0.65$$

$$x = 2.6 \text{ square units}$$

Exercise 9.2

1. Copy the following diagram onto graph paper. $\Delta A'B'C'$ is an enlargement of ΔABC.

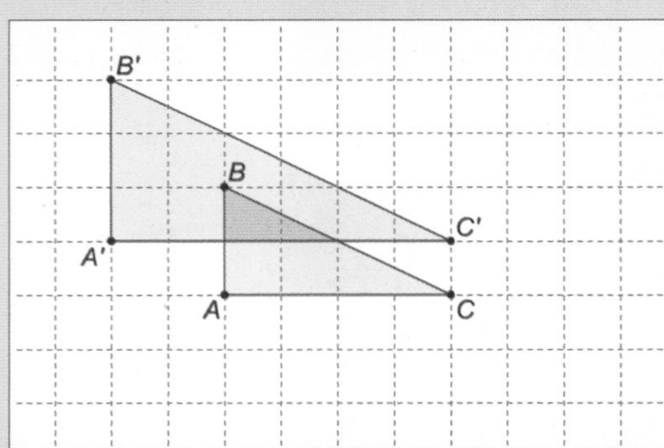

(i) Find the centre of enlargement.

(ii) Find the scale factor.

2. Copy this diagram of two rectangles onto graph paper. $AB'C'D'$ is the image of the rectangle $ABCD$ under an enlargement.

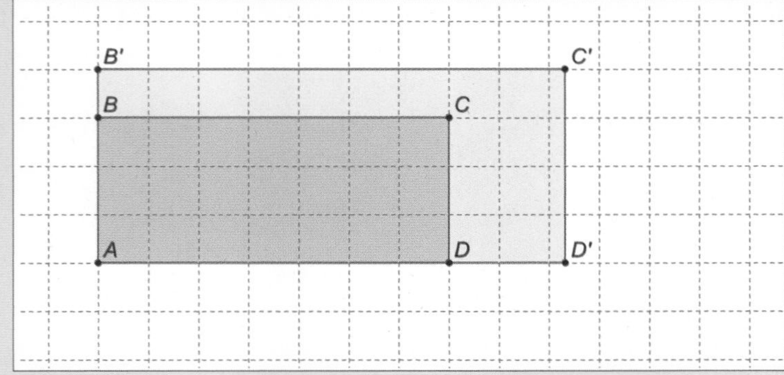

(i) Find the centre of enlargement.

(ii) Find the scale factor, k.

(iii) Find the ratio Area of $AB'C'D'$: Area of $ABCD$.

3. The square $P'Q'R'S'$ is the image of $PQRS$ under an enlargement.

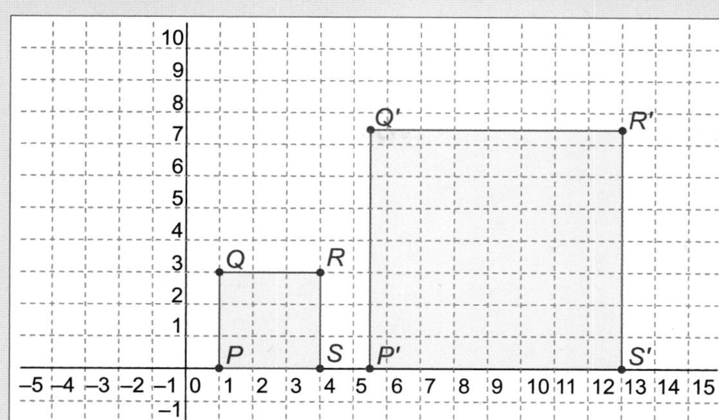

(i) Find the scale factor.

(ii) Find the ratio Area of $P'Q'R'S'$: Area of $PQRS$.

(iii) Find the ratio Perimeter of $P'Q'R'S'$: Perimeter of $PQRS$.

4. ΔABC is the image of ΔXYZ under an enlargement of scale factor k and centre O.

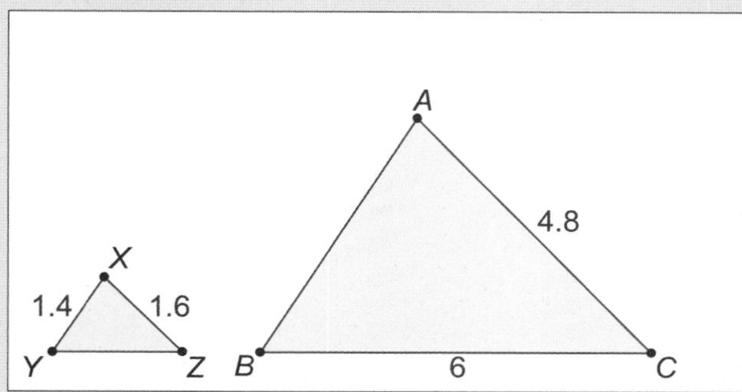

(i) Find the value of k.

(ii) Find $|AB|$.

(iii) Find $|YZ|$.

5. The rectangle $D'E'F'G'$ is the image of the rectangle $DEFG$ under an enlargement with centre O.

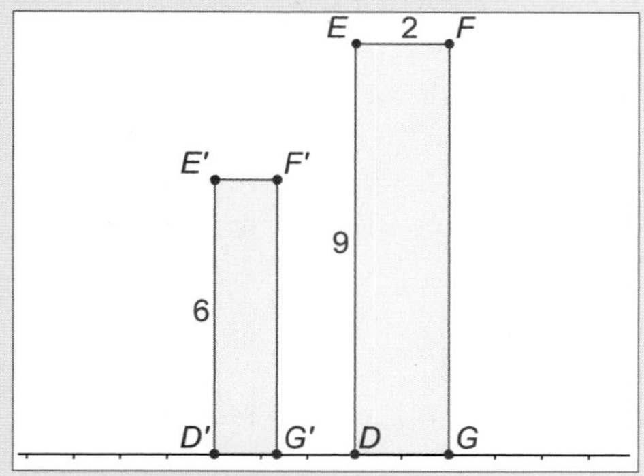

(i) Find the scale factor.

(ii) Find $|E'F'|$.

(iii) Write as a fraction in its simplest form:

$$\frac{\text{Area of rectangle } D'E'F'G'}{\text{Area of rectangle } DEFG}$$

6. Plot the points $A(2,6)$, $B(8,4)$ and $C(8,1)$ on the x–y co-ordinate plane.

(i) Draw ΔABC.

(ii) Find the area of ΔABC.

(iii) Draw $\Delta A'B'C'$, the image of ΔABC under an enlargement of scale factor $\frac{1}{2}$ and centre $O(0,0)$.

(iv) Find the ratio $\dfrac{\text{Area } \Delta A'B'C'}{\text{Area } \Delta ABC}$.

7. The triangle ADE is the image of the triangle ABC under an enlargement of scale factor k and centre A.

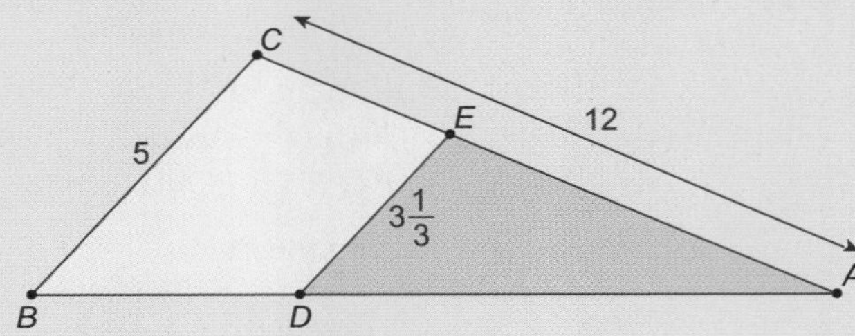

$|AC| = 12$ cm, $|BC| = 5$ cm and $|DE| = 3\frac{1}{3}$ cm.

(i) Find the scale factor, k.

(ii) Find $|AE|$.

(iii) The area of the triangle ADE is 9.85 cm^2. Find the area of the triangle ABC.

(iv) Write down the area of the region $BCED$.

8. ΔPQR is an enlargement of ΔXYR. Both triangles are right-angled, as shown.

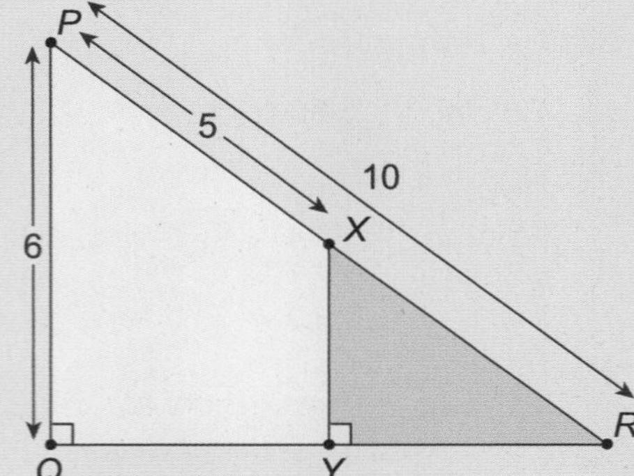

(i) Name the centre of enlargement.

(ii) Write down the value of k, the scale factor.

(iii) Find $|QR|$.

(iv) Find $|XR|$ and $|YR|$.

(v) Calculate the ratio Area ΔPQR : Area ΔXYR.

9. (i) Construct an equilateral triangle DEF of side 8 cm.

(ii) Construct the image of the triangle DEF under the enlargement of scale factor 0.45 and centre D.

(iii) Given that the area of the triangle DEF is $16\sqrt{3}$, find the area of the image (of the triangle) to the nearest whole number.

10. The right-angled triangle ABC is the image of the triangle DEC under the enlargement of centre C and scale factor k.

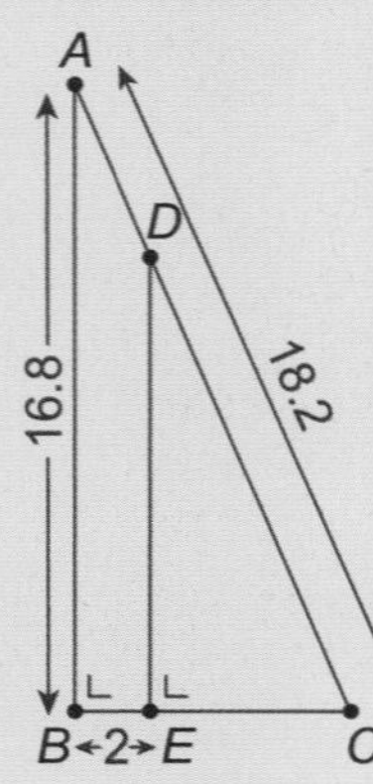

Find:

(i) $|EC|$

(ii) The scale factor, k

(iii) $|DE|$

(iv) The area of the triangle DEC

(v) The area of the figure $ADEB$

11. (a) $A(1,0)$, $B(2,5)$ and $C(5,0)$ are three points. Show the triangle ABC on the x–y plane.

(b) Find: (i) The area of ΔABC

(ii) $|BC|$

(c) Show also $\Delta A'B'C'$, the enlargement of ΔABC, centre (0,0), of scale factor $k = 2$.

(d) Find: (i) The area of $\Delta A'B'C'$

(ii) $|B'C'|$

(e) Verify that:

(i) $\dfrac{\text{Area } \Delta A'B'C'}{\text{Area } \Delta ABC} = k^2$

(ii) $\dfrac{|B'C'|}{|BC|} = k$

12. Square $ABCD$ is the image of square $NMSD$ under an enlargement. $|DS| = |SC|$.

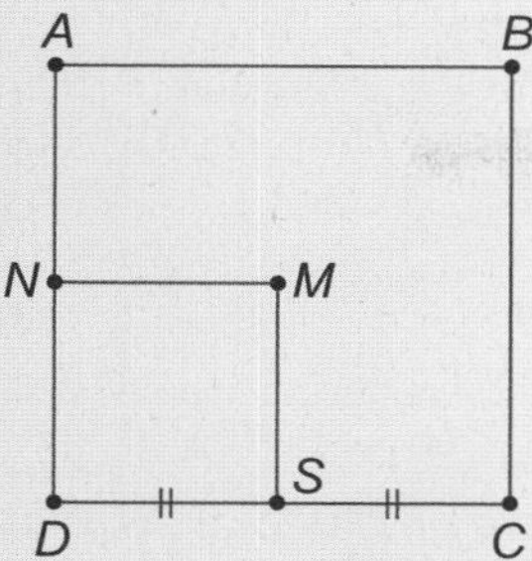

(i) What point is the centre of this enlargement?

(ii) What is the scale factor of the enlargement?

(iii) What is the ratio Area of $ABCD$: Area of $NMSD$?

13. The triangle OPQ is the reduction of triangle ORS, of scale factor k and centre O. $|OP| = 2$ and $|PR| = 7$.

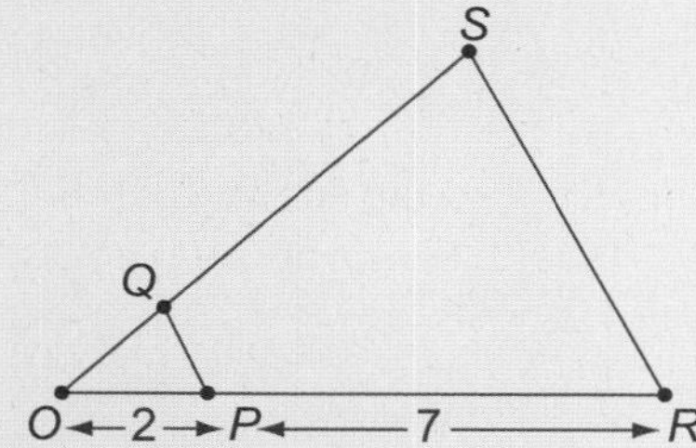

Find:

(i) The value of k

(ii) The ratio $|OQ| : |OS|$

(iii) Area ΔOPQ : Area ΔORS

(iv) The area of the quadrilateral $PRSQ$, given that the area of triangle ORS is $20\frac{1}{4}$ square units.

14. Triangle ABC has a right angle at B. $|AB| = 7\frac{1}{2}$ cm and $|BC| = 4$ cm.

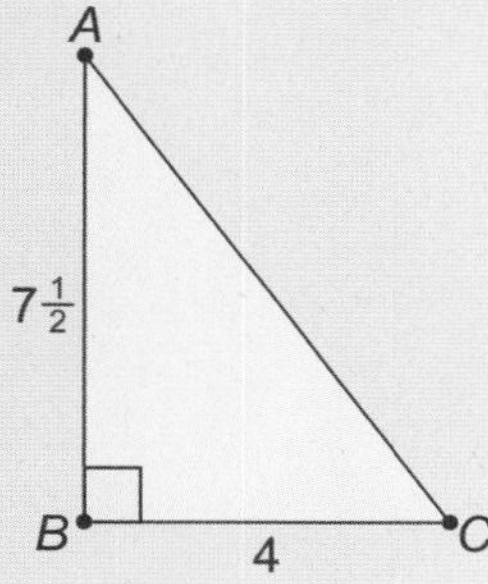

(i) Find $|AC|$.

(ii) Construct triangle $A'BC'$, the image of triangle ABC under a reduction, centre B, of scale factor 0.75.

(iii) Find $|A'B|$.

(iv) Find the area of $\Delta A'BC'$.

15. $A(0,2)$, $B(4,0)$, $C(2,-2)$ and $D(-2,2)$ are four points.

(i) Illustrate these points on the x–y co-ordinate plane.

(ii) Show that $ABCD$ is a parallelogram by showing that AB is parallel to CD and that AD is parallel to BC.

(iii) Show the enlargement of $ABCD$ of scale factor 1.5, centre the origin.

(iv) Investigate if the enlargement is also a parallelogram.

16. Draw any triangle PQR.
Show $\Delta PQ'R'$, the enlargement of ΔPQR, centre P, of scale factor 3.

Explain why QR is parallel to $Q'R'$.

17. Triangle ABC has sides x, $x - 1$ and $x + 1$ as shown.

(a) If $|\angle ABC| = 90°$, find the value of x.

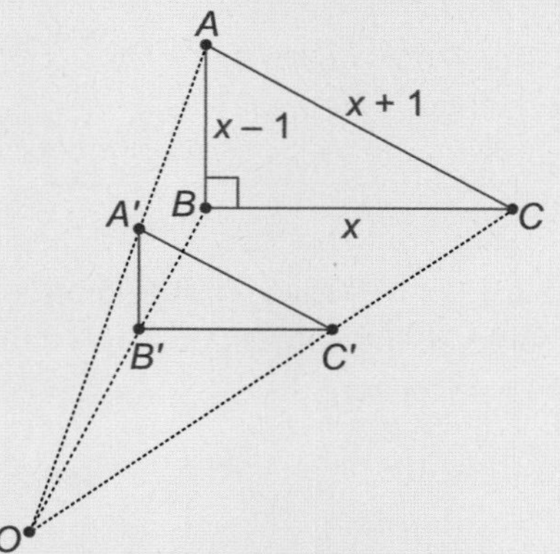

(b) Triangle $A'B'C'$ is the image of triangle ABC under a reduction, centre O, of scale factor $\frac{4}{5}$.

Find the lengths of the sides of triangle $A'B'C'$ and verify that it is also right-angled.

18. $\Delta AB'C'$ is the image of ΔABC under an enlargement with centre A, of scale factor 2.

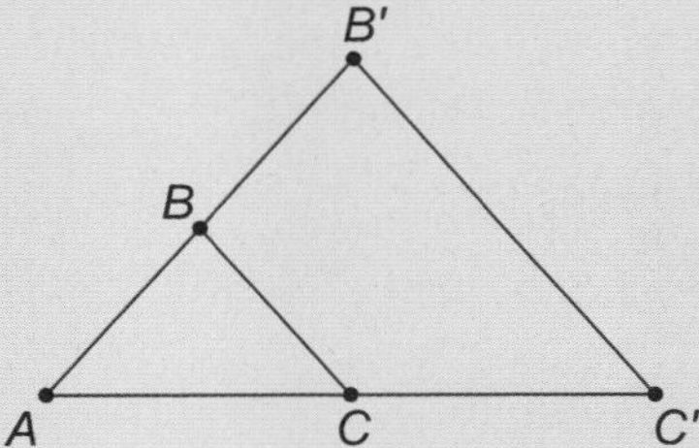

State whether the following are true or false:

(i) $\dfrac{|AB'|}{|AB|} = 2$

(ii) $\dfrac{|BC|}{|B'C'|} = \dfrac{1}{2}$

(iii) $|AC'| = \frac{1}{2}|AC|$

(iv) $\dfrac{\text{Area } \Delta AB'C'}{\text{Area } \Delta ABC} = 2$

(v) $\dfrac{\text{Area } \Delta AB'C'}{\text{Area } \Delta ABC} = 4$

(vi) $|\angle AB'C'| = 2|\angle ABC|$

(vii) $B'C' \parallel BC$

19. $ABCD$ is a square of side 10 cm. P is the midpoint of $[AB]$.

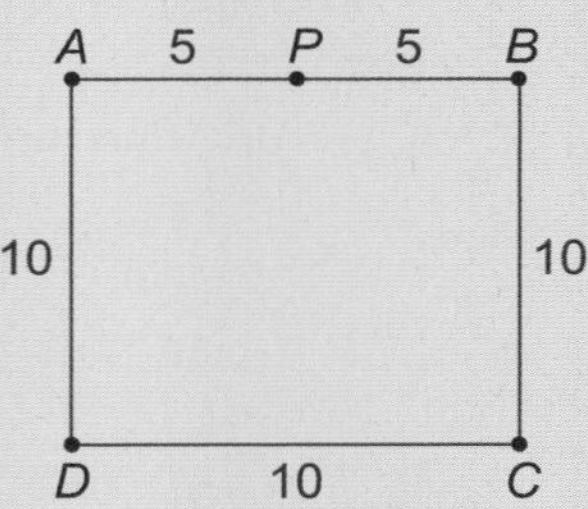

$A'B'C'D'$ is the image of $ABCD$ under the enlargement, centre P, of scale factor 0.4 (i.e. a reduction).

Illustrate $ABCD$ and $A'B'C'D'$ on a diagram.

Write down:

(i) $|A'B'|$

(ii) The area of $A'B'C'D'$

(iii) The ratio $|A'B'| : |AB|$

(iv) The ratio Area $A'B'C'D'$: Area $ABCD$.

20. (i) Construct a right-angled triangle ABC such that:

$|\angle BAC| = 90°$, $|AC| = 6$ cm, $|AB| = 2.5$ cm and $|BC| = 6.5$ cm

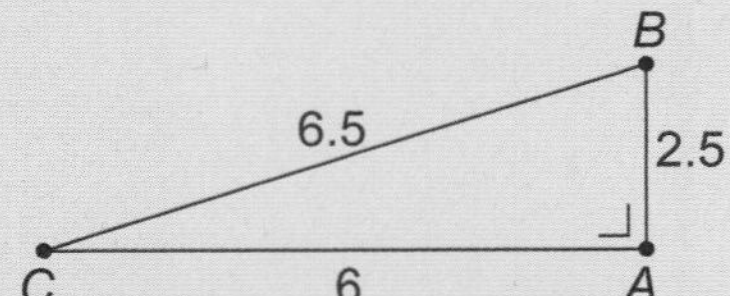

(ii) Verify Pythagoras' theorem in this case: $|BC|^2 = |AB|^2 + |AC|^2$

(iii) Construct $\Delta AB'C'$, the enlargement of ΔABC, centre A, of scale factor 2.

(iv) Investigate if: $|B'C'|^2 = |AB'|^2 + |AC'|^2$

(v) What does this prove about $\Delta AB'C'$?

21. A regular hexagon of side 12 cm has a perpendicular height of x cm as shown.

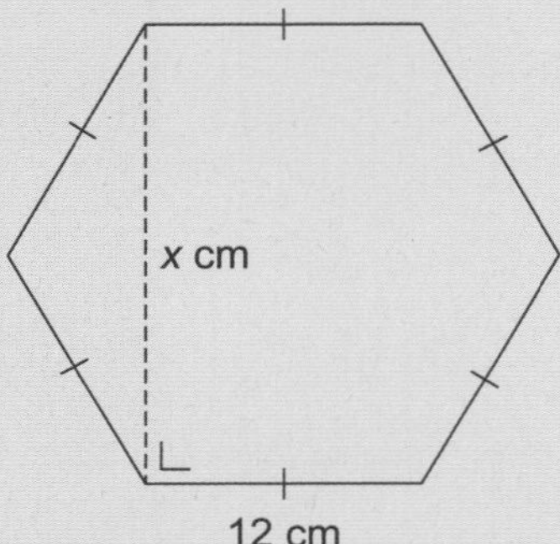

(i) Calculate the value of x.

(ii) Calculate the area of the hexagon.

(iii) When the hexagon is enlarged by a scale factor k, its area is $1{,}944\sqrt{3}$ cm^2.

Calculate the perpendicular height of the enlarged hexagon.

22. The diagram shows two similar cuboids.

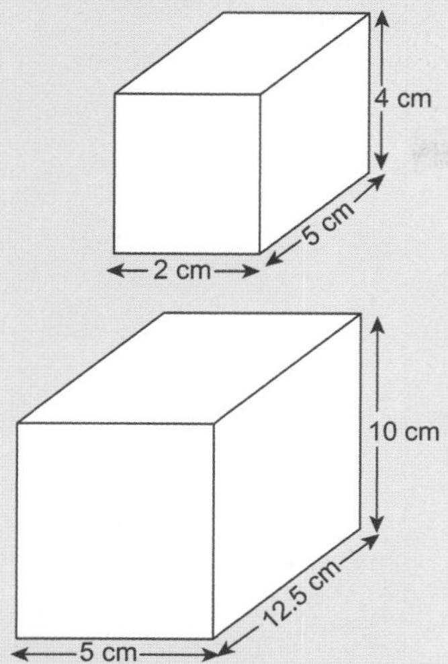

Calculate the ratio of their:

(i) Lengths
(ii) Breadths
(iii) Heights
(iv) Surface areas
(v) Volumes

23. Three spheres are shown.

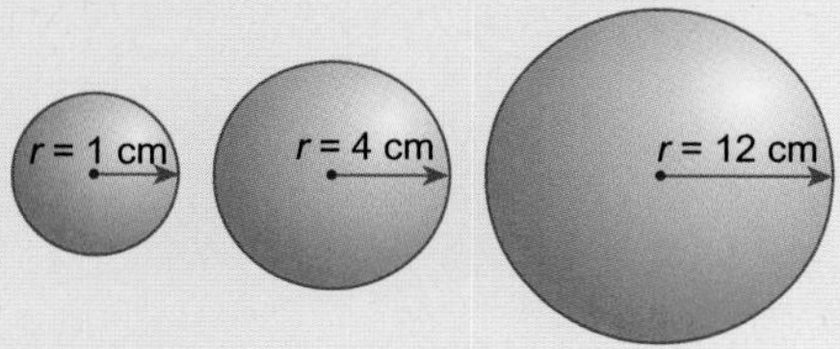

Calculate the ratio of their:

(i) Radii
(ii) Surface areas
(iii) Volumes

What do you notice?

24. Two cones, A and B, are similar to each other. Cone A has a height of 75 cm and a total surface area of 3,240 cm^2. Cone B has a total surface area of 90 cm^2. How tall is cone B?

25. A model for the design of a ship is shown. If the scale used is 1 : 200, find the height and length of the hull of the ship.

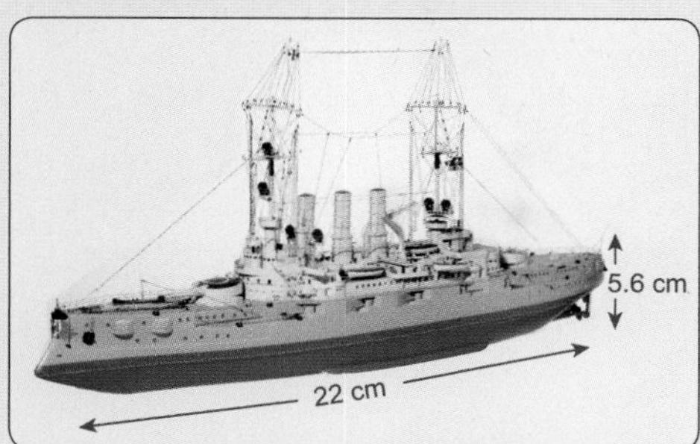

26. Three similar bottles of water have radii of 2 cm, 4 cm and 10 cm, respectively.

The second smallest bottle holds 50 ml of water and requires 75 cm^2 of plastic to make (assuming no wastage). Find:

(i) The amount of plastic, to the nearest cm^2, to make the other bottles
(ii) The volume of water that the other bottles hold, to the nearest ml

27. A projector projects a rectangular image onto a rectangular screen. Both screen and image are similar. The image covers an area one third the size of the screen.
If the screen has an area of 189 m^2, find the area covered by the image.

28. Four different types of paper are used in an office: A1, A2, A3 and A4. All types are similar to each other.

A1 paper is double the area of A2, which is double the area of A3, which is double the area of A4.

If A2 paper has a length of 594 mm and A4 has a width of 210 mm, calculate the dimensions (to the nearest mm) and area (to the nearest cm^2) of each type of paper.

Co-ordinate Geometry: The Line

Learning Outcomes

In this chapter you will learn to:

- Calculate the distance between two points
- Calculate the slope of a line through two points and consolidate the understanding of the concept of slope
- Find the equation of a line, given the slope and a point
- Find the equation of a line, given two points
- Calculate the area of a triangle
- Recognise the fact that the relationships $y = mx + c$ and $y - y_1 = m(x - x_1)$ are linear and use these relationships to solve problems
- Find the equation of lines parallel to and perpendicular to a given line and through a given point
- Find the point of intersection of two lines
- Recognise the fact that $ax + by + c = 0$ represents a linear relationship and use this relationship to solve problems
- Calculate the length of the perpendicular from (x_1, y_1) to $ax + by + c = 0$
- Calculate the angle θ between two lines with slopes of m_1 and m_2 using $\tan \theta = \pm \dfrac{m_1 - m_2}{1 + m_1 m_2}$
- Divide a line segment in a given ratio $m : n$

Co-ordinate geometry was invented by the French mathematician René Descartes (1596–1650). His work on co-ordinate geometry first appeared in 1631 in a book entitled *Discourse on Method*. Descartes' co-ordinate system was much easier to work with than Euclid's geometry, and even today it is the foundation for many branches of modern mathematics. It is sometimes called Cartesian geometry in honour of Descartes.

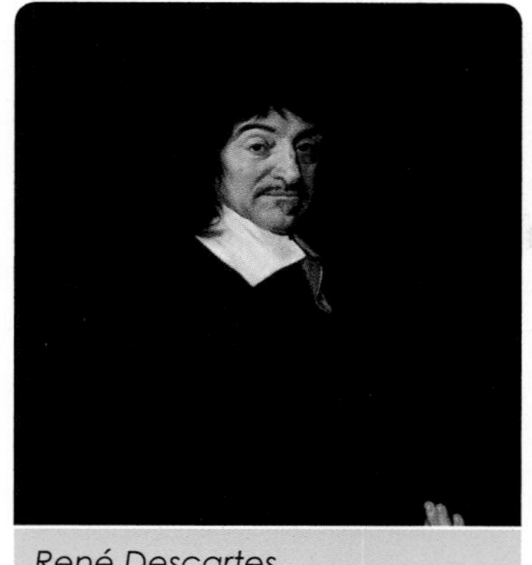

René Descartes

Co-ordinate geometry has applications in such diverse areas as geography, astronomy, engineering and economics. For example, when you look up the location of a place on a map, it is usually given as a set of co-ordinates.

Co-ordinate geometry is used by accountants and business managers regularly when they calculate break-even points and profit margins.

The Crab Nebula viewed from the NASA Hubble Space Telescope

YOU SHOULD REMEMBER...

- The theorem of Pythagoras
- How to find the area of a parallelogram
- How to find the area of a triangle
- How to find the area of a rectangle
- A circle is the set of all points that are a fixed distance from a given point
- Distance = Speed × Time

KEY WORDS

- **Distance**
- **Midpoint**
- **Slope of a line**
- **Equation of a line**

In co-ordinate geometry, we refer to the plane on which we work as the *x*–*y* plane, or the Cartesian plane.

10.1 REVISION OF FORMULAE

Given the points *A* and *B*:

1. Distance between two points

Finding the distance between two points *A* and *B* is the equivalent of finding the length of the line segment [*AB*]. Therefore, the distance formula will also be used to find the length of a line segment.

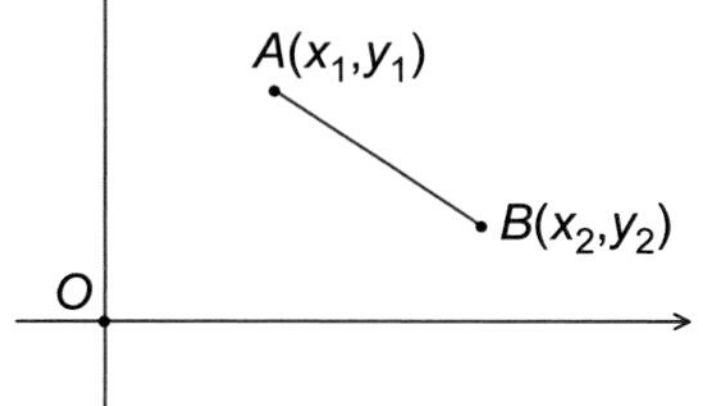

In the previous activity, you derived the formula for the distance between two points.

FORMULA

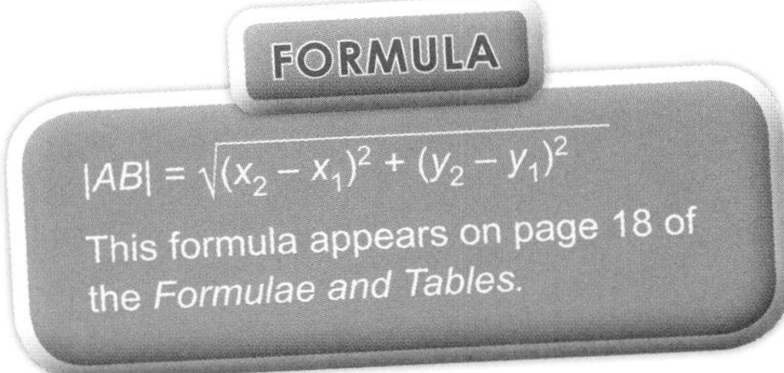

$|AB| = \sqrt{(x_2 - x_1)^2 + (y_2 - y_1)^2}$

This formula appears on page 18 of the *Formulae and Tables*.

2. **Midpoint of a line segment**

The point that bisects a line segment is called the midpoint of the line segment. If C is the midpoint of $[AB]$, then $|AC| = |CB|$.

In the next activity, you will derive a formula for finding the midpoint of a line segment.

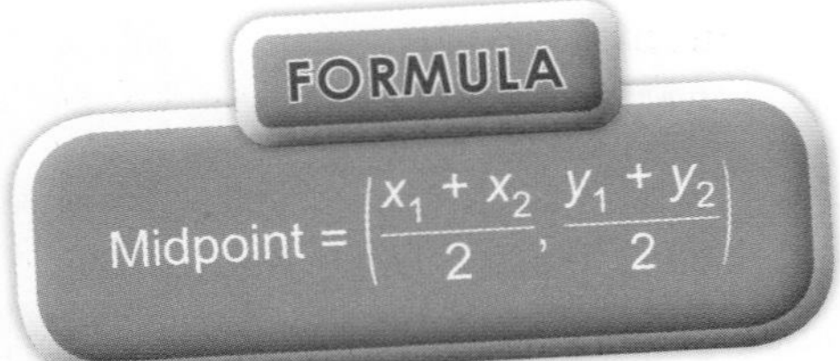

This formula appears on page 18 of the *Formulae and Tables*.

3. **Slope of a line given two points**

The slope of a line is a measure of the 'steepness' of the line. We measure the slope of a line by finding how much the line rises or falls as we move from left to right along it.

Consider the line l, which contains the points $A(1,1)$ and $B(4,3)$.

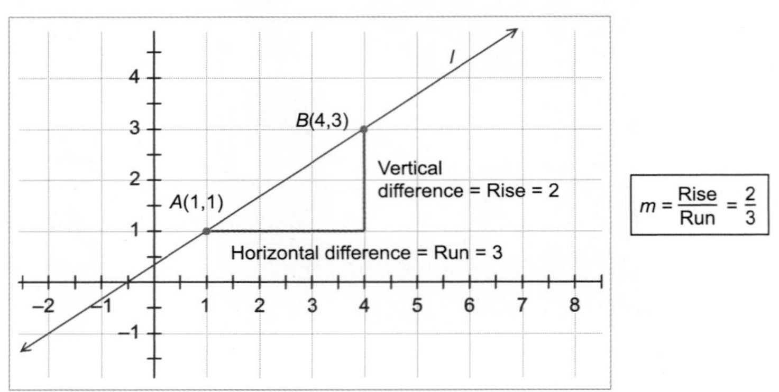

The horizontal difference between A and B is 3. We sometimes call this number the **run**.

The vertical difference between A and B is 2. This number is called the **rise**.

The slope of l is $\frac{\text{rise}}{\text{run}} = \frac{2}{3}$. We use the letter m to denote slope; therefore, $m = \frac{2}{3}$ for our line l.

Consider the line k, which contains the points $C(-2,3)$ and $D(2,1)$.

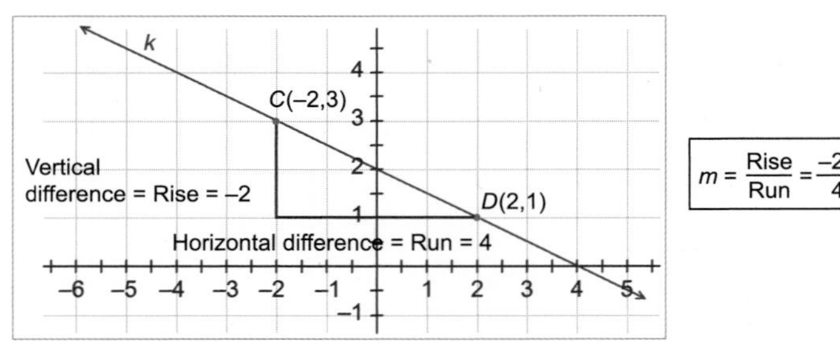

- The horizontal difference (the run) between C and D is 4. The vertical difference (the rise) between C and D is -2. The rise is negative here, as we are dropping down from C to D.
- The slope of k is: $m = \frac{\text{rise}}{\text{run}} = \frac{-2}{4} = -\frac{1}{2}$.
- The slope is negative because the line goes down from left to right.

In the next activity, you will derive the formula for finding the slope of a line:

This formula appears on page 18 of the *Formulae and Tables*.

4. Equation of *AB*

The equation of a line tells us how the x co-ordinate and the y co-ordinate of every point on the line are related to each other.

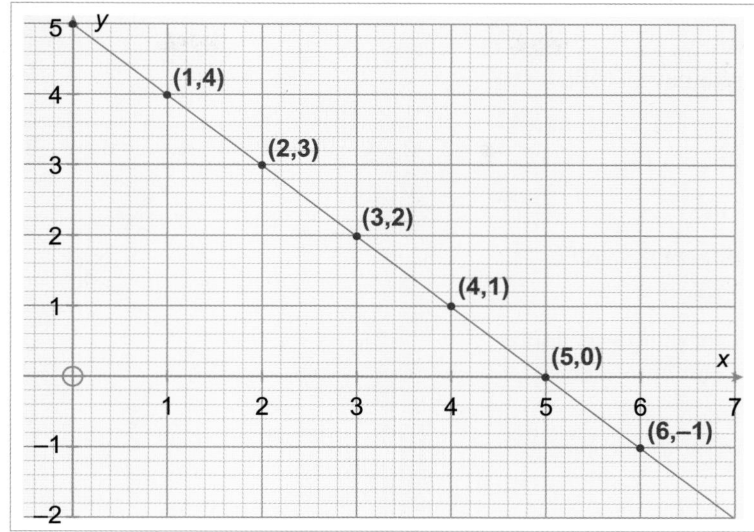

For example, consider the equation $x + y = 5$. This equation tells us that, for every point on this line, the x co-ordinate added to the y co-ordinate equals 5. Therefore, points on this line would include (0,5), (5,0), (1,4), (4,1), (2,3), (3,2), (6,–1), (–1,6), and so on.

Equations are written in three main forms:

(i) $y - y_1 = m(x - x_1)$

(ii) $y = mx + c$ [m = slope; c is called the y-intercept – this is where the line cuts the y-axis]

(iii) $ax + by + c = 0$

5. Slope of *AB*, given its equation

(i) $y - y_1 = m(x - x_1)$ slope is m

(ii) $y = mx + c$ slope is m

(iii) $ax + by + c = 0$ $m = \frac{-a}{b}$

6. Point of intersection of a line with the *x*- and *y*-axes

- When a line cuts the x-axis, the value of the y coordinate is 0.
- When a line cuts the y-axis, the value of the x coordinate is 0.

7. Point of intersection of two lines

Use the method of solving simultaneous equations to find the point of intersection.

8. Slope of parallel and perpendicular lines

If two lines a and b have slopes m_1 and m_2 respectively, then:

$$a \parallel b \Leftrightarrow m_1 = m_2$$

$$a \perp b \Leftrightarrow m_1.m_2 = -1$$

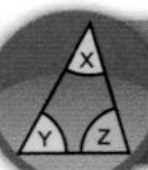

Worked Example 10.1

The line k: $6x - 8y - 71 = 0$ and the points $A(8,-6)$ and $B(5,-2)$ are shown.

(i) Find $|AB|$.

(ii) Find the midpoint of $[AB]$.

(iii) Show that the line k contains the midpoint of $[AB]$.

(iv) Find the slope of AB.

(v) Find the slope of the line k: $6x - 8y - 71 = 0$.

(vi) Find the point of intersection of the line k and the x-axis.

(vii) From the graph, find the intersection of AB and the line k.

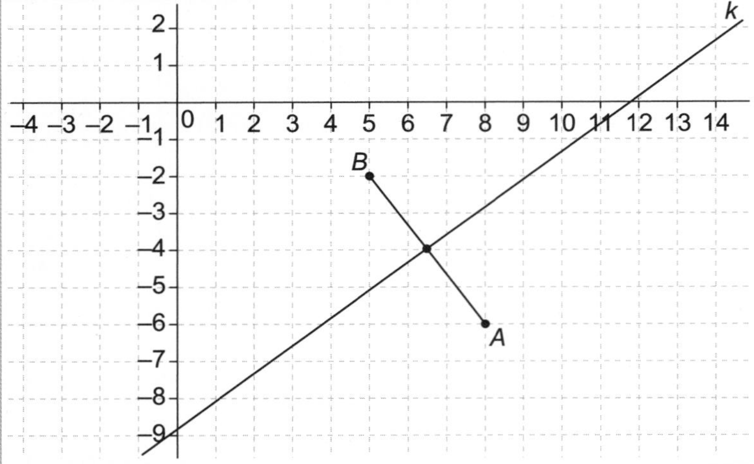

(viii) Given that the equation of AB is $4x + 3y = 14$, verify the point of intersection found in part (vii).

(ix) What can you conclude about the lines AB and k?

Solution

(i) $|AB| = \sqrt{(x_2 - x_1)^2 + (y_2 - y_1)^2}$

$A(8,-6)$ $B(5,-2)$
$x_1\ y_1$ $x_2\ y_2$

$= \sqrt{(5-8)^2 + (-2+6)^2}$

$= \sqrt{(-3)^2 + (4)^2}$

$= \sqrt{9 + 16}$

$= \sqrt{25}$

$\therefore |AB| = 5$

(ii) Midpoint of $[AB]$

Midpoint $= \left(\frac{x_1 + x_2}{2}, \frac{y_1 + y_2}{2}\right)$

$= \left(\frac{8+5}{2}, \frac{-6-2}{2}\right)$

$= (6.5,-4)$

(iii) $(6.5,-4) \in 6x - 8y - 71 = 0$?

$6(6.5) - 8(-4) - 71 = 0$

$39 + 32 - 71 = 0$

$71 - 71 = 0$

$0 = 0$

$\therefore (6.5,-4)$ is on the line k

(iv) Slope of AB

$m = \frac{y_2 - y_1}{x_2 - x_1}$

$= \frac{-2+6}{5-8}$

Slope of $AB = -\frac{4}{3}$

(v) k: $\boxed{\begin{matrix}6\\a\end{matrix}}\,x\,\boxed{\begin{matrix}-8\\b\end{matrix}}\,y\,\boxed{\begin{matrix}-71\\c\end{matrix}} = 0$

$m = \frac{-a}{b} = \frac{-6}{-8} = \frac{3}{4}$

(vi) $y = 0$

$\therefore 6x - 8(0) - 71 = 0$

$\therefore 6x = 71$

$\therefore x = \frac{71}{6}$ $\left(\frac{71}{6}, 0\right)$

(vii) $(6.5,-4)$ is the midpoint of $[AB]$, and from part (iii), it also lies on k.

$\therefore$ Point of intersection $= (6.5,-4)$

(viii)

$$4x + 3y = 14 \cdots\cdots ①$$
$$6x - 8y = 71 \cdots\cdots ②$$
$$12x + 9y = 42 \quad ① \times 3$$
$$12x - 16y = 142 \quad ② \times 2$$
$$\ominus \quad \oplus \quad \ominus$$
$$25y = -100$$
$$y = -4$$

① $4x + 3(-4) = 14$

$$4x - 12 = 14$$
$$4x = 26$$
$$x = 6.5 \qquad (6.5, -4)$$

$\therefore$ Point of intersection is verified.

(ix) Slope of $AB = -\frac{4}{3}\ (m_1)$

Slope of $k = \frac{3}{4}\ (m_2)$

$$m_1 \times m_2 = -\frac{4}{3} \times \frac{3}{4} = -1$$

$\therefore AB \perp k$

Exercise 10.1

1. (i) Find $|AB|$ for each of these pairs of points:

(a) $A(3,2)$ and $B(8,14)$

(b) $A(-6,-1)$ and $B(3,-4)$

(c) $A(6,9)$ and $B(6,12)$

(d) $A(-4,-2)$ and $B(3,-7)$

(ii) Find the midpoint of $[AB]$ for each line segment in part (i).

2. l: $2x - y = 12$. Find:

(i) The slope of l

(ii) The point of intersection of l and

(a) the x-axis

(b) the y-axis

3. Find the point of intersection of

l: $2x - y - 10 = 0$

k: $2x = 14y - 146$

4. P,Q and R are the points $(3,-3)$, $(-5,1)$ and $(1,3)$ respectively.

(i) Show that the triangle PQR is isosceles.

(ii) Find the co-ordinates of S the midpoint of $[QP]$.

(iii) Show that $SR \perp QP$.

5. Find a and b if the point $(6,3)$ is the midpoint of the line joining $(2a, 2a - b)$ and $(a - 2b, 4a + 3b)$.

6. l: $2x - 3y + 4 = 0$ and k: $3x + 2y - 6 = 0$ are two lines. Prove that $l \perp k$.

7. a: $2x + 3y - 8 = 0$ and b: $4x + 6y - 9 = 0$. Prove that $a \parallel b$.

8. m: $3x - 4y = 8$ and n: $ax - 8y = 12$. If $m \parallel n$, find the value of a.

9. $A(2,-2)$ and $B(4,4)$ are two points.

(i) Find $|AB|$.

(ii) Find C, the midpoint of $[AB]$.

The equation of AB is $3x - y - 8 = 0$.

(iii) Verify that $(3,1)$ is on AB.

l: $x + 3y = 14$

(iv) Find the point of intersection of l and AB.

(v) Find the slope of l and the slope of AB.

What can you conclude about the lines l and AB?

10.2 FINDING THE EQUATION OF A LINE

In the given diagram, l is a line containing the point (x_1,y_1), and (x,y) is any other point on l.

Then, $\frac{y - y_1}{x - x_1} = m$, where m is the slope of the line l.

$\Rightarrow y - y_1 = m(x - x_1)$

This is the equation of the line. Therefore, to find the equation of a line, we need the slope of the line, m, and a point on the line, (x_1,y_1).

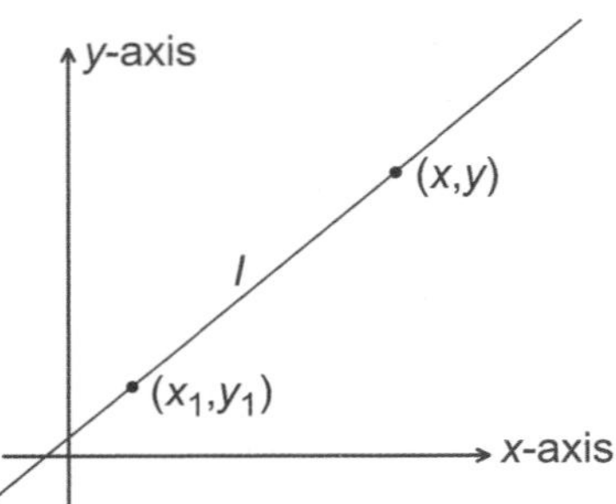

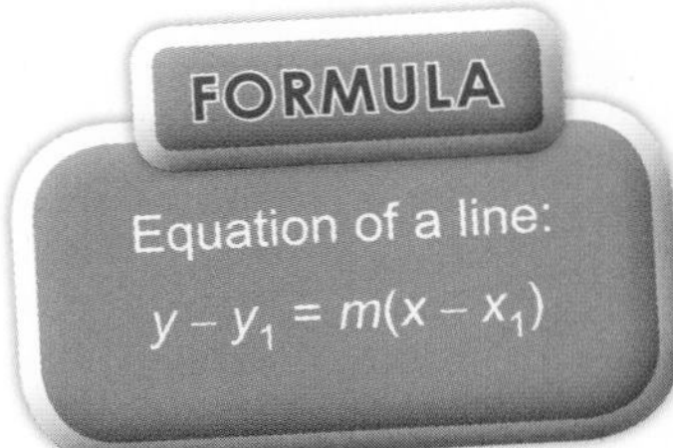

This formula appears on page 18 of the *Formulae and Tables*.

The general form of the equation of a straight line is: $ax + by + c = 0$, where a, b and $c \in R$.
One frequently used form of the equation of a straight line is $y = mx + c$.

The Equations of Parallel and Perpendicular Lines

A line parallel to $ax + by + c = 0$ is $ax + by + d = 0$ (where $d \in R$).
A line perpendicular to $ax + by + c = 0$ is $bx - ay + d = 0$ (where $d \in R$).

Equations of the Form $y = mx + c$

Many equations that model or represent real-life situtations are of the form $y = mx + c$.
So, it makes sense to study equations of the form $y = mx + c$.

When we use equations to solve everyday problems, we usually refer to the equation as a **model** of the problem.

Given the equation $y = mx + c$, m is the slope and $(0,c)$ is the y-intercept, i.e. the point where the line crosses the y-axis.

For example, the equation for the total cost of manufacturing a product could be given as:

TC $= 0.5Q + 5$, where Q = Quantity produced (in 10,000 unit batches) and TC = Total cost (in €000s).

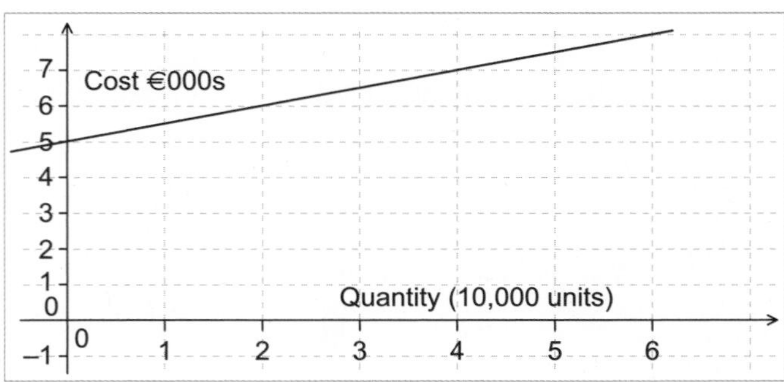

From the graph and equation, $m = 0.5$.
This means that for every 10,000 units produced, the cost increases by €500 (0.5 × €1,000)

From the graph and equation, $c = 5$. This indicates that, regardless of how many units are produced, there is a fixed cost of €5,000.

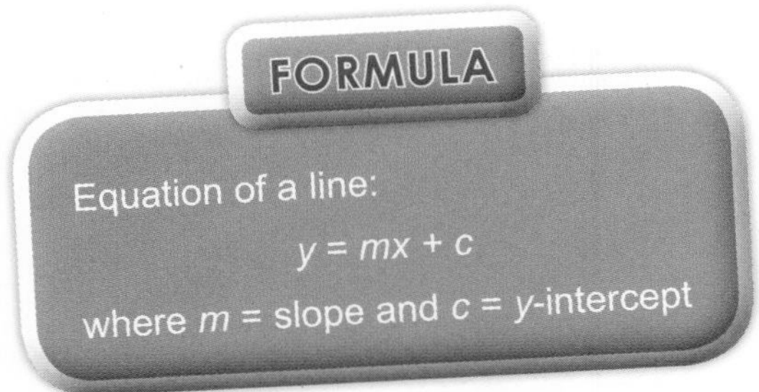

FORMULA
Equation of a line:
$y = mx + c$
where m = slope and c = y-intercept

This formula appears on page 18 of the *Formulae and Tables*.

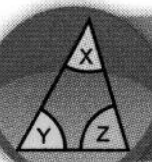

Worked Example 10.2

(i) Find the equation of the line which passes through $A(3,4)$ with slope $\frac{1}{2}$.

(ii) Find the equation of the line which passes through $A(-2,0)$ and $B(2,-3)$.

(iii) Find the equation of the line which passes through (2,3) and is parallel to $3x + 4y + 6 = 0$.

(iv) l is the line $4x + 3y + 8 = 0$. The line m contains (2,–3) and is perpendicular to l. Find the equation of m.

Solution

(i) Equation: $y - y_1 = m(x - x_1)$ Point $A(3, 4)$ ($x_1\ y_1$) Slope $m = \frac{1}{2}$

$$(y - 4) = \frac{1}{2}(x - 3)$$
$$2(y - 4) = 1(x - 3)$$
$$2y - 8 = x - 3$$
$$x - 2y + 5 = 0$$

(ii) Equation: $y - y_1 = m(x - x_1)$ Points $A(-2, 0)$ ($x_1\ y_1$) and $B(2,-3)$ ($x_2\ y_2$)

Slope $m\ \frac{y_2 - y_1}{x_2 - x_1} = \frac{-3 - 0}{2 + 2} = -\frac{3}{4}$

$$y - 0 = -\frac{3}{4}(x + 2)$$
$$4y = -3x - 6$$
$$3x + 4y + 6 = 0$$

(iii) Equation: $y - y_1 = m(x - x_1)$ Point $(2, 3)$ ($x_1\ y_1$)

Parallel to $3x + 4y + 6 = 0$

$\Rightarrow$ Slope $m = -\frac{a}{b} = -\frac{3}{4}$

$$y - 3 = -\frac{3}{4}(x - 2)$$
$$4y - 12 = -3x + 6$$
$$3x + 4y - 18 = 0$$

(iv) Equation: $y - y_1 = m(x - x_1)$ Point $(2,-3)$ ($x_1\ y_1$)

$l: 4x + 3y + 8 = 0$

$\perp$ to l $\Rightarrow m = \frac{b}{a}$

$\therefore m = \frac{3}{4}$

$$y + 3 = \frac{3}{4}(x - 2)$$
$$4(y + 3) = 3(x - 2)$$
$$4y + 12 = 3x - 6$$
$$3x - 4y - 18 = 0$$

Exercise 10.2

1. Find the equations of the lines containing the point A with slope m.

	A	m
(i)	(6,8)	–3
(ii)	(–4,–2)	$\frac{2}{3}$
(iii)	$\left(4, -\frac{1}{2}\right)$	$-\frac{2}{5}$
(iv)	(0,–3)	2

2. Find the equation of the line through the points A and B.

(i) $A(2,1)$; $B(3,2)$

(ii) $A(-1,3)$; $B(2,4)$

(iii) $A(-5,-1)$; $B(-2,5)$

(iv) $A(-3,6)$; $B(5,-2)$

(v) $A(1,-3)$; $B(2,-10)$

3. Find the equation of the line through the points X and Y.

   (i) $X(-2,2)$; $Y(-5,3)$

   (ii) $X(1,7)$; $Y(-2,4)$

   (iii) $X(6,-5)$; $Y(-3,9)$

   (iv) $X(1,1)$; $Y(-2,-1)$

   (v) $X(-3,4)$; $Y(-2,-5)$

4. Find the equation of the line that passes through the origin and has a slope of -1.

5. Find the equation of the lines labelled j, k and l.

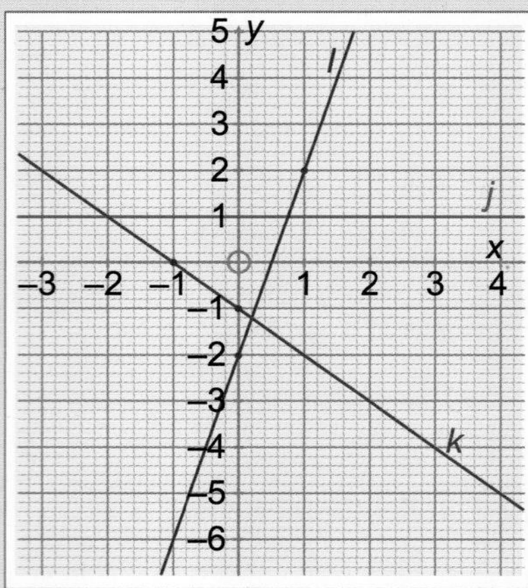

6. Find the equation of the line passing through the point of intersection of $3x + 2y - 1 = 0$ and $5x + 6y + 1 = 0$, and which is perpendicular to $3x - y = 0$.

7. A line crosses the x-axis at $x = 3$ and the y-axis at $y = 2$.

   Find the equation of the line.

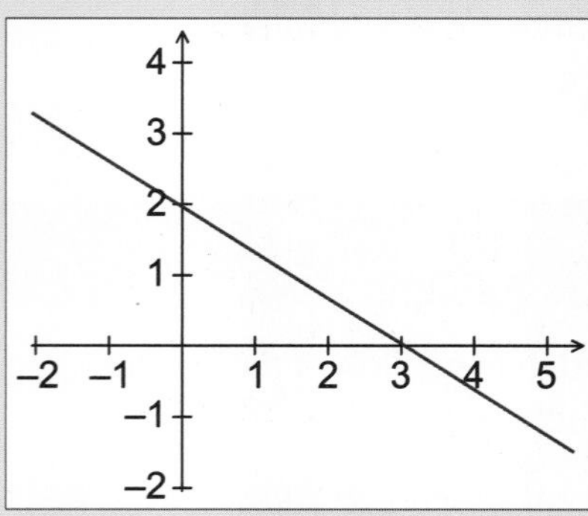

8. l is the line $3x - 2y + 4 = 0$.
   The line k contains the point $(2,-3)$ and is parallel to l. Find the equation of k.

9. m is the line $x - 6y + 12 = 0$.
   The line n contains the point $(-3,2)$ and is perpendicular to m. Find the equation of n.

10. p is the line $2x - y + 14 = 0$.
    The line q contains the point $(-1,2)$ and is parallel to p. Find the equation of q.

11. l is the line $x - y + 2 = 0$.
    The line k contains the point $(2,2)$ and is perpendicular to l. Find the equation of k.

12. $A(-1,4)$ and $B(5,-4)$ are two points.
    Find the equation of the perpendicular bisector of $[AB]$.

13. Find the equation of the line through the point $(1,0)$ that also passes through the point of intersection of the lines $2x - y + 6 = 0$ and $10x + 3y - 2 = 0$.

14. Find the equation of the straight line joining the origin to the midpoint of the line joining $A(3,2)$ and $B(5,-1)$.

15. One side of a rhombus is the line $y = 2x$ and two opposite vertices are the points $(0,0)$ and $(4.5,4.5)$.

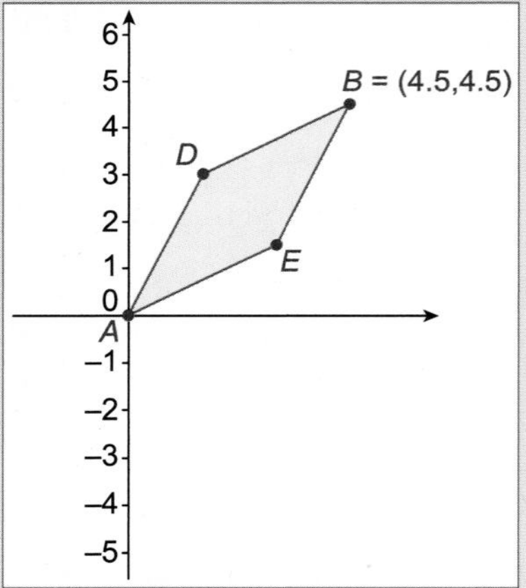

    Find:

    (i) The equations of the diagonals

    (ii) The co-ordinates of the other two vertices

    (iii) The length of a side of the rhombus

10.3 THE AREA OF A TRIANGLE

Graphical Approach

The diagram on the right shows a triangle with vertices (2,1), (3,–2) and (–1,–1). The area of the triangle can be found using the following graphical approach:

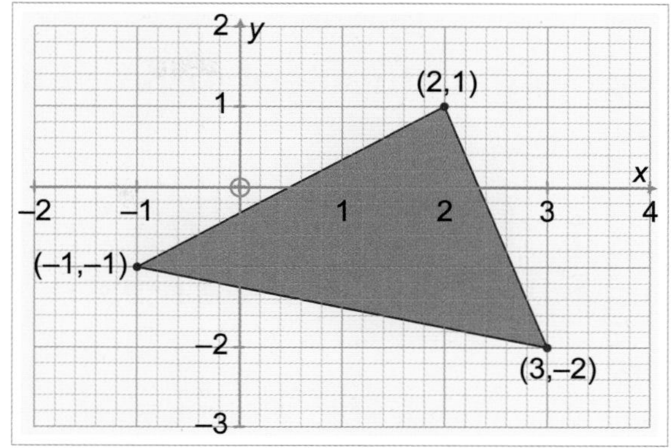

Step 1
Construct a rectangle *ABCD* around the triangle as shown, and find its area:

Area of rectangle = 4 × 3 = 12 units^2

Step 2
Find the area of each of the triangles labelled *P*, *Q* and *R*:

- Area of $\Delta P = \frac{1}{2}(2)(3) = 3$ units^2
- Area of $\Delta Q = \frac{1}{2}(1)(3) = 1.5$ units^2
- Area of $\Delta R = \frac{1}{2}(4)(1) = 2$ units^2
- Area of ΔP + Area of ΔQ + Area of $\Delta R = 3 + 1.5 + 2 = 6.5$ units^2

Step 3
The area of the required triangle is found by subtracting the areas of *P*, *Q* and *R* from the area of *ABCD*.

Area = 12 – 6.5 = 5.5 units^2

Formula Approach

The diagram below shows a triangle with vertices (0,0), (x_1, y_1) and (x_2, y_2).

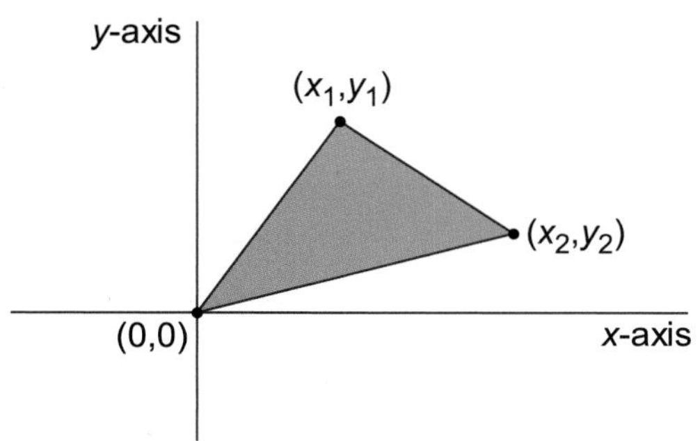

The area of this triangle is given by:

This formula appears on page 18 of the *Formulae and Tables*.

To use this formula, one vertex must be (0,0).

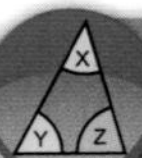

Worked Example 10.3

Find the area of the triangle with vertices (0,0), (7,3) and (15,0).

Solution 1: Graphical Approach

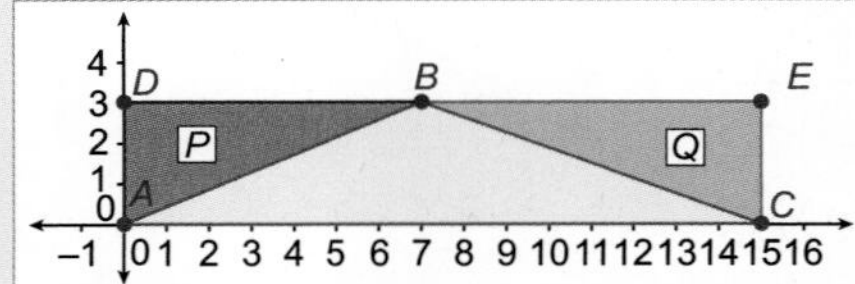

Step 1

Construct a rectangle *ADEC* around the given triangle *ABC* as shown.

The area of the rectangle = 3 × 15 = 45 units^2

Step 2

Find the area of each of the triangles labelled *P* and *Q*.

- Area of $\Delta P = \frac{1}{2}(7)(3) = 10.5$ units^2
- Area of $\Delta Q = \frac{1}{2}(8)(3) = 12$ units^2
- Area of $\Delta P + \Delta Q = 22.5$ units^2

Step 3

Area of given triangle =

Area of rectangle – [Area of ΔP + Area of ΔQ]

Area = 45 – 22.5 = 22.5 units^2

Solution 2: Formula Approach

(0,0) (7, 3) (15, 0)

$x_1\ y_1$ $x_2\ y_2$

$$\text{Area} = \frac{1}{2}|x_1y_2 - x_2y_1|$$
$$= \frac{1}{2}|(7)(0) - (15)(3)|$$
$$= \frac{1}{2}|0 - 45|$$
$$= \frac{1}{2}|-45|$$
$$= \frac{1}{2}(45)$$

∴ Area = 22.5 sq units

Solution 3

$$\text{Area} = \frac{1}{2}\text{ base} \times \text{perpendicular height}$$
$$= \frac{1}{2}(15)(3)$$

∴ Area = 22.5 units^2

Worked Example 10.4

Find the area of the triangle with vertices (–3,4), (4,2) and (6,10).

Solution

Translate the triangle so that one vertex is at (0,0).

(–3, 4)	(4, 2)	(6, 10)
+3 ↓ –4	+3 ↓ –4	+3 ↓ –4
(0, 0)	(7, –2)	(9, 6)
	x_1 y_1	x_2 y_2

$$\text{Area} = \frac{1}{2}|x_1y_2 - x_2y_1|$$
$$= \frac{1}{2}|(7)(6) - (9)(-2)|$$
$$= \frac{1}{2}|42 + 18|$$
$$= \frac{1}{2}(60)$$

= 30 square units

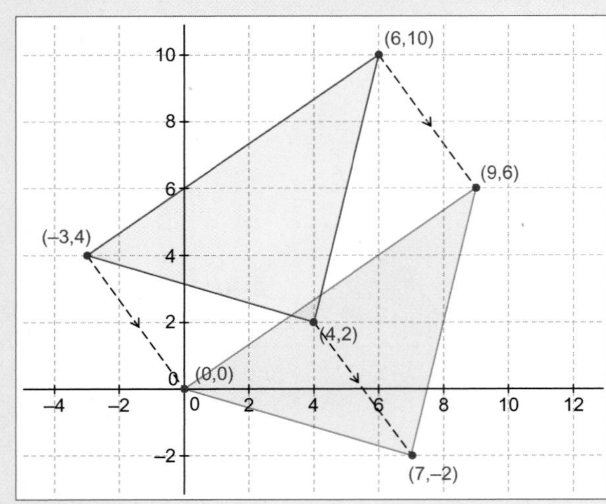

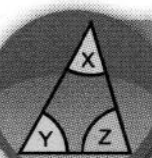

Worked Example 10.5

$A(8,2)$, $B(-3,-4)$, $C(6,k)$ are three vertices of a triangle of area 50 square units.

Find two values of k.

Solution

$(8, \quad 2) \qquad (-3, \quad -4) \qquad (6, \quad k)$

$-8 \downarrow -2 \qquad -8 \downarrow -2 \qquad -8 \downarrow -2$

$(0, \quad 0) \qquad (\underset{x_1}{-11}, \quad \underset{y_1}{-6}) \qquad (\underset{x_2}{-2}, \quad \underset{y_2}{k-2})$

$$\text{Area} = \frac{1}{2}|-11(k-2) - (-2)(-6)| = 50$$

$$\Rightarrow |-11(k-2) - (-2)(-6)| = 100$$

$$|-11k + 22 - 12| = 100$$

$$|-11k + 10| = 100$$

Square both sides:

$$121k^2 - 220k + 100 = 10{,}000$$

$$121k^2 - 220k - 9900 = 0$$

$$11k^2 - 20k - 900 = 0$$

$$(11k + 90)(k - 10) = 0$$

$$\boxed{k = \frac{-90}{11}}$$

$$\boxed{k = 10}$$

Exercise 10.3

1. Find the areas of the triangles with vertices:

	A	B	C
(i)	(0,0)	(2,−3)	(3,5)
(ii)	(5,2)	(0,0)	(3,10)
(iii)	(2,2)	(0,0)	(3,7)
(iv)	(−5,6)	(−1,1)	(5,0)
(v)	(1,5)	(−5,−3)	(4,1)
(vi)	(−1,−4)	(−2,3)	(2,−1)
(vii)	(1,3)	(3,4)	(2,6)
(viii)	(−1,−3)	(4,1)	(3,5)

2. A triangle has vertices $(-1,-1)$, $(6,1)$ and $(-2.5,-5)$.

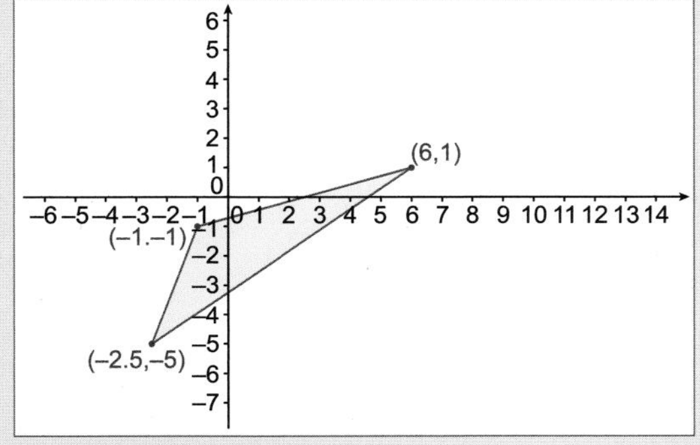

Find the area of the triangle.

3. Find the area of the triangle with vertices $(1,1)$, $(8,-5)$ and $(5,-2)$.

4. $X(-3,1)$, $Y(1,3)$ and $Z(3,0)$ are vertices of a triangle. Find the area of ΔXYZ.

5. The area of ΔABC is 8 square units. $A(1,-2)$, $B(8,-3)$ and $C(x,y)$.

If C is a point on the x-axis, calculate the two possible sets of co-ordinates for C.

6. Find the area of the quadrilateral $ABCD$ with vertices $A(3,3)$, $B(1,4)$, $C(-3,1)$ and $D(3,-5)$.

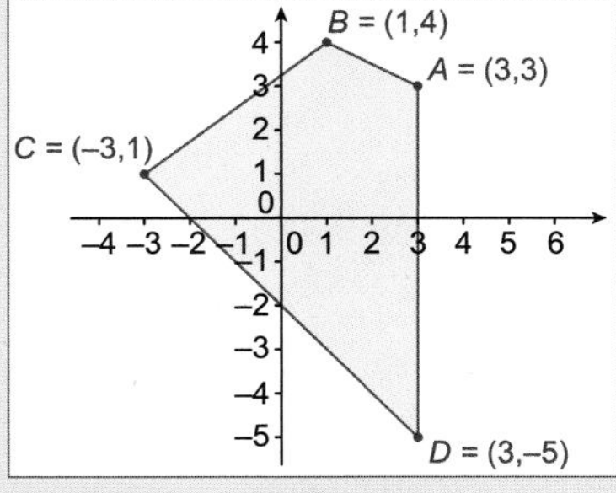

7. $(0,0)$, $(6t,t)$, $(2t,3t)$ are the vertices of a triangle of area 72 square units.

Find two possible values of t.

8. $A(2,1)$, $B(0,3)$ and $C(2k,-1)$ are vertices of a triangle of area 4 square units.
Find the values of k.

10.4 THE PERPENDICULAR DISTANCE FROM A POINT TO A LINE

ACTIVITY 10.6

The shortest distance from a point to a line is the perpendicular distance.

The distance from a point (x_1,y_1) to the line $ax + by + c = 0$ is given by:

This formula appears on page 19 of the *Formulae and Tables*.

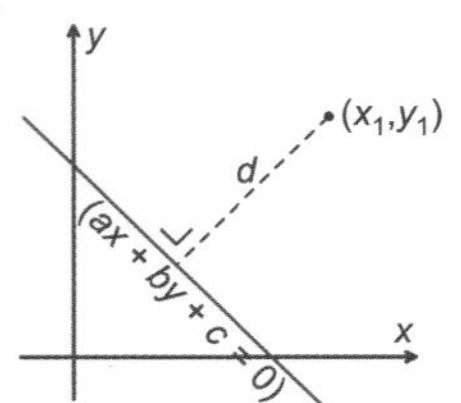

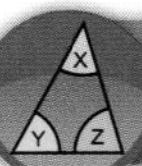

Worked Example 10.6

Find the distance from the point (3,1) to the line $4x + 3y + 10 = 0$.

Solution

$$\boxed{\begin{matrix}4\\a\end{matrix}}\,x\,\boxed{\begin{matrix}+3\\b\end{matrix}}\,y\,\boxed{\begin{matrix}+10\\c\end{matrix}} = 0 \qquad \begin{matrix}(3,1)\\x_1\ y_1\end{matrix}$$

$$d = \frac{|4(3) + 3(1) + 10|}{\sqrt{4^2 + 3^2}}$$

$$= \frac{|12 + 3 + 10|}{\sqrt{16 + 9}}$$

$$= \frac{25}{\sqrt{25}} = \frac{25}{5}$$

$$= 5$$

$$\therefore d = 5$$

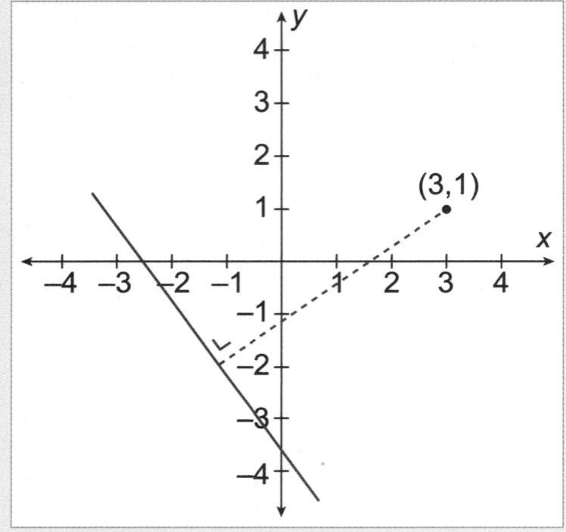

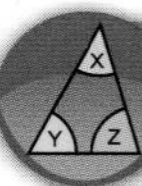

Worked Example 10.7

Find the equation of two lines which are parallel to the line $x + 2y = 5$ and a distance of $3\sqrt{5}$ from it.

Solution

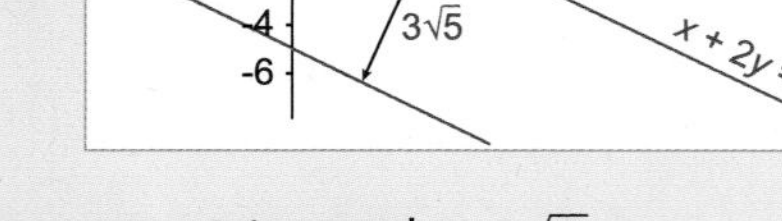

- Any line parallel to $x + 2y = 5$ is of the form $x + 2y + c = 0$.
- Any point on $x + 2y = 5$ will be a distance of $3\sqrt{5}$ from $x + 2y + c = 0$.

(5,0) is on the line $x + 2y = 5$.

$\therefore$ The perpendicular distance from (5,0) to $x + 2y + c = 0$ is equal to $3\sqrt{5}$.

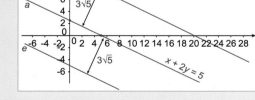

$$\frac{|1(5) + 2(0) + c|}{\sqrt{1^2 + 2^2}} = 3\sqrt{5}$$

$$|5 + c| = 3\sqrt{5}\,\sqrt{5}$$

$$\therefore |5 + c| = 15$$

Note: The absolute value or modulus symbol | | indicates we take the positive value of the answer, for example, |−10| = 10 and |10| = 10. The absolute value of a number may be thought of as its distance from zero.

Square both sides:

$$c^2 + 10c + 25 = 225$$
$$c^2 + 10c - 200 = 0$$
$$(c + 20)(c - 10) = 0$$
$$\therefore c = -20 \quad \textbf{or} \quad c = 10$$

Equations:

$$x + 2y - 20 = 0$$
$$x + 2y + 10 = 0$$

Exercise 10.4

1. Find the distance from:
   (i) $(3,-1)$ to $6x + 8y - 31 = 0$
   (ii) $(1,3)$ to $3x + 4y + 10 = 0$
   (iii) $(3,8)$ to $12x - 5y - 9 = 0$
   (iv) $(3,2)$ to $2x - y + 1 = 0$
   (v) $(3,4)$ to $x - y - 1 = 0$

2. Find, in surd form, the perpendicular distance from:
   (i) $(-1,1)$ to $x - 2y = 2$
   (ii) $(0,0)$ to $x + y - 8 = 0$
   (iii) $(10,0)$ to $x = 2y$
   (iv) $(11,-10)$ to $x = \frac{3y}{2}$

3. Find the perpendicular distance from the point $(5,6)$ to the line $2x + 3y + 4 = 0$.

4. Find the distance from the point $(-3,7)$ to the line $5y = 6x + 2$.

5. Show that $(2,-1)$ is equidistant from the lines with equations $4x + 3y - 20 = 0$ and $y = \frac{12x + 10}{5}$.

6. Investigate if the point $(3,1)$ is equidistant from $3x - 4y + 5 = 0$ and $12x + 5y - 15 = 0$.

7. The distance from $(0,0)$ to $x + y + k = 0$ is $4\sqrt{2}$.

   Find two possible values for $k \in R$.

8. The line l has equation $5x - 3y + 10 = 0$.

   The point K has co-ordinates $(6,2)$.

   Show that the perpendicular distance from K to l is $\sqrt{34}$.

9. k is the line $3x - 4y + 9 = 0$.

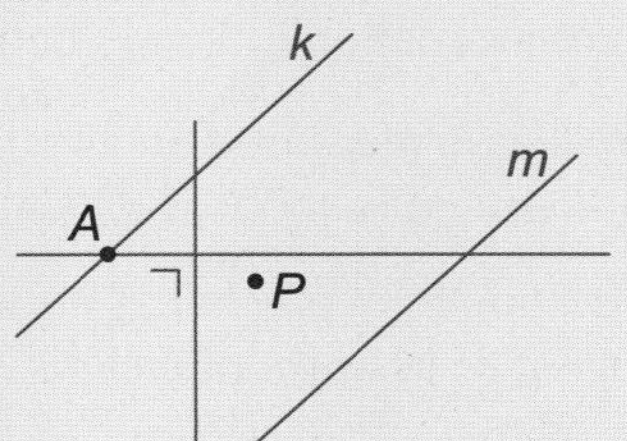

   The point $A(-3,0)$ is on k.
   The line m is parallel to k. The point $P(2,-1)$ is midway between k and m.

   (i) Find the equation of m.
   (ii) Calculate the distance between k and m.

10. (i) Calculate the distance from the point $(-1,-5)$ to the line $3x - 4y - 2 = 0$.
    (ii) The point $(-1,-5)$ is equidistant from the lines $3x - 4y - 2 = 0$ and $3x - 4y + k = 0$, where $k \neq -2$.
    Find the value of k.

11. Find the distance between the parallel lines:

    a: $3x - 4y + 10 = 0$
    b: $3x - 4y + 15 = 0$

12. Find the equations of the lines that pass through the point $(-3,-4)$ and that are a distance of $\sqrt{10}$ from the point $(2,1)$.

13. Find the equations of the lines that are perpendicular to $8x + 15y + 1 = 0$ and that are a distance of 5 units from $(1,1)$.

14. If p is the length of the perpendicular from the origin to the line $\frac{x}{a} + \frac{y}{b} = 1$,

    prove that $\frac{1}{p^2} = \frac{1}{a^2} + \frac{1}{b^2}$.

10.5 THE ANGLE BETWEEN TWO LINES AND THE ANGLE OF INCLINATION

The Angle of Inclination

The **angle of inclination** is the angle formed between a line and the positive side of the x-axis.

The angle of inclination is always between 0° and 180°.

- It is always measured anticlockwise from the positive side of the x-axis.
- The slope m of any line is equal to the tangent of its angle of inclination:

  then $m = \tan \alpha$ (where α = angle of inclination)

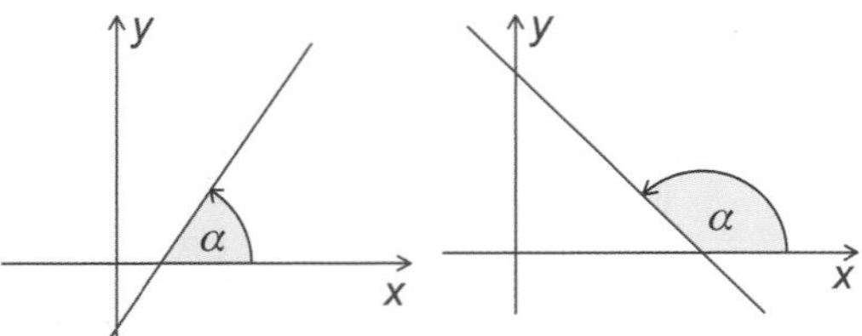

- All horizontal lines have an angle of inclination of 0°.
  Their slopes are zero.
- All vertical lines have an angle of inclination of 90°.
  Their slopes are infinitely steep.

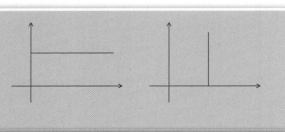

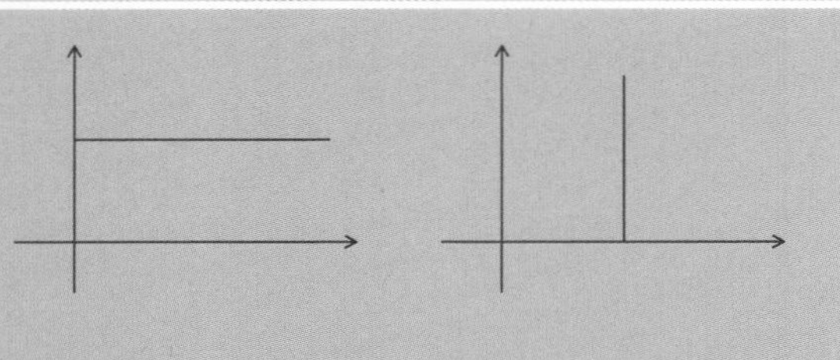

The Angle Between Two Lines

When two lines intersect, the angle between them is defined as the angle through which one of the lines must be rotated to make it coincide with the other line.

Generally, find the acute angle first ($\tan \theta$ is positive), and use $180° - \theta$ to find the obtuse angle.

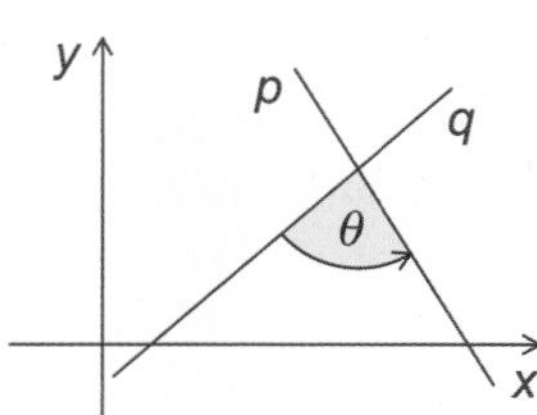

FORMULA

If two lines p and q have slopes m_1 and m_2 respectively, and θ is the angle between them, then:

$$\tan \theta = \pm \frac{m_1 - m_2}{1 + m_1 m_2}$$

This formula appears on page 19 of the *Formulae and Tables*.

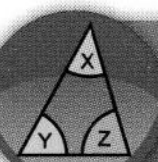

Worked Example 10.8

Find the measure of the angles between the two lines:

$2x + y - 6 = 0$ and $3x - 2y + 2 = 0$.

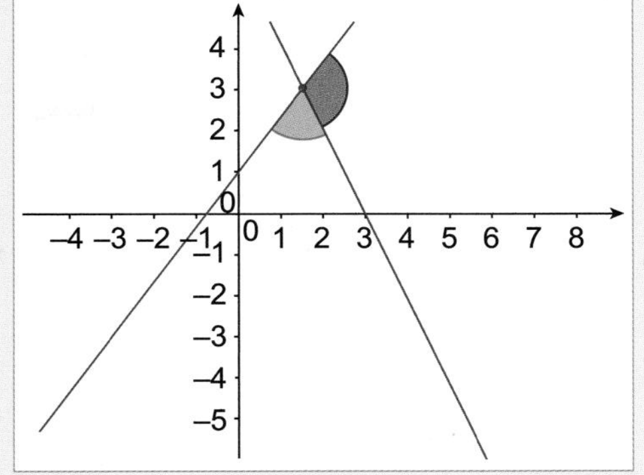

Solution

$$m = -\frac{a}{b}$$

$2x + y - 6 = 0$ $\quad$ $3x - 2y + 2 = 0$

$a = 2 \quad b = 1$ $\quad$ $a = 3 \quad b = -2$

$m_1 = \frac{-2}{1} = -2$ $\quad$ $m_2 = \frac{-3}{-2} = \frac{3}{2}$

$$\tan\theta = \pm\frac{m_1 - m_2}{1 + m_1 m_2}$$

$$\tan\theta = \pm\frac{-2 - \frac{3}{2}}{1 + (-2)\left(\frac{3}{2}\right)}$$

$$= \pm\left(\frac{-4 - 3}{2 + (-2)(3)}\right)$$

$$= \pm\left(\frac{-7}{-4}\right) = \pm\frac{7}{4}$$

$$\tan\theta = \pm\frac{7}{4}$$

$\theta = \tan^{-1}\left(\frac{7}{4}\right)$ … for acute angle

$\therefore \theta = 60.26°$

or $\theta = 180° - 60.26°$ … for obtuse angle

$\therefore \theta = 119.74°$

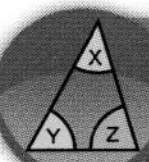

Worked Example 10.9

Find the equations of the lines through the point (4,3) that make an angle of 45° with the line $6x + y - 5 = 0$.

Solution

Find the slope of $6x + y - 5 = 0$.

$$m_1 = \frac{-6}{1} = -6$$

Let the slope of the line(s) through (4,3) = m.

$$\tan\theta = \pm\frac{m_1 - m_2}{1 + m_1 m_2}$$

$$= \pm\left(\frac{-6 - m}{1 - 6m}\right)$$

But $\tan\theta = \tan 45° = 1$

$$\therefore \tan 45° = \left|\frac{-6 - m}{1 - 6m}\right|$$

$$\therefore 1 = \left|\frac{-6 - m}{1 - 6m}\right|$$

$$\therefore 1 = \frac{36 + 12m + m^2}{1 - 12m + 36m^2}$$

$$\therefore 1 - 12m + 36m^2 = 36 + 12m + m^2$$

$$\therefore 35m^2 - 24m - 35 = 0$$

$$\therefore (7m + 5)(5m - 7) = 0$$

$$\therefore m = -\frac{5}{7} \quad \text{or} \quad m = \frac{7}{5}$$

Case 1

Point (4,3)

Slope $m = -\frac{5}{7}$

$$y - 3 = -\frac{5}{7}(x - 4)$$

$$7y - 21 = -5x + 20$$

$$\boxed{5x + 7y - 41 = 0}$$

Case 2

Point (4,3)

Slope $m = \frac{7}{5}$

$$y - 3 = \frac{7}{5}(x - 4)$$

$$5y - 15 = 7x - 28$$

$$\boxed{7x - 5y - 13 = 0}$$

Exercise 10.5

1. (a) Find the acute angle between the two lines that have the following slopes:

	m_1	m_2
(i)	3	7
(ii)	$\frac{3}{5}$	$-\frac{1}{4}$
(iii)	2	−1
(iv)	$-\frac{1}{2}$	$\frac{1}{3}$
(v)	2	$\frac{1}{3}$

(b) Find the obtuse angle between the two lines that have the following slopes:

	m_1	m_2
(i)	2	6
(ii)	$\frac{4}{5}$	−3
(iii)	−1	$\frac{1}{3}$
(iv)	$\frac{1}{2}$	$\frac{1}{4}$
(v)	$\frac{1}{3}$	3

2. Find, to the nearest degree, the measures of the angles between these pairs of lines:

   (i) $2x + y - 6 = 0$ and $3x - 2y + 2 = 0$

   (ii) $x + 2y + 7 = 0$ and $2y = 5 - 3x$

   (iii) $2x + 5y = 10$ and $5x - 2y = 9$

   (iv) $6x - 2y + 5 = 0$ and $2x - 1 = 4y$

   (v) $x + y - 5 = 0$ and $2x + y + 3 = 0$

3. Find the measure of the acute angle between $x - y - 6 = 0$ and $3x - y + 1 = 0$.

4. Find the measure of the obtuse angle between $3x + y = 0$ and $2x - y = 11$.

5. Find the equations of the two lines that pass through the origin and make an angle of 45° with the line $6x - y = 9$.

6. Find the equations of the lines that pass through the point (2,3) and make 45° angles with the line $x - 2y - 1 = 0$.

7. $A(-3,0)$, $P(2,-1)$ $\quad k: 3x - 4y + 9 = 0$

   Calculate the measure of the acute angle between AP and k.
   Give your answer correct to the nearest degree.

8. A triangle has vertices (1,−1), (5,1) and (−2.5,−5).

   Calculate the value of the smallest angle in this triangle.

9. A line containing the point (−4,−2) has slope m. This line intercepts the x-axis at $(x_1,0)$ and the y-axis at $(0,y_1)$. Given that $x_1 + y_1 = 3$, find the slopes of the two lines that satisfy this condition, and find the acute angle between these two lines (to the nearest degree).

10. Part of an obstacle course is called the 'vertical ramp'. If the ramp is on flat ground and its slope is 6, what is the angle of inclination of the ramp?

11. For rain to run off a roof with no risk of water damage, the roof must have a pitch of at least 15°. If the gradient of the roof is 0.25, is there a risk of water damage?

12. An architect is designing a museum for modern art. In keeping with his philosophy, he decides on a very angular building. In the foyer, the wall is at an angle of 55°, while the glass roof is sloped, with a gradient of −0.25.

    Find the interior angle where the wall a and glass roof b meet.

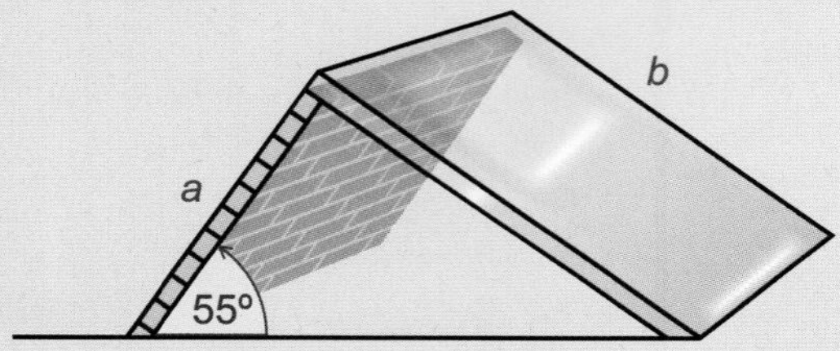

10.6 DIVIDING A LINE SEGMENT IN A GIVEN RATIO a : b

If $P(x_1,y_1)$ and $Q(x_2,y_2)$ are two points, then $[PQ]$ can be divided either internally or externally by a point R.

1. Internal division

If R divides $[PQ]$ internally in the ratio $a:b$:

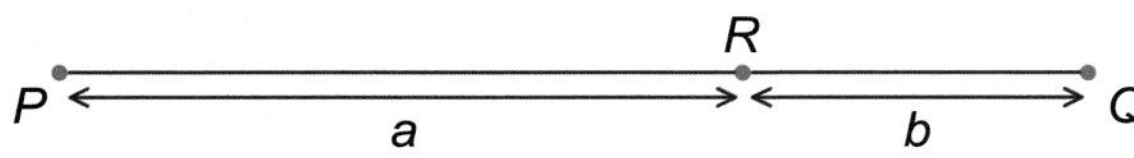

$$R = \left(\frac{bx_1 + ax_2}{b + a}, \frac{by_1 + ay_2}{b + a}\right)$$

This formula appears on page 18 of the *Formulae and Tables*.

2. External division

If R divides $[PQ]$ externally in the ratio $a:b$:

$$R = \left(\frac{-bx_1 + ax_2}{-b + a}, \frac{-by_1 + ay_2}{-b + a}\right)$$

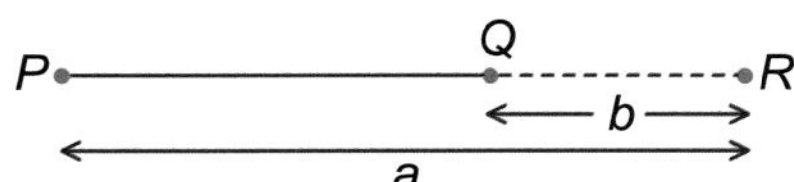

Worked Example 10.10

$X(-5,3)$ and $Y(3,-1)$ are two points. Find the co-ordinates of Z, which divides $[XY]$ in the ratio 3 : 1.

(i) Internally (ii) Externally

Solution

(i)

X(–5,3) Z Y(3,–1)
x_1 y_1 x_2 y_2
3, 1

$$Z = \left(\frac{bx_1 + ax_2}{b + a}, \frac{by_1 + ay_2}{b + a}\right) \qquad 3 : 1 \quad a : b$$

$$= \left(\frac{1(-5) + 3(3)}{1 + 3}, \frac{1(3) + 3(-1)}{1 + 3}\right)$$

$$= \left(\frac{-5 + 9}{4}, \frac{3 - 3}{4}\right)$$

$\therefore Z = (1,0)$

(ii)

X(–5,3) Y(3,–1) Z
x_1 y_1 x_2 y_2
a = 3, b = 1

$$Z = \left(\frac{-bx_1 + ax_2}{-b + a}, \frac{-by_1 + ay_2}{-b + a}\right)$$

$$= \left(\frac{-1(-5) + 3(3)}{-1 + 3}, \frac{-1(3) + 3(-1)}{-1 + 3}\right) = \left(\frac{5 + 9}{2}, \frac{-3 - 3}{2}\right)$$

$\therefore Z = (7,-3)$

Exercise 10.6

1. $A(1,-2)$ and $C(-4,8)$ are two points. B divides $[AC]$ in the ratio $3:2$. Find the co-ordinates of B when B divides $[AC]$:

   (i) Internally (ii) Externally

2. $Q(-2,6)$ and $R(12,27)$ are two points. Find the co-ordinates of P when P is a point on $[QR]$ such that $|QP|:|PR| = 3:4$.

3. $A(-1,4)$ and $B(9,-1)$ are two points and P is a point on $[AB]$. Given that $|AP|:|PB| = 2:3$, find the co-ordinates of P.

4. $P(-2,5)$ and $Q(1,3)$ are two points. The point R is on $[PQ]$ produced, such that $|PQ|:|QR| = 1:2$. Find two possible sets of co-ordinates for R.

5. $P(2,-5)$ and $Q(-5,9)$ are two points. Find the co-ordinates of $K(x,y)$ on the line PQ where $|PK|:|KQ| = 4:3$.

   (i) If $K \in [PQ]$ (ii) If $K \notin [PQ]$

6. $X(-2,-1)$, $Y(2,1)$ and $Z(4,2)$ are three points.

   (i) Prove that X, Y and Z are collinear.

   (ii) Find the ratio by which Y divides $[XZ]$.

   (iii) Find the ratio by which Z divides $[XY]$ produced to Z.

7. A is a point on the y-axis and E is a point on the x-axis. $D(2,1)$ divides $[AE]$ internally in the ratio $4:1$. Find the co-ordinates of A and E.

8. $A(8,-6)$ and $B(5,-2)$ are two points. In what ratio does the line $6x - 8y - 71 = 0$ divide $[AB]$?

9. $A(x,y)$, $B(0,1)$ and $C(-2,2)$ are three points. C divides $[AB]$ externally in the ratio $5:1$.

   (i) Find the ratio $|AB|:|BC|$.

   (ii) Find the value of x and the value of y.

Revision Exercises

1. Using the points given in the table, find:

   (a) The distance between the points

   (b) The midpoint of line segment $[AB]$

   (c) The equation of line AB

	(i)	(ii)	(iii)	(iv)	(v)
A	(2,1)	(–3,2)	$\left(\frac{1}{2},1\right)$	(–2,0)	$\left(\frac{2}{3},-\frac{1}{3}\right)$
B	(4,5)	(3,–2)	$\left(-\frac{3}{2},-5\right)$	$(0,\sqrt{2})$	$\left(\frac{5}{6},1\right)$

2. Write down the slope of each of the following line segments:

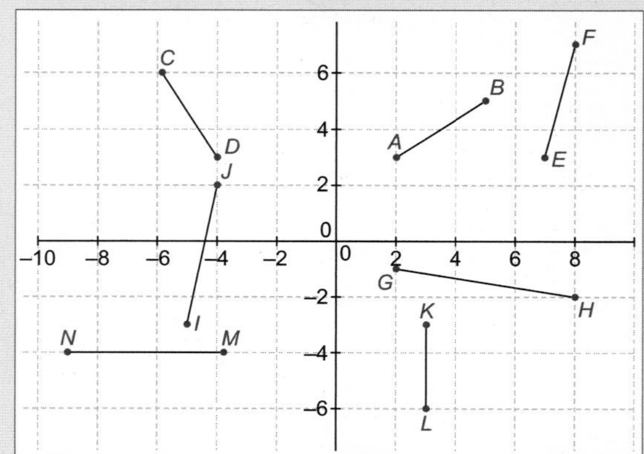

3. $A(2,1)$, $B(10,7)$, $C(14,10)$ and $D(7,3)$ are four points.

   (i) Plot A, B, C and D on the plane.

   (ii) Verify that $|AB| = 2|BC|$ and that $|AB| = 2|BD|$.

4. $A(-2,1)$ and $B(4,-5)$ are two points.
   (i) Plot the two points on graph paper.
   (ii) Find M, the midpoint of $[AB]$.
   (iii) Verify that $|AM| = |MB|$.
   (iv) Find the slope of AB.
   (v) Find the equation of AB.
   (vi) Find the co-ordinates of the point where AB cuts the x-axis.

5. Find two values of x such that the distance between $A(0,0)$ and $B(x,-4)$ is 5.

6. Find two values of y such that the distance between $(5,1)$ and $(5,y)$ is 8.

7. l: $3x + y + 12 = 0$ and k: $x + 2y - 1 = 0$ are two lines. Find:
   (i) The acute angle between them
   (ii) The distance of their point of intersection from the origin
   (iii) The area of the triangle enclosed by l, k and the x-axis
   (iv) The equation of the line m, through $(2,3)$ and perpendicular to l
   (v) The perpendicular distance from $(4,4)$ to m

8. The line p contains the points $(6,-2)$ and $(-4,10)$.

   The line q with equation $ax + by + 21 = 0$ is perpendicular to p.

   Express a in terms of b.

9. Show that the line containing the points $(2,-6)$ and $(-8,12)$ is perpendicular to the line $5x - 9y + 6 = 0$.

10. The equation of the line l is $14x + 6y + 1 = 0$.

    Find the equation of the line perpendicular to l that contains the point $(5,-3)$.

11. The line l_1: $3x - 2y + 1 = 0$ and the line l_2: $5x + y + 3 = 0$ intersect at the point P. Find the equation of the line through P parallel to l_2.

12. (i) The line $3x - 5y + k = 0$ cuts the x-axis at P and the y-axis at Q. Write down the co-ordinates of P and Q in terms of k.
    (ii) The area of the triangle OPQ is 10 square units, where O is the origin. Find the two possible values of k.

13. Find the equations of the two lines that pass through the point $(6,1)$ and make an angle of $45°$ with the line $x + 2y = 0$.

14. Find the area of the triangle with vertices $(5,-3)$, $(-5,-1)$ and $(8,7)$.

15. The line k has a positive slope and passes through the point $P(2,-9)$. k intersects the x-axis at Q and the y-axis at R and $|PQ| : |PR| = 3 : 1$.

    Find the co-ordinates of Q and the co-ordinates of R.

16. (a) The distance from $(5,6)$ to $(k,2)$ is $2\sqrt{5}$. Find two possible values of k.
    (b) (i) Show that $P(k-2, 7k-7)$ is on the line m: $7x - y + 7 = 0$.
    (ii) Find the equation of the line n, on which the point $Q(t + 1, 3 - t)$ lies for all values of $t \in R$.

17. The co-ordinates of three points A, B, and C are: $A(2,2)$, $B(6,-6)$, $C(-2,-3)$ (see diagram).
    (a) Find the equation of AB.
    (b) The line AB intersects the y-axis at D. Find the co-ordinates of D.
    (c) Find the perpendicular distance from C to AB.
    (d) Hence, find the area of the triangle ADC.

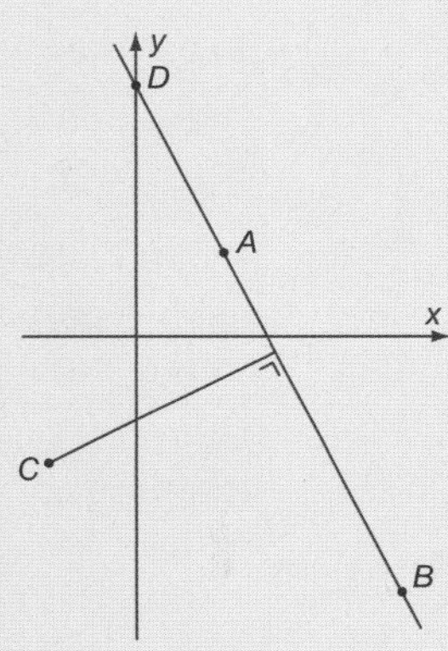

SEC Project Maths Sample Paper 2, Leaving Certificate Higher Level, 2010

18. Three points A, B, and C have co-ordinates: $A(-2,9)$, $B(6,-6)$ and $C(11,6)$.

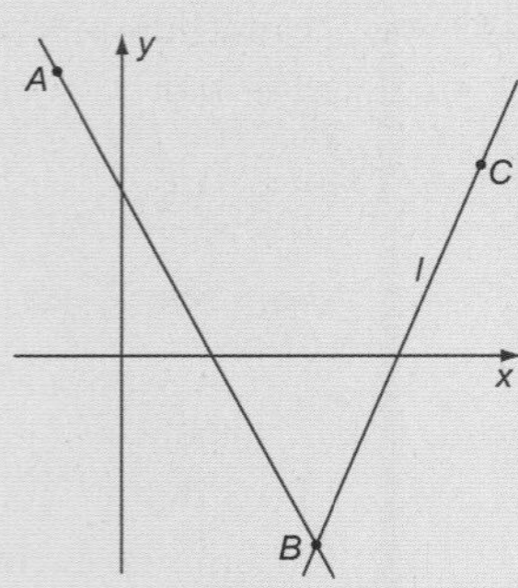

The line l passes through B and has the equation $12x - 5y - 102 = 0$.

(a) Verify that C lies on l.

(b) Find the slope of AB, and hence, find tan ($\angle ABC$), as a fraction.

SEC Project Maths Paper 2, Leaving Certificate Higher Level, 2010

19. In the co-ordinate diagram shown, the lines j, k and l are parallel, and so are the lines m and n. The equations of four of the five lines are given in the table below.

Equation	Line
$x + 2y = -4$	
$2x - y = -4$	
$x + 2y = 8$	
$2x - y = 2$	

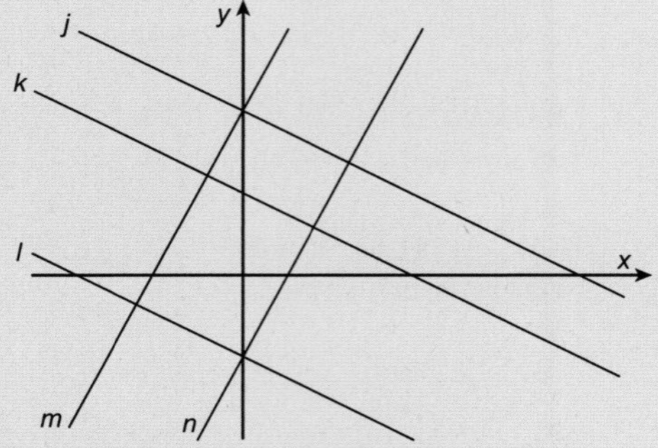

(a) Complete the table by matching four of the lines to their equations.

(b) Hence, insert scales on the x-axis and y-axis.

(c) Hence, find the equation of the remaining line, given that its x-intercept and y-intercept are both integers.

SEC Project Maths Paper 2, Leaving Certificate Higher Level, 2011

20. Find the value of b if the lines $x + (b - 4)y = 4$ and $bx + y = 18$ are perpendicular to each other.

21. (i) Write down the equation of any line parallel to $x - 2y = 4$.

(ii) If a particular parallel line contains the point $(7,-2)$, find its equation.

22. (i) Write down the equation of any line perpendicular to $x + 3y = 10$.

(ii) If a particular perpendicular line contains the point $(7,-6)$, find its equation.

23. The line l_1 in the diagram has slope 3 and y-intercept 2.

(a) Write down the equation of this line, in the form $y = mx + c$.

(b) On the diagram, draw and label the lines l_2 and l_3, where:
l_2 has slope 3 and y-intercept 7
l_3 has slope 1 and y-intercept 8

(c) On the diagram, draw and label the line l_4, which is perpendicular to l_1 and passes through the point $(0,4)$.

(d) Determine whether l_4 passes through the point $(27,-4)$.

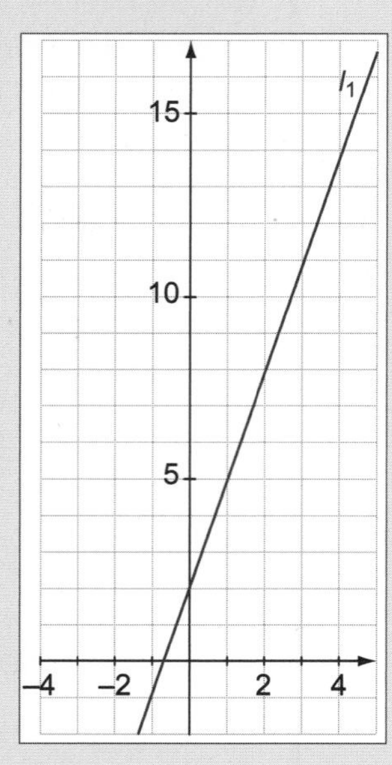

NCCA Pre-Leaving Certificate Higher Level Project Maths Paper 2, February 2010

24. Two common units of measurement in cooking are the tablespoon and the cup. The table below gives some conversions.

Tablespoon	4	8	12	16
Cup	$\frac{1}{4}$	$\frac{1}{2}$	$\frac{3}{4}$	1

(i) Using suitable axes and scales, draw a straight line graph of the conversion.

(ii) Using the graph, convert 6 tablespoons to cups.

(iii) Find the slope of the line.

(iv) Hence, write down the equation of the line in the form $y = mx$.

(v) Use your equation to convert 50 tablespoons to cups.

25. A car passes a traffic light travelling at a speed of 30 km/h. The graph below gives the speed of the car during the 20-second period after passing the traffic light.

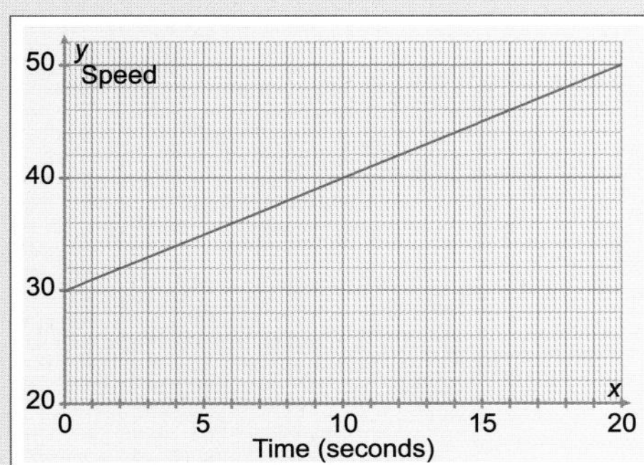

(i) What is the speed of the car 10 seconds after passing the light?

(ii) How many seconds does it take the driver to reach a speed of 48 km/h?

(iii) Find the equation of the line.

(iv) What is the y-intercept of this line? What value does it represent?

(v) By how many kilometres per hour does the speed change in the 20-second period?

(vi) If the driver continues to change his speed (accelerates) at the same rate over the next 10-second period, then what will the speed of the car be 25 seconds after passing the light?

26. The charge for repairing a washing machine is made up of a fixed charge and a fee that depends on the time taken to repair the machine.

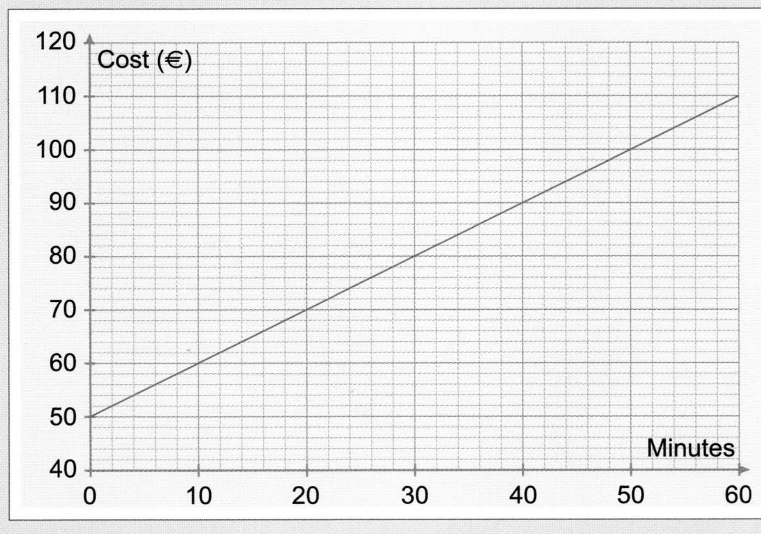

(i) What is the fixed charge for a repair?

(ii) What is the charge for a repair that takes 40 minutes?

(iii) Calculate the slope of the line.

(iv) What does the slope represent?

(v) Find the equation of the line.

(vi) Use your equation to find the cost of a repair that takes two hours.

27. The graph below shows the cost of production for a given product. The total cost of production is made up of fixed costs and variable costs.

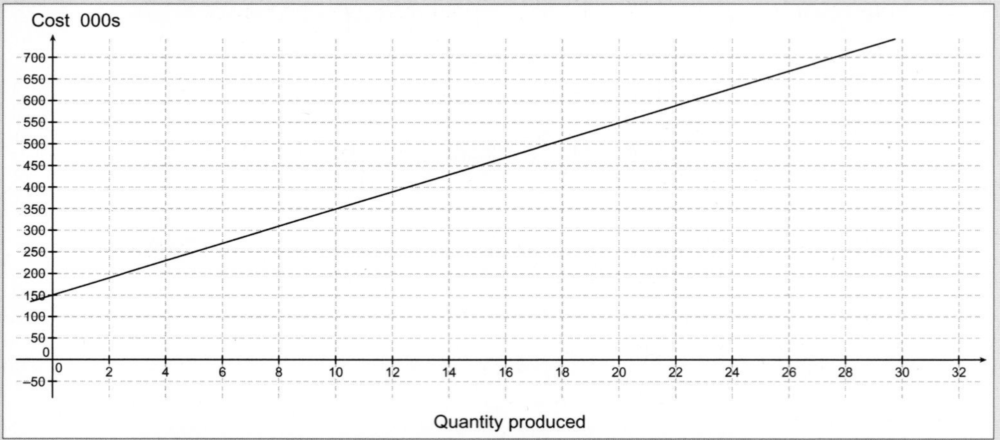

(i) What is the fixed cost associated with this product?

(ii) What is the variable cost per unit produced?

(iii) Find the equation of the line graphed above.

28. The following equation gives the time (T) in minutes for cooking a turkey whose weight (w) is in kilograms:

$T = 44w + 20$

(i) Plot the graph for $0 \leqslant w \leqslant 10$.

(ii) Find the time needed to cook a turkey whose weight is 4.8 kg.

(iii) A turkey was cooked for 5 hours. Using the equation above, find an approximation for its weight in kilograms.

29. A student is asked to design a flag for her team for a school sports day. She has the basic colour scheme for the design. Her teacher told her to get prices on the material needed before she adds any designs.

Below is her basic pattern. Each unit measurement represents 10 cm.

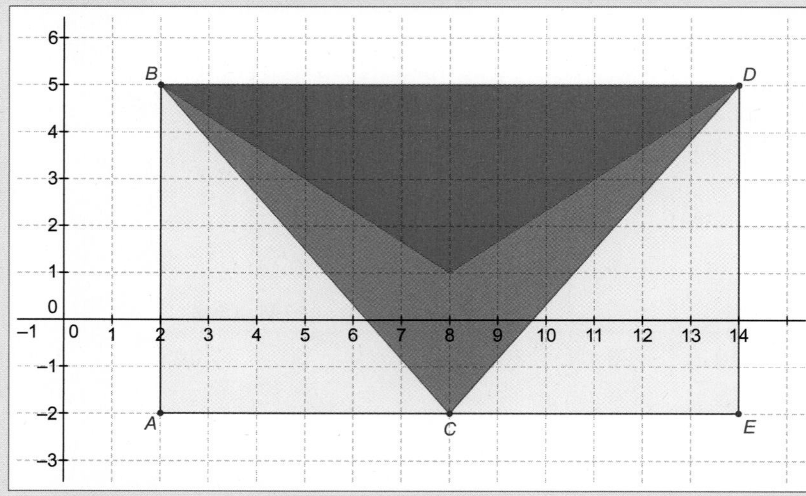

(i) Find correct to the nearest cm^2 the amount of colour material she will need for each section of the flag.

(ii) The budget for material is €70 and the material costs are as follows:

- Blue material 79 cents per 100 cm^2
- Green material 64 cents per 100 cm^2
- Red material 40 cents per 100 cm^2

Does she have enough money for this design?

30. The following graph represents the total sales and total costs of a firm for selling a particular product:

(i) Find the slope of the Total Sales line.

Indicate which answer is correct – the slope of this line gives us:

(a) Total sales

(b) The selling price per unit

(c) The cost of selling 10,000 shirts

(ii) Find the equation of the Total Sales line.

(iii) Find the equation of the Total Costs line.

(iv) The break-even point is the level of production at which sales cover costs.

Find the break-even point from the graph, and verify your answer using algebraic methods.

31. Rory and Paula are mooring their boat along a pier wall. Paula can jump from three of the points marked on the side of the boat. Which is the shortest distance to jump?
The pier wall is given by the line $x + 4y = 20$.

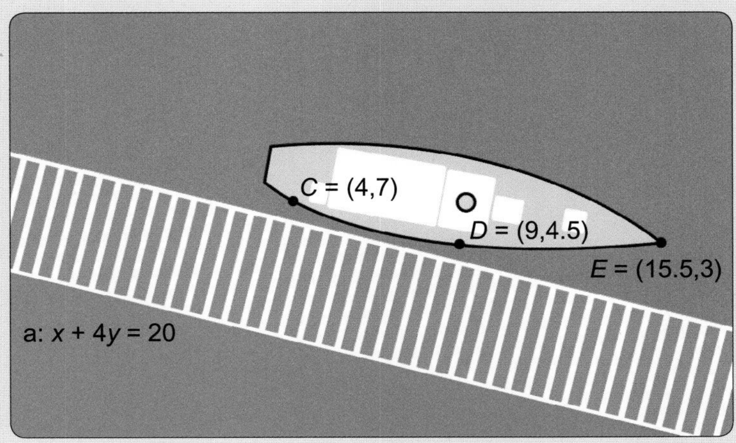

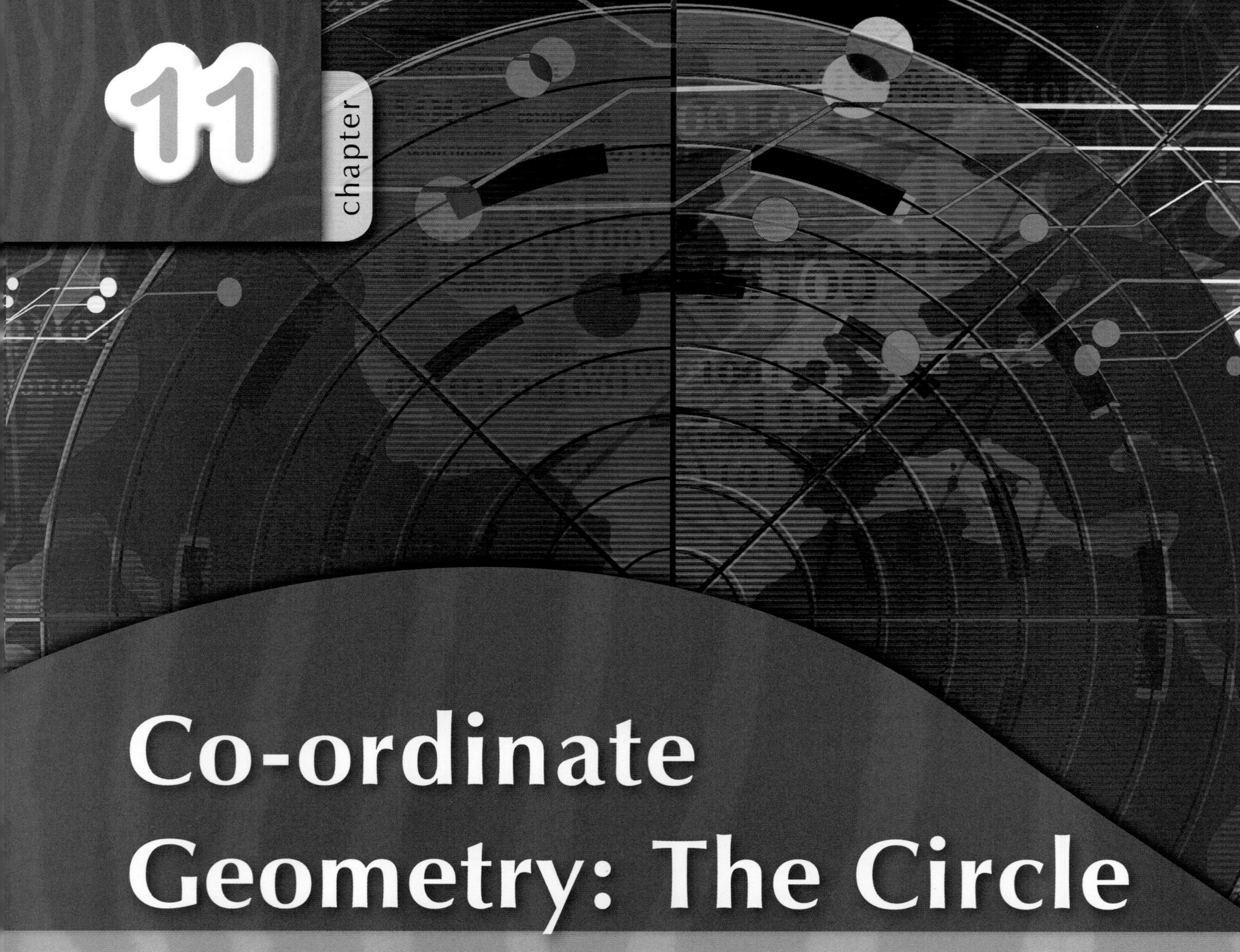

11 chapter

Co-ordinate Geometry: The Circle

Learning Outcomes

In this chapter you will learn how to:

- Find the equation of a circle with centre (0,0) and radius length r
- Find the equation of a circle with centre (h,k) and radius length r
- Work with equations of the form $x^2 + y^2 + 2gx + 2fy + c = 0$
- Calculate the points of intersection of a line and a circle
- Prove that a line is a tangent to a circle
- Prove that a line does not intersect a circle
- Show whether a point is inside, outside or on a circle
- Find the equation of tangents to a circle

The ancient Greeks believed that the **circle** was the perfect form, because circular forms occurred so frequently in nature. They also thought that the stars and planets travelled in circular paths around the universe.

A **circle** is the set of all points in the plane which are equidistant from a fixed point, the centre. The distance from the centre to any point on the circle is called the **radius length** of the circle.

YOU SHOULD REMEMBER...

- How to find the distance between two points
- How to find the midpoint of two points
- How to find the perpendicular distance of a point from a line
- How to solve quadratic equations

KEY WORDS

- **Equation of a circle**
- **Radius length**
- **Tangent**

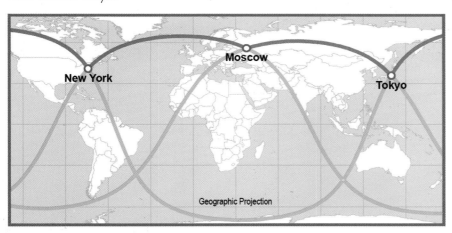

An interesting modern-day application of co-ordinate geometry of the circle is the mapping of 'great circle' routes. A great circle of a sphere is a circle that runs along the surface of the sphere so as to cut it into two equal halves. As the earth is almost spherical, we can draw imaginary great circles on the surface of the earth. The shortest route between any two points on the surface of a sphere will lie along a great circle. This is why intercontintental airlines fly along great circle routes – it minimises the distance they have to travel. On the map below we can see examples of three great circle routes: New York to Moscow, Moscow to Tokyo and New York to Tokyo.

New York
Moscow
Tokyo
Geographic Projection

11.1 CIRCLES WITH CENTRE (0,0)

Consider a circle with centre $O(0,0)$ and radius length r. Let $P(x, y)$ be the co-ordinates of any point on the circle.

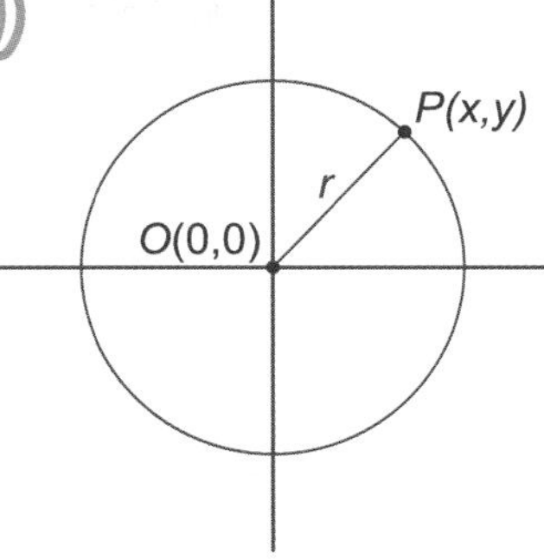

$$|OP| = \sqrt{(x-0)^2 + (y-0)^2} = \sqrt{x^2 + y^2}$$

$$|OP| = \text{radius length} = r$$

Therefore,

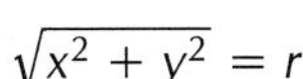

$$\sqrt{x^2 + y^2} = r$$

and hence,

$$x^2 + y^2 = r^2$$

This is the **equation of a circle with centre (0,0) and radius length *r*.**

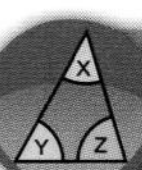

Worked Example 11.1

Find the equation of the following circles:

(i) s_1: centre (0,0) and radius length 9 (ii) s_2: centre (0,0) and contains the point (2,3)

Solution

(i) $x^2 + y^2 = r^2$ Given: $r = 9$

$\Rightarrow x^2 + y^2 = 9^2$

$\therefore x^2 + y^2 = 81$ ......s_1

(ii) **Radius length**

$r = \sqrt{(2-0)^2 + (3-0)^2}$

$r = \sqrt{4+9}$

$r = \sqrt{13}$

Equation

$x^2 + y^2 = r^2$

$\therefore x^2 + y^2 = 13$ ......s_2

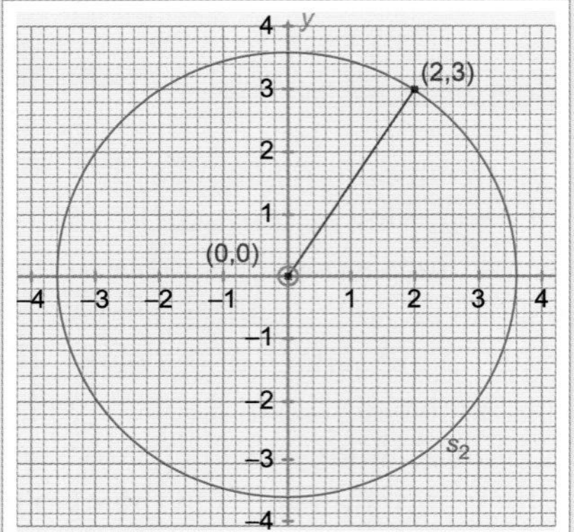

Worked Example 11.2

Find the equation of the circle, with centre (0,0), which has the line $2x - 3y - 6 = 0$ as a tangent.

Solution

Step 1 A useful approach is to sketch the line (by finding the intercepts) and then draw the circle with this line as tangent.

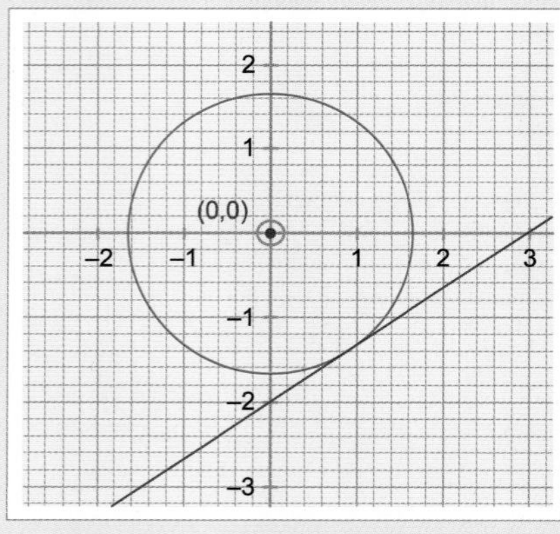

Step 2 We will use the following geometry theorem to find the equation:

The perpendicular distance from the centre of a circle to a tangent of the circle is equal to the radius length of the circle.

Radius length

$$r = \frac{|2(0) - 3(0) - 6|}{\sqrt{2^2 + (-3)^2}}$$

$$r = \frac{6}{\sqrt{13}}$$

Equation

$$x^2 + y^2 = \left(\frac{6}{\sqrt{13}}\right)^2$$

$$\therefore x^2 + y^2 = \frac{36}{13}$$

$$\therefore 13x^2 + 13y^2 = 36$$

Exercise 11.1

1. Write down the equation of the circle with centre $O(0,0)$ and radius length:

(i) 5	(iv) 13	(vii) $\sqrt{3}$	(x) 1.8
(ii) 8	(v) 17	(viii) $\frac{3}{4}$	(xi) $5\sqrt{3}$
(iii) 1	(vi) $\sqrt{2}$	(ix) $\frac{1}{2}$	(xii) $3\sqrt{7}$

2. Write down the radius length of each of the following circles:

(i) $x^2 + y^2 = 64$

(ii) $x^2 + y^2 = 81$

(iii) $x^2 + y^2 = 2^2$

(iv) $x^2 + y^2 = 7^2$

(v) $x^2 + y^2 = 3$

(vi) $4x^2 + 4y^2 = 9$

(vii) $9x^2 + 9y^2 = 100$

(viii) $x^2 + y^2 = a^2$

(ix) $25x^2 + 25y^2 = 49$

(x) $x^2 + y^2 = \frac{1}{a^2}$

(xi) $a^2x^2 + a^2y^2 = b^2$

(xii) $b^4x^2 + b^4y^2 = a^6$

3. Find the distance from $O(0,0)$ to $B(-6,-8)$, and hence, write down the equation of the circle with centre O and which contains the point B.

4.

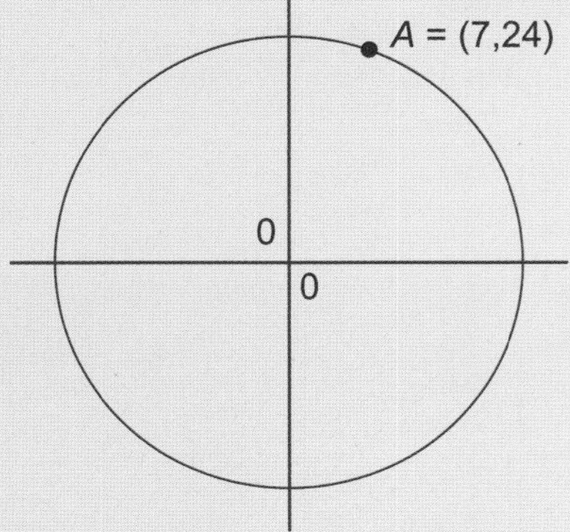

(i) Find the radius length of the circle shown above.

(ii) Hence, write its equation in the form $x^2 + y^2 = r^2$

5. Find the area and circumference of each of the following circles:

Give your answer in terms of π, m, n and a.

(i) $4x^2 + 4y^2 = 9$

(ii) $x^2 + y^2 = \frac{1}{a^2}$

(iii) $x^2 + y^2 = \frac{m^4}{n^4}$

(iv) $x^2 + y^2 = a^2 + 2a + 1$

6. The line segment joining $A(-3,4)$ and $B(3,-4)$ is the diameter of a circle.

(i) Find the centre of the circle.

(ii) Find the radius length of the circle.

(iii) Write down the equation of the circle.

7. The line segment joining $A(-6,2)$ and $B(6,-2)$ is the diameter of a circle.

(i) Find the centre of the circle.

(ii) Find the radius length of the circle.

(iii) Write down the equation of the circle.

(iv) Draw a sketch of the circle.

(v) Using the formula $A = \pi r^2$, find the area of the circle. Give your answer correct to two decimal places.

(vi) Find the area of the square in which the circle can be inscribed.

8. A circle c has equation $x^2 + y^2 = 5$.

(i) Write down the equation of the circle k, which has its centre at the origin and whose area is 25 times greater than the area of c.

(ii) If the point $P(t,-2)$ is on k, find the value of t, where $t \in N$.

9. Find the equation of the circle which has centre (0,0) and which touches the line $4x - 3y = 25$ at one point only.

10. Find the equation of the circle which has centre (0,0) and which touches the line $x - 3y - 9 = 0$ at one point only.

11. Find the equation of the circle which has centre (0,0) and which has the line $x - 4y - 1 = 0$ as a tangent.

12.

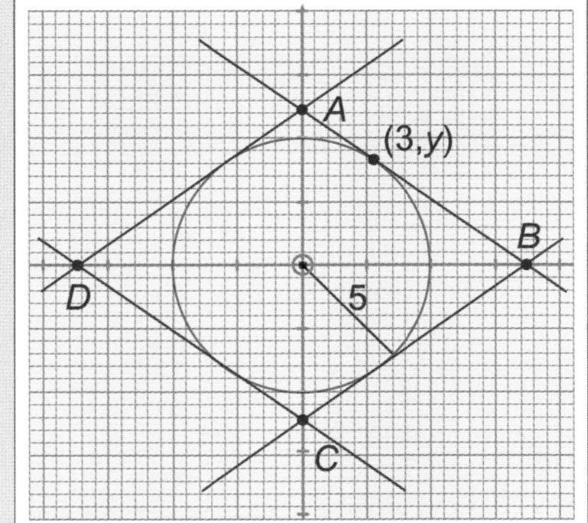

(i) Find the value of y.

(ii) Hence find the area of the parallelogram $ABCD$.

11.2 CIRCLES WITH CENTRE (h,k) AND RADIUS LENGTH r

We will now derive the equation of a circle centred outside of (0,0).

You should have derived the equation of the circle with centre (h,k) and radius length r. Here once again is the derivation:

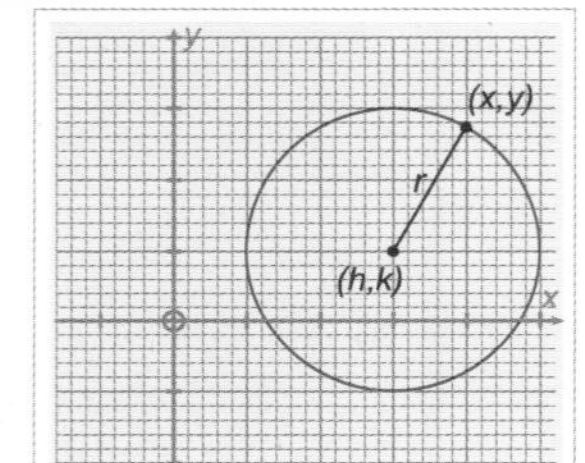

s is the circle with centre $Q(h,k)$.

Let $P(x,y)$ be any point on s.

Let r be the length of the radius of s.

$|QP| = \sqrt{(x-h)^2 + (y-k)^2} = r$

$\therefore (x-h)^2 + (y-k)^2 = r^2$

The equation above represents the equation of any circle with centre (h,k) and with radius length r.

This formula appears on page 19 of *Formulae and Tables*.

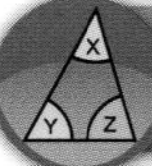

Worked Example 11.3

Find the centre and radius length of the circle $(x-5)^2 + (y+3)^2 = 25$.

Solution

Given equation: $(x-5)^2 + (y+3)^2 = 25$

General equation: $(x-h)^2 + (y-k)^2 = r^2$

Comparing: $-h = -5$, $-k = 3$, $r^2 = 25$

$\therefore h = 5, k = -3, r = 5$

$\therefore$ The centre of the circle is $(5,-3)$ and the radius length is 5.

Worked Example 11.4

The circle shown has a diameter with endpoints $(2,-3)$ and $(6,-8)$. Find:

(i) The centre of the circle

(ii) The radius length of the circle

(iii) The equation of the circle

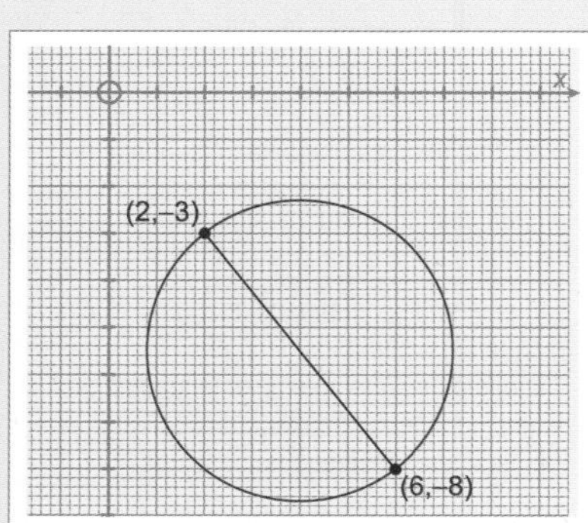

Solution

(i) The centre of the circle is the midpoint of the endpoints of the diameter.

Midpoint $= \left(\frac{x_1 + x_2}{2}, \frac{y_1 + y_2}{2}\right)$

Centre $= \left(\frac{2+6}{2}, \frac{-3-8}{2}\right) = \left(\frac{8}{2}, -\frac{11}{2}\right) = \left(4, -\frac{11}{2}\right)$.

(ii) The radius of the circle is the distance from an endpoint of a diameter to the centre of the circle.

Distance $= \sqrt{(x_2 - x_1)^2 + (y_2 - y_1)^2}$ Points (2,–3) and $\left(4, -\frac{11}{2}\right)$

$$r = \sqrt{(4-2)^2 + \left(-\frac{11}{2} + 3\right)^2}$$

$$r = \sqrt{4 + \frac{25}{4}} = \sqrt{\frac{41}{4}} \text{ or } \frac{\sqrt{41}}{2}$$ (Leave in square root form)

(iii) Equation

$(x - h)^2 + (y - k)^2 = r^2$ Centre $\left(4, -\frac{11}{2}\right)$ $r = \sqrt{\frac{41}{4}}$

$$(x-4)^2 + \left(y + \frac{11}{2}\right)^2 = \frac{41}{4}$$

Intercepts on the *x*-Axis and *y*-Axis

The points where a circle crosses the x-axis are called the x-intercepts of the circle, and the points where a circle crosses the y-axis are called the y-intercepts of the circle.

The co-ordinates of points on the x-axis are always of the form (a,0) and the co-ordinates of points on the y-axis are always of the form (0,b). Hence:

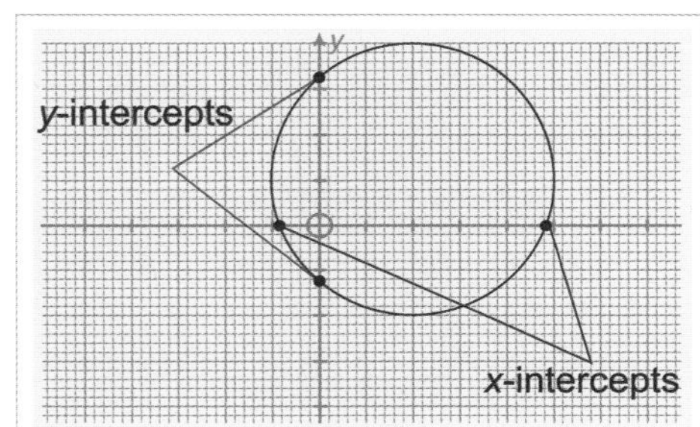

- We let $y = 0$ in the equation of a circle and solve for x to find the co-ordinates of the **x-intercepts**.
- We let $x = 0$ in the equation of a circle and solve for y to find the co-ordinates of the **y-intercepts**.

Worked Example 11.5

Find the x-intercepts and the y-intercepts of the circle $(x + 3)^2 + (y - 2)^2 = 13$.

Solution

(i) ***x*-intercepts**

Let $y = 0$ in the equation of the circle.

$$(x + 3)^2 + (0 - 2)^2 = 13$$
$$(x + 3)^2 + 4 = 13$$
$$(x + 3)^2 = 9$$
$$x + 3 = \pm 3$$
$$x = 0 \textbf{ or } x = -6$$

Therefore, the co-ordinates of the x-intercepts are (0,0) and (–6,0).

(ii) ***y*-intercepts**

Let $x = 0$ in the equation of the circle.

$$(0 + 3)^2 + (y - 2)^2 = 13$$
$$9 + (y - 2)^2 = 13$$
$$(y - 2)^2 = 4$$
$$y - 2 = \pm 2$$
$$y = 4 \textbf{ or } y = 0$$

Therefore, the co-ordinates of the y-intercepts are (0,4) and (0,0).

Exercise 11.2

1. Find the equations of the following circles.

(i) Centre = $(3,-5)$, radius length = 2

(ii) Centre = $(0,7)$, radius length = 4

(iii) Centre = $(-8,1)$, radius length = 4

(iv) Centre = $(0,0)$, radius length = $\sqrt{5}$

(v) Centre = $\left(\frac{1}{2},-\frac{1}{4}\right)$, radius length = 12

(vi) Centre = $(-3,-8)$, radius length = $\frac{1}{2}$

(vii) Centre = $(-2,-\frac{3}{4})$, radius length = $3\sqrt{2}$

(viii) Centre = $(-1,6)$, radius length = $\frac{7}{2}$

2. A circle s with centre $(1,1)$ and which contains the point $(5,6)$ is shown below.

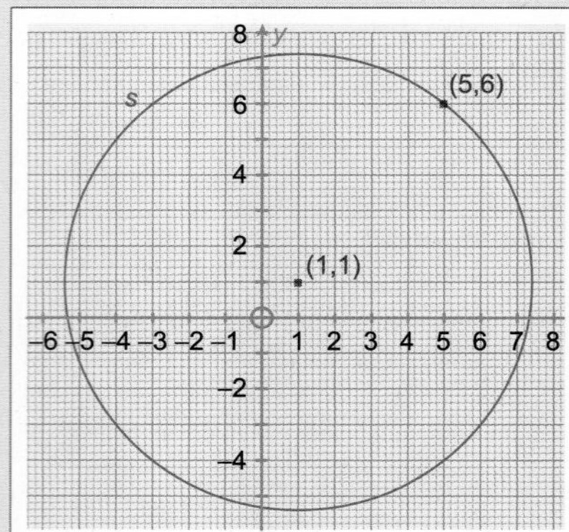

(i) Find the radius length of s.

(ii) Write down the equation of s.

3. A circle t with centre $(-2,-1)$ and which contains the point $(2,-3)$ is shown below.

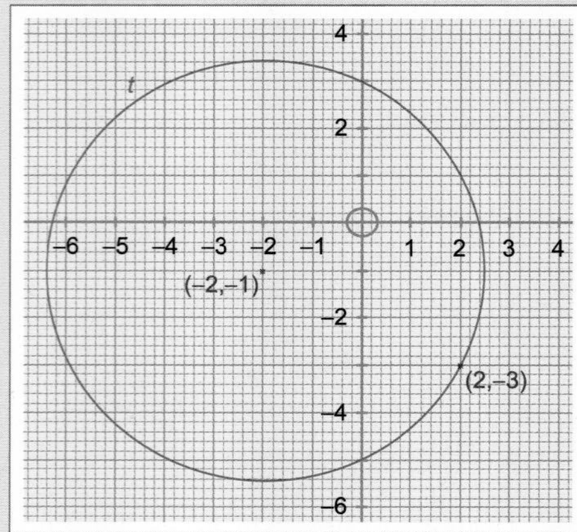

(i) Find the radius length of t.

(ii) Write down the equation of t.

4. The circle z shown in the diagram has a diameter with endpoints $(-1,4)$ and $(3,-2)$.

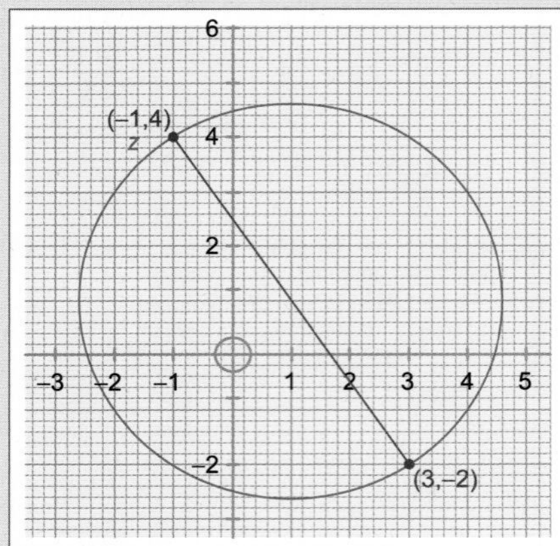

(i) Find the centre of z.

(ii) Find the radius length of z.

(iii) Write down the equation of z.

5. Find the centre and radius length of each of the following circles:

(i) $(x-5)^2 + (y-2)^2 = 81$

(ii) $(x+2)^2 + (y+5)^2 = 49$

(iii) $(x-1)^2 + (y+3)^2 = 100$

(iv) $x^2 + (y-8)^2 = 49$

(v) $x^2 + y^2 = 100$

6. Find the equation of the circle with centre $(-3,2)$ and having the line $x - y + 4 = 0$ as a tangent.

7. Find the equation of the circle with centre $(5,-2)$ and having the line $3x - y + 4 = 0$ as a tangent.

8. The lines k: $2x + 3y - 6 = 0$ and l: $x + \frac{3}{2}y + 12 = 0$ are tangents to the circle s. s touches k on the y-axis.

(i) Sketch k, l and s.

(ii) Find the equation of s.

9. For each of the following circles, write down the co-ordinates of the x-intercepts:

(i) $(x-2)^2 + (y+3)^2 = 34$

(ii) $(x+3)^2 + (y-2)^2 = 40$

(iii) $(x+5)^2 + (y-8)^2 = 164$

(iv) $(x+1)^2 + (y-1)^2 = 50$

10. For each of the following circles, write down the co-ordinates of the y-intercepts:

(i) $(x-3)^2 + (y-4)^2 = 90$

(ii) $(x+2)^2 + (y-5)^2 = 104$

(iii) $(x-6)^2 + (y+1)^2 = 72$

(iv) $(x-1)^2 + (y+1)^2 = 10$

11. Find the equation of the circle having the lines $x + 1 = 0$ and $x - 3 = 0$ as tangents and with its centre lying on the line $y = 3$.

12. The centre of a circle s is in the second quadrant. s touches both the x-axis and the y-axis at the points P and Q, respectively. s has a radius length of $5\sqrt{2}$.

(i) Find the equation of s.

(ii) Find the equation of the circle that contains the points P and Q and has a radius length of 5.

11.3 EQUATIONS OF THE FORM $x^2 + y^2 + 2gx + 2fy + c = 0$

In Activity 11.7 you showed that $x^2 + y^2 + 2gx + 2fy + c = 0$ represents the equation of a circle with centre $(-g,-f)$ and radius length $\sqrt{g^2 + f^2 - c}$.

FORMULA

The formula $x^2 + y^2 + 2gx + 2fy + c = 0$ represents a circle with

- Centre $(-g,-f)$
- Radius length $\sqrt{g^2 + f^2 - c}$

Remember a second degree equation represents a circle if:

- The coefficient of x^2 and y^2 must be equal.
- The highest power is 2.
- There cannot be an xy term.

This formula appears on page 19 of *Formulae and Tables*.

Worked Example 11.6

Find the centre and radius length of the circle $x^2 + y^2 - 4x - 6y - 12 = 0$.

Solution

Comparing $x^2 + y^2 + 2gx + 2fy + c = 0$

and $x^2 + y^2 - 4x - 6y - 12 = 0$

we get $2g = -4$ and $2f = -6$

$\therefore g = -2$ and $f = -3$

$\therefore (-g,-f) = (2,3)$

The co-ordinates of the centre are $(2,3)$.

The radius length $= \sqrt{g^2 + f^2 - c} = \sqrt{(-2)^2 + (-3)^2 - (-12)} = 5$.

Points Inside, Outside or On a Circle

In Activity 11.8 you showed that, in a circle of the form $(x - h)^2 + (y - k)^2 = r^2$, a point (x_1, y_1) is:

(i) inside the circle if $(x_1 - h)^2 + (y_1 - k)^2 < r^2$

and (ii) outside the circle if $(x_1 - h)^2 + (y_1 - k)^2 > r^2$

Note also that a point (x_1, y_1) is:

on the circle if $(x_1 - h)^2 + (y_1 - k)^2 = r^2$

Worked Example 11.7

Investigate if the points (7,–5) and (8,–6) are outside, inside or on the following circle:

$$(x - 4)^2 + (y + 1)^2 = 25$$

Solution

$(x - 4)^2 + (y + 1)^2 = 25$

Substitute (7,–5) into the left-hand side of the equation:

Is $(7 - 4)^2 + (-5 + 1)^2 = 25$?

$$(3)^2 + (-4)^2 = 25$$

$$9 + 16 = 25$$

$$25 = 25 \quad \text{True}$$

Therefore, the point (7,–5) is **on** the circle.

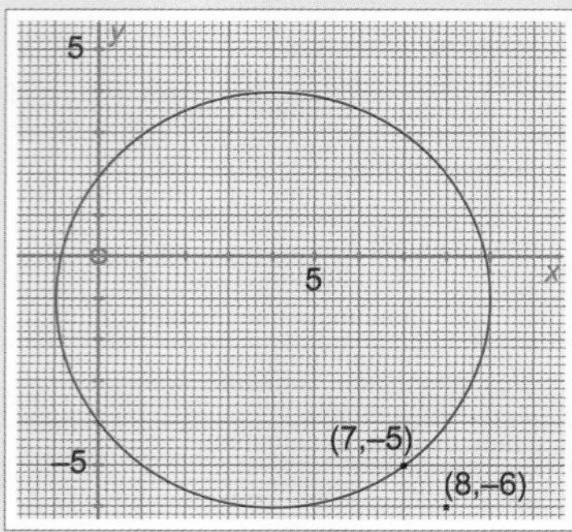

Substitute (8,–6) into the left-hand side of the equation:

Is $(8 - 4)^2 + (-6 + 1)^2 = 25$?

$$(4)^2 + (-5)^2 = 25$$

$$16 + 25 = 25$$

$$41 = 25 \quad \text{False}$$

$$41 > 25$$

Therefore, the point (8,–6) is **outside** the circle.

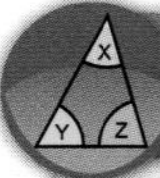

Worked Example 11.8

Investigate if the point (5,4) lies inside, outside or on the circle $x^2 + y^2 + 2x - 6y - 15 = 0$.

Solution

Step 1

Write the equation in the form $(x - h)^2 + (y - k)^2 = r^2$:

$$x^2 + y^2 + 2x - 6y - 15 = 0$$

$$x^2 + 2x + y^2 - 6y - 15 = 0 \quad \text{(group together } x\text{-terms and } y\text{-terms)}$$

$$x^2 + 2x + 1 + y^2 - 6y + 9 - 15 = 1 + 9 \quad \text{(complete the square on the } x \text{ and the } y\text{)}$$

$$(x + 1)^2 + (y - 3)^2 = 10 + 15$$

$$(x + 1)^2 + (y - 3)^2 = 25$$

Step 2

Substitute (5,4) into the modified equation:

Is $(5 + 1)^2 + (4 - 3)^2 = 25$?

$$6^2 + 1^2 = 25$$

$$37 = 25 \quad \textbf{False}$$

$$37 > 25$$

Therefore, the point (5,4) is outside the circle.

Alternative Method

If the equation of a circle is of the form $x^2 + y^2 + 2gx + 2fy + c = 0$, then it can be shown that the point (x_1, y_1) lies:

(i) Inside the circle if $x_1^2 + y_1^2 + 2gx_1 + 2fy_1 + c < 0$

(ii) Outside the circle if $x_1^2 + y_1^2 + 2gx_1 + 2fy_1 + c > 0$

(iii) On the circle if $x_1^2 + y_1^2 + 2gx_1 + 2fy_1 + c = 0$

$5^2 + 4^2 + 2(5) - 6(4) - 15 = 12 > 0$; therefore, the point (5,4) is outside the circle.

Exercise 11.3

1. Find the centre and radius length of each of these circles:

(i) $x^2 + y^2 - 4x + 6y - 3 = 0$

(ii) $x^2 + y^2 - 2x - 2y + 1 = 0$

(iii) $x^2 + y^2 + 2x + 8y + 8 = 0$

(iv) $x^2 + y^2 + 10x - 8y - 8 = 0$

(v) $9x^2 + 9y^2 - 12x + 18y + 4 = 0$

(vi) $x^2 + y^2 - 6x - 7 = 0$

(vii) $x^2 + y^2 + 10x - 6y + 21 = 0$

(viii) $y^2 = -x(x - 1)$

(ix) $x^2 + y^2 + 10y = 0$

(x) $2x^2 + 2y^2 + 6x - 14y - 3 = 0$

(xi) $9x^2 + 9y^2 - 24x - 12y + 11 = 0$

(xii) $9x^2 + 9y^2 - 6x + 18y + 1 = 0$

2. Complete the table by stating whether the points lie inside, outside or on the circle. Show all your workings.

c_1: $(x - 2)^2 + (y - 3)^2 = 9$	$T(2,1)$	Inside
c_2: $(x + 3)^2 + (y - 1)^2 = 25$	$U(0,5)$	
c_3: $x^2 + y^2 = 25$	$V(4,4)$	
c_4: $x^2 + y^2 = 26$	$W(5,1)$	
c_5: $(x - 2)^2 + (y - 3)^2 = 49$	$X(0,0)$	
c_6: $x^2 + y^2 - 4x + 6y - 3 = 0$	$Y(-2,-3)$	
c_7: $x^2 + y^2 - 6x - 7 = 0$	$Z(3,-6)$	

3. For each of the following circles, write down the co-ordinates of the *x*-intercept:

(i) $x^2 + y^2 - 4x - 10y + 3 = 0$

(ii) $x^2 + y^2 + 10x - 16y - 75 = 0$

(iii) $x^2 + y^2 - 2x - 2y - 3 = 0$

(iv) $x^2 + y^2 - 2x - 8y - 35 = 0$

4. For each of the following circles, write down the co-ordinates of the *y*-intercept:

(i) $x^2 + y^2 - 2x - 4y - 21 = 0$

(ii) $x^2 + y^2 + 4x - 6y + 5 = 0$

(iii) $x^2 + y^2 - 6x - 8y = 0$

(iv) $x^2 + y^2 - 2x + 2y - 8 = 0$

5. The circle $x^2 + y^2 + ax - 2y - 15 = 0$ contains the point $P(-6,5)$. Find the value of a.

6. The circle $x^2 + y^2 - a^2x + ay - 22 = 0$ contains the point $Q(2,4)$.
Find the value of a.

7. The circle $x^2 + y^2 + ax + by + 6 = 0$ contains the points $P(1,1)$ and $Q(3,2)$.
Find the value of a and the value of b.

8. The circle $x^2 + y^2 - 2x - my - n = 0$ contains the points $A(2,1)$ and $B(-1,2)$.
Find the value of m and the value of n.

9. Find the range of values of a for which the point $P(a,3)$ lies inside the circle $x^2 + y^2 + 6x - 2y - 6 = 0$. Give your answer in the form $-n - 2\sqrt{n} < a < -n + 2\sqrt{n}$.

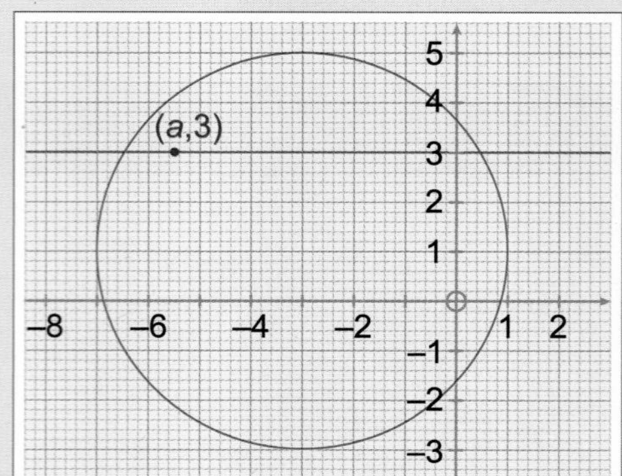

10. Show that the point $Q(5,a)$ lies outside the circle $x^2 + y^2 - 5x - y + 4 = 0$, for all $a \in R$.

11. Find the values of b for which the line $5x + by = 169$ is a tangent to $x^2 + y^2 = 169$.

For $b > 0$, show that the line is also a tangent to the circle $x^2 + y^2 - 20x - 48y + 507 = 0$.

12. A circle touches both the x-axis and y-axis. It has a radius length of 4.

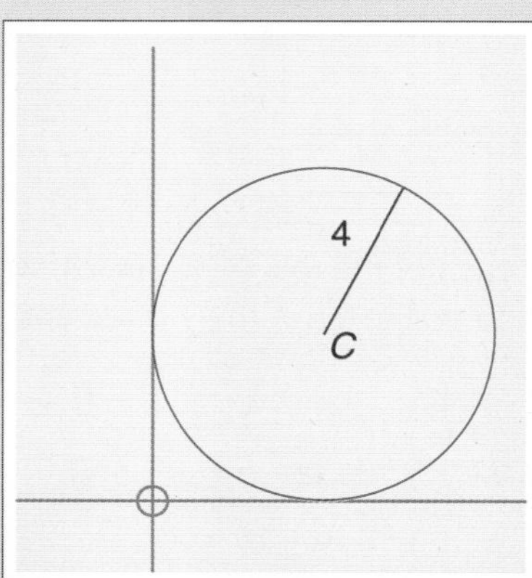

(i) Write down the coordinates of C, the centre of the circle.

(ii) Hence find the equation of the circle.

13. The diagram shows four circles, each of radius length 5.

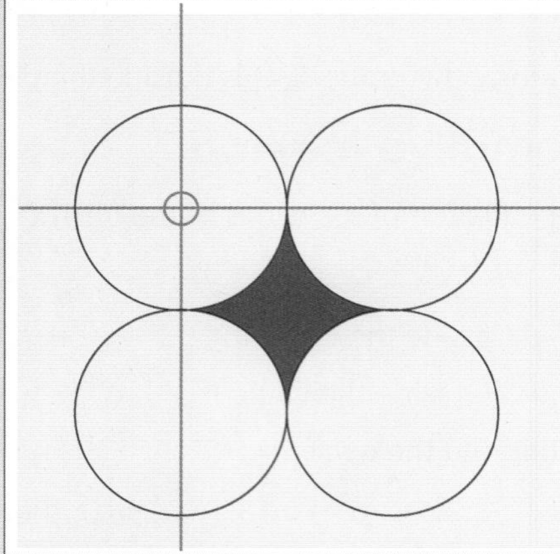

(i) Find the equation of the circle whose centre lies in the fourth quadrant.

(ii) Calculate the area of the shaded region. Explain your reasoning.

14. The line $3x - y + 6 = 0$ is a tangent to the circle at the point $(-3,-3)$. The circle also passes through the point $(-4,-1)$.

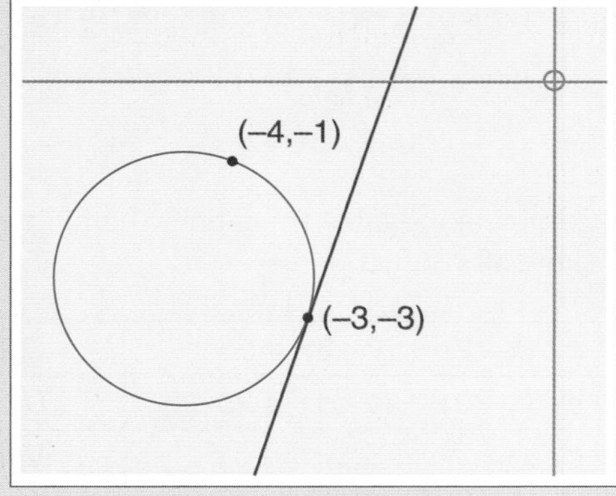

(i) Find the equation of the line, perpendicular to the given tangent, containing the centre of the circle.

(ii) Show that the co-ordinates of the centre of the circle can be written in the form: $\left(a, -4 - \frac{a}{3}\right)$

(iii) Find the value of a.

(iv) Hence find the equation of the circle.

(v) Find the equation of the tangent to the circle parallel to the tangent through $(-3,-3)$.

11.4 INTERSECTION OF A LINE AND A CIRCLE

If a line and a circle are drawn on the plane, then the line and the circle may meet at two points or at one point, or they may not meet at all. This is illustrated in the diagrams below.

Two points of intersection

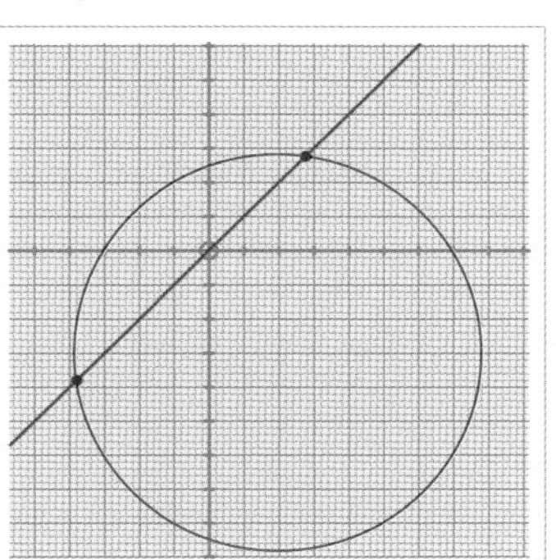

One point of intersection

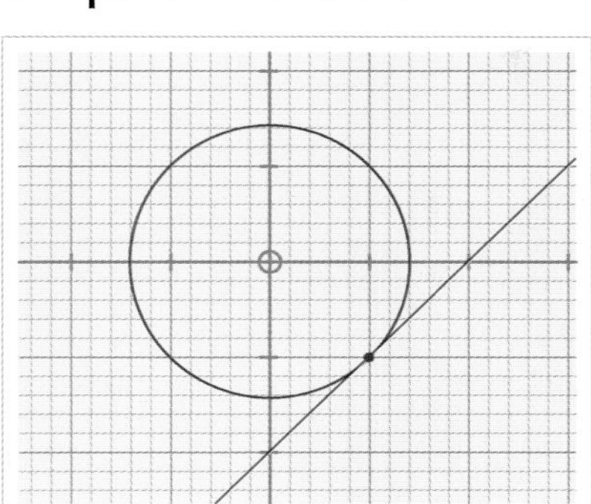

No points of intersection

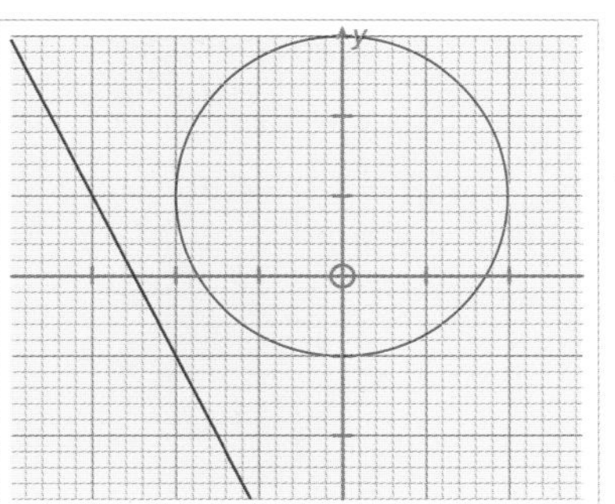

Worked Example 11.9

Find the co-ordinates of the points of intersection of the line l: $5x + y = 24$ and the circle s: $x^2 + y^2 - 4x - 2y - 8 = 0$.

Solution

Step 1

Take the equation of the line and write y in terms of x (or x in terms of y):

$$y = 24 - 5x$$

Step 2

Substitute this expression for y into the equation of the circle:

$$x^2 + (24 - 5x)^2 - 4x - 2(24 - 5x) - 8 = 0$$

$$x^2 + 576 - 240x + 25x^2 - 4x - 48 + 10x - 8 = 0$$

$$26x^2 - 234x + 520 = 0 \quad \text{(divide by 26)}$$

$$x^2 - 9x + 20 = 0$$

$$(x - 4)(x - 5) = 0$$

$$x = 4 \quad \textbf{or} \quad x = 5$$

Step 3

Substitute, separately, $x = 4$ and $x = 5$ into the equation of the **line** in Step 1 to find the y co-ordinates.

- When $x = 4$, $y = 24 - 5(4) = 4$.
- When $x = 5$, $y = 24 - 5(5) = -1$.

Therefore, the co-ordinates of the points of intersection are (4,4) and (5,–1).

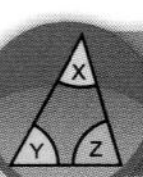

Worked Example 11.10

Show that the line $3x - 4y + 10 = 0$ is a tangent to the circle $x^2 + y^2 - 10x = 0$.

Solution

If the line is a tangent to the circle, then the perpendicular distance from the centre of the circle to the line will be equal to the length of the radius.

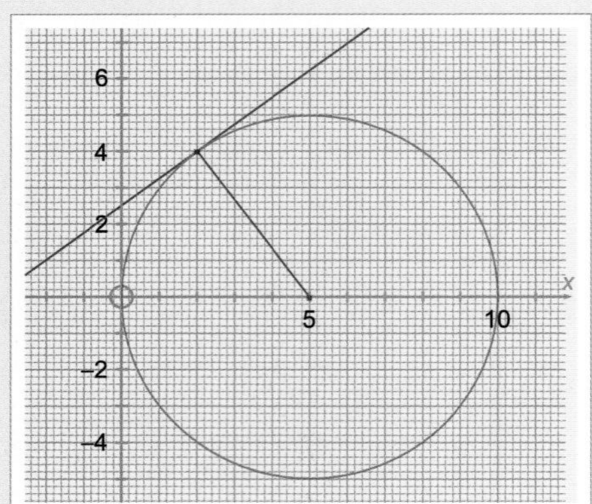

Centre (5,0), $r = \sqrt{(5)^2 + (0)^2 - 0} = 5$

Distance from the centre of the circle to the line $= \dfrac{|3(5) - 4(0) + 10|}{\sqrt{3^2 + 4^2}}$

$= \dfrac{25}{\sqrt{25}}$

$= 5$

$=$ radius length

Therefore, the line is a tangent to the circle.

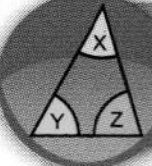

Worked Example 11.11

Show that the line l: $5x - y - 20 = 0$ does not intersect the circle s: $x^2 + y^2 - 2x - 2y - 2 = 0$.

Solution

If the line does not intersect the circle, then the perpendicular distance from the centre of the circle to the line will be greater than the length of the radius.

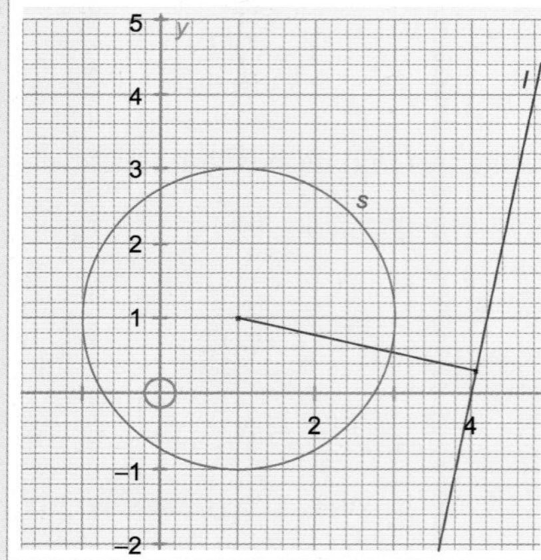

Centre $= (-g, -f)$

$\Rightarrow$ Centre $= (1,1)$

Radius length

$r = \sqrt{g^2 + f^2 - c}$

$r = \sqrt{1 + 1 + 2} = 2$

Perpendicular distance

Distance from centre to $l = \dfrac{|5(1) - (1) - 20|}{\sqrt{(5)^2 + (-1)^2}} = \dfrac{16}{\sqrt{26}} \approx 3.14$

The distance from the centre to l is greater than the length of the radius; therefore, the line does not intersect the circle.

Locus of a Point

A point A, which moves so that its distance from another fixed point C is always constant, traces out a circle. A mathematician would say that the **locus** of the point A is a circle.

> A **locus** is the path traced out by a moving point, satisfying certain given conditions.

Worked Example 11.12

$A(-12,0)$, $B(0,0)$ and $P(x,y)$ are three points. If $|AP| = 5|BP|$, then show that the locus of P is a circle.

Solution

$$|AP| = 5|BP|$$
$$\sqrt{(x+12)^2 + (y-0)^2} = 5\sqrt{(x-0)^2 + (y-0)^2}$$
$$(x+12)^2 + y^2 = 25(x^2 + y^2)$$
$$x^2 + 24x + 144 + y^2 = 25x^2 + 25y^2$$
$$24x^2 + 24y^2 - 24x - 144 = 0$$
$$x^2 + y^2 - x - 6 = 0$$

This is the equation of a circle with centre $\left(\frac{1}{2},0\right)$ and radius length $\sqrt{\left(\frac{1}{2}\right)^2 + (0)^2 + 6} = \sqrt{6.25} = 2.5$.

Exercise 11.4

1. Find the points of intersection of the line $x + y = 4$ and the circle $x^2 + y^2 = 10$.

2. Find the points of intersection of the line $x - y = 1$ and the circle $x^2 + y^2 = 13$.

3. l is the line $2x + y - 3 = 0$ and s is the circle $x^2 + y^2 = 26$. Find the points of intersection of l and s.

4. m is the line $x + 7y - 4 = 0$ and n is the circle $x^2 + y^2 = 10$. Find the points of intersection of m and n.

5. Find the co-ordinates of the point or points of intersection of the following lines and circles:

   (i) $l: x + y = 3$; $s: x^2 + y^2 = 5$

   (ii) $l: x - y + 1 = 0$; $s: x^2 + y^2 - 2x + 2y - 3 = 0$

   (iii) $l: x + y - 8 = 0$; $s: x^2 + y^2 + 4x - 8y + 2 = 0$

   (iv) $l: 5x + y = 24$; $s: x^2 + y^2 - 4x - 2y - 8 = 0$

6. $A(-3,1)$, $B(0,-5)$ and $P(x,y)$ are three points.

   (i) If $|AP| = 2|BP|$, prove that x and y satisfy the equation $x^2 + y^2 - 2x + 14y + 30 = 0$.

   (ii) Say why this is a circle.

   (iii) Find the centre and radius length of this circle.

7. $A(-3,1)$, $B(0,-5)$ and $P(x,y)$ are three points.

   (i) If $|AP| = 3|BP|$, prove that x and y satisfy the equation $8x^2 + 8y^2 - 6x + 92y + 215 = 0$.

   (ii) Say why this is a circle.

   (iii) Find the centre and radius length of this circle.

8. $A(-3,1)$, and $B(0,-5)$ are two points. A point $P(x,y)$ moves so that $|AP| = \frac{1}{2}|BP|$.

   (i) Show that the locus of P is a circle.

   (ii) Find the centre and radius length of this circle.

9. A circle s has equation $(x-2)^2 + (y-3)^2 = 9$. $A(-1,3)$ and $B(5,3)$ are the co-ordinates of two points.

   (i) Show that the x-axis is a tangent to s.

   (ii) Prove that $[AB]$ is a diameter of s.

   (iii) If a point $P(x,y)$ moves so that $|AP| = \frac{1}{3}|BP|$, show that the locus of P is a circle. Label this circle t.

(iv) Find the centre and radius length of t.

(v) Prove that t does not intersect the x-axis.

(vi) Using the same axes and scales draw s and t.

10. $A(-3,0)$, and $B(0,-5)$ are two points. A point $P(x,y)$ moves so that $|AP| = a|BP|$, for some $a \in R$, $a \neq \pm 1$.

(i) Show that the locus of P is a circle.

(ii) For what values of a does the circle pass through the origin?

(iii) Find the range of values of a for which the centre of the circle lies in the fourth quadrant.

(iv) Can the centre of the circle ever lie in the third quadrant? Explain clearly how you got your answer.

11.5 TANGENTS AND TOUCHING CIRCLES

A **tangent** to a circle touches the circle at one point and is perpendicular to the radius that joins the centre of the circle to the point of tangency.

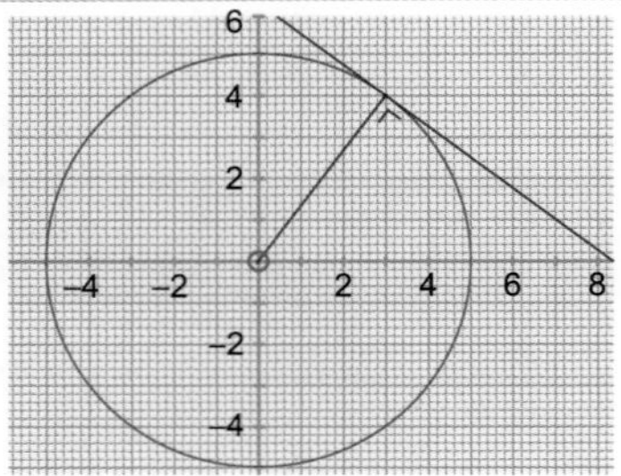

On this course, you will learn:

(1) how to find the equation of a tangent to a point **on** the circle, and

(2) how to find the equation of a tangent from a point **outside** the circle

The Equation of a Tangent to a Point On a Circle

Step 1 Find the slope of the radius that contains the point of contact.

Step 2 As the tangent is perpendicular to the radius, it is now possible to find the slope of the tangent.

Step 3 Find the equation of the tangent.

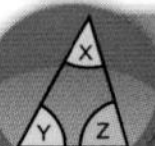

Worked Example 11.13

Find the equation of the tangent to the circle $x^2 + y^2 - 2x + 4y - 20 = 0$ at the point $(-2,2)$.

Solution

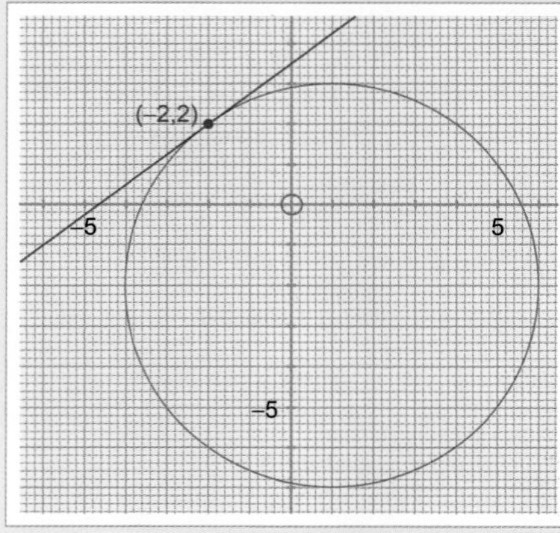

Step 1 The centre of the circle is $(1,-2)$, and the point on the circle is $(-2,2)$.

$\therefore$ The slope of the radius is $\frac{2-(-2)}{-2-1} = -\frac{4}{3}$.

Step 2 $\therefore$ The slope of the tangent is $\frac{3}{4}$ (as $\perp$ to radius).

Step 3 **Equation of the tangent**

$$y - y_1 = m(x - x_1) \qquad \text{Point } (-2,2)\ m = \frac{3}{4}$$

$$y - 2 = \frac{3}{4}(x + 2)$$

$$4y - 8 = 3x + 6$$

$$3x - 4y + 14 = 0$$

The Equation of a Tangent From a Point Outside a Circle

Step 1 Find the centre and radius length of the circle.

Step 2 Let the slope of the tangent be m.

Step 3 Find the equation of the tangent using m as the slope. (Remember that you will have a point on the tangent). Write the equation in the form $ax + by + c = 0$.

Step 4 Find in terms of m the perpendicular distance from the tangent to the centre of the circle and set this equal to the radius length. Solve for m.

Step 5 Rewrite the equation from Step 3, using the value for m.

Worked Example 11.14

Find the equations of the tangents from (1,0) to the circle $x^2 + y^2 - 12x - 10y + 51 = 0$.

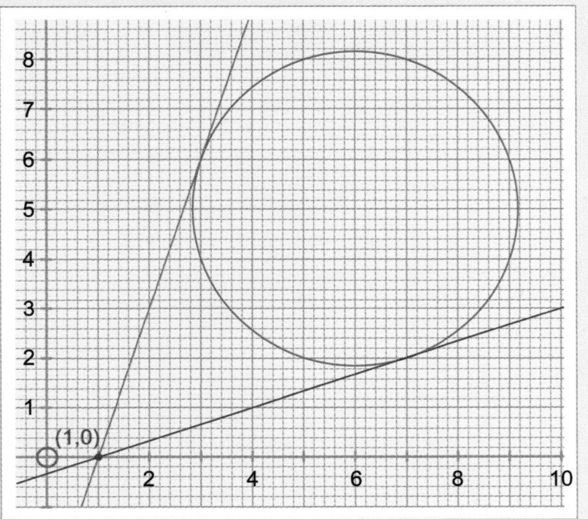

Solution

The centre of the circle is (6,5) and the radius length is $\sqrt{36 + 25 - 51} = \sqrt{10}$.

Here we are unable to find the slope directly, as we do not have the point of contact. For now, we will let the slope of the tangent be m.

Therefore, the equation of the tangent will be of the form:

$y - y_1 = m(x - x_1)$ Point (1,0) Slope $= m$

$y - 0 = m(x - 1)$

$\therefore mx - y - m = 0$

Therefore, the distance from (6,5) to $mx - y - m = 0$ equals $\sqrt{10}$.

$$\frac{|6m - 5 - m|}{\sqrt{m^2 + 1}} = \sqrt{10}$$

$$\frac{|5m - 5|}{\sqrt{m^2 + 1}} = \sqrt{10}$$

$$|5m - 5| = \sqrt{10}\sqrt{m^2 + 1}$$

$$\therefore 25m^2 - 50m + 25 = 10m^2 + 10 \quad \text{(squaring both sides)}$$

$$15m^2 - 50m + 15 = 0$$

$$3m^2 - 10m + 3 = 0$$

$$(3m - 1)(m - 3) = 0$$

$$\therefore m = \frac{1}{3} \quad \textbf{OR} \quad m = 3$$

Therefore, the equations of the tangents are: (1) $\frac{1}{3}x - y - \frac{1}{3} = 0$ (or $x - 3y - 1 = 0$)

and (2) $3x - y - 3 = 0$

Touching Circles

Two circles s_1 and s_2 have centres c_1 and c_2 and radii lengths r_1 and r_2, respectively.

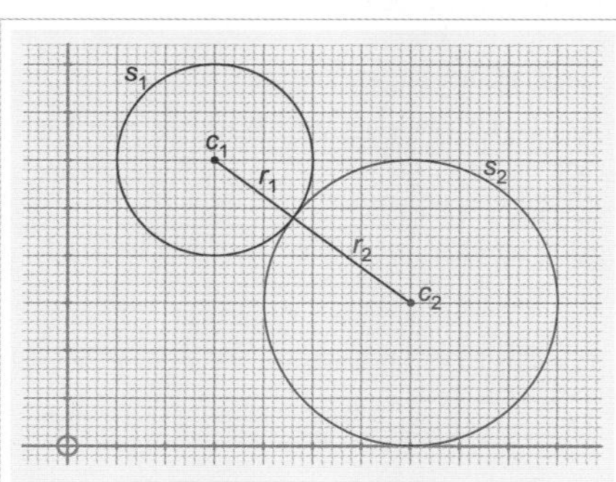

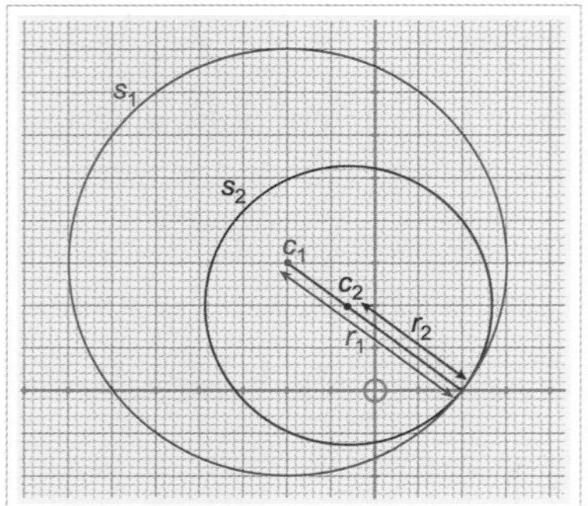

- If $|c_1c_2| = r_1 + r_2$, then the circles touch externally.
- If $|c_1c_2| = |r_1 - r_2|$, then the circles touch internally.

Worked Example 11.15

Prove that the circles $x^2 + y^2 - 14x - 6y + 49 = 0$ and $x^2 + y^2 - 6x - 12y + 41 = 0$ touch externally.

Solution

$c_1 = (7,3) \qquad r_1 = \sqrt{49 + 9 - 49} = 3$

$c_2 = (3,6) \qquad r_2 = \sqrt{9 + 36 - 41} = 2$

$\therefore r_1 + r_2 = 3 + 2 = 5$

$|c_1c_2| = \sqrt{(3-7)^2 + (6-3)^2} = \sqrt{16 + 9} = 5$

$r_1 + r_2 = |c_1c_2|$, therefore the circles touch externally.

Exercise 11.5

1. Find the equations of the tangents to these circles at the points given.
   (i) $x^2 + y^2 = 10$; $(3,1)$
   (ii) $x^2 + y^2 = 20$; $(-4,2)$
   (iii) $(x + 3)^2 + (y + 4)^2 = 25$; $(0,0)$
   (iv) $(x - 6)^2 + (y + 3)^2 = 20$; $(2,-1)$
   (v) $(x - 1)^2 + (y + 2)^2 = 13$; $(3,1)$
   (vi) $x^2 + y^2 - 6x + 4y = 0$; $(6,-4)$
   (vii) $x^2 + y^2 + 2x + 4y - 12 = 0$; $(3,-1)$
   (viii) $x^2 + y^2 + 2x - 2y - 8 = 0$; $(2,2)$

2. s is the circle $x^2 + y^2 = 5$ and P is the point $(2,1)$.
   (i) Verify that P is a point on s.
   (ii) Find the equation of l, the tangent to the circle s at the point P.
   (iii) Find the equation of the tangent to s that is parallel to l.

3. Find the values of k for which $x + 4y + k = 0$ is a tangent to $x^2 + y^2 - 2x + 2y - 15 = 0$.

4. Find the equation of the tangents to the circle $x^2 + y^2 - 6x - 2y - 15 = 0$ which are parallel to the line $3x + 4y + 10 = 0$.

5. Find the equations of the tangents to the circle $x^2 + y^2 - 8x + 4y + 7 = 0$ which are perpendicular to the line $2x + 3y = 6$.

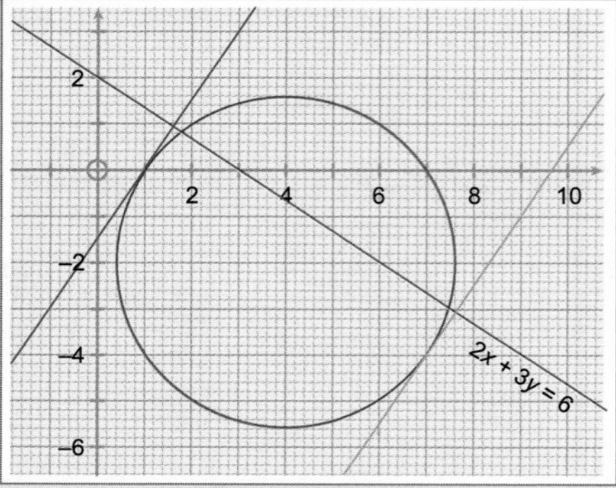

6. Find the equations of the tangents from the point P to the given circle.

   (i) $x^2 + y^2 - 2x - 2y + 1 = 0$ $\quad P(3,4)$

   (ii) $x^2 + y^2 + 2x + 8y + 8 = 0$ $\quad P(6,-1)$

7. Find the equations of the tangents to the circle $x^2 + y^2 - 4x + 6y - 3 = 0$ from the point $P(6,7)$.

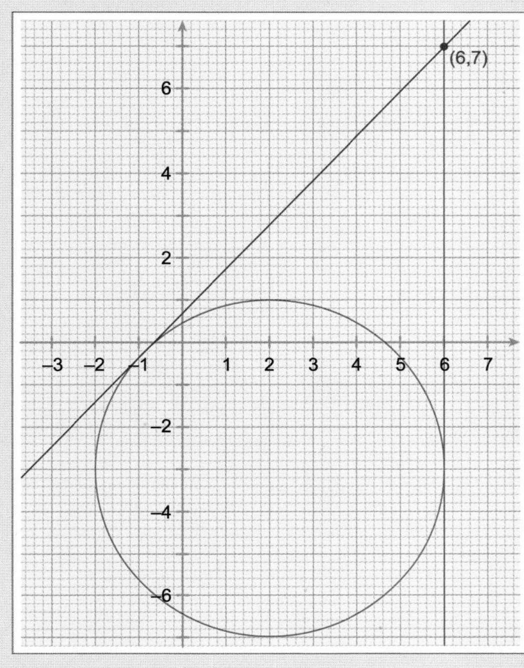

8. Sketch the two circles $x^2 + y^2 = 16$ and $x^2 + y^2 - 6x - 8y + 24 = 0$. Prove that they touch externally.

9. Investigate if the circles $x^2 + y^2 - 6x - 16y + 9 = 0$ and $x^2 + y^2 + 4x - 6y + 12 = 0$ touch internally.

10. Prove that the circles $x^2 + y^2 - 12x + 6y - 76 = 0$ and $x^2 + y^2 + 4x - 6y + 12 = 0$ touch each other, and state whether this is internal or external.

11. Draw a rough sketch of the circles $x^2 + y^2 - 2x - 15 = 0$ and $x^2 + y^2 - 14x - 16y + 77 = 0$. Prove that they touch externally.

12. $s: x^2 + y^2 = 25$ and $t: x^2 + y^2 - 10x + 24y + k = 0$ touch each other externally. Find the value of k.

13. Sketch the circles $x^2 + y^2 = 9$ and $x^2 + y^2 - 18x + 72 = 0$. Find the equation of the circle whose centre is on the x-axis and which touches both of these circles:

    (i) Externally

    (ii) Internally

11.6 PROBLEMS IN g, f AND c

In this section we will be given limited information on a circle and asked to solve or find the equation of the circle.

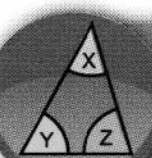

Worked Example 11.16

Find the equation of the circle s, which passes through the points (1,1), (2,3) and (3,–1).

Solution

Let the equation be $x^2 + y^2 + 2gx + 2fy + c = 0$.

(1,1) is on s $\quad \therefore 1^2 + 1^2 + 2g(1) + 2f(1) + c = 0$ $\quad \therefore 2g + 2f + c = -2$ $\quad$ **Eq. I**

(2,3) is on s $\quad \therefore 2^2 + 3^2 + 2g(2) + 2f(3) + c = 0$ $\quad \therefore 4g + 6f + c = -13$ $\quad$ **Eq. II**

(3,–1) is on s $\quad \therefore 3^2 + (-1)^2 + 2g(3) + 2f(-1) + c = 0$ $\quad \therefore 6g - 2f + c = -10$ $\quad$ **Eq. III**

We have three simultaneous equations. We eliminate c by subtracting Eq. II from Eq. I, and subtracting Eq. II from Eq. III. This gives us:

$-2g - 4f = 11$ $\quad$ **Eq. IV**

$2g - 8f = 3$ $\quad$ **Eq. V**

Add Eq. IV and Eq. V:

$$-12f = 14 \qquad \therefore f = -\frac{7}{6}$$

Substituting $f = -\frac{7}{6}$ into Eq. IV gives:

$$-2g - 4\left(-\frac{7}{6}\right) = 11 \qquad \therefore g = -\frac{19}{6}$$

Substituting $f = -\frac{7}{6}$ and $g = -\frac{19}{6}$ into Eq. I gives:

$$2\left(-\frac{19}{6}\right) + 2\left(-\frac{7}{6}\right) + c = -2 \qquad \therefore c = \frac{20}{3}$$

We now substitute these values for g, f and c into the general equation:

$$x^2 + y^2 + 2\left(-\frac{19}{6}\right)x + 2\left(-\frac{7}{6}\right)y + \frac{20}{3} = 0 \quad \text{(multiply across by 6)}$$

$$6x^2 + 6y^2 - 38x - 14y + 40 = 0 \ldots \text{ equation of circle } s$$

Worked Example 11.17

Find the equation of the circle k, which passes through the points (1,1) and (2,–1) and whose centre lies on the line $3x - y = 7$.

Solution

Let the equation of the circle be $x^2 + y^2 + 2gx + 2fy + c = 0$.

(1,1) is on k $\quad \therefore 1 + 1 + 2g + 2f + c = 0 \quad \therefore 2g + 2f + c = -2$ **Eq. I**

(2,–1) is on k $\quad \therefore 4 + 1 + 4g - 2f + c = 0 \quad \therefore 4g - 2f + c = -5$ **Eq. II**

$(-g,-f)$ is on $3x - y = 7$ $\quad \therefore -3g + f = 7$ **Eq. III**

Subtracting Eq. II from Eq. I gives:

$$-2g + 4f = 3 \quad \textbf{Eq. IV}$$

Now solve between Eq. III and Eq. IV. Multiply Eq. III by –4:

$$12g - 4f = -28$$
$$-2g + 4f = 3$$

Adding the above equations gives: $\quad 10g = -25 \quad \therefore g = -\frac{5}{2}$

Substituting $g = -\frac{5}{2}$ into Eq. III gives: $\quad \frac{15}{2} + f = 7 \quad \therefore f = -\frac{1}{2}$

Putting these into Eq. I gives: $\quad 2\left(-\frac{5}{2}\right) + 2\left(-\frac{1}{2}\right) + c = -2$

$$\therefore -5 - 1 + c = -2$$
$$\therefore c = 4$$

Hence, the equation of the circle k is $x^2 + y^2 - 5x - y + 4 = 0$.

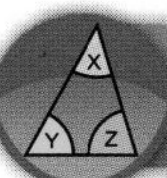

Worked Example 11.18

The line $2x - y - 17 = 0$ is a tangent to the circle k at the point $(6,-5)$. The circle also contains the point $(4,1)$. Find the equation of the circle k.

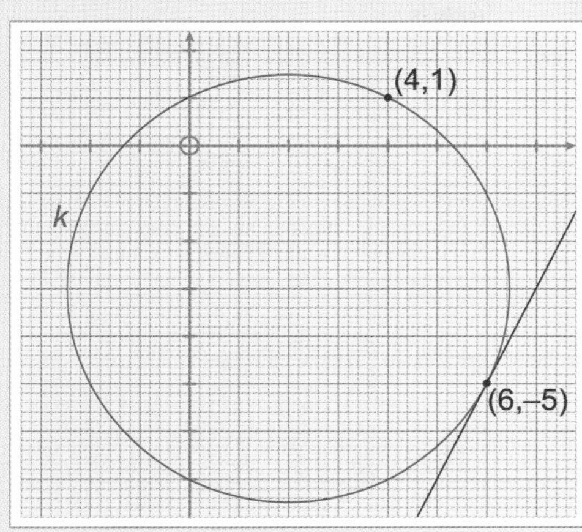

Solution

Step 1 Let the equation of k be $x^2 + y^2 + 2gx + 2fy + c = 0$.

Step 2 Find the equation of the line through $(6,-5)$ which contains the centre of the circle. This line is perpendicular to $2x - y - 17 = 0$, and therefore its slope is $-\frac{1}{2}$.

Equation: $y - y_1 = m(x - x_1)$

$$\therefore y + 5 = -\frac{1}{2}(x - 6)$$

$$\therefore 2y + 10 = -x + 6$$

$$\therefore x + 2y + 4 = 0$$

Step 3 This line contains $(-g,-f)$, the centre of the circle: $-g - 2f + 4 = 0$ **Eq. I**

Step 4 Substitute $(4,1)$ and $(6,-5)$ into the equation of k:

$(4)^2 + (1)^2 + 8g + 2f + c = 0$

$8g + 2f + c = -17$ **Eq. II**

$(6)^2 + (-5)^2 + 12g - 10f + c = 0$

$12g - 10f + c = -61$ **Eq. III**

Eliminate c from Eq. II and Eq. III:

$4g - 12f = -44$ **Eq. IV**

Step 5 Solve between Eq. I and Eq. IV:

$$-g - 2f = -4$$
$$4g - 12f = -44$$
$$-4g - 8f = -16$$
$$4g - 12f = -44$$
$$-20f = -60$$
$$f = 3$$

Substitute $f = 3$ into Eq. IV:

$\Rightarrow g = -2$

Substitute $f = 3$ and $g = -2$ into Eq. II:

$-16 + 6 + c = -17$

$c = -7$

Therefore, the equation of k is $x^2 + y^2 - 4x + 6y - 7 = 0$.

Exercise 11.6

1. Find the equation of the circle which passes through the points A, B and C.

   (i) $A(1,2)$, $B(4,-3)$, $C(0,-2)$

   (ii) $A(3,0)$, $B(4,-3)$, $C(5,-2)$

   (iii) $A(-2,2)$, $B(2,4)$, $C(2,-5)$

   (iv) $A(0,0)$, $B(4,0)$, $C(3,-1)$

   (v) $A(1,2)$, $B(4,5)$, $C(7,-2)$

   (vi) $A(11,2)$, $B(3,-2)$, $C(10,-2)$

2. Find the equation of the circle which contains the two points $O(0,0)$ and $P(4,2)$, and whose centre is on the line $x + y = 3$.

3. Find the equation of the circle which contains the two points $A(0,-1)$ and $B(3,0)$, and whose centre is on the line $x - 3y + 2 = 0$.

4. Find the equation of the circle which contains the two points $Q(0,2)$ and $P(1,5)$, and whose centre is on the line $x + 5y = 15$.

5. (i) Show that if the circle $x^2 + y^2 + 2gx + 2fy + c = 0$ touches the x-axis, then $g^2 = c$.

(ii) Using the result from part (i), find the equations of the two circles which contain the points $A(3,4)$ and $B(5,2)$ and which touch the x-axis.

6. (i) Show that if the circle $x^2 + y^2 + 2gx + 2fy + c = 0$ touches the y-axis, then $f^2 = c$.

(ii) Using the result from part (i), find the equation of the circle which contains the points $A(2,3)$ and $B(2,-5)$ and which touches the y-axis.

7. Find the equations of the circles which contain the point (4,3), have their centre on the line $3x - 2y = 0$ and touch the y-axis.

8. The equation of a circle is $x^2 + y^2 - 4x - 4y + 4 = 0$.

(i) Write down the co-ordinates of the centre of the circle.

(ii) Find the radius length of the circle.

(iii) Draw a sketch of the circle.

(iv) Explain why the circle touches both axes.

9. There are two circles which have radii lengths of $\sqrt{5}$ and which pass through the points (–3,1) and (1,1). Find their equations.

10. Find the equations of the two circles which contain the point (2,1), have their centres on the line $y = x$ and have radii of length 5 units.

11. Find the equation of the circle which passes through the points $P(-3,-2)$ and $Q(0,-1)$ and has the line $2x - y + 4 = 0$ as a tangent at the point $P(-3,-2)$.

12. Find the equation of the circle which passes through the points $A(-2,2)$ and $B(5,-5)$ and has the line $3x - 4y = 35$ as a tangent at the point $B(5,-5)$.

Revision Exercises

1. The point (1,–7) is on a circle k which has its centre at $O(0,0)$.

(a) Sketch the circle k.

(b) Find the equation of k.

(c) If (p,p) is a point on k, find two possible values of p.

(d) If the point $(3,n)$ is inside the circle k, find the greatest possible value of $n \in N$.

2. (a) A circle with centre (1,1) passes through the point (–2,–3). Find the equation of the circle.

(b) The line $2x + y + k = 0$ is a tangent to the circle $x^2 + y^2 - 6x + 10y + 29 = 0$. Find the two possible values of k.

(c) A circle has the line $y = 2x$ as a tangent at the point (2,4). The circle also passes through the point (4,–2).
Find the equation of the circle.

3. (a) Find the centre and radius length of the circle $2x^2 + 2y^2 - 2x + 6y - 1 = 0$.

(b) Find the equation of the circle which passes through the points (0,–2), (1,1) and (2,2).

(c) $A(-1,-1)$, $B(2,5)$ and $C(x,y)$ are three points. If $|AC| = 2|BC|$, prove that $x^2 + y^2 - 6x - 14y + 38 = 0$.

4. $A(3,1)$ and $B(-1,-1)$ are points on a circle of centre $(k,-3k)$.

(a) Find the value of k.

(b) Find the equation of the circle.

(c) Find the equations of the two tangents, l and m, to the circle at A and B.

(d) Find the measure of the acute angle between l and m.

5. (a) The equation of a circle is $(x-4)^2 + (y-9)^2 = 80$.

The line $2x - y + 1 = 0$ intersects the circle at the points A and B.
Find the co-ordinates of A and B and hence investigate if $[AB]$ is a diameter of the circle.

(b) Find the equation of the circle which passes through (1,0) and (0,2) and has its centre on the line $x + 3y - 11 = 0$.

Prove that the origin is outside the circle.

6. (a) Prove that the circles $x^2 + y^2 + 6x - 8y - 55 = 0$ and $x^2 + y^2 + 4y - 1 = 0$ touch internally.

(b) A line containing the point $P(5,6)$ touches $x^2 + y^2 - 4x - 4y + 4 = 0$ at K. Find $|PK|$.

(c) If $y = mx + c$ is a tangent to the circle $x^2 + y^2 + 2ax = 0$, prove that $a^2 + 2acm - c^2 = 0$.

7. (a) Find the equation of the tangent to the circle $x^2 + y^2 = 25$ at the point $(-3,-4)$.

(b) Two circles intersect at $A(1,0)$ and $B(-3,2)$. The distance from the centre of each circle to the chord $[AB]$ is $\sqrt{5}$. Find the equation of the two circles.

8. The diagram shows two concentric circles, centred at the origin, of radius length r_1 and r_2, respectively. The area of the shaded region is 144π.

(i) If $r_2 - r_1 = 8$, find the equation of the larger circle.

(ii) Find the value of y in the co-ordinate A.

(iii) Find the equation of the tangent to the larger circle at the point A.

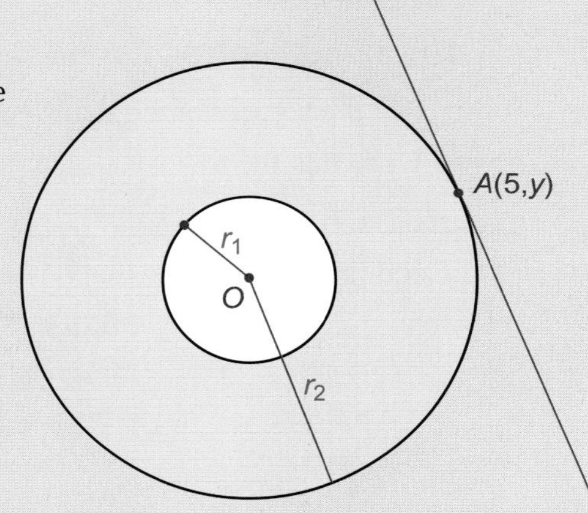

9. P is the point (0,7) and Q is the point (8,11).

(a) Find the equation of the circle with diameter PQ.

(b) Find the equation of the tangent at Q.

(c) This tangent crosses the x-axis at the point R. Find the co-ordinates of R.

NCCA Pre-Leaving Certificate Project Maths Paper 2, February, 2010

10. (a) Write down the equation of the circle with centre $(-3,2)$ and radius 4.

(b) A circle has equation $x^2 + y^2 - 2x + 4y - 15 = 0$.
Find the values of m for which the line $mx + 2y - 7 = 0$ is a tangent to this circle.

SEC Project Maths Sample Paper 2, Leaving Certificate Higher Level, 2010

11. (a) The centre of a circle lies on the line $x - 2y - 1 = 0$. The x-axis and the line $y = 6$ are tangents to the circle. Find the equation of this circle.

(b) A different circle has equation $x^2 + y^2 - 6x - 12y + 41 = 0$.
Show that this circle and the circle in part (a) touch externally.

SEC Project Maths Paper 2, Leaving Certificate Higher Level, 2010

12. (a) A circle has centre (–2,3) and passes through the point (5,6). Find the equation of the circle.

(b) k is the circle $x^2 + y^2 + 2x + 2y - 7 = 0$, and l is the line $4x + 3y = 12$.

(i) Show that the line l does not intersect the circle k.

(ii) Find the co-ordinates of the point on k that is closest to l.

(c) The equation of a circle is $(x + 2)(x - 4) + (y + 1)(y - 1) + 3 = 0$.

(i) Show that the centre of the circle lies on the x-axis.

(ii) Find the radius length of the circle.

(d) Show that the equation of the tangent to the circle $x^2 + y^2 = r^2$ at the point (x_1,y_1) is $xx_1 + yy_1 = r^2$.

13. (a) (1,2) and (3,4) are the endpoints of the diameter of a circle.

(i) Write down the equation of the circle.

(ii) Construct the circle.

(iii) Construct the tangent l to the circle at the point (3,4).

(iv) Find the equation of l.

(b) Find the equations of the circles that pass through the points (–3,6) and (–6,3) and have the y-axis as a tangent.

(c) (–2,4), (0,–10) and (6,–2) are the vertices of a triangle.

(i) Plot the vertices of the triangle.

(ii) Verify that the triangle is right-angled.

(iii) Construct the circumcircle of the triangle.

(iv) Find the equation of the circumcircle.

14. The line $x + 3y = 20$ intersects the circle $x^2 + y^2 - 6x - 8y = 0$ at the points P and Q. Find the equation of the circle that has $[PQ]$ as diameter.

SEC Project Maths Paper 2, Leaving Certificate Higher Level, 2011

Appendix: Formal Proofs of Theorems

Students should become familiar with the formal proofs of the specified theorems. Note that you may be asked to give formal proofs of the following theorems in examination. Theorems 4, 6, 9, 14 and 19 are on the Junior Certificate Higher Level syllabus but may also be examined at Leaving Certificate level.

Theorem 4

The angles in any triangle add up to 180°.

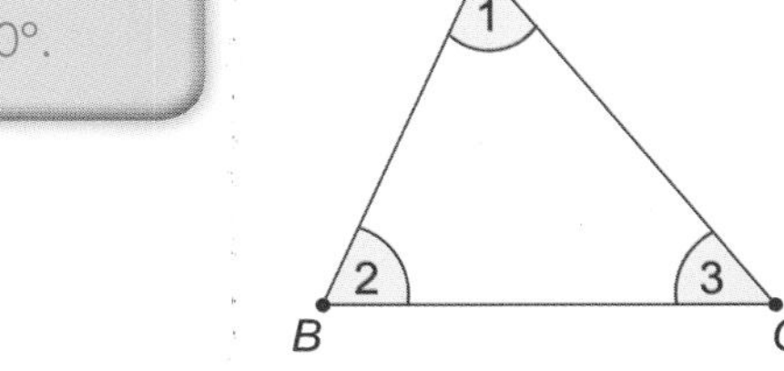

Given: A triangle with angles ∠1, ∠2 and ∠3.

To prove: $|\angle 1| + |\angle 2| + |\angle 3| = 180°$.

Construction: Draw a line through A, parallel to BC. Label angles 4 and 5.

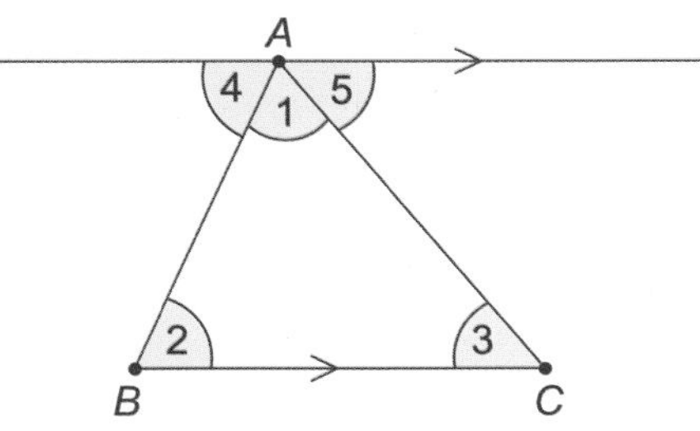

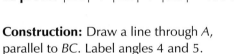

Proof:

Statement	Reason
$\|\angle 4\| + \|\angle 1\| + \|\angle 5\| = 180°$	Straight angle
$\|\angle 2\| = \|\angle 4\|$	Alternate
$\|\angle 3\| = \|\angle 5\|$	Alternate
$\Rightarrow \|\angle 4\| + \|\angle 1\| + \|\angle 5\| = \|\angle 2\| + \|\angle 1\| + \|\angle 3\|$	
$\Rightarrow \|\angle 1\| + \|\angle 2\| + \|\angle 3\| = 180°$	
Q.E.D.	

Theorem 6

Each exterior angle of a triangle is equal to the sum of the interior remote angles.

Given: A triangle with interior angles ∠1, ∠2 and ∠3, and an exterior angle ∠4.

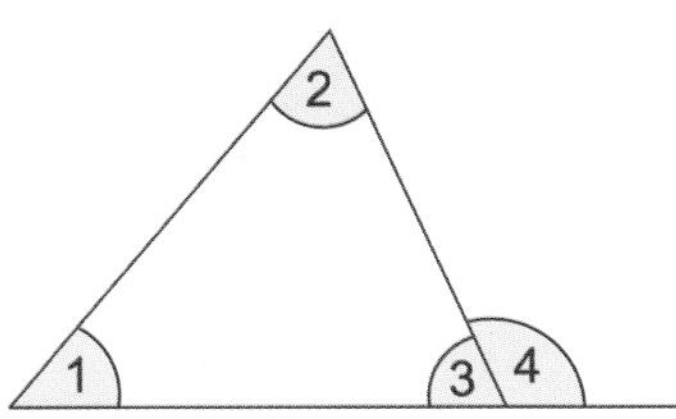

To prove: $|\angle 1| + |\angle 2| = |\angle 4|$.

Proof:

Statement	Reason
$\|\angle 3\| + \|\angle 4\| = 180°$	Straight angle
$\|\angle 1\| + \|\angle 2\| + \|\angle 3\| = 180°$	Angles in a triangle
$\Rightarrow \|\angle 1\| + \|\angle 2\| + \|\angle 3\| = \|\angle 3\| + \|\angle 4\|$	Both = 180°
$\Rightarrow \|\angle 1\| + \|\angle 2\| = \|\angle 4\|$	Subtracting $\|\angle 3\|$
Q.E.D.	

Theorem 9

In a parallelogram, opposite sides are equal and opposite angles are equal.

Given: A parallelogram $ABCD$.

To prove:

(i) $|AB| = |CD|$ and $|BC| = |AD|$ (opposite sides are equal)

(ii) $|\angle ABC| = |\angle ADC|$, $|\angle BAD| = |\angle BCD|$ (opposite angles are equal)

Construction: Draw the diagonal $[AC]$.

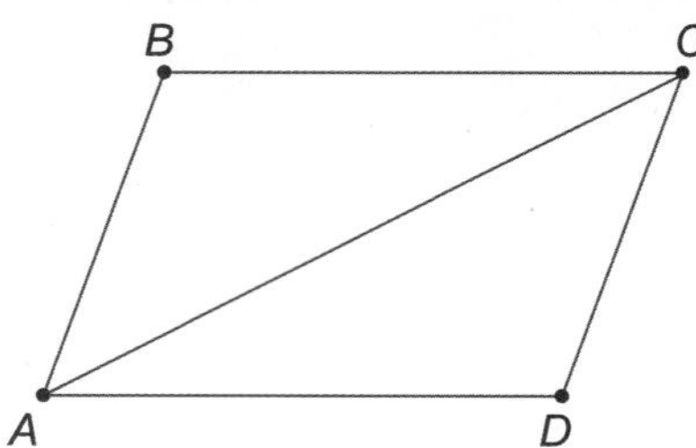

Proof:

Statement	Reason
$\lvert\angle BCA\rvert = \lvert\angle CAD\rvert$	Alternate
$\lvert AC\rvert = \lvert AC\rvert$	Common (shared)
$\lvert\angle BAC\rvert = \lvert\angle ACD\rvert$	Alternate
$\Rightarrow \Delta BAC \equiv \Delta ADC$	ASA
$\Rightarrow \lvert AB\rvert = \lvert CD\rvert$ and $\lvert BC\rvert = \lvert AD\rvert$	Corresponding sides
Also, $\lvert\angle ABC\rvert = \lvert\angle ADC\rvert$	Corresponding angle
Similarly, $\lvert\angle BAD\rvert = \lvert\angle BCD\rvert$	
Q.E.D.	

Theorem 14: Theorem of Pythagoras

In a right-angled triangle, the square of the hypotenuse is the sum of the squares of the other two sides.

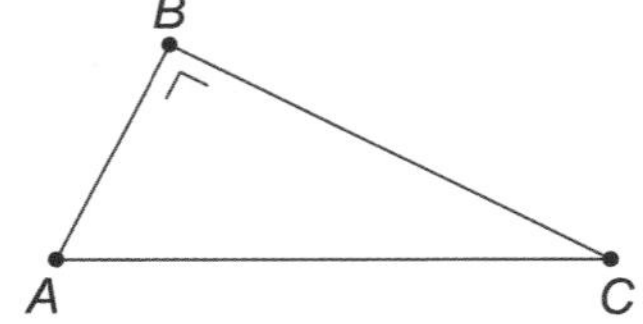

Given: A right-angled triangle ABC with $|\angle ABC| = 90°$.

To prove: $|AC|^2 = |AB|^2 + |BC|^2$.

Construction: Draw $BD \perp AC$.

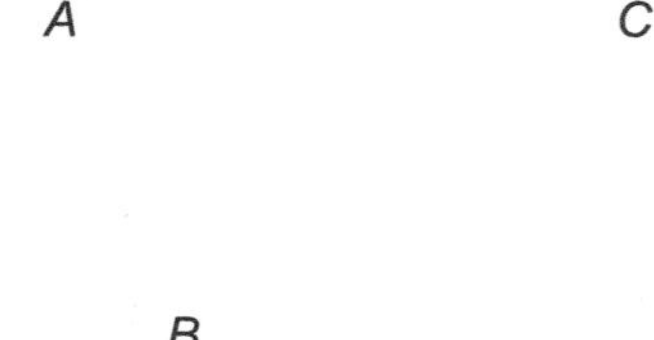

Proof:

Step 1

Consider the triangles ABC and ADB.

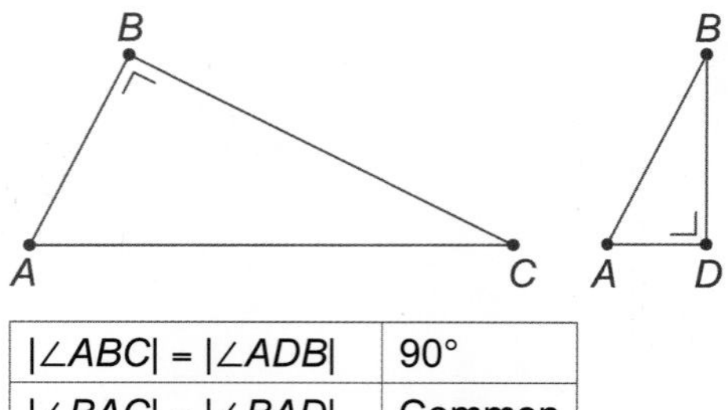

$\lvert\angle ABC\rvert = \lvert\angle ADB\rvert$	90°
$\lvert\angle BAC\rvert = \lvert\angle BAD\rvert$	Common

$\therefore$ ΔABC and ΔADB are similar.

Statement	Reason
ΔABC and ΔADB are similar.	Construction
$\Rightarrow \dfrac{\lvert AC\rvert}{\lvert AB\rvert} = \dfrac{\lvert AB\rvert}{\lvert AD\rvert}$	Theorem
$\Rightarrow \lvert AB\rvert . \lvert AB\rvert = \lvert AC\rvert . \lvert AD\rvert$	
$\Rightarrow \lvert AB\rvert^2 = \lvert AC\rvert . \lvert AD\rvert$	

Step 2

Consider the triangles *ABC* and *BDC*.

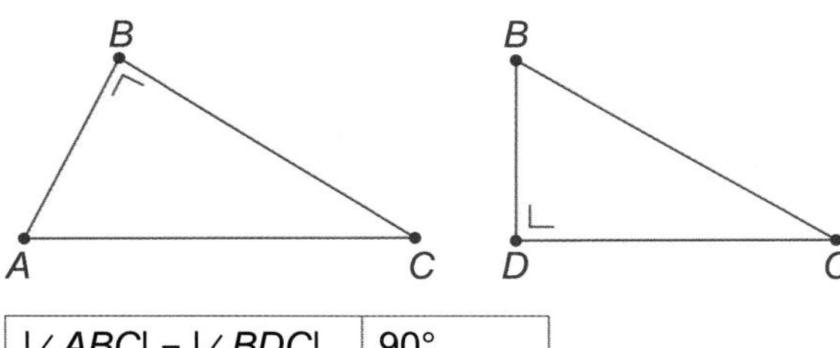

$\|\angle ABC\| = \|\angle BDC\|$	90°
$\|\angle ACB\| = \|\angle DCB\|$	Common

∴ ΔABC and ΔBDC are similar.

Statement	Reason
ΔABC and ΔBDC are similar.	Construction
$\Rightarrow \frac{\|AC\|}{\|BC\|} = \frac{\|BC\|}{\|DC\|}$	Theorem
$\Rightarrow \|BC\|.\|BC\| = \|AC\|.\|DC\|$	
$\Rightarrow \|BC\|^2 = \|AC\|.\|DC\|$	

Step 3

$\|AB\|^2 + \|BC\|^2 = \|AC\|.\|AD\| + \|AC\|.\|DC\|$
$= \|AC\|.(\|AD\| + \|DC\|)$
$\Rightarrow \|AB\|^2 + \|BC\|^2 = \|AC\|.\|AC\|$ (Since $\|AD\| + \|DC\| = \|AC\|$)
$\|AB\|^2 + \|BC\|^2 = \|AC\|^2$
Q.E.D.

Theorem 19

The angle at the centre of a circle standing on a given arc is twice the angle at any point of the circle standing on the same arc.

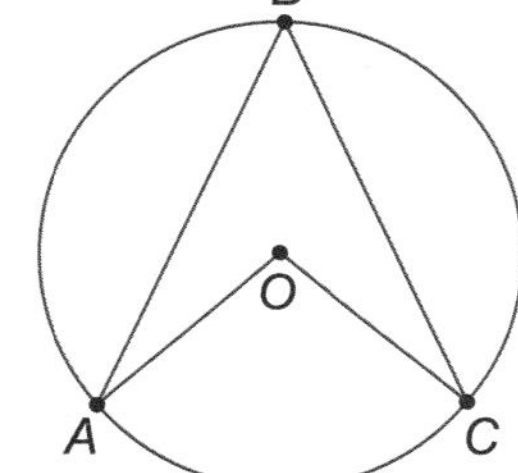

Given: A circle with centre *O* and an arc *AC*.
A point *B* on the circle.

To prove: $|\angle AOC| = 2|\angle ABC|$.

Construction: Join *B* to *O* and continue to a point *D*. Label angles 1, 2, 3, 4, 5 and 6.

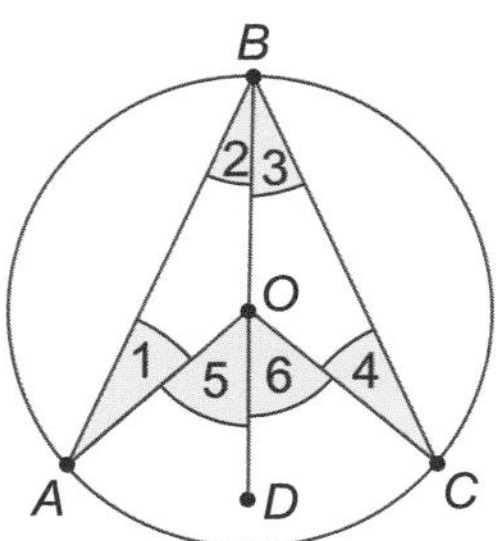

$|\angle AOC| = |\angle 5| + |\angle 6|$

$|\angle ABC| = |\angle 2| + |\angle 3|$

Proof:

Statement	Reason
$\|OA\| = \|OB\|$	Radii
$\|\angle 1\| = \|\angle 2\|$	Isosceles triangle
$\|\angle 5\| = \|\angle 1\| + \|\angle 2\|$	Exterior angle
$\Rightarrow \|\angle 5\| = 2\|\angle 2\|$	Since $\|\angle 1\| = \|\angle 2\|$
Similarly, $\|\angle 6\| = 2\|\angle 3\|$	
$\|\angle 5\| + \|\angle 6\| = 2\|\angle 2\| + 2\|\angle 3\|$	
$\Rightarrow \|\angle 5\| + \|\angle 6\| = 2(\|\angle 2\| + \|\angle 3\|)$	
$\|\angle AOC\| = 2\|\angle ABC\|$	
Q.E.D.	

Theorem 11

If three parallel lines cut off equal segments on some transversal line, then they will cut off equal segments on any other transversal.

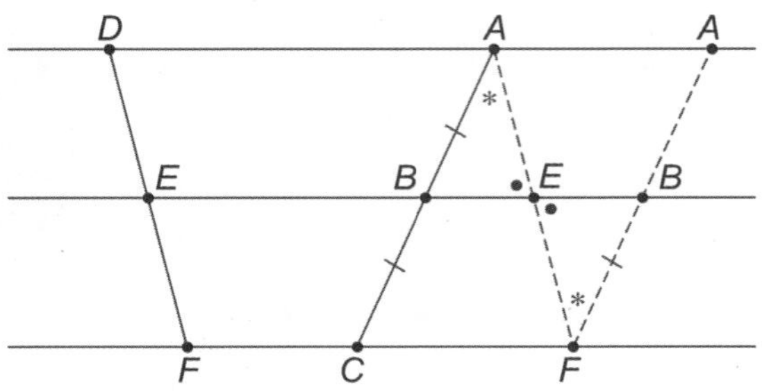

Given: $AD \parallel BE \parallel CF$, as in the diagram, with $|AB| = |BC|$.

To prove: $|DE| = |EF|$.

Construction: Draw $AE' \parallel DE$, cutting EB at E' and CF at F'.

Draw $F'B' \parallel AB$, cutting EB at B', as in the diagram.

Proof:

Statement	Reason
$\lvert B'F'\rvert = \lvert BC\rvert$	Opposite sides in a parallelogram
$= \lvert AB\rvert$	By assumption
$\lvert\angle BAE'\rvert = \lvert\angle E'F'B'\rvert$	Alternate angles
$\lvert\angle AE'B\rvert = \lvert\angle F'E'B'\rvert$	Vertically opposite angles
$\therefore \Delta ABE'$ is congruent to $\Delta F'B'E'$	ASA
Therefore, $\lvert AE'\rvert = \lvert F'E'\rvert$.	
But $\lvert AE'\rvert = \lvert DE\rvert$ and $\lvert F'E'\rvert = \lvert FE\rvert$	Opposite sides in a parallelogram
$\therefore \lvert DE\rvert = \lvert EF\rvert$	
Q.E.D.	

Theorem 12

Let ABC be a triangle. If a line l is parallel to BC and cuts $[AB]$ in the ratio $s : t$, then it also cuts $[AC]$ in the same ratio.

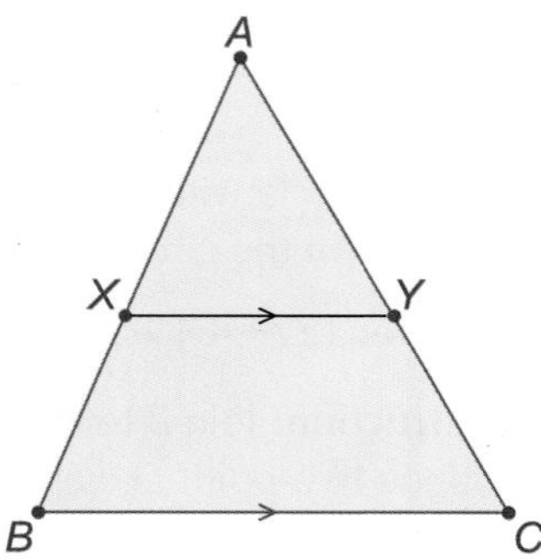

Given: A triangle ABC and a line XY parallel to BC which cuts $[AB]$ in the ratio $s : t$.

To prove: $|AY| : |YC| = s : t$

Construction: Divide $[AX]$ into s equal parts and $[XB]$ into t equal parts. Through each point of division, draw a line parallel to BC.

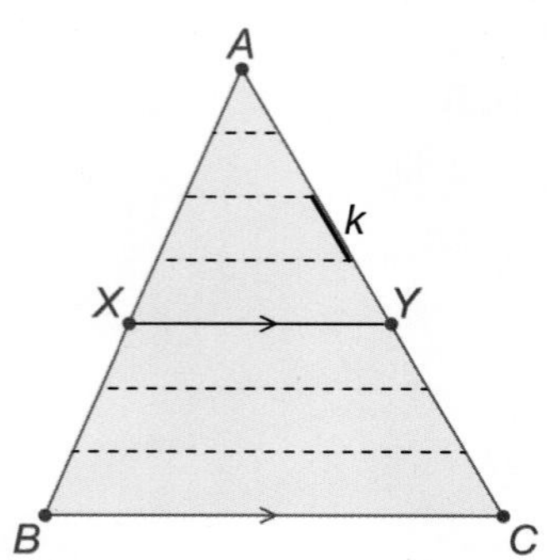

Proof: According to Theorem 11, the parallel lines cut off segments of equal length along $[AC]$.

Let k be the length of each of these equal segments.

$\Rightarrow |AY| = sk$ and $|YC| = tk$

$\Rightarrow |AY| : |YC| = sk : tk = s : t$

Q.E.D.

Theorem 13

If two triangles *ABC* and *DEF* are similar, then their sides are proportional, in order:
$\frac{|AB|}{|DE|} = \frac{|BC|}{|EF|} = \frac{|AC|}{|DF|}$

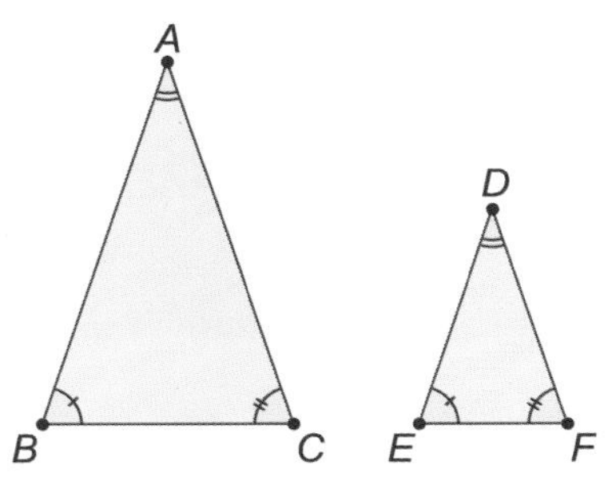

Given: Similar triangles *ABC* and *DEF*.

To prove: $\frac{|AB|}{|DE|} = \frac{|BC|}{|EF|} = \frac{|AC|}{|DF|}$

Construction: Assume triangle *DEF* is smaller than triangle *ABC*.

- Mark a point *X* on [*AB*] such that $|AX| = |DE|$, and mark a point *Y* on [*AC*] such that $|AY| = |DF|$ as shown.
- Draw [*XY*].

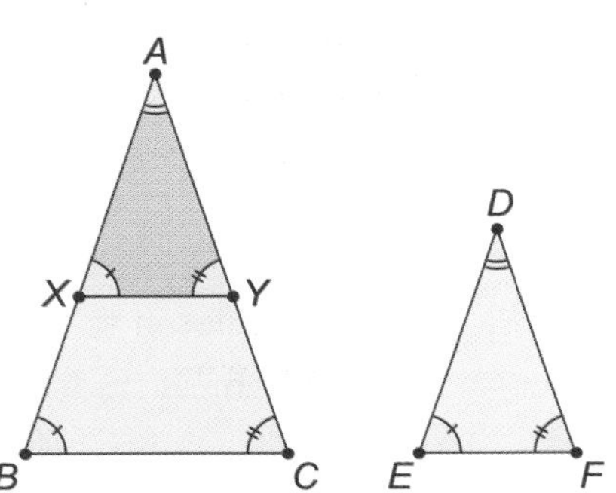

Proof:

Statement	Reason
ΔAXY is congruent to ΔDEF.	SAS
$\Rightarrow |\angle AXY| = |\angle ABC|$	
$\Rightarrow XY \parallel BC$	Corresponding angles equal
$\Rightarrow \frac{|AB|}{|AX|} = \frac{|AC|}{|AY|}$	Theorem 12
But $|AX| = |DE|$ and $|AY| = |DF|$.	Construction
$\Rightarrow \frac{|AB|}{|DE|} = \frac{|AC|}{|DF|}$	
Similarly, $\frac{|BC|}{|EF|} = \frac{|AB|}{|DE|}$	
$\Rightarrow \frac{|AB|}{|DE|} = \frac{|BC|}{|EF|} = \frac{|AC|}{|DF|}$	
Q.E.D.	

Answers

Chapter 1

Exercise 1.1

1. (i) Heights of plants, colour of leaves (ii) Heights (numerical), colour (categorical) (iii) Continuous (iv) Centimetres (v) Nominal **4.** (i) Discrete (ii) Continuous (iii) Discrete (iv) Discrete **5.** Continuous numerical, continuous numerical, discrete numerical, discrete numerical, nominal categorical **8.** Central Statistics Office; Central Bank of Ireland **9.** (i) and (ii) are incorrect

Exercise 1.2

1. Simple random sample **2.** (i) A – 20, B – 35, C – 5, D – 10 (ii) Stratified random sample **3.** (i) Systematic random sampling (ii) Cluster sampling (iii) Quota sampling **4.** (i) Simple random sampling (ii) Convenience sampling (iii) Census **6.** No **7.** (i) Yes (ii) Use a stratified random sample

Exercise 1.3

1. (i)

Scores	1	2	3	4	5	6
Frequency	10	10	7	5	8	10

(ii) 10 (iii) 10 (iv) 10%

2. (i)

Mode	Walks	Bus	Car	Rail
Frequency	9	5	4	2

(ii) Walks (iii) Rail

3. (i)

Number of Goals	0	1	2	3	4
Frequency	7	9	11	3	5

(ii) 35 (iii) 7 (iv) 23 (v) 7

4. (i)

Result	3Hs	2Hs	1H	0H
Frequency	3	11	9	2

(ii) 36%

5. (i)

Marks	1	2	3	4	5
Frequency	4	2	7	3	4

(iii) 4 (iv) 80%

6. (i) 47

(ii)

Age	Frequency
20–29	8
30–39	9
40–49	15
50–59	10
60–69	5

7. (i) 20 (ii) 55% **8.** It is a leading question.
9. You may tick more than one box.
10. (i) There are no clear boundaries between the three categories offered.

Exercise 1.4

1. (iii) 76 (iv) 29 **2.** (ii) Height of students (in cm) (iii) Numerical (iv) 28%
3. (i) Numerical discrete **4.** (ii) 17 (iii) 2 (iv) 55% **5.** (ii) Yes **6.** (ii) 27 cm (iii) 49 cm (iv) ⅓ **7.** (ii) Yes
(iii) He could have used a larger sample size.
8. (i) 18 (ii) 1 (iii) Running increases your pulse.
10. (ii) 7 minutes (iii) 38 minutes (iv) Group 1 has the fastest and slowest times. **12.** (ii) 75 mm

Exercise 1.5

1. (i)

Weight (kg)	Frequency
0.5–1.5	6
1.5–2.5	2
2.5–3.5	14
3.5–4.5	18
4.5–5.5	9
5.5–6.5	15
6.5–7.5	8
7.5–8.5	6

(iii) There are two clusters, one between 2.5 and 4.5 and the other between 4.5 and 7.5.

2. (i)

Weight (kg)	Frequency
2–2.5	5
2.5–3	8
3–3.5	13
3.5–4	4

2. (iv)

Weight (kg)	Relative Frequency (%)
2–2.5	16.6
2.5–3	26.6
3.5–3.5	43.3
3.5–4	13.3

3.

Time (minutes)	Frequency (%)
0–1	2
1–2	3
2–3	5
3–4	2
4–5	1

(i) 10 (ii) 15.38%

4. (ii) 35 (iii) 15

5. (iii)

Price	Frequency
0.8–0.9	1
0.9–1	4
1–1.1	3
1.1–1.2	4
1.2–1.3	3
1.3–1.4	0
1.4–1.5	5
1.5–1.6	4
1.6–1.7	1
1.7–1.8	1

6. (i)

Time (Sec)	Frequency
2–3	3
3–4	4
4–5	5
5–6	2
6–7	1

7. (a) Skewed right (b) Reasonably symmetric (c) Skewed left **8.** (ii) Reasonably symmetric distribution **9.** (ii) Skewed right **10.** (ii) Skewed right

Exercise 1.6

1. (ii) 0.94 (iii) Strong positive correlation **2.** (i) Weak positive (ii) 0.6 (iii) Systolic = 112, Diastolic = 44 (mmHg) **3.** (i) Strong positive correlation (ii) 0.8 (iii) 3.6, 3.7, 3.9 and 3.9 (iv) 14.1 **4.** (i) Moderately strong positive correlation (ii) Very strong negative correlation (iii) Weak positive correlation (iv) Close to perfect negative correlation (v) No correlation **5.** (ii) 0.82 (iii) Strong positive correlation **6.** (ii) 0.18 (iii) No, as the correlation co-efficient indicates an extremely weak positive correlation. **7.** (ii) 0.93 (iii) Very strong positive correlation **8.** (i) 7.9 litres / 100 km (ii) 1,000 cc (iii) 0.98 A near-perfect positive correlation (iv) False **9.** (ii) Strong positive correlation **10.** (ii) 0.90 (iii) Strong positive correlation **11.** (i) Strong positive correlation (iii) 0.96

Exercise 1.7

1. (ii) 0.93 **2.** (ii) –0.82 (iv) Strong negative correlation **3.** (ii) 0.95 (iv) Strong positive correlation (v) $y = 1.3x - 7$
4. (ii) 0.96 (iii) Strong positive correlation (v) $y = 4x + 6$ (vi) €18,000 **5.** (ii) 1.00 (iv) Perfect positive correlation (v) $y = \frac{11}{7}(x - \frac{51}{7})$
6. (ii) 0.99 (iii) Near-perfect positive correlation (v) $y = 2.5x + 14$ (vi) 39%

Revision Exercises

1. (i) Discrete numerical (ii) Continuous numerical (iii) Categorical (nominal) (iv) Discrete numerical (v) Discrete numerical **2.** (ii) Discrete data (iii) Group 1: skewed right. Group 2: Slightly skewed right (iv) Stratified random sample (v) 225 (vi) Yes (Group 1) **3.** (ii) 0.86 (iii) Strong positive correlation (v) $y = 0.7x - 1$ (vi) 43.1 days **4.** (i) Adults living in Ireland (ii) 1,000 adults, randomly selected (iii) Inferential (iv) Frequency of use of Internet for shopping (v) Categorical **5.** (i) Quota sampling (ii) No (iii) Busy people, shy people, people without strong opinions **6.** (i) Test score (ii) Discrete numerical data (of only whole number scores were possible) (iv) Slightly skewed right

7.

	Explanatory	Response
(i)	Weight	Cost
(ii)	Mock mark	Final mark
(iii)	Distance	Time
(iv)	Volume of water	Amount of electricity

8. (i) Convenience sampling (ii) Simple random sampling (iii) Systemic random sampling (iv) Convenience sampling **10.** (i) 0.10 (ii) Almost no correlation (iii) (a) 0.1 (b) 0.9 **11.** (ii) Skewed right (iii) 60% **12.** (b) (i) 0 (ii) The pattern suggests a quadratic relationship. **13.** (a) –0.75 (b) Age: 47 years; max. heart rate: 137 bpm (c) 176 bpm (d) –0.7 (e) $MHR = 207 - 0.7 \times \text{(age)}$ (g) He should exercise a bit more intensely.

Chapter 2

Exercise 2.1

1. (i) 6 (ii) 26 (iii) 4,320 (iv) 8 (v) 504 (vi) 10 (vii) 11 (viii) 14 (ix) 20 (x) 420 **2.** 42 **3.** 30 **4.** 260 **5.** (a) (i) No (ii) No (iii) Yes (b) (i) 6 (ii) 120 (iii) 40,320 **6.** (i) 120 (ii) 360 (iii) 720 **7.** 24 (i) 6 (ii) 18 (iii) 12 **8.** (i) 5,040 (ii) 2,520 (iii) 42 **9.** (i) 720 (ii) 120 (iii) 24 (iv) 240 (v) 480 **10.** (i) 5,040 (ii) 1,440 (iii) 3,600 (iv) 1,440 (v) 3,600 **11.** (i) 40,320 (ii) 720 (iii) 4,320 (iv) 10,080 (v) 30,240 **12.** (i) 362,880 (ii) 30,240 (iii) 17,280 (iv) 40,320 (v) 151,200 **13.** (a) (i) 10 (ii) 330 (iii) 23 (iv) 156 (b) (i) n (ii) $n + 1$ (iii) $n - 1$ (c) (i) 18 (ii) 192 **14.** 245 **15.** 15 **16.** 48 **17.** (i) 468,000 (ii) 1,800 **18.** 80 **19.** 78,000 **20.** 59,280 **21.** 32 **22.** 200 **23.** (i) 120 (ii) 12 **24.** 144 **25.** (i) 362,880 (ii) 80,640 (iii) 282,240 (iv) 2,880 **26.** (i) 720 (ii) 240 (iii) 168 **27.** (i) 72 (ii) 42

Exercise 2.2

1. 45; 165; 35; 14; 190; 84; 84; 78; 3,060; 3,060 **4.** $k = 5$ **7.** 1,365 **8.** (i) 35 (ii) 15 (iii) 20 **9.** (i) 715 (ii) 315 (iii) 15 **10.** (i) 105 (ii) 91 **11.** (i) 56 (ii) 35 (iii) 21 (iv) 20 **12.** 91 **13.** 78 **14.** 132 **15.** (i) 126 (ii) 81 (iii) 5 **16.** 8,145,060 **17.** (i) 252 (ii) 126 (iii) 35 (iv) 462 **18.** 300 **19.** (i) 210 (ii) 252 (iii) 378 **20.** 660 **21.** (i) 66 (ii) 220 **22.** (i) 2,598,960 (ii) 249,900 (iii) 2,349,060 (iv) 48 (v) 4,512 **23.** $n = 21$ **24.** $n = 11$ **25.** $x = 11$

Exercise 2.3

1. Fifty–fifty C; Certain E; Very unlikely B; Impossible A; Very likely D **2.** (i) 0.8 (ii) 48 **3.** Getting tails on single flip of a fair coin – R; Getting a 4 on a single roll of a fair six-sided die – Q; Getting a 7 on a single roll of a fair six-sided die – P; A person being born on a day that ends with the letter 'y' – T; A person not being born on a Sunday – S. **4.** (i) 13% (ii) Conor's punctuality has disimproved. He is late ≈15% of the time vs. 13% last year. **5.** (ii) After 40: 0.4; after 60: 0.4833; after 80: 0.5125; after 100: 0.49 (iii) Yes **6.** (i) 76% (ii) 35 (iii) Pundit A is most accurate; Pundit B is least accurate. **7.** (i) 57.5% (ii) No **8.** (i) Relative frequency: after 20 flips = 0.55; after 30 flips = 0.5666; after 40 flips = 0.525; after 50 flips = 0.48 (ii) No **9.** (i) 52.5% (ii) 31 successes (iv) No **10.** (i) Cathal's data (ii) 20 times **11.** (i) Relative frequency: 1: 0.296; 2: 0.170; 3: 0.110; 4: 0.094; 5: 0.078; 6: 0.072; 7: 0.065; 8: 0.057; 9: 0.058 (ii) Yes

Exercise 2.4

1. $\frac{1}{2}$ **2.** (i) $\frac{1}{2}$ (ii) $\frac{2}{3}$ (iii) $\frac{1}{2}$ **3.** (i) $\frac{3}{8}$ (ii) $\frac{3}{8}$ (iii) $\frac{5}{8}$ **4.** (i) $\frac{8}{15}$ (ii) $\frac{7}{15}$ (iii) $\frac{1}{6}$ (iv) $\frac{1}{10}$ A girl who wears glasses would be chosen on 12 days. **5.** (i) $\frac{1}{4}$ (ii) $\frac{1}{2}$ (iii) $\frac{1}{13}$ (iv) $\frac{3}{4}$ (v) $\frac{4}{13}$ (vi) $\frac{7}{13}$ **6.** (i) $\frac{2}{7}$ (ii) $\frac{4}{7}$ (iii) $\frac{7}{7} = 1$ (iv) 0 **7.** (i) Yes (iii) No (iii) Yes (iv) No (v) Yes (vi) No (vii) No (viii) Yes (ix) No (x) Yes **8.** P(E) = 0.4 P(F) = 0.6 P(E∩F) = 0.1 P(E∪F) = 0.9 **9.** (a) (i) $\frac{1}{2}$ (ii) $\frac{1}{4}$ (iii) $\frac{3}{20}$ (iv) $\frac{3}{5}$ (v) $\frac{7}{20}$ (vi) $\frac{9}{20}$ (vii) $\frac{1}{2}$ (viii) $\frac{2}{5}$ (b) (i) $\frac{7}{20} = \frac{10}{20} - \frac{3}{20}$ (ii) $\frac{3}{5} = \frac{10}{20} + \frac{5}{20} - \frac{3}{20}$, $\frac{3}{5} = \frac{12}{20}$ **10.** (i) $\frac{3}{4}$ (ii) $\frac{11}{24}$ (iii) $\frac{1}{3}$ (iv) $\frac{7}{8}$ (v) $\frac{1}{4}$ (vi) F (vii) T (viii) F (ix) T (x) T **11.** (a) (i) $\frac{1}{13}$ (ii) $\frac{1}{2}$ (iii) $\frac{1}{4}$ (iv) $\frac{1}{26}$ (v) $\frac{6}{13}$ (vi) $\frac{7}{13}$ (vii) $\frac{3}{4}$ (viii) $\frac{10}{13}$ **12.** (a) (i) 0.4 (ii) 0.9 **13.** (i) $\frac{1}{12}$ (ii) $\frac{1}{6}$ (iii) $\frac{1}{6}$ (iv) $\frac{1}{2}$ (v) $\frac{1}{2}$ (vi) $\frac{17}{36}$ (vii) $\frac{11}{12}$ **14.** S = {(H,H,H), (H,H,T), (H,T,T), (H,T,H), (T,H,H), (T,H,T), (T,T,H), (T,T,T)} (i) 8 (ii) $\frac{1}{8}$ (iii) $\frac{7}{8}$ (iv) $\frac{1}{2}$ **15.** (i) $\frac{1}{12}$ (ii) $\frac{1}{4}$ (iii) $\frac{1}{2}$ **16.** (a) (i) $\frac{1}{5}$ (ii) $\frac{7}{10}$ (iii) $\frac{3}{4}$ (iv) $\frac{3}{5}$ (v) $\frac{1}{4}$ (b) Yes **17.** $n = 8$ **18.** (i) $\frac{33}{50}$ (ii) $\frac{2}{5}$ (iii) $\frac{1}{10}$ (iv) $\frac{27}{50}$ **19.** (i) 216 (ii) $\frac{1}{216}$ (iii) $\frac{5}{216}$ (iv) $\frac{1}{24}$ **20.** (i) 0.085 (ii) 0.077 (iii) 0.162 **21.** (i) 0.1 (ii) No (iii) P(E) = 0.4; P(F) = 0.3; P(E∩F) = 0.1; P(E∪F) = 0.6; (iv) 0.6 = 0.4 + 0.3 – 0.1 **22.** (i) 0.65 (ii) 0.35 (iii) 0.8 = 0.35 + 0.65 – 0.2 **23.** (i) 10% (ii) 25% (iii) 20% **24.** (i) 0.13 (ii) 0.6 (iii) 0.36 (iv) 0.3 **25.** (a) (i) $k = 0.08$ (ii) 0.65 (iii) 0.15 (iv) 0.3 (v) 0.65 (b) (i) 0.75 = 0.53 + 0.35 – 0.13 (ii) 0.47 = 1 – 0.53 **26.** (b) (i) P(E) = $\frac{3}{25}$, P(F) = $\frac{14}{25}$ (ii) Yes (iii) P(E∪F) = $\frac{17}{25}$ (iv) No **27.** (iii) Yes (iv) {7,8,9,10}, {4,5,6,7}

Exercise 2.5

1. (i) 0.25 (ii) 0.1667 **2.** (a) A = {(6,3), (6,4), (6,5), (6,6), (5,4), (5,5), (5,6), (4,5), (4,6), (3,6)} B = {(6,1), (6,2), (6,3), (6,4), (6,5), (6,6), (1,6), (2,6), (3,6), (4,6), (5,6)} A ∩ B = {(6,3), (6,4), (6,5), (6,6), (3,6), (4,6), (5,6)} (b) (i) P(B|A) = $\frac{7}{10}$ (ii) P(A|B) = $\frac{7}{11}$ **3.** (i) 0.75 (ii) 0.25 **4.** 0.25 **5.** (i) 0.75 (ii) 0.5 (iii) 0.25 (iv) 0.375 (v) 0.5833 (vi) 0.8571 **6.** (i) 0.7059 (ii) 0.8 **7.** 0.8537 **8.** P(B) = 0.4 **9.** (i) $\frac{1}{18}$ (ii) $\frac{5}{36}$ (iii) $\frac{38}{45}$ **10.** (i) $\frac{2}{3}$ (ii) $\frac{1}{3}$ **11.** P(E) = $\frac{1}{6}$ P(F) = $\frac{11}{36}$ P(E ∩ F) = $\frac{2}{36}$ P(F|E) = $\frac{1}{3}$ P(E|F) = $\frac{2}{11}$ **12.** P(A) = $\frac{5}{11}$ P(B) = $\frac{5}{11}$

$P(A \cap B) = \frac{2}{11}$ $P(A|B) = \frac{2}{5}$ $P(B|A) = \frac{2}{5}$
13. (i) 0.6 (ii) $\frac{1}{3}$ (iii) 0.33 (iv) 0.67
14. $P(A|B) = 0.4$ $P(B|A) = 0.6667$ **16.** (i) 0.66
(ii) 0.16 (iii) $\frac{8}{15}$ (iv) $\frac{8}{33}$ (v) $\frac{26}{55}$ (vi) 0.4375
17. (i) $x = 0.1, y = 0.2$ (ii) $P(B|C) = \frac{13}{30}$
$P(C|B) = \frac{26}{37}$ (iii) $\frac{33}{77}$ (iv) 0.175 (v) 0.26
18. (i) $x = 0.2, y = 0.3$ (ii) 0.4 **19.** (i) $x = 0.08$
(ii) $\frac{19}{49}$ (iii) $\frac{13}{43}$ (iv) $\frac{4}{15}$ **20.** (i) $\frac{1}{5}$ (ii) No

Revision Exercises

1. (a) (i) 5,040 (ii) 240 (b) (i) $\frac{1}{36}$ (ii) $\frac{11}{36}$
(iii) $\frac{5}{36}$ **2.** (i) 336 (ii) 56 (iii) $\frac{1}{56}$ (iv) $\frac{55}{56}$
3. (i) $k = 0.2$ (ii) $P(X) = 0.4$ $P(Y) = 0.7$
$P(X \cap Y) = 0.3$ (iii) $0.8 = 0.4 + 0.7 - 0.3$
(iv) $\frac{3}{7}$ (v) No **4.** (i) You are more likely to get a sum of 3 (ii) P(sum of 2) = $\frac{1}{12}$; P(sum of 3) = $\frac{1}{4}$; P(sum of 4) = $\frac{1}{3}$; P(sum of 5) = $\frac{1}{3}$ **5.** (a) 72
(b) (i) 5,040 (ii) 360 (iii) 720 (iv) $\frac{1}{8}$
6. (i) 120 (ii) 112 (iii) $\frac{1}{15}$ **7.** (i) $\frac{2}{3}$ (ii) $\frac{1}{5}$
(iii) $\frac{7}{9}$ **8.** (i) 720 (ii) 144 (iii) $\frac{1}{5}$
9. (i) 35 (ii) 20 (iii) 15 (iv) $\frac{4}{7}$ **10.** (i) Things have improved slightly. (ii) 10 muggings
11. (a) (i) 0.625 (ii) 0.375 (b) $n = 14$
12. (i) {HH1, HH2, HH3, HH4, HT1, HT2, HT3, HT4, TH1, TH2, TH3, TH4, TT1, TT2, TT3, TT4}
(ii) $\frac{1}{16}$ (iii) $\frac{1}{8}$ (iv) $\frac{1}{4}$ **13.** (i) 84 (ii) 30 (iii) $\frac{1}{84}$
(iv) False **14.** (i) Fred Harry Murphy (ii) 2,600

Chapter 3

Exercise 3.1

1. (i) $\frac{1}{4}$ (ii) $\frac{3}{4}$ **2.** (i) $\frac{1}{216}$ (ii) $\frac{1}{24}$ **3.** (i) $\frac{1}{16}$
(ii) $\frac{15}{16}$ **4.** (i) $\frac{1}{32}$ (ii) $\frac{31}{32}$ **5.** (i) $\frac{8}{29}$ (ii) $\frac{91}{435}$
(iii) $\frac{344}{435}$ **6.** (i) $\frac{4}{663}$ (ii) $\frac{1}{221}$ (iii) $\frac{188}{221}$
(iv) $\frac{33}{221}$ **7.** (i) $\frac{1}{5525}$ (ii) $\frac{5524}{5525}$ **8.** (a) 0.6
(b) (i) 0.36 (ii) 0.16 (iii) 0.84 **9.** (a) 0.875
(b) (i) 0.766 (ii) 0.670 (iii) 0.513 **10.** (i) $\frac{1}{24}$
(ii) $\frac{1}{4}$ (iii) $\frac{3}{4}$

Exercise 3.2

1. $\frac{10}{21}$ **2.** $\frac{13}{102}$ **3.** $\frac{5}{18}$ **4.** $\frac{1}{2}$ **5.** $\frac{3}{8}$ **6.** 0.0625
7. 0.42 **8.** (i) $\frac{5}{42}$ (ii) $\frac{5}{21}$ **9.** (i) $\frac{5}{33}$ (ii) $\frac{13}{66}$
(iii) $\frac{19}{66}$ (iv) $\frac{47}{66}$ (v) $\frac{16}{33}$ **10.** (i) $\frac{67}{560}$ (ii) $\frac{117}{280}$
(iii) $\frac{3}{14}$ (iv) $\frac{11}{14}$ **11.** (i) $\frac{1}{6}$ (ii) $\frac{4}{9}$ (iii) $\frac{5}{9}$
12. (i) $\frac{1}{4}$ (ii) $\frac{9}{400}$ (iii) $\frac{169}{400}$ (iv) $\frac{1}{80}$ **13.** (i) 0.10
(ii) 0.09 **14.** (i) $\frac{55}{72}$ (ii) $\frac{17}{72}$ **15.** (i) 0.0005
(ii) 0.0020 **16.** (i) $\frac{2041}{2401}$ (ii) $\frac{89}{144}$
17. (i) 0.0164 **18.** (i) $\frac{1}{4}$ (ii) $\frac{120}{343}$ **19.** (i) $\frac{1}{6561}$
(ii) $\frac{1}{81}$ (iii) $\frac{112}{243}$ **20.** (i) $\frac{1}{100}$ (ii) $\frac{18}{25}$ (iii) $\frac{7}{25}$
21. (i) $\frac{1}{4}$ (ii) $\frac{13}{32}$ (iii) $\frac{1}{16}$ **22.** (i) $\frac{25}{196}$ (ii) $\frac{15}{196}$
(iii) $\frac{15}{28}$ (iv) $\frac{1}{28}$ **23.** 5 **24.** 26, 7 **25.** (i) $\frac{1}{3}$ (ii) $\frac{2}{9}$
(iii) $\frac{6}{27}$ **26.** (i) 0.0061 (ii) 0.11 (iii) 0.94
27. (a) (i) $\frac{1}{3}$ (ii) $\frac{1}{2}$ (iii) $\frac{1}{2}$ (iv) $\frac{2}{3}$ (v) $\frac{1}{2}$ (vi) $\frac{1}{3}$
(vii) 0 (viii) $\frac{1}{6}$ (b) (i) N (ii) Y (iii) Y (iv) N
28. (a) (i) 6 (ii) 2 (iii) 24 **29.** (i) 0.275
(ii) 0.2375 (iii) 0.072 **30.** $\frac{5}{108}$ **31.** (i) 0.108
(ii) 0.892 (iii) 0.162 (iv) 0.108 (v) 0.345
32. (i) 0.395 (ii) 0.089 (iii) 0.107 **33.** (i) $\frac{4}{5}$
(ii) $\frac{1}{3}$ (iii) $\frac{41}{60}$ **34.** 0.5138

Exercise 3.3

1. 3.5 **2.** 6 **3.** €11 **4.** (ii) 8 (iii) No **5.** No
6. (ii) 7 (iii) Yes **7.** (ii) 7.75 **8.** 7.875 **9.** Yes
10. (i) 7.5 **11.** (i) B (ii) 6.42 (iii) 10.29
12. (i) Choice 2: €769.23, Choice 3: €2777.78
(ii) Pick Choice 3 **13.** (i) 8,145,060 (ii) 0.000000122
(iii) No **14.** (a) 0.101 (b) 0.086 (c) €616.91
(d) €520.39 (e) €1,071.09, €503.61 (f) €448
15. (ii) 1.1 (iii) $\frac{1}{18}$ **16.** (i) 0.3 (ii) $\frac{1}{3}$

Exercise 3.4

2. (i) $\frac{3}{8}$ (ii) 0.875 or $\frac{7}{8}$ **3.** Not independent
4. 0.6 **5.** 20 **6.** (i) Independent (ii) Not independent **7.** $\frac{1}{3}$ **9.** Independent **10.** (i) 2
(ii) 0.4, 0.5, 0.2 (iii) Independent **11.** (i) 400
(ii) $P(E) = \frac{320}{400}$; $P(F) = \frac{21}{400}$; $P(E \cap F) = \frac{14}{400}$
(iii) Not independent

Exercise 3.5

2. 0.3125 **3.** 0.3858 **4.** (i) 0.2734 (ii) 0.03125
(iii) 0.0352 **5.** (i) 0.2373 (ii) 0.3955
(iii) 0.3672 **6.** 125 **7.** 0.2871 **8.** 0.2508
9. 0.8208 **12.** 0.103 **13.** (i) 0.0512
(ii) 0.05792 **14.** (i) 0% (ii) 25% (iii) 94%
15. (i) 0.29 (ii) 0.16 (iii) 0.0037 **16.** (i) 0.60
(ii) 0.0849 **17.** (i) 0.01 (ii) 0.29 (iii) 0.7969
18. 0.27 **19.** (i) 0.36 (ii) 0.64

Exercise 3.6

1. 0.15625 **2.** 0.058 **3.** (i) 0.25 (ii) 0.125
4. 0.0604 **5.** 0.0779 **6.** 0.0481 **7.** 0.09261
8. 0.0352 **9.** 0.0356 **10.** 9 **11.** 13 **12.** 7

Exercise 3.7

1. (i) 0.9452 (ii) 0.0548 (iii) 0.0548 (iv) 0.0792
(v) 0.1359 (vi) 0.1218 (vii) 0.1151 (viii) 0.8973
(ix) 0.871 (x) 0.3094 (xi) 0.3094 (xii) 0.9876
(xiii) 0.0215 (xiv) 0.0206 (xv) 0.8664
(xvi) 0.9616 (xvii) 0.0094 (xviii) 0.7372
(xix) 0.95 (xx) 0.9 **2.** (i) 68% (ii) 95%
(iii) 100% **3.** (i) 1.84 (ii) 0.92 (iii) –0.63
(iv) 0.69 (v) 0.44 **4.** 1.96 **5.** 0.43 **6.** 2.3
7. 0.32 **8.** $x = 0.6755$; $x = 0$; $x = -0.6755$
9. $t \approx 0.52$; $k \approx -0.84$ **10.** $k \approx 2.58$

Exercise 3.8

1. 2.28% **2.** 4.46% **3.** 0.0228 **4.** (i) 0.242 (ii) 0.383 (iii) 0.0301 **5.** True **6.** (i) 0.0668 (ii) 105 **7.** (i) 0.2266 (ii) No **8.** 4% **9.** (i) 0.0475 (ii) 0.0475 (iii) 0.905 **10.** 22% **11.** (i) 0.0271 (ii) 10 (iii) Yes **12.** 40 **13.** 20 **14.** 176.92

Revision Exercises

1. (a) (i) 0.4019 (ii) 0.4019 (iii) 0.1962 (b) 0.0670 (c) (i) $\frac{1}{8}$ (ii) $\frac{7}{10}$ **2.** (a) (i) 0.733 (ii) 1.22 (b) (i) $0.06\dot{6}$ (ii) $\frac{1}{3}$ (iii) $\frac{1}{6}$ **3.** (i) $\frac{5}{8}$ (ii) $\frac{3}{64}$ (iii) $\frac{5}{32}$ **4.** (i) $x = 11$, $y = 24$ (ii) No (iii) Not independent **5.** (a) (i) 0.7257 (ii) 0.4514 (b) (i) $\frac{4}{25}$ (ii) $\frac{8}{13}$ (iii) 0.13824 **6.** (a) (i) $\frac{2}{17}$ (ii) $\frac{15}{17}$ (b) (i) $\frac{32}{72}$ (ii) $\frac{10}{63}$ (iii) $\frac{53}{63}$ **7.** (a) 0.4, 0.1 (b) (i) 0.336 (ii) 0.024 (iii) 0.976 **8.** (a) (i) $\frac{55}{144}$ (ii) $\frac{89}{144}$ (b) Yes **9.** (i) Sum (ii) $\frac{1}{12}$, $\frac{1}{4}$, $\frac{1}{3}$ **10.** (i) $\frac{9}{25}$ (ii) $\frac{72}{625}$ (iii) 0.3088 (iv) No (v) 0.1174 **11.** (i) $\frac{385}{1728}$ (ii) $\frac{1343}{1728}$ (iii) Karen (iv) 13 **12.** (a) (i) $x = 0.25$, $y = 0.1$ (ii) Not independent (b) (i) $\frac{1}{12}$ **13.** (i) 216 (ii) $\frac{1}{54}$ (iii) $\frac{53}{54}$ (iv) $\frac{5}{9}$ (v) 0.3568 (vi) 0.1673 **14.** (i) P(E) = 0.3; P(F) = 0.5; P(E ∩ F) = 0.2 (ii) 0.4 (iv) Not independent **15.** (a) 0.0668 (b) (i) 50.5 **16.** (iii) 0.3280 (v) No **17.** (b) 0.2 (c) 0.2 (d) Independent **18.** (i) $\frac{21}{32}$ (ii) $\frac{1}{64}$ (iii) $\frac{21}{64}$ (iv) −€0.28 (v) No (vi) €42 (vii) No (viii) 13.5% **19.** (i) 0.04 (ii) No

Chapter 4

Exercise 4.1

1. (i) mean = 78.95; median = 78.4 (ii) mean = 40.38; median = 40.6 (iii) mean = 6.3; median = 6.1 (iv) mean = $29.3\dot{2}$; median = 27.9; (v) mean = 97.57; median = 98 **2.** (i) Almost perfectly symmetric. (ii) mean = 44.49 g; median = 45 g **3.** (i) sampling variability (ii) 225.3125 (iii) $1.28\dot{3}$ (iv) 18.46 (v) Yes **4.** (i) ≈ 10.91 °C (ii) ≈ 10.38 °C. The mean temperature in 2009 is higher than for 1961–1990. (iii) Not really **5.** (i) 2000 (ii) 2009 (iii) 155,048.8 (iv) 155,696.5 **6.** (i) 43.62 mins (ii) 16 **7.** (i) 96 (ii) 33.91 years (iii) 25% **8.** (i) Continuous

(ii)

Hours	Tally	No. of days
0–1	𝍸 |	6
1–2	𝍸 𝍸	10
2–3	||||	4
3–4	|||	3
4–5	|||	3
5–6	||||	4

(iv) Skewed right (v) 0.2, 0.33, 0.5, 0.7, 0.8, 0.9, 1.1, 1.12, 1.2, 1.22, 1.4, 1.5, 1.6, 1.79, 1.8, 1.9, 2.3, 2.5, 2.51, 2.8, 3.1, 3.2, 3.3, 4, 4, 4.21, 5, 5.2, 5.9. Median = 1.85 hrs (vi) $2.4\dot{6}$ hours (vii) 2.376 hrs (viii) $3.\dot{5}\dot{3}\%$ **9.** (i) 159.03 cm (iii) Quite symmetric **10.** (i) Continuous

(ii)

Temp	Tally	No. of days
29–31	||	6
31–33	𝍸 |||	10
33–35	𝍸 |||	4
35–37	𝍸 |||	3
37–39	||	3
39–41	||	4

(iv) Slightly skewed right (v) 34.25 °C (vi) 34.4 °C (vii) ≈ 34.53 °C (viii) ≈ 0.37%

Exercise 4.2

1. (i) Mean or median (ii) Mode (iii) Mean or median (iv) Mode (v) Median **2.** (i) Mean (ii) Mode (iii) Median **3.** (i) Categorical (nominal) (ii) Mode **4.** (i) Median (ii) Not really (iii) Mean **5.** Mean = $32.\dot{8}\%$, Median = 18. I would use the median, as the mean is raised in value by the outlier value of 188.

Exercise 4.3

1. (i) $Q_1 = 2$; $Q_3 = 7$; IQR = 5; (ii) $Q_1 = 4$; $Q_3 = 7$; IQR = 3 (iii) $Q_1 = 2.5$; $Q_3 = 6.5$; IQR = 4 (iv) $Q_1 = 4$; $Q_3 = 7$; IQR = 3 (v) $Q_1 = -2$; $Q_3 = 2$; IQR = 4 (vi) $Q_1 = -3$; $Q_3 = 7$; IQR = 10

2.

Stem	Leaf
12	1, 1, 6
13	0, 1, 1, 1, 6, 9
14	1, 1, 3, 5
15	0

Key: 14|1 = 141

(ii) $Q_1 = 130$; $Q_3 = 141$ (iii) 57.14% (iv) 11 **3.** (i) 59 (ii) 72 (iii) 13 (iv) Skewed left

4. (i)

Stem	Leaf
0	7, 7, 7, 8, 9, 9, 9, 9
1	0, 1, 1, 1, 1, 1, 2, 3, 3, 3, 4
1	6

Key: 1|1 = 11 kWh

(ii) Skewed right (iii) 9 (iv) 11 (v) 3.5

5. (i)

Stem	Leaf
8	3, 6, 8
9	
10	5, 7, 8
11	0, 1, 2, 3, 4, 4, 7
12	0, 9, 9
13	3, 7, 8
14	0, 2, 5
15	
16	0, 3
17	3, 5, 9
18	0, 0
19	
20	6

Key: 17|3 = 17.3 inches

(ii) Skewed right (iii) 12.3 (iv) 12.9 (v) 4.9 **6.** (a) (i) 29.165 (ii) 29.025 (iii) 20.77 (iv) 34.82 (v) 14.05 (vi) 6.2 (b) (i) 0.14 (ii) The distribution does not contain outliers.

7.

	Area 1	Area 2	Area 3
Mean	37.31	40.10	38.89
Minimum	36.71	39.38	38.24
Q1	37.01	39.73	38.53
Median	37.18	39.78	38.80
Q3	37.50	40.62	39.05
Maximum	38.85	40.80	40.08
IQR	0.49	0.89	0.52
Range	2.14	1.42	1.84

Exercise 4.4

1. (i) Neither. $\sigma_A = 2.83$, $\sigma_B = 2.83$ (ii) Neither. $\sigma_A = 3.22$, $\sigma_B = 3.22$ (iii) A. $\sigma_A = 111.80$, $\sigma_B = 11.18$ (iv) Neither. $\sigma_A = 2.74$, $\sigma_B = 2.74$ **2.** (i) Neither. $\sigma_X = 2.83$, $\sigma_Y = 2.83$ (ii) Neither. $\sigma_X = 1.12$, $\sigma_Y = 1.12$ (iv) Neither. $\sigma_X = 2.74$, $\sigma_Y = 2.74$ **3.** 10.71% **4.** (a) (i) 15 (ii) €1.30 (iii) €2.90 (iv) €2.05 (v) €0.53 **5.** Mean = 150,711 (€m), Standard deviation = 11,763.67 (€m) (iii) 2007 (iv) 2009 (v) Yes

6. (ii)

Stem	Leaf
12	1, 1, 6
13	0, 1, 1, 1, 6, 9
14	1, 1, 4, 5
15	0

Key: 12|6 = 126 (mmHg) (systolic pressure)

(iii) 0 (iv) Symmetric (v) Mean = 134.71, $\sigma = 8.55$ (vi) Less **7.** (i) 70 mins (ii) ≈ 27 mins **8.** (i) 32 years (ii) ≈ 18 years **9.** (i) €32 (ii) ≈ €17 **10.** (i) 71.96 cm (ii) 5.30 cm

11. (i)

Regular Coke			
Weight (g)	360–365	365–370	370–375
Frequency	2	5	3

Diet Coke			
Weight (g)	345–350	350–355	355–360
Frequency	1	8	1

(iii) Regular Coke (iv) $\sigma_{\text{Regular Coke}} = 3.5$, $\sigma_{\text{Diet Coke}} = 2.24$

Exercise 4.5

1. (i)

Stem	Leaf
5	1, 2, 3, 3, 3, 4, 4, 4, 5, 6, 6, 9
6	0, 1, 2, 8
7	2, 3, 3, 4, 5, 7, 8
8	0, 0, 0, 1, 1, 3, 5

Key: 7|3 = 7.3

(ii) 81 (iii) 53 (iv) 54 (v) 78 (vi) 73 (vii) 59.5

2. (i)

Stem	Leaf
1	8
2	
3	
4	2, 3, 7, 8
5	6, 6, 8
6	1, 5, 7
7	1, 4, 6, 7
8	3, 6, 7, 7, 8, 9, 9
9	0, 4, 5, 5, 7, 8, 9
10	0

Key: 7|4 = 7.4

(ii) 72.5 9 (iii) 89 (v) 27th percentile

3. (i)

Stem	Leaf
5	3
5	5, 5, 7, 8, 8, 9, 9
6	2, 2, 3, 3, 3, 3, 3, 3, 4
6	5, 5, 7, 8, 8, 8, 9, 9, 9
7	0, 0, 1, 3
7	5
8	0, 0, 3, 4

Key: 6|5 = 65 bpm

(ii) Skewed right (iii) 73 bpm (iv) 58 bpm (vi) 23 bpm **4.** (i) Skewed right (ii) €29 (iii) €21 (iv) €31

5. (i)

Distance (m)	Frequency
14.25–15.00	1
15.00–15.75	0
15.75–16.50	2
16.50–17.25	4
17.25–18.00	9
18.00–18.75	7
18.75–19.50	4
19.50–20.25	1

(iii) Slightly skewed left (iv) 19.12 m (v) ≈ 40th percentile **6.** The units are standard deviations from the mean. **8.** (i) 23 cm (ii) 3.29 (iii) –3.29 (iv) Yes **9.** (i) 60 IQ points (ii) 3.75 (iii) 3.75 (iv) Yes **10.** (i) –3 (ii) 2 (iii) –4 (iv) 6 **11.** The English score is better.

Exercise 4.6

1. (i) 68% (ii) 95% (iii) 99.7% **2.** (i) 18.6 (ii) 4.22 (iii) [14.38, 22.82] **3.** (i) [175, 225] (ii) [80, 120] (iii) [18, 22] (iv) [22.5, 27.5] **4.** (i) [210, 350] (ii) [60, 180] (iii) [21, 29] (iv) [24, 46] **5.** (i) [75, 225] (ii) [255, 345] (iii) [14, 26] (iv) [85, 115] **6.** (i) [270, 330] (ii) [95, 135] (iii) [37, 43] (iv) [32.5, 37.5] **7.** (i) [150, 250] (ii) [60, 140] (iii) [16, 24] (iv) [20, 30] **8.** (i) [35, 55] (ii) [55, 145] (iii) [4, 40] (iv) [24, 36] **9.** Eoin is incorrect. **10.** 186.5 cm **11.** Yes **12.** 68%

Exercise 4.7

1. $\sigma_A > \sigma_B$ **2.** $\sigma_A = \sigma_B$ **3.** $\sigma_A > \sigma_B$ **4.** $\sigma_A > \sigma_B$ **5.** $\sigma_A < \sigma_B$ **6.** $\sigma_A < \sigma_B$ **7.** $\sigma_A > \sigma_B$ **8.** $\sigma_A < \sigma_B$ **9.** $\sigma_A = \sigma_B$ **10.** σ_B is greater

Exercise 4.8

1. (i) Approximately normal distribution (ii) Mean $= \mu$; SD $= \frac{\sigma}{20}$ **2.** 0.0011 **3.** (i) 0.6628 (ii) 0.9812 (iii) The underlying population is normally distributed. **4.** (i) 0.5222 (ii) ≈ 1 **5.** (i) 0.5675 (ii) 0.7257 (iii) No **6.** (i) 42.86% (ii) 0.0367 **7.** $n = 12$ **8.** (i) Approximately normal distribution (ii) Mean $= \mu$; SD $= \frac{\sigma}{\sqrt{n}}$ **10.** (i) ≈ 29.66% (ii) Approximately normal distribution (iii) ≈ 103 or ≈ 104 **11.** (i) 0.34% (ii) Assumption: Population from which sample was chosen has mean of 6 ppb and SD of 10 ppb. **12.** (i) ≈ 0.0158 hours (iii) 2.87% (iv) 43 (v) Expected distribution would be very similar to actual sample distribution of sample means found in part (i)

Exercise 4.9

1. $-0.0247 < p < 0.0647$
2. $0.6587 < p < 0.8413$
3. (i) $0.7084 < p < 0.7716$ (ii) Yes
4. $0.2384 < p < 0.3016$ **5.** 625
6. Accept the alternative hypothesis that $p \neq 50\%$ **7.** Accept the null hypothesis that the coin is fair. **8.** No, the die is fair. **9.** The new drug is not different. **10.** (ii) 50% (iii) Yes (iv) Range: 9.5 cm

Revision Exercises

1. (i)

Survival time (days)	Frequency
0–250	6
250–500	10
500–750	7
750–1000	5
1000–1250	2
1250–1500	3
1500–1750	2
1750–2000	3
2000–2250	2
2250–2500	2
2500–2750	1

Note: 0–250 includes 0 but not 250.

(ii) 925.12 days (iii) Skewed right (iv) Majority of patients don't survive. (v) No (vi) Both (vii) Yes

2. (i)

Price (€)	Frequency
0–3	2
3–6	9
6–9	10
9–12	5
12–15	1
15–18	3

Note: 0–3 includes €0 but not €3.

(iii) Almost symmetric (iv) Mean = 7.82
(v) $\sigma = 3.65$ (standard deviation)
(vi) Minimum: increases by €2;
Maximum: increases by €2; Mean: increases by €2;
Standard deviation: unchanged;
Median: increases by €2; IQR: unchanged

3. (i)

Level of cholesterol (mg/dl)	Frequency
0–200	11
200–400	11
400–600	5
600–800	6
800–1000	2
1000–1200	1

Note: 0–200 includes 0 but not 200.

(ii) Skewed right (iii) 702 (iv) 127 (vi) 684
4. (i) 74 cm (ii) 11.84 (iii) 11.84 (iv) Highly unusual

5.

	68%	95%	99.7%
	$[\bar{x} \pm \sigma]$	$[\bar{x} \pm 2\sigma]$	$[\bar{x} \pm 3\sigma]$
(i)	[175, 225]	[150, 250]	[125, 275]
(ii)	[80, 120]	[60, 140]	[40, 160]
(iii)	[18, 22]	[16, 24]	[14, 26]
(iv)	[22.5, 27.5]	[20, 30]	[17.5, 32.5]

6. She does not have a different success rate.
7. (a) (i) 0 (ii) –0.9 (iii) 0.3 (iv) –0.2 (b) 0.76

8. (a)

Boys							
No. of sports	0	1	2	3	4	5	6
Frequency	1	10	12	20	4	3	0

Girls							
No. of sports	0	1	2	3	4	5	6
Frequency	0	9	6	22	9	3	1

(b) Similarity: 3 is the modal and median number of sports for both groups.
Difference: boys' mean = 2.5; girls' mean = 2.88.
(c) Yes (d) Improvements
(i) Use stratified random sampling
(ii) Survey teenagers, not just those enrolled in GAA club.

9. (a)

	A	B	C	D
Data skewed left	✘	✘	✔	✘
	✔	✘	✘	✘
	✘	✔	✘	✔
	✔	✘	✘	✘
	✔	✔	✔	✘

(b) D

10. (a)

Market capital ($bn)	Frequency
150–200	7
200–250	2
250–300	1
300–350	1
350–400	1

Note: 150–200 includes 150 but not 200.

(b) Median = $196.5 bn (c) IQR = $60.5 bn
(d) Yes. $345 bn and $390 bn.

(e)

Absolute value of % decline	Frequency
0–10	2
10–20	4
20–30	1
30–40	4
40–50	1

Note: 0–10 includes 0 but not 10.

(f)

Summary stats	2008	2009
Count	12	12
Max	$733 bn	$390 bn
Min	$192 bn	$166 bn
Range	$541 bn	$224 bn
Mean	$307.92 bn	$219.83 bn
Median	$246.5 bn	$196.5 bn
St. Dev.	$154.3 bn	$70.64 bn
Q_1	$205.5 bn	$169.5 bn
Q_3	$344.5 bn	$230 bn
IQR	$139 bn	$60.5 bn

(g) The following statistics show reductions indicating the effects of a recession: max, min, mean, median, Q_1, Q_3 **11.** (a) 0.0062 (b) 0.0262 **12.** (a) $97,300 (b) $4,242.64 (c) Approximately normal distribution (e) –1.838 (f) 3.29%

Chapter 5

Exercise 5.1

6. (i) $8\frac{8}{9}$ (ii) $\frac{43}{3}$ (iii) 7 (iv) 12 (v) 15 (vi) 6

Exercise 5.2

3. (i) A = 55°, B = 125° (ii) A = 40°, B = 40°, C = 110°, D = 70° (iii) A = 110°, B = 110°, C = 70° (iv) A = 45°, B = 55°, C = 135° (v) A = 105°, B = 50°, C = 50° (vi) A = 67°, B = 67°, C = 53° (vii) A = 100° **4.** (i) $x = 30°$, $-30° < y < 150°$ (ii) $x = \frac{293}{44}$, $y = 7\frac{6}{11}$

Exercise 5.3

1. (i) A = 51°, B = 66° (ii) A = 75°, B = 60°, C = 60° (iii) A = 30°, B = 120°, C = 150° (iv) A = B = 64.25°, C = 51.5 (v) A = 54°, B = 63°, C= 64° (vii) A = 48°, B = 14° (viii) A = 93°, B = 96°, C = 120° **2.** (i) 36 (ii) 66, 47 (iii) 59, 11

Exercise 5.5

2. (i) N (ii) Y (iii) Y (iv) N (v) Y (vi) Y
3. (i) 7 (ii) 13 (iii) $7 \le n \le 13$
4. (i) 9 (ii) 14 (iii) $9 \le a \le 14$

5. (i) 9 (ii) 16 (iii) $9 \le a \le 16$
6. (i) Triangles with sides 2,3,4; 2,5,4; 3,4,5; 3,4,6; 3,5,6; 4,5,6
(ii) Triangle with sides 2,5,4 (22.3°)
(iii) Triangle with sides 3,4,6 (117.28°)
7. $1 \le c \le 22$

Exercise 5.6

1. (i) A = 41°, B = 49°, C = 90° (ii) A = 90°, B = 52.5°, C = 37.5° (iii) A = 40°, B = 80°, C = 60° (iv) A = 71°, B = 103°, C = 67°, D = 71°, E = 61° (v) A = 60°, B = 60°, C = 30°, D = 70°
2. (i) $x = 2, y = 3$ (ii) $x = 7, y = 3$

Exercise 5.7

1. (i) $x = 3, y = 8$ (ii) $x = 1, y = \frac{7}{2}$ (iii) $x = 1, y = 2$ **2.** (i) $\frac{2}{5}$ (ii) $\frac{1}{4}$ (iii) $\frac{4}{1}$ (iv) $\frac{3}{7}$ **3.** (i) $\frac{28}{3}$ (ii) 22.5 (iii) 8 (iv) 11.85 **4.** (i) 1 (ii) 5 (iii) 8 (iv) $\frac{3}{2}$ **5.** (i) 3 : 5 (ii) 3 : 2 (iii) 5 : 2 **6.** (i) $\frac{3}{7}$ (ii) $\frac{3}{7}$ (iii) $\frac{7}{4}$ **7.** No **8.** No **9.** (i) 9.1 (ii) 7 (iii) 2 **10.** (i) 16.31 (ii) 8 (iii) 39.65

Revision Exercises

1. (a) (i) 117° (ii) 117° (iii) 63° (iv) 117° (v) 63° (vi) 63° (vii) 63° (viii) 117° (b) (i) 112° (ii) 68° (iii) 34° (iv) 34° (v) 56° (vi) 90° (vii) 90° (viii) 112° **2.** (a) (i) 70° (ii) 110° (iii) 70° (iv) 110° (b) 15° **3.** (a) (i) $x = 4.5, y = 7.5$ (ii) ∠1 = 120°, ∠2 = 60°, ∠3 = 120°, ∠4 = 120°, ∠5 = 60° (b) (ii) 900° (iii) 129° **4.** (a) (i) 72° (ii) 114° (iii) 39° (iv) 27° (b) (i) $x = 1, y = 2$ (ii) |AB| = 10 |DC| = 10 |AD| = 11
8. (a) $x = 3, 7$ (b) 800 m

Chapter 6

Exercise 6.2

26. (ii) 11.5276 units² **27.** (i) $[BC] \approx 1.15$ m (ii) $[DF] \approx 0.375$ m; $[EG] \approx 0.75$ m

Revision Exercises

18. (iii) 3 units (iv) 9 units² **30.** (iii) ≈ 18.88 m²

Chapter 7

Exercise 7.1

1. (i) 29 (ii) 85 (iii) 3 (iv) 24 (v) 24 (vi) 40
2. (i) $x = \sqrt{10}$ (ii) $x = \sqrt{2}$ (iii) $x = \sqrt{34}$ (iv) $x = 2\sqrt{6}$ **3.** 2.5 m **4.** (i) $x = 5, y = 12$ (ii) $x = 85, y = 77$ (iii) $x = 96, y = 4$ (iv) $x = 10, y = 24$ **5.** (i) 60 cm (ii) 100 cm (iii) 4,800 cm²

6. (a)

a	b	c
12	16	20
15	20	25
18	24	30
21	28	35

(b)

a^2	b^2	c^2
36	64	100
81	144	225
144	256	400
225	400	625
324	576	900
441	784	1,225

7. (i) $\sin A = \frac{5}{13}$, $\cos A = \frac{12}{13}$, $\tan A = \frac{5}{12}$ (ii) $\sin A = \frac{21}{29}$, $\cos A = \frac{20}{29}$, $\tan A = \frac{21}{20}$
8. (i) $\sin A = \frac{20}{29}$, $\sin B = \frac{21}{29}$, $\cos A = \frac{21}{29}$, $\cos B = \frac{20}{29}$, $\tan A = \frac{20}{21}$, $\tan B = \frac{21}{20}$
(ii) $\sin A = \frac{3}{\sqrt{13}}$, $\sin B = \frac{2}{\sqrt{13}}$, $\cos A = \frac{2}{\sqrt{13}}$, $\cos B = \frac{3}{\sqrt{13}}$, $\tan A = \frac{3}{2}$, $\tan B = \frac{2}{3}$
(iii) $\sin A = \frac{1}{\sqrt{5}}$, $\sin B = \frac{2}{\sqrt{5}}$, $\cos A = \frac{2}{\sqrt{5}}$, $\cos B = \frac{1}{\sqrt{5}}$, $\tan A = \frac{1}{2}$, $\tan B = 2$
9. (i) 0.2588 (ii) 0.8660 (iii) 3.7321 (iv) 0.2419 (v) 0.9004 (vi) 0.0872 (vii) 0.2126 (viii) 0.5000 (ix) 5.6713 (x) 0.4791 (xi) 0.7218 (xii) 0.9823 (xiii) 0.5210 (xiv) 0.2830 (xv) 0.8581 (xvi) 0.5490 (xvii) 0.8934 (xviii) 7.4947 (xix) 0.0307 (xx) 0.8923 **10.** (i) 38.26° (ii) 29.61° (iii) 19.76° (iv) 25.94° (v) 20.62° (vi) 82.84° (vii) 58.54° (viii) 46.23° (ix) 64.93° (x) 63.11° (xi) 8.26° (xii) 41.23° **11.** (i) 2°30′ (ii) 2°15′ (iii) 2°45′ (iv) 25°24′ (v) 1°12′ (vi) 0°20′ **12.** (i) 2.52° (ii) 10.67° (iii) 25.83° (iv) 70.37° (v) 11.62° (vi) 33.55° **13.** (i) 75°57′ (ii) 48°14′ (iii) 43°55′ (iv) 41°34′ (v) 17°42′ (vi) 26°49′ (vii) 73°54′ (viii) 13°57′ (ix) 22°12′ (x) 58°01′ (xi) 25°36′ (xii) 23°4′ **14.** 13° **15.** 28°04′ **16.** (i) 8.66 (ii) 5 (iii) 10.32 (iv) 11.47 (v) 8 (vi) 28.28 **17.** (i) 4.4 (ii) 24.2 (iii) 14.8 (iv) 6.9 (v) 19.9 (vi) 5 **18.** $x = 64.28, y = 11.33$ **19.** $x \approx 3.6, y \approx 4.7, z = 12$ **20.** (i) 7.2 km (ii) 34° (iii) E 4°N **21.** (i) 118 km (ii) 23 km/hr (iii) 59 km/hr **22.** $h = 449.1740$ m
23. $d = 346.4102$ m

Exercise 7.2

1.

Degrees	90°	180°	270°	360°	30°	45°	60°
Radians	$\frac{\pi}{2}$	π	$\frac{3\pi}{2}$	2π	$\frac{\pi}{6}$	$\frac{\pi}{4}$	$\frac{\pi}{3}$

2. (i) 90° (ii) 270° (iii) 450° (iv) 240° (v) 225° (vi) 50° (vii) 720° (viii) 1080° (ix) 135° (x) 330° (xi) 80° (xiii) 144° **3.** (i) $\frac{\pi}{2}$ (ii) $\frac{3\pi}{2}$ (iii) $\frac{\pi}{4}$ (iv) $\frac{\pi}{12}$ (v) 3π (vi) $\frac{\pi}{6}$ (vii) $\frac{12\pi}{5}$ (viii) $\frac{5\pi}{2}$ (ix) $\frac{5\pi}{12}$ (x) $\frac{5\pi}{24}$ (xi) $\frac{7\pi}{6}$ (xii) $\frac{49\pi}{9}$
4. (i) 2nd (ii) 1st (iii) 1st (iv) 3rd (v) 3rd (vi) 3rd (vii) 4th (viii) 1st (ix) 2nd (x) 2nd (xi) 4th (xii) 3rd

Exercise 7.3

1. (i) 0 (ii) –1 (iii) 0 (iv) 1 (v) 0 (vi) –1 (vii) 0 (viii) 1 (ix) 0 (x) 0 (xi) 1 (xii) 0 (xiii) 0 **2.** (a) (i) $-\frac{1}{\sqrt{2}}$ (ii) ½ (iii) –½ (iv) –½ (v) $\frac{1}{\sqrt{3}}$ (vi) $\frac{1}{\sqrt{2}}$ (vii) $\frac{\sqrt{3}}{2}$ (viii) $\frac{-\sqrt{3}}{2}$ (ix) $-\sqrt{3}$ (x) $\sqrt{3}$ (b) (i) –0.82 (ii) 0.34 (iii) –0.64 (iv) –0.09 (v) 0.84 (vi) 0.82 (vii) 0.64 (viii) –0.64 (ix) –0.18 (x) –0.36
3. (i) $\frac{1}{\sqrt{2}}$ (ii) ½ (iii) $\sqrt{3}$ (iv) $\frac{\sqrt{3}}{2}$ (v) $-\frac{\sqrt{3}}{2}$ (vi) 0 (vii) $-\sqrt{3}$

Exercise 7.4

1. (i) $\frac{-13\pi}{7}, \frac{-6\pi}{7}, \frac{\pi}{7}, \frac{8\pi}{7}$ (ii) θ =60°, 120°, 420°, 480° (iii) $\theta = \frac{4\pi}{3}, \frac{5\pi}{3}, \frac{10\pi}{3}, \frac{11\pi}{3}$

2. sin θ: Period 2π, Range: [–1,1]; cos θ: Period 2π, Range: [–1,1]; tan θ: Period π, Range: [–∞,∞]

3.

	Period	Range
(i)	$\frac{\pi}{2}$ or 90°	[–1, 1]
(ii)	2π or 360°	[–2, 2]
(iii)	2π or 360°	[–3, 3]
(iv)	π or 180°	[–1, 1]
(v)	π or 180°	[–3, 3]
(vi)	$\frac{\pi}{2}$ or 90°	[–2, 2]
(vii)	$\frac{\pi}{2}$ or 90°	[–∞,∞]

4.

	Period	Range
(i)	2π	[–1, 1]
(ii)	$\frac{\pi}{2}$	[–1, 1]
(iii)	$\frac{\pi}{2}$	[–∞,∞]
(iv)	$\frac{\pi}{3}$	[–∞,∞]
(v)	$\frac{2\pi}{3}$	[–2, 2]
(vi)	$\frac{\pi}{2}$	[–4, 4]
(vii)	$\frac{2\pi}{3}$	[–a,a]
(viii)	$\frac{2\pi}{k}$	[–3,3]

5. (i) g(x) = 3sin 2x (ii) g(x) = 3sin 2x (iv) Yes, at (–π,0), (0,0) and (π,0) **6.** $0 < \theta < \frac{7\pi}{2}$
7. (i) $(\frac{-\pi}{2},-1), (\frac{\pi}{6},\frac{1}{2}), (\frac{5\pi}{6},\frac{1}{2})$ **8.** (i) (a) (0,0), (±π,0), (±2π,0), (±3π,0), (±4π,0)
(b) Max = 1, Min = –1 (ii) $h(x) = \sin(\frac{x}{2})$ (iii) $g(x) = 3\sin(\frac{x}{2})$ (iv) Period = 4π, Range = [–3, 3] (v) $h(x) = \sin\left(\frac{1}{2}x\right)$

Exercise 7.5

1.

A	30°	45°	60°
sin A	½	$\frac{1}{\sqrt{2}}$	$\frac{\sqrt{3}}{2}$
cos A	$\frac{\sqrt{3}}{2}$	$\frac{1}{\sqrt{2}}$	½
tan A	$\frac{1}{\sqrt{3}}$	1	$\sqrt{3}$

2. (i) $|\angle BAC| = 30°$ (ii) $|AB| = \sqrt{3}$ (iii) $|AC| = 2$ **3.** (i) 45° (ii) 7 **4.** (i) x = y = 4 (ii) 45° **5.** (i) $\frac{-1}{\sqrt{2}}$ (ii) –½ (iii) $-\sqrt{3}$ (iv) $\frac{-\sqrt{3}}{2}$ (v) $\frac{1}{\sqrt{2}}$ (vi) $\frac{-1}{\sqrt{2}}$ (vii) $\frac{-1}{\sqrt{2}}$ (viii) $\frac{1}{\sqrt{2}}$ (ix) $\frac{1}{\sqrt{3}}$ (x) $\frac{1}{\sqrt{2}}$ (xi) $-\frac{\sqrt{3}}{2}$ (xii) –1 (xiii) $\sqrt{3}$ (xiv) $\frac{-2}{\sqrt{3}}$ (xv) –2
6. 1 **7.** 4 **8.** ⁴⁄₃ **10.** (i) 1 (ii) $\sqrt{3} - 1$ (iii) $-\frac{2}{\sqrt{3}}$

Exercise 7.6

1. (i) 60° or 300° (ii) 45° or 225° (iii) 60° or 120° (iv) 135° or 225° (v) 60° or 120° (vi) 135° or 225° (vii) 45°, 135°, 225°, 315° (viii) 135° or 315° (ix) 60°, 120°, 240°, 300° **2.** (i) $\frac{\pi}{6}$ or $\frac{5\pi}{6}$ (ii) $\frac{\pi}{6}$ or $\frac{7\pi}{6}$ (iii) $\frac{\pi}{4}$ or $\frac{7\pi}{4}$ (iv) $\frac{5\pi}{4}$ or $\frac{7\pi}{4}$ (v) 0, π, 2π (vi) x = π **3.** (i) A = 23.6° or 156.4° (ii) 115.4° or 244.6° (iii) A = 105.9° or 285.9° (iv) 53.1° or 306.9° (v) A = 10.5° or 169.5° (vi) A = 142.3° or 322.3° **4.** (i) sin θ = ³⁄₅, tan θ = ¾ (ii) cos θ = –¹²⁄₁₃, tan θ = –⁵⁄₁₂
5. (i) θ = 15°, 75°, 195°, 255° (ii) θ = 30°, 150°, 210°, 330° (iii) θ = 58.1°, 118.1°, 178.1°, 238.1°, 298.1°, 358.1° (iv) θ = 90° or 210° or 330° (v) θ = 300°
6. (i) $\frac{\pi}{2} + 2n\pi, n \in Z$ (ii) $\frac{\pi}{2} + \frac{2n\pi}{3}, n \in Z$ (iii) $\frac{3\pi}{4} + 2n\pi, \frac{5\pi}{4} + 2n\pi, n \in Z$ (iv) $\frac{\pi}{2} + 2n\pi, \frac{3\pi}{2} + 2n\pi, n \in Z$ (v) $\frac{\pi}{4} + 2n\pi, \frac{3\pi}{4} + 2n\pi, n \in Z$
7. First design is in line with regulations, second is not
8. $\theta > 40°$, not economical

Exercise 7.7

1. (i) $|\angle YZX| = 21.2°$, $|\angle YXZ| = 98.8°$, $|YZ| = 13.7$ (ii) $|\angle RQS| = 70°$, $|QR| = 8.8$, $|RS| = 10.9$ (iii) $|\angle CAB| = 87.8°$ or 92.2°, $|\angle BCA| = 32.2°$ or 27.8°, $|AB| = 8.0°$ or 7.0° (iv) $|\angle UTV| = 19°$, $|UV| = 4.5$, $|TV| = 8.3$ (v) $|\angle RQP| = 34.8°$ or 145.2°, $|\angle QRP| = 125.2°$ or 14.8°, $|QP| = 14.3$, $|QP| = 4.5$ (vi) $|\angle XWY| = 90°$, $|XY| = 5.2$,

$|WY| = 4.1$ **2.** (i) $7.5°$, $x = 3\frac{\sqrt{2}}{4}$, $y = \frac{3 + 2\sqrt{3}}{4}$ (ii) $30°$, $x = 1$, (iii) $60°$, $60°$, 2 **3.** (i) $a = 4.58$, (ii) $a = 9.53$, (iii) $a = 13.69$ (iv) $a = 3.87$, (v) $a = 18.37$ **4.** (i) $A \approx 82°$ (ii) $A = 120°$ (iii) $A = 41°$ (iv) $A = 17°$ (v) $A = 90°$ **5.** $|AD| = 79$, $|AC| = 130$ **6.** $\theta = 108°$ **8.** (i) $|WYX| \approx 42.5$ (ii) $|XY| = 14.9$ (iii) $|WZ| = 24.2$ **9.** $|DC| = 4.9$ **10.** (i) $\frac{\cos x = p^2 + d^2 - c^2}{2pd}$, $\frac{\cos B = q^2 + d^2 - b^2}{2qd}$

12. $|PQ| = 73.73$ m, $|PR| = 65.22$ m **13.** (i) $100°$ (ii) 101.54 m (iii) 77.8 m **14.** (b) 1.885 m (c) 10.37 m **15.** (i) $|AB| = 3.66$ m (ii) 20.296 m

Exercise 7.8

1. 73.72 sq. units **2.** 123.61 sq. units **3.** 80.99 sq. units **4.** 158.48 sq. units **5.** 46.98 sq. units **6.** 70.91 sq. units **7.** (i) 45.51 sq. units (ii) 23.66 sq. units (iii) 24.63 sq. units **8.** (i) $x = 6$ cm (ii) $x = 4.1$ cm (iii) $x = 38.3°$ **9.** 8 cm **10.** (i) 35 cm^2; 7 cm (ii) 2.704 cm^2; 1.04 cm (iii) 308.39 m^2; 51.40 cm **11.** $\frac{3}{2}$ radians **12.** 45.71 cm, area of slice = 117.81 cm^2 **13.** (i) 9 cm^2 (ii) 4.09 cm^2 (iii) 4.91 cm^2 **14.** (i) $|AB| = \sqrt{3}r$ cm (ii) $\pi\sqrt{3}r$ cm **15.** 87.586 cm^2

Exercise 7.9

1. (i) 14 m (ii) $2\sqrt{41}$ m (iii) $66°$ **2.** (i) 20 m (ii) 30.6 m **3.** (i) 5 cm (ii) 13 cm (iii) $13.34°$ (iv) $14.04°$ **4.** (i) 33.0995 m (ii) $40.8285°$ **5.** $32.07°$ **6.** (i) ≈ 8.13 cm (ii) ≈ 9.96 cm (iii) $55°$

Exercise 7.10

1. (i) $\frac{4}{5}$ (ii) $\frac{4}{3}$ (iii) $\frac{5}{13}$ (iv) $\frac{5}{12}$ (v) $\frac{16}{65}$ (vi) $\frac{63}{16}$ **2.** (i) $\frac{\sqrt{3}-1}{2\sqrt{2}}$ (ii) $\frac{\sqrt{3}+1}{2\sqrt{2}}$ (iii) $\frac{\sqrt{3}-1}{2\sqrt{2}}$ (iv) $2 + \sqrt{3}$ (v) $\frac{\sqrt{3}-1}{2\sqrt{2}}$ (vi) $-\frac{1}{2}$ (vii) $\frac{\sqrt{3}+1}{2\sqrt{2}}$ (viii) -2 (ix) $\frac{1}{\sqrt{2}}$ (x) $\frac{1}{2}$ **3.** $\frac{16}{13}$ **4.** $\frac{5}{12}$ **7.** (i) $\frac{14}{13}$ (ii) $\lambda = 45°$ **8.** $\tan A = \frac{1}{2}$ or $\tan A = -2$ **9.** $\tan A = \pm \frac{1}{5}$ **11.** $\tan B = \frac{3}{5}$ **12.** (i) $\frac{4}{7}$ (ii) $\frac{3}{11}$ (iii) 1 **14.** (i) $\sin 8\theta + \sin 4\theta$ (ii) $\frac{1}{2}(\cos 4\theta + \cos 2\theta)$ (iii) $\frac{1}{2}(\sin 4A - \sin 2A)$ (iv) $\frac{1}{2}(\cos 2x - \cos 8x)$ (v) $\cos(5\theta) + \cos(3\theta)$ (vi) $\frac{1}{2}(\sin 8x + \sin 4x)$ (vii) $[\cos 5\theta - \cos 3\theta]$ (viii) $\sin\theta$ (ix) $\frac{1}{2}[\sin 6x + \sin 4x]$ (x) $\cos(2x) + \cos(\pi)$

15. (i) $\frac{1}{4}$ (ii) $\frac{\sqrt{3}+2}{2}$ **16.** (i) $2\sin 3x\cos x$ (ii) $2\cos 2x\sin x$ (iii) $2\cos 6x\cos 3x$ (iv) $2\sin 2x\cos x$ (v) $2\cos\frac{3x}{2}\sin\frac{x}{2}$ (vi) $2\sin 6x\cos 4x$ (vii) $-2\sin 5\theta\sin 3\theta$ (viii) $2\sin 3x\sin 2x$ (ix) $-2\sin 30°\sin x$ (x) $2\sin x\cos 60°$ **17.** (i) $\frac{1}{\sqrt{2}}$ (ii) $-\frac{1}{\sqrt{2}}$

Revision Exercises

1. 5 cm = x

2.

Degrees	Radians
90°	$\frac{\pi}{2}$
180°	π
270°	$\frac{3\pi}{2}$
360°	2π
120°	$\frac{2\pi}{3}$
45°	$\frac{\pi}{4}$
60°	$\frac{\pi}{3}$

3. (i) $216°$ (ii) $36°$ (iii) $300°$ **4.** (i) $\frac{5\pi}{6}$ (ii) $\frac{8\pi}{5}$ (iii) $\frac{3\pi}{5}$ **5.** (i) 17 m (ii) $30°$ **7.** (a) $\sin\alpha = Q$, $\cos\alpha = P$, $\tan\alpha = \frac{Q}{P}$ (b) (i) 10.64 (ii) $y = 10.96$ **8.** (i) $\frac{1}{\sqrt{2}}$ (ii) $\frac{\sqrt{3}}{2}$ (iii) -14.301 (iv) 0.978 (v) -0.901 **10.** (i) Red = $\cos\theta$, Green = $\sin\theta$ (ii) Red = $\sin 2x$, Green = $2\cos x$ (iii) $\tan\theta$ (iv) $\tan 2\theta$ **17.** (i) $2\cos 4x\sin x$ (ii) $2\cos 4x\cos 3x$ **18.** $\frac{1}{2\sqrt{2}} - \frac{1}{4}$

19.

A	30°	45°	60°
$\sin A$	$\frac{1}{2}$	$\frac{1}{\sqrt{2}}$	$\frac{\sqrt{3}}{2}$
$\cos A$	$\frac{\sqrt{3}}{2}$	$\frac{1}{\sqrt{2}}$	$\frac{1}{2}$
$\tan A$	$\frac{1}{\sqrt{3}}$	1	$\sqrt{3}$

(i) $A = 30° \pm n(360°)$ or $150° \pm n(360°)$, $n \in N$ (ii) $B = 45° \pm n(180°)$, $n \in N$ (iii) $C = 45° \pm n(180°)$, $n \in N$ (iv) $D = 60° + n(360°)$ or $120° + n(360°)$, $n \in N$ **20.** (a) (i) $A = 23.6°$ or $156.4°$ (ii) $A = 115.4°$ or $244.6°$ (iii) $A = 105.9°$ or $285.9°$ (iv) $A = 120°$ or $240°$ (v) $A = 60°$ or $120°$ (b) (i) $\theta = 20°$ or $100°$... (ii) $\theta = 30°$ or $60°$... **21.** (i) $\approx 24°$ (ii) Carol **22.** (i) 1, 186.628 cm^2 (ii) 476.003 cm^2 **23.** (i) $14.036°$ (ii) 6.185 (iii) $d = 0.7697$ m **24.** (i) $d = 110.2799$ km (ii) 4 hours 31 minutes (iii) 1 hour 29 minutes **25.** (i) 4 cm (ii) 8.378 cm^2 (iii) 84.87 cm^2 (iv) 68.114 cm^2 **26.** $\theta = 18.43°$ **27.** (i) 19.06 m (ii) $5.4°$ **28.** (i) 7.36 m (ii) 242 cm (iii) $14°$ **29.** (i) 1.31 m (ii) 1.9 m **30.** $|\angle PRQ| = 120°$ **31.** (i) 1 m (ii) 2.97 m (iii) $56°$ **33.** 23.125 m **34.** (i) 3.42 m (ii) 31.71 m^2

(iii) 26.72 $m^2 \leqslant$ area of roof $\leqslant$ 37.07 m^2
35. (b) $h \approx 194.1750$ m
(c) 2nd estimate: $h \approx 194.0727$ m; 3rd estimate: $h \approx 194.1149$ m (d) $h \approx 19{,}412$ cm (g) Range = 3.8 m

Chapter 8

Exercise 8.1

1. (i) $x = 7, y = 20$ (ii) $x = 40/3, y = 50/3$ (iii) $x = 26/3, y = 64/3$ (iv) $x = \sqrt{220}, y = \sqrt{120}$ (v) $x = 7.25, y = 2.75$ (vi) $x = 3\sqrt{5}, y = \sqrt{20}$ (vii) $x = 12.25, y = 8.75$ **2.** (i) Not similar (ii) Similar **3.** (ii) 20 (iii) 16 (iv) 8 **4.** (i) 18.75 (ii) 22.5 (iii) $\approx$ 59.92 units^2 (iv) $\approx$ 210.67 units^2 (v) 71.25 **5.** (ii) 40/3 (iii) 10/3 (iv) 5 **6.** (ii) 128/3 **7.** (i) 14 (ii) 12 (iii) 26 **8.** (i) 10 : 3 (ii) 3 : 7 (iii) 7 : 10 **9.** 2.4

Exercise 8.2

1. (i) $x = 20$ (ii) $x = \sqrt{23}$ (iii) $x = \sqrt{2}$ (iv) $x = 0.45$ **2.** (i) $x = 8\sqrt{3}, y = 4\sqrt{3}$ (ii) $x = 13.44, y = 3.92$ (iii) $x = \sqrt{65}, y = \sqrt{145}$ (iv) $x = \frac{13\sqrt{29}}{2}, y = 7\sqrt{26}$ **3.** (ii) 101, 99, 20 **4.** (ii) $x = 84, y = 13$ **5.** $\approx$ 3.10 **7.** (i) $2\sqrt{74}$ (ii) $2\sqrt{113}$ (iii) $\sqrt{356}$ **8.** (i) $20\sqrt{2}$ (ii) $5\sqrt{17}$ (iii) $5\sqrt{21}$ **9.** (ii) 3

Exercise 8.3

1. (i) 7.665 units^2 (ii) 17.63 units^2 (iii) 8.05 units^2 (vi) 65 units^2 (v) 14.7 units^2 (vi) 432 units^2 **2.** (i) $\approx$ 9 units^2 (ii) $\approx$ 28 units^2 (iii) 90 units^2 (iv) $\approx$ 6 units^2 (v) 31.5 units^2 (vi) 120 units^2 (vii) $\approx$ 228 units^2 **3.** (i) 6.75 (ii) 4.28 (iii) $\approx$ 5.17 **4.** (i) 5 cm (ii) 15 cm^2 **5.** 8 : 1 **6.** $\frac{4\sqrt{3}}{3}$

Exercise 8.4

1. (i) $|\angle A| = 55°, |\angle B| = 35°$ (ii) $|\angle A| = 25°, |\angle B| = 130°$ (iii) $|\angle A| = 48°, |\angle B| = 48°$ (iv) $|\angle A| = 40°, |\angle B| = 40°$ (v) $|\angle A| = 52.5°, |\angle B| = 105°$ (vi) $|\angle A| = 98°, |\angle B| = 41°$ (vii) $|\angle A| = 34°, |\angle B| = 90°$ **2.** (i) 112° (ii) 80° (iii) 100° (iv) 80° **3.** (i) 10 (ii) $\approx$10.5463 **4.** (i) 90° (ii) 40° (iii) 70° (iv) 40° (v) 30° (vi) 30° **5.** (i) $\angle RCS$ (ii) $\angle QRP$ (iii) $\angle QPS$ **7.** (i) 7 (ii) 1 (iii) 49 (iv) $35\sqrt{2}$ **8.** (i) 30 cm (ii) 14 cm

9. (i) 12 cm (ii) $3\sqrt{17}$ cm (iii) $12\sqrt{2}$ cm **10.** 48 cm **11.** (i) $\approx$ 49.29° (ii) 27.5281 (iii) $\approx$ 69.74

Revision Exercises

1. (a) 9 (b) (i) 50.27 cm^2 (ii) $\approx$ 41.57 cm^2 (c) (i) $\frac{\sqrt{2y^2}}{2}$ **or** $\frac{\sqrt{2}y}{2}$ (ii) $r = \frac{y}{2}$ (iii) 2 : 1 **2.** (a) (i) 84 sq. units (ii) $r = 12.5$ (b) (i) 2017.2 m^2 (ii) €10,086 (iii) Area ΔBCD = 634.63 units^2; Area ΔABD = 1,382.57 units^2; length of fence $[BD]$ = 86.505 m (c) (i) $ay - y^2$ (ii) $a^2 - ay$ (iii) ay **3.** (a) (i) 4.36 m (ii) 6.3936 (b) 10 units^2 (c) (i) $12\sqrt{3}$ (ii) 187.0615 units^2 **4.** (b) (i) 8 (ii) 18 m (c) (i) $\approx$ 8.57 m (ii) Distance to A = 57.14 m, Distance to B = 42.86 m **5.** (c) (ii) 9 (iii) $4.5x$ units^2 **6.** (b) $\approx$ 2.33 m **7.** (b) 5 (c) (i) $\frac{7y}{7-y}$ (ii) $\frac{14y^2 - 70y + 175}{10 - 2y}$ **8.** (a) (i) Triangles PQS and PQR (ii) Triangles PXQ and SXR (b) $r\sqrt{3}$ (c) (ii) 125 cm **9.** (a) $\approx$ 13.86 km (c) (ii) $x\sqrt{5}$ (iii) $\sqrt{\frac{x^2}{25} + 4x^2}$ **10.** (a) $\approx$ 7.79 (b) (ii) $r^2 - \frac{y^2}{4}$ (c) (i) $\sqrt{\frac{3}{4}}\,x$ (ii) $\frac{x}{\sqrt{3}}$ (iii) $\frac{x}{2\sqrt{3}}$ (iv) 4 : 1

Chapter 9

Exercise 9.2

1. (ii) 1.5 **2.** (ii) 4/3 (iii) 16.9 **3.** (i) 2.5 (ii) 25 : 4 (iii) 5 : 2 **4.** (i) 3 (ii) 4.2 (iii) 2 **5.** (i) 2/3 (ii) 4/3 (iii) 4/9 **6.** (iv) 1 : 4 **7.** (i) 2/3 (ii) 8 (iii) 22.1625 (iv) 12.3125 **8.** (i) R (ii) 2 (iii) 8 (iv) 4 (v) 4:1 **9.** (iii) 6 units^2 **10.** (i) 5 (ii) 1.4 (iii) 12 (iv) 30 (v) 28.8 **11.** (b) (i) 10 sq units (ii) $\sqrt{34}$ (d) (i) 40 sq. units (ii) $2\sqrt{34}$ **12.** (ii) 2 (iii) 4 : 1 **13.** (i) 2/9 (ii) 2 : 9 (iii) 4 : 81 (iv) 19.25 **14.** (i) 8.5 (iii) 5.625 (iv) 8.4375 cm^2 **17.** (a) $x = 4$ (b) $|A'B'| = 2.4$; $|B'C'| = 3.2$; $|A'C'| = 4$ **18.** (i) T (ii) T (iii) F (iv) F (v) T (vi) F (vii) T **19.** (i) 4 (ii) 16 (iii) 0.4 : 1 or 2 : 5 (iv) 4 : 25 **21.** (i) $12\sqrt{3}$ cm (ii) $216\sqrt{3}$ cm^2 (iii) $36\sqrt{3}$ cm **22.** (i) 2 : 5 (ii) 2 : 5 (iii) 2 : 5 (iv) 4 : 25 (v) 8 : 125 **23.** (i) 1 : 4 : 12 (ii) 1 : 16 : 144 (iii) 1 : 64 : 1,728 **24.** 12.5 cm **25.** h = 11.2 m, l = 44 m **26.** (i) Bottle A: 19 cm^2, Bottle C: 469 cm^2 (ii) Bottle A: 6 ml, Bottle C: 781 ml **27.** 21 m^2 **28.** Dimensions: A4 = 297 × 210 mm; A3 = 420 × 297 mm; A2 = 594 × 420 mm; A1 = 840 × 594 mm; Area: A4 = 624 cm^2, A3 = 1,247 cm^2, A2 = 2,495 cm^2, A1 = 4,990 cm^2

Chapter 10

Exercise 10.1

1. (i) (a) 13 (b) $3\sqrt{10}$ (c) 3 (d) $\sqrt{74}$
(ii) (a) $(1\frac{1}{2}, 8)$ (b) $(-\frac{3}{2}, -\frac{5}{2})$ (c) $(6, 2\frac{1}{2})$
(d) $(-\frac{1}{2}, -\frac{9}{2})$ **2.** (i) 2 (ii) (a) (6,0) (b) (0,–12)
3. (11,12) **4.** (i) $|PQ| = 4\sqrt{5}$; $|PR| = 2\sqrt{10}$; $|QR| = 2\sqrt{10}$; isosceles as $|PR| = |QR| \neq |PQ|$
(ii) (–1,–1) **5.** $b = -3$; $a = 2$ **8.** $a = 6$
9. (i) $2\sqrt{10}$ (ii) (3,1) (iv) (3.8,3.4)
(v) Slope $l = -\frac{1}{3}$; Slope $AB = 3$; $AB \perp l$

Exercise 10.2

1. (i) $3x + y - 26 = 0$ (ii) $2x - 3y + 2 = 0$
(iii) $4x + 10y - 11 = 0$ (iv) $2x - y - 3 = 0$
2. (i) $x - y - 1 = 0$ (ii) $x - 3y + 10 = 0$
(iii) $2x - y + 9 = 0$ (iv) $x + y - 3 = 0$
(v) $7x + y - 4 = 0$ **3.** (i) $x + 3y - 4 = 0$
(ii) $x - y + 6 = 0$ (iii) $14x + 9y - 39 = 0$
(iv) $2x - 3y + 1 = 0$ (v) $9x + y + 23 = 0$
4. $x + y = 0$ **5.** j: $y = 1$; l: $4x - y - 2 = 0$; k: $x + y + 1 = 0$ **6.** $x + 3y + 2 = 0$
7. $2x + 3y - 6 = 0$ **8.** $3x - 2y - 12 = 0$
9. $6x + y + 16 = 0$ **10.** $2x - y + 4 = 0$
11. $x + y - 4 = 0$ **12.** $3x - 4y - 6 = 0$
13. $2x + y - 2 = 0$ **14.** $x - 8y = 0$
15. (i) DE: $x + y - 4.5 = 0$; AB: $x - y = 0$
(ii) $D(1.5,3)$; $E(3,1.5)$ (iii) ≈ 3.35 units

Exercise 10.3

1. (i) 9.5 sq. units (ii) 22 sq. units (iii) 4 sq. units
(iv) 13 sq. units (v) 24 sq. units (vi) 12 sq. units
(vii) $\frac{5}{2}$ sq. units (viii) 12 sq. units **2.** 12.5 sq. units
3. $\frac{3}{2}$ sq. units **4.** 8 sq. units **5.** $C(3,0)$ or (–29,0)
6. 29 sq. units **7.** ±3 **8.** $k = 0$ or $k = 4$

Exercise 10.4

1. (i) 2.1 units (ii) 5 units (iii) 1 unit
(iv) $\sqrt{5}$ units (v) $\sqrt{2}$ units **2.** (i) $\sqrt{5}$ units
(ii) $4\sqrt{2}$ units (iii) $2\sqrt{5}$ units (iv) $4\sqrt{13}$ units
3. $\frac{32\sqrt{13}}{13}$ units **4.** $\frac{51\sqrt{61}}{61}$ units
6. Point is equidistant. **7.** $k = \pm 8$
9. (i) $3x - 4y - 29 = 0$ (ii) $\frac{38}{5}$ units
10. (i) 3 units (ii) $k = -32$ **11.** 1 unit
12. $x - 3y - 9 = 0$ or $3x - y + 5 = 0$
13. $15x - 8y + 78 = 0$ or $15x - 8y - 92 = 0$

Exercise 10.5

1. (a) (i) ≈ 10.30° (ii) 45° (iii) ≈ 71.57°
(iv) 45° (v) 45° (b) (i) 162.9° (ii) 110.22°
(iii) 116.57° (iv) 167.47° (v) 126.87° **2.** (i) 60° or 120° (ii) 30° or 150° (iii) 90° (iv) 45° or 135° (v) 18° or 162° **3.** ≈ 26.57° **4.** 135°
5. $7x + 5y = 0$ or $5x - 7y = 0$ **6.** $3x - y - 3 = 0$ or $x + 3y - 11 = 0$ **7.** ≈ 48° **8.** 10.15°
9. $m = \frac{1}{4}$ or 2; ≈ 49° **10.** ≈ 85.54°
11. There is a risk of water damage. **12.** 110.96°

Exercise 10.6

1. (i) (–2,4) (ii) (–14,28) **2.** (4,15) **3.** (3,2)
4. (7,–1) or (–5,7) **5.** (i) (–2,3) (ii) (–26,51)
6. (ii) 2 : 1 (iii) 3 : 1 **7.** $A(0,5)$; $E(\frac{5}{2},0)$
8. 1 : 1 **9.** (i) 4 : 1 (ii) $x = 8, y = -3$

Revision Exercises

1. (a) (i) $2\sqrt{5}$ (ii) $2\sqrt{13}$ (iii) $2\sqrt{10}$ (iv) $\sqrt{6}$
(v) $\frac{\sqrt{65}}{6}$ (b) (i) (3,3) (ii) (0,0) (iii) $(-\frac{1}{2},-2)$
(iv) $(-1,\frac{1}{\sqrt{2}})$ (v) $(\frac{3}{4},\frac{1}{3})$ (c) (i) $2x - y - 3 = 0$
(ii) $2x + 3y = 0$ (iii) $6x - 2y - 1 = 0$
(iv) $x - \sqrt{2}y + 2 = 0$ (v) $24x - 3y - 17 = 0$
2. $[AB]\ \frac{2}{3}$, $[CD] = -\frac{3}{2}$, $[EF] = 4$, $[GH] = -\frac{1}{6}$, $[IJ] = 5$, $[KL]$ = No slope, $[MN] = 0$
4. (ii) (1,–2) (iv) –1 (v) $x + y + 1 = 0$
(vi) (–1, 0) **5.** ±3 **6.** 9 or –7 **7.** (i) 45°
(ii) $\sqrt{34}$ (iii) $\frac{15}{2}$ sq. units
(iv) $x - 3y + 7 = 0$ (v) $\frac{\sqrt{10}}{10}$ **8.** $a = -\frac{5}{6}b$
10. $3x - 7y - 36 = 0$ **11.** $5x + y + 3 = 0$
12. (i) $P(\frac{-k}{3},0)$, $Q(0,\frac{k}{5})$ (ii) $\pm 10\sqrt{3}$
13. $x - 3y - 3 = 0$ or $3x + y - 19 = 0$
14. 53 sq. units **15.** $Q(8,0)$, $R(0,-12)$
16. (a) $k = 7$ or $k = 3$ (b) (ii) $x + y - 4 = 0$
17. (a) $2x + y - 6 = 0$ (b) $D(0,6)$
(c) $\frac{13\sqrt{5}}{5}$ (d) 13 sq. units
18. (b) Slope $AB = -\frac{15}{8}$, $\tan(\angle ABC) = \frac{171}{140}$
19. (a) $x + 2y = -4$: Line l, $2x - y = -4$: Line m, $x + 2y = 8$: Line j, $2x - y = 2$: Line n
(c) $x + 2y = 4$ **20.** $b = 2$ **21.** (i) $x - 2y = k$, $k \in R$ (ii) $x - 2y - 11 = 0$ **22.** (i) $-3x + y = k$, $k \in R$
(ii) $x + 3y + 11 = 0$ **23.** (a) $y = 3x + 2$ (d) No
24. (ii) $\frac{3}{8}$ cups (iii) $\frac{1}{16}$ (iv) $y = \frac{1}{16}x$ (v) 3.125 cups
25. (i) 40 km/h (ii) 18 secs (iii) $y = x + 30$
(iv) $y = 30$; initial speed (on passing traffic light)
(v) 20 km/h (vi) 55 km/h **26.** (i) €50 (ii) €90 (iii) 1
(iv) Cost per minute of fixing a washing machine
(v) $y = x + 50$ (vi) €170 **27.** (i) €150, 000
(ii) €20/unit (iii) $y = 20x + 150$ **28.** (ii) 231.2 mins
(iii) $6.\dot{3}\dot{6}$ kg **29.** (i) Red: 2,400 cm^2, Green: 1,800 cm^2 Blue: 4,200 cm^2 (ii) Yes
30. (i) 20; (b) Selling price per unit (ii) $y = 20x$
(iii) $y = 10x + 40$

(iv) Break-even point is 40,000 units.
31. From point D

Chapter 11

Exercise 11.1

1. (i) $x^2 + y^2 = 25$ (ii) $x^2 + y^2 = 64$
(iii) $x^2 + y^2 = 1$ (iv) $x^2 + y^2 = 169$
(v) $x^2 + y^2 = 289$ (vi) $x^2 + y^2 = 2$
(vii) $x^2 + y^2 = 3$ (viii) $16x^2 + 16y^2 = 9$
(ix) $4x^2 + 4y^2 = 1$ (x) $x^2 + y^2 = 3.24$
(xi) $x^2 + y^2 = 75$ (xii) $x^2 + y^2 = 63$ **2.** (i) 8
(ii) 9 (iii) 2 (iv) 7 (v) $\sqrt{3}$ (vi) $\frac{3}{2}$ (vii) $\frac{10}{3}$
(viii) a (ix) $\frac{7}{5}$ (x) $\left|\frac{1}{a}\right|$ (xi) $\left|\frac{b}{a}\right|$ (xii) $\left|\frac{a^3}{b^2}\right|$
3. $x^2 + y^2 = 100$ **4.** (i) $r = 25$ (ii) $x^2 + y^2 = 625$
5. Area: (i) $\frac{9\pi}{4}$ (ii) $\frac{\pi}{a^2}$ (iii) $\frac{m^4}{n^4}\cdot\pi$ (iv) $(a + 1)^2\,\pi$
Circumference: (i) 3π (ii) $\frac{2\pi}{a}$ (iii) $\frac{2m^2}{n^2}\cdot\pi$
(iv) $2|a + 1|\pi$ **6.** (i) (0,0) (ii) 5 (iii) $x^2 + y^2 = 25$
7. (i) (0,0) (ii) $2\sqrt{10}$ (iii) $x^2 + y^2 = 40$
(v) 125.66 sq. units (vi) 160 sq. units
8. (i) $x^2 + y^2 = 125$ (ii) $t = 11$ **9.** $x^2 + y^2 = 25$
10. $10x^2 + 10y^2 = 81$ **11.** $17x^2 + 17y^2 = 1$
12. (i) $y = 4$ (ii) Area $ABCD = \frac{625}{6}$ units^2

Exercise 11.2

1. (i) $(x - 3)^2 + (y + 5)^2 = 2^2$ (ii) $x^2 + (y - 7)^2 = 16$
(iii) $x^2 + y^2 = 25$ (iv) $x^2 + y^2 = 5$
(v) $(x - \frac{1}{2})^2 + (y + \frac{1}{4})^2 = 144$
(vi) $(x + 3)^2 + (y + 8)^2 = \frac{1}{4}$
(vii) $(x + 2)^2 + (y + \frac{3}{4})^2 = 18$
(viii) $(x + 1)^2 + (y - 6)^2 = \frac{49}{4}$ **2.** (i) $\sqrt{41}$
(ii) $(x - 1)^2 + (y - 1)^2 = 41$ **3.** (i) $\sqrt{20}$
(ii) $(x + 2)^2 + (y + 1)^2 = 20$ **4.** (i) (1, 1)
(ii) $\sqrt{13}$ (iii) $(x - 1)^2 + (y - 1)^2 = 13$
5. (i) Centre: (5,2), Radius length: 9
(ii) Centre: (–2, –5), Radius length: 7
(iii) Centre: (1,–3), Radius length: 10
(iv) Centre: (0,8), Radius length: 7
(v) Centre: (0,0), Radius length: 10
6. $(x + 3)^2 + (y - 2)^2 = 2$
7. $(x - 5)^2 + (y + 2)^2 = \frac{441}{10}$
8. (ii) $(x - 30)^2 + (y + \frac{19}{13})^2 = \frac{225}{13}$
9. (i) (7,0) or (–3,0) (ii) (3,0) or (–9,0)
(iii) (5,0) or (–15,0) (iv) (6,0) or (–8,0)
10. (i) (0,13) or (0,–5) (ii) (0,15) or (0,–5)
(iii) (0,5) or (0,–7) (iv) (0,2) or (0,–4)
11. $(x - 1)^2 + (y - 3)^2 = 4$
12. (i) $(x + 5\sqrt{2})^2 + (y - 5\sqrt{2})^2 = 50$
(ii) $x^2 + y^2 + 5\sqrt{2}x - 5\sqrt{2}y = 0$

Exercise 11.3

1. (i) Centre: (2,–3), Radius length: 4
(ii) Centre: (1,1), Radius length: 1
(iii) Centre: (–1,–4), Radius length: 3
(iv) Centre: (–5,4), Radius length: 9
(v) Centre: ($\frac{2}{3}$,–1), Radius length: 1
(vi) Centre: (3,0), Radius length: 4
(vii) Centre: (–5,3), Radius length: $\sqrt{13}$
(viii) Centre: (0,10), Radius length: 1
(ix) Centre: (0,–5), Radius length: 5
(x) Centre: ($-\frac{3}{2}$,$\frac{7}{2}$), Radius length: 4
(xi) Centre: ($\frac{4}{3}$,$\frac{2}{3}$), Radius length: 1
(xii) Centre: ($\frac{1}{3}$,–1), Radius length: 1
2. c_2: $u(0,5)$ on circle; c_3: $v(4,4)$ outside circle;
c_4: $w(5,1)$ on circle; c_5: $x(0,0)$ inside circle;
c_6: $y(-2,-3)$ on circle; c_7: $z(3,-6)$ outside circle
3. (i) (3,0) or (1,0) (ii) (–15,0) or (5,0)
(iii) (3,0) or (–1,0) (iv) (7,0) or (–5,0)
4. (i) (0,7) or (0,–3) (ii) (0,5) or (0,1)
(iii) (0,0) or (0,8) (iv) (0,–4) or (0,2) **5.** $a = 6$
6. $a = 1$ **7.** $b = -5$ **8.** $n = -5$; $m = 6$
9. $-3 - 2\sqrt{3} < a < -3 + 2\sqrt{3}$ **11.** $b = \pm 12$
12. (i) C(4,4) (ii) $(x - 4)^2 + (y - 4)^2 = 16$
13. (i) $(x - 10)^2 + (y + 10)^2 = 25$
(ii) $100 - 25\pi$ units^2 **14.** (i) $x + 3y + 12 = 0$
(ii) C $(a, -4 - \frac{a}{3})$ (iii) $a = -4.5$
(iv) $\left(x + \frac{9}{2}\right)^2 + \left(y + \frac{5}{2}\right)^2 = \frac{5}{2}$ (v) $3x - y + 16 = 0$

Exercise 11.4

1. (3,1) or (1,3) **2.** (3,2) or (–2,–3)
3. ($\frac{17}{5}$,$-\frac{19}{5}$) or (–1,5) **4.** ($\frac{79}{25}$,$\frac{3}{25}$) or (–3,1)
5. (i) (2,1) or (1,2) (ii) (–1,0) or (0,1) (iii) (1,7)
(iv) (5,–1) or (4,4) **6.** (iii) Centre: (1,–7),
Radius: $2\sqrt{5}$ **7.** (iii) Centre: ($\frac{3}{8}$,$-\frac{23}{4}$), Radius: 8
8. (ii) Centre: (–6,7), Radius: $3\sqrt{10}$
9. (iv) Centre: ($-\frac{7}{4}$,3), Radius: $\frac{9}{4}$ **10.** (ii) $a = \frac{3}{5}$
or $a = -\frac{3}{5}$ (iii) $-1 < a < 0$ (iv) No

Exercise 11.5

1. (i) $3x + y = 10$ (ii) $2x - y + 10 = 0$
(iii) $3x + 4y = 0$ (iv) $2x - y - 5 = 0$
(v) $2x + 3y - 9 = 0$ (vi) $3x - 2y - 26 = 0$
(vii) $4x + y - 10 = 0$ (viii) $3x + y - 8 = 0$
2. (ii) $2x + y - 5 = 0$ (iii) $2x + y + 5 = 0$
3. $k = 20$ or $k = -14$
4. $3x + 4y + 12 = 0$ or $3x + 4y - 38 = 0$
5. $3x - 2y - 3 = 0$ or $3x - 2y - 29 = 0$
6. (i) $(2 + \frac{2\sqrt{3}}{3})x - y - 2 - 2\sqrt{3} = 0$ or
$(2 - \frac{2\sqrt{3}}{3})x - y - 2 + 2\sqrt{3} = 0$
(ii) $y = -1$ or $21x - 20y - 146 = 0$
7. $21x - 20y + 14 = 0$; $x = 6$ **9.** Circles don't touch internally. **10.** Circles touch internally.

12. $k = 105$ **13.** Externally: $(x - \frac{9}{2})^2 + y^2 = \frac{9}{4}$
Internally: $(x - \frac{9}{2})^2 + y^2 = \frac{225}{4}$

Exercise 11.6

1. (i) $3x^2 + 3y^2 + 17x - 5y - 22 = 0$
(ii) $x^2 + y^2 - 7x + 3y + 12 = 0$
(iii) $2x^2 + 2y^2 - 7x + 2y - 34 = 0$
(iv) $x^2 + y^2 - 4x - 2y = 0$
(v) $5x^2 + 5y^2 + 48x - 12y + 47 = 0$
(vi) $x^2 + y^2 - 13x - 2y + 22 = 0$
2. $x^2 + y^2 - 4x - 2y = 0$ **3.** $x^2 + y^2 - 2x - 2y - 3 = 0$
4. $x^2 + y^2 - 10x - 4y + 4 = 0$
5. (ii) $x^2 + y^2 - 6x - 4y + 9 = 0$
or $x^2 + y^2 - 22x - 20y + 121 = 0$
6. (ii) $x^2 + y^2 - 10x + 2y + 1 = 0$
7. $x^2 + y^2 - 4x - 6y + 81 = 0$
and $9x^2 + 9y^2 - 100x - 150y + 625 = 0$
8. (i) (2,2) (ii) $r = 2$
9. $x^2 + y^2 + 2x - 4 = 0$ or $x^2 + y^2 + 2x - 4y = 0$
10. $x^2 + y^2 - 10x - 10y + 25 = 0$
or $x^2 + y^2 + 4x + 4y - 17 = 0$
11. $x^2 + y^2 + 2x + 6y + 5 = 0$
12. $x^2 + y^2 - 4x + 2y - 20 = 0$

Revision Exercises

1. (b) $x^2 + y^2 = 50$ (c) $p = \pm 5$ (d) $n = 6$
2. (a) $(x - 1)^2 + (y - 1)^2 = 25$ (b) $k = 4$ or -6
(c) $x^2 + y^2 - 12x - 4y + 20 = 0$
3. (a) Centre: $(\frac{1}{2}, -\frac{3}{2})$, Radius: $\sqrt{13}$
(b) $x^2 + y^2 - 10x + 4y + 4 = 0$
(c) $x^2 + y^2 - 6x - 14y + 38 = 0$ **4.** (a) $k = -2$
(b) $(x + 2)^2 + (y - 6)^2 = 50$
(c) $x - y - 2 = 0$; $x - 7y - 6 = 0$ (d) 36.87°
5. (a) $A(0,1)$, $B(8,17)$; $[AB]$ is a diameter.
(b) $x^2 + y^2 - 7x - 5y + 6 = 0$ **6.** (b) $\sqrt{21}$
7. (a) $3x + 4y + 25 = 0$ (b) $x^2 + y^2 - 6y - 1 = 0$;
$x^2 + y^2 + 4x + 2y - 5 = 0$ **8.** (i) $x^2 + y^2 = 169$
(ii) $y = 12$ (iii) $5x + 12y = 169$
9. (a) $(x - 4)^2 + (y - 9)^2 = 20$ (b) $2x + y - 27 = 0$
(c) $R(\frac{27}{2},0)$ **10.** (a) $(x + 3)^2 + (y - 2)^2 = 16$
(b) $-\frac{41}{19}$ or 1 **11.** (a) $x^2 + y^2 - 14x - 6y + 49 = 0$
12. (a) $(x + 2)^2 + (y - 3)^2 = 58$ (b) (ii) $(\frac{7}{5},\frac{4}{5})$
(c) (ii) $\sqrt{7}$ **13.** (a) (i) $(x - 2)^2 + (y - 3)^2 = 2$
(iv) $x + y - 7 = 0$
(b) $x^2 + y^2 + 30x - 30y + 225 = 0$
or $x^2 + y^2 + 6x - 6y + 9 = 0$
(c) (iv) $x^2 + y^2 + 2x + 6y - 40 = 0$
14. $\left(x - \frac{7}{2}\right)^2 + \left(y - \frac{11}{2}\right)^2 = \frac{45}{2}$